The Harrowsmith Sourcebook

Edited by James Lawrence

A Consumer Guide for the Conserver Society

Compiled by the Editors, Contributors and Readers of *Harrowsmith*, Canada's National Award Winning Magazine of Country Living and Alternatives to Bigness

Camden House

ISBN 0-920656-04-8 (Hardcover)
ISBN 0-920656-02-1 (Softcover)
Trade distribution by Firefly Books, Toronto
ISBN 0-920668-06-2 (Hardcover)
ISBN 0-920668-07-0 (Softcover)

Printed in Canada for
Camden House Publishing Ltd.
Queen Victoria Road
Camden East, Ontario
K0K 1J0

Cover by Pat Michener

The Harrowsmith Sourcebook

Editor
James Lawrence

Associate Editors
Pamela Cross, Alice O'Connell

Art Director
Ian S.R. Grainge

Editorial Staff
Jennifer Bennett, Frank B. Edwards,
Thomas Pawlick, Elinor Lawrence

Art Staff
Pamela McDonald, Lynn Dumbleton, Elaine Bird

Copy Editors
Jean Macleod, Susan Cross, Dorrie Matthews

Typesetting
Johanna Troyer

Business & Distribution
John R. Page

Contributors
J. Adams, Sharon Airhart, Kenneth Allan, Lynn Anstett, Frank Appleton,
Michael Asti-Rose, Kerry Banks, Dianne Baker, Mikell Billoki,
Betsy Brierley, Larry Brierley, Vicki Cameron, Karen Casselman,
Margaret Coulter, Ann Creighton, David Creighton, Sandra Cumming,
Ron and Ellen Dean, Jeffrey Dinsdale, Jo Frohbeiter-Mueller, Larry Geno,
Katherine Gifford, John Gow, Paula Gustafson, Kathleen Haslem,
Norbert Hirschkorn, Ann Jeffries, Clark Jeffries, George Johnson, Stephen Lambert,
Drew Langsner, Louise Langsner, Tim Matson, Nyla Maurer,
Norman McKinney, William McLeish, Molly Miron, Merilyn Mohr,
Phillip Monner, Ian Murray, Roger Nixon, Andrejs Ozdins, Ken Parejko,
Barbara Palm White, Catharine Reed, Paul Reed, Hank Reinink,
Mary Ann Robertson, Bernadine Roslyn, Lesley Rowsome, Michael Schultz,
Miriam Scott, Michael Shook, Kathryn Sinclair, W.J. Smart, Joe Smillie,
Hal Smith, A. Southgate, Douglas Steele, Douglas Stewart, Elmo Stoll,
Andrew Terris, Nicole Webb, Joan Wells, E.J. Woytuik, Janet Young, Henni Zakes

Cohorts
Lorraine Adams, David Archibald, Dianne Bartlett, Maxine McLaren,
Nancy Pepper, A. Tadd Rustey, Susan Thompson, Daniel Wilson, Diane Young

Contents

CREDITS

Illustrators:

Gustav Russ Youngreen, pp.17, 21, 22, 43, 66, 67, 68, 70, 72, 127, 149, 153, 162, 168, 185, 195, 212, 222, 224, 249, 251, 256, 310; John Bianchi, pp.16, 77, 79, 82, 88, 108, 120, 138, 139, 140, 157, 168, 208, 223, 257, 312, 315; Ian S.R. Grainge, pp.64, 65, 81, 83, 84, 109, 125; F. Allyn Massey from ''The Vermont Bean Seed Co. Catalogue'', pp.20, 172; Graham Pilsworth, p.298; Sherry Streeter from Woodstove Cookery, *Garden Way Pub., p.71.*

Photographers:

Library of Congress, pp.10-11, 13, 15, 37, 47, 52, 218-219; James Lawrence, pp.175, 191, 274, 280-281, 290; Eric Hayes, pp.294-295, 303, 305, 307; Ernie Sparks, pp.282, 285, 286, 292; Agriculture Canada, pp.86, 255, 261; U.S. Dept. of Agriculture, pp.203, 215, 229; J.D. Wilson/Y.A. Grue, pp.252-253, 258, 260; Don McCallum, pp.18, 198; Bill Milliken, pp.74-75, 189; J.W. Stevenson, pp.232-233; E. Bork/NFB Phototheque, pp.230-231; Stephen Brooks, pp.170-171; Lisl Dennis/Image Bank of Canada, pp.118-119; Courtesy Headwaters, pp.308-309; Courtesy Heidinger Marketing Services, pp.158-159; Bruce Kendall, pp.268-269; B. Allan Mackie from Log House Plans, *pp.136-137; George Thomas, pp.228-229; Barry Estabrook, p.244; Courtesy Farallones Institute, p.161; Katherine Gifford, p.148; Ted Grant/NFB Phototheque, p.270; Stephen Homer, p.267; Bill Hutchinson, p.73; P.J. Hutchinson, p.254; Rosann Hutchinson, p.262; C. and A. Jeffries, p.64; Jurgen Mohr, p.23; National Photography Collection, Public Archives Canada, p.199; Patrick O'Connell, p.296; Ontario Ministry of Agriculture and Food, p.205; F. Royal/NFB Phototheque, p.239; R.R. Sallows, p.250; Courtesy Solerco Inc., p.76; Alan B. Stone, p.180; Bob Warrick, p.263.*

CAVEATS: The listing of any product or company in *The Harrowsmith Sourcebook* does not imply a blanket recommendation by the editors or publisher, and opinions expressed by contributors are their own and do not necessarily coincide with those of the publisher. In any mail order dealings it is wise to exercise a degree of caution until the quality and reliability of the product and/or source are known. All prices listed are subject to change and readers should request current information from a source before ordering. Unless otherwise indicated, most sources will supply free information, but smaller businesses and cottage industries appreciate receiving a self-addressed, stamped envelope with each query.

"**R**ight, the *Whole Earth Catalog* again."

Although offered by a new friend who had not seen the book, this instant analysis seems to portend the reception this *Sourcebook* may receive. Some reviewers, we may speculate with fair certainty, will call this book *The Canadian Whole Earth Catalogue.*

It is not. For starters, something called the *Canadian Whole Earth Almanac* was published in 1970, conceived in California by a staff member of the original *Whole Earth Catalog* and in response to demand for more extensive listings of Canadian tools and sources.

This *Almanac,* launched with financial aid from the *Whole Earth Catalog,* Portola Institute, Rochdale College, Coach House Press and others, lasted for five issues, spread over a period of about two years. It had gathered about a thousand subscribers and some not very good reviews, and, after an optimistic beginning, seemed to lose focus and the attention of its readers. Toward the end, the editorial explanations of what was happening within the *Almanac* became enigmatic but not without hints of the demise to come:

"Our promised dream issue never appeared. It seems impossible to issue a new magazine every season — and unnecessary. As a tactical gesture we are issuing a combination issue once a year. If you subscribe, you get four, whether or not we bring out four in a year."

The *Almanac* was being published out of Rochdale College, a modern high-rise structure on Toronto's Bloor Street that housed what was to become one of the brightest failures of alternative education and housing ever to spring up in North America. The incongruity of a *Whole Earth* publication coming out of this ultra-urban environment was not missed by everyone, and the Toronto *Star* sniped:

"One is forced to the conclusion that the people who buy the *Almanac* aren't really going to do or buy anything it recommends. It is all escapism, with even less reality than the plywood flamingoes on the lawns of York Mills."

Meanwhile, in the United States, the *Whole Earth Catalog* was also dying, by ritual suicide. Despite booming sales and rising profits, Stewart Brand pulled the plug on his brainchild in 1971, explaining it by saying, "As I was driving up the hill to work one day it suddenly hit me that I didn't want to. Instead of a golden opportunity, the publication was becoming a grim chore." In his farewell note to readers of the *Last Whole Earth Catalog,* Brand explained how the idea had come about — flying home from his father's funeral, thinking about friends moving to the country and in need of tools and information, and remembering the L.L. Bean catalogue, a family favourite, as an example of the useful and unusual made accessible. Click. Also included in the last edition was a piece entitled "How To Do A Whole Earth Catalog," with Brand's invitation for someone else to pick up the pieces of a success stopped in its prime.

Unrelated predecessors: The Canadian Whole Earth Almanac *began optimistically, engraved beaver and all, in 1970, but died two years later after attracting roughly 1,000 subscribers.*

By 1974, Brand was back with the *Whole Earth Epilog* and this explanation:

"In May 1971 we ceased making the *Whole Earth Catalog* forever, sincerely enough, on the expectation that someone would quickly come along and fill the niche better than we did. Well,

1) They didn't.

2) The *Last Whole Earth Catalog* continued to sell 5,000 copies a week with increasingly outdated information;

3) The North American economy began to lose its mind, putting more people in need of tools for independence and the economy as a whole in need of greater local resilience; and

4) After burning our bridges we reported before the Throne to announce, 'We're here for our next terrific idea.' The Throne said, 'That was it.' "

In Canada, the *Whole Earth Almanac* remained dead and the "back to the land" movement, for want of a better cliché, was generally written off as a '60s phenomenon that had died with it. *Saturday Night,* in fact, had dismissed the *Whole Earth Almanac* as moribund even before it slipped from sight, stating with authority that those who read such things "are on a nostalgia trip."

The next chapter in this continuing saga opens in June, 1976, with the appearance of *Harrowsmith* magazine, an idea for a local weekly rural newspaper that got out of control. There was, at the time, not even a glimmer of interest in creating an access catalogue.

By 1978, however, mail from readers asking for information about sources within Canada or that would serve Canadians began to overload our copy editors. In response we put together a slim booklet optimistically called *Sourcebook One* and gave something like 75,000 of them away free to *Harrowsmith* subscribers. At some point in this process, we discovered that the booklet's postage and printing costs were running upwards of $30,000 and adding substantially to the magazine's financial turmoil.

At the same time, source information — gleaned from *Harrowsmith* and augmented by reader input — began to increase almost exponentially, as did the number of requests for help on locating things missed in *Sourcebook One.* I'm not just sure when we decided that a full-blown sourcebook should be compiled, but the choice hardly seemed our own. The need to attempt a comprehensive sourcebook was clear, the magazine, with self-imposed advertising limitations, was unable to support itself without help from the sale of books and the first *Harrowsmith* anthology, and a new source directory seemed the answer.

We would like to think that this is not just another *Whole Earth Catalog* of the North, that somehow we have *Harrowsmith's* editorial stamp on the thing. The tone is different, the approach is different, and, as we push the final printer's forms out the door tonight, we are very aware that this book is far from "whole."

Despite three and a half years of experience in seeking out source information in Canada, we embarked on this project with great trepidation: could we fill a 288-page book without puffing, padding and creative use of white space? Determined not to fall short of our promised length, we threw the project open to *Harrowsmith* readers and contributors in an eleventh hour attempt to assure that we would have enough copy.

The result is the 320-page book you hold in your hands. That we ended up shelving perhaps 75 pages of prepared, typeset material, that the book could easily have gone to more than 500 pages without diluting its effect, is a source of no small amount of anguish here. Having set the price months prior to publication — allowing our national distributor to begin sales to book shops

— and having told our printer that it would be a 288-page book, we found ourselves suddenly trapped by financial constraints, paper shortages and our own faulty planning. To the credit of our new financial watchdog, John Page, he did not balk when we presented him with the compromise addition of 32 pages and no increase in the cover price.

In the end, the reader ends up with something of a bargain and we come away feeling heartened that "alternative" sources in Canada and serving Canadians are either growing in number or coming out of the woodwork for the first time. It is, I think, a fairly strong argument against those who would claim that "the back-to-basics thing is dead." The sheer numbers in the wood heat and solar chapters — along with 30 pages of natural foods sources we cut in last minute desperation — indicate, at least to us, that there are palpable changes afoot in this country.

Because this book has been produced largely in the spare time of art and editorial staffs who had no real time to spare, with weeks of evening hours, many past-midnight sessions and the knowledge that we had undertaken too much, too late, it is difficult to be objective about this *Sourcebook.* Surely there will be endless letters and calls telling us about those we missed, complaining about the service or quality of sources we have listed, offering personal experiences that either augment or fly in the face of descriptions included here. Fair enough. Having done the book once in gonzo fashion, we are more than ready to do it again, with even more reader input. Associate Editors Alice O'Connell and Pamela Cross (who shamed us all continually by staying at her desk "for just a couple hours more" after the rest of us had staggered out in the early morning hours), are already collecting material for the next edition, if there is to be one. (No firm plans have been set, but a supplement or revised edition will appear when enough readers let us know that one is due.)

We are reminded again of a quotation from Camus that we used when the first issue of *Harrowsmith* was sent off to the printer, hot from the kitchen table and with a great amount of uncertainty as to what we had created. "All great things," said the existentialist, "have ridiculous beginnings." While we would be the last to make claims of greatness for this particular book, we have a feeling of having relived the ridiculous once again. The best we can hope for is the kind of reader response that will allow us — or someone else — to move on to a Canadian source directory worthy of being called whole.

—*JL*

Confessions Of A Wood Stove Dealer

"Consumers should be aware that our guardians of fire are like rival clergy, none of whom has the Holy Book...."

It was a noble goal, my dream of retiring at 35. But now that I'm 34, the game plan will have to be revised. Last year, our first in the wood stove business, I thought I would finally get myself free of the nine-to-five rat race. I'm still working on it.

Wood stoves! Why not sell wood stoves? In a time of soaring fuel prices, living in a dairy county that is 60 per cent forest, why not sell wood stoves? Sure, there's competition — from hardware to drug stores — but they're all selling junk and the salesmen can't tell a baffle plate from china. And the factories can't keep up with the demand. Wood stoves. Why not sell wood stoves?

Our market research consisted of getting an assignment from the editor of a Sunday newspaper magazine for an article on the wood heat renaissance. Then I made the rounds of the wood stove dealers in the area, reporting what they had to say about the strength of their businesses. The dealers were delighted to be interviewed and to receive valuable publicity. And I was paid — shamefully little — for doing my research.

Here's what I learned initially: Few wood stove dealers are open for business year-round, full-time. Just as it is hopeless to push ski equipment in the summer, stove sales are brisk primarily from September to Christmas and then quickly fall off. Consequently, in our area the shops selling stoves exclusively are largely staffed by owners who have a full-time job by day — teaching school, for example — and sell stoves from low-rent quarters by night. This is not much of a handicap since husband and wife normally shop **together in the evening, when**

neither of them is working, for a ''major appliance.'' Some dealers, like us, sell stoves from their houses, garages or other structures adjoining their homes. The remaining dealers are retailers and other businessmen. The largest dealer in our area is a rural building contractor for whom the stove business is an excellent seasonal complement. The department stores and big hardware and lumber chains sell stoves, too, but they usually dispense the mass market El Cheapos.

Naturally you can't take too seriously retailers' raves about their businesses when they talk to interviewers. No one reported business was bad. (It was only later, in dealer-to-dealer conversations, that I got more frank appraisals.) But I did get some important numbers. It was mid-October of 1977 when one salesman said his boss' part-time shop was selling 15 stoves a week; another dealer's salesman (his son) reported that they had sold 300 units for the season. A brick manufacturing company, with a retail outlet selling fireplaces and stoves, was clearing out its hardware department to double the floor space allotted to stoves.

With this raw intelligence, my partner and I made some preliminary mail enquiries to stove manufacturers and discovered that wholesale stove prices are generally about 30 per cent less than list prices. If a good, medium-sized, heavy-duty, airtight stove generally costs $300 to $600, then dealers are grossing about $90 to $180 per sale, or so we thought. Simple arithmetic convinced us that a part-time shop could make a gross profit of $15,000 to $30,000 in a three- to four-month season.

Sobering Thoughts

At this point we were pretty high on the stove business, ready to drain the bank account, maybe even borrow money and fill the barn with more stoves than we could afford. Coming from working-class stock and being naturally cautious with sweaty cash, we managed to restrain ourselves until we could get some predictable but nevertheless sobering advice from small-business consultants (the casual kind you can sometimes get free from Chamber of Commerce people or management schools associated with universities). We heard the frightening statistics — one-third of small businesses fail in their first year and one-half in the second year; two-thirds never last five years. But, of course, we figured that statistics are what happen to other people.

Next, we turned to the problem of finding a manufacturer or distributor who would do business with us. We wanted to start a business with about $2,000 — would anybody take us seriously?

Contrary to a bum steer we got from another dealer, most stove manufacturers are continually beating the bush for new retailers. In most cases, if you've got enough cash for an initial order of X number of stoves, presto! You're a dealer. Usually manufacturers want you to buy at least three of their stoves (if they make only one model), or one of each model, sometimes as many as 10 stoves. But a hungry company with a large inventory, especially in spring and early summer, will negotiate on the terms of setting up a dealership. One young local company will set up a dealer with no conditions other than the novice retailer pay

cash in advance for one stove. In fact, few manufacturers will sell stoves to *any* small dealer without cash up front.

Since we wanted to carry several lines but had less than $2,000 for showroom models, we had to very carefully analyse our options. We found two young companies manufacturing one basic wood-burner, both of whom were happy to sell us single units; the terms were cash in advance and a vague promise from us to order a specified number of stoves later if they generated customer interest. After more rummaging, we opened up our shop in August, 1978, with seven floor models representing four manufacturers; we sell add-on units made by a fifth stovemaker who hasn't required us to keep a floor model in stock.

Next, our only problem was to sell stoves, and we turned our attention to the hard realities of advertising. Following the practice of some of our competitors, we decided to limit off-season

advertising to occasional classi-fieds; we'd budget something like 90 per cent of our advertising dollars for peak-season display ads. Even in the most humble weekly newspaper, large display ads are expensive to run regularly and, having been associated with newspapers for years, we know that some publications ''pull'' better than others — and some don't pull at all.

How else would we know where to advertise except by trial and error? At least three weeklies, two ''shoppers,'' and two dailies circulate in the sales territory we have staked out for ourselves. Then there are at least six radio and television stations.

One very large dealer told us that he blew $5,000 on advertising in a daily newspaper before he realized he couldn't trace a single sale to it. We decided to ask every prospect who came to the shop how they heard about us; we would keep careful records of the answers, sales activities, phone enquiries, etc.

This raw data hasn't produced a magic ad formula, partly because lots of customers don't know where they saw our ad or think, for example, that they heard about us on the radio even though we have never used costly airwaves. We think we have identified the most effective — for us at least — print medium: a multi-edition shoppers' newspaper delivered free to all of the rural homes in the county. In the fall we run a four-column-inch ad every week in the edition that covers a 20-mile radius from the shop. We cautiously plan to test a radio station soon.

By bartering our services as reporters, we gave three area weeklies the old college try: We traded feature stories and photos for equal amounts of display space. One weekly — with which we had no contract or barter agreement — even ran our new-business news release (the 8''x10'' glossies were irresistible); another paper carried our news release with photos on the front page.

Volatile Business

If there is one thing that seasoned dealers agree on, it is this: The wood stove business is volatile, and what was true last year may not be true this year. Yes, stove sales are *usually* slow in the spring and summer, but a decision by OPEC oil ministers can suddenly change that. In short, the business is unpredictably whiplashed by headlines about the energy crisis. Or the weather.

Last October, at the time when stove sales should have been building toward a feverish flurry, the weather was unusually mild in our region. Just as many drivers wait until it snows before buying snow tires, many homeowners finally decide what stove to buy only because their central heating systems are again beginning to eat them alive. But last October the oil burners weren't slurping their usual share, and by the time they developed an appetite, the cash registers were ringing merrily in tune with Christmas carols. Consumers don't buy wood stoves as stocking stuffers. And after the holidays they are either tapped out or paying off their bills. Then the worst of winter roars in; it's too cold for chimney work and they "can't afford" a quality stove. Maybe next year.

Consequently, last autumn was one of the leanest of recent sales seasons in our area.

Before consulting our accountant, a peer who will work for sweet corn, we could account for all of the money we invested: What little money we made — maybe $800— was tied up in unsold inventory; most of our other profits went to advertising. Not figuring our labour, we broke even. Not so, the accountant said, invoking the mumbo jumbo of tax laws and balance sheets (my partner keeps the books). Since the shop occupied one-third of the square footage of its owners' residence (the shop is confined to one wing of the house), it ought to pay one-third of the real estate taxes and utility bills; since we never wanted more than one telephone and the telephone company required us to have a business line (which costs more than residential service), the shop could properly be made to pay the telephone bill (excepting personal long distance calls); since our 1973 Toyota pickup is our personal as well as delivery vehicle, the shop could properly be charged for its use — never mind that its rusted-out fenders flutter in the wind, we are entitled to the same flat mileage allowance as the dealer who drives a shiny new one-ton V-8 with dual wheels and a hydraulic tailgate. And so on.

The bottom line, the accountant said confidently, is that the business lost money and didn't owe any taxes; its owners, therefore, could deduct the amount of the loss from their personal taxable income. We'll be getting an income tax refund.

We survived our first year without incurring any debt. By the business consultants' rule of thumb — that breaking even augurs well for one-year-old businesses — we are a qualified success. We have established a beachhead.

To place our balance sheet in a clearer perspective, we should say something about our location. Our shop-home is five miles from a village of 1,500 and 15 miles from a city of 60,000. While we're one and a half miles from an interstate highway connecting the village and city, our shop isn't visible from any road. In fact, our customers have to drive uphill for one mile on a dirt road; at the point where the road was abandoned 30 years ago, they turn into our 1,000-foot driveway and don't see a sign of civilization until our place suddenly appears in a clearing in the woods. Some of our city-slicker customers get out of their cars in a disbelieving, mild state of euphoria. Wood heat aficionados will drive long distances to see a particular stove — we've sold stoves to shoppers who drove 75 miles in one direction. You can't sell newspapers and chewing gum on a back country road, but you *can* sell wood stoves.

Shake-Out Coming

A trendy, hot new business is a business nevertheless, subject to the axiom that money begets money. Modest investments don't usually turn into fortunes overnight, and while big investment is generally a prerequisite to the big payoff, it is no guarantee. One of the biggest and best financed dealers we know says he is not sure he is making money. Wood stove retailers face the same headaches as other retailers: shipments delayed by strikes or shortages, damaged freight, poor quality control at the factory, expensive advertising costs, sales cycles, bad (good) weather, high costs of credit and tough competition.

We know of many dealers — kings and gypsies alike — who made large initial inventory purchases to get "exclusive" territories and thus gain a competitive edge. However, when another dealer came along with cash in hand, some slippery manufacturers had a ready answer. If a dealer hasn't sold enough units to keep the manufacturer happy, the manufacturer must dump him in favour of new blood, claiming the rights of rational self-interest, self-preservation and sound business practice. If the dealer is doing well, the manufacturer congratulates him and says the territory is now big enough for two.

The name of the game is Intense Competition. The toll it takes on the psyche of the small retailer is one of the hidden costs of doing business. The only way to avoid excessive anxiety about going bankrupt — or sweating through the lesser states thereof — is not to take risks. We could have mortgaged our farmstead for more start-up cash, but decided not to go for broke. Naturally our anxiety level would have been considerably higher if we had obtained a business loan. Even so, before our first season was over, we had $4,000 tied up in the business, double what we had anticipated. That represented just about everything we could scrape together, all of it saved from wages.

Don Lancaster, in his no-nonsense book about starting a small business, *The Incredible Secret Money Machine,* points out the advantage of being under-capitalized: *Having enough advance financing for your money machine is about the* worst *possible thing you can do and is almost certain to scuttle the whole machine.*

A glib but accurate reason is that if you have the money, you are only going to spend it. And spend it on things that are totally unnecessary and in ways that will commit you down the road to even higher future costs. For your money machine to work, you have to start out scared, lean and hungry . . . It's really difficult for any beginner to increase the amount of money he is handling by more than 20 per cent or so a year without starting to do stupid things with it or worrying too much about it.

If starting up a stove shop is risky, founding a stove manufacturing company is high-stakes gambling. Apparently, a great many entrepreneurs think wood stoves are the pet rocks of the energy crisis. According to Hal Illingworth, editor of the *National Woodstove and Fireplace Journal,* a trade publication, over 600 manufacturers are making wood stoves in the United States and Canada; there were perhaps one-twentieth that number in 1973, when an Arab-Israeli war precipitated an oil boycott and the stove manufacturers were deluged with orders.

About 75,000 stoves were manufactured annually in 1973, Illingworth says, while he conservatively estimates that 1979 production will reach at least 750,000. Most plants are operating at capacity.

Dealers are wary of the industry's rapid growth, and "the great shake-out" is expected by some within a few years. It is a normal and predictable phenomenon in a more or less capitalist economy: A sudden surge in demand produces a sudden surge in supply until suppliers are pruned back by saturation of the marketplace. This truism has important implications for wood stove consumers as well as those flirting with the idea of opening a stove shop. Unless a member of the latter group enjoys some unusual advantages, it may be too late to jump in now. The market for stoves may have already peaked or will peak in less than three years, the length of time it takes most small businesses to become solid and profitable. Then again, the OPEC sheiks can change the scenario overnight. Who can say whether we "got in on the ground floor"? Where's the ceiling? Differences of opinion are what make a horse race or a livelihood for market research analysts.

The most notable casualty so far is the Portland Stove Foundry of Maine, which manufactured stoves for 102 years before filing for bankruptcy last year. In recent years the company had back orders for as many as 4,000 stoves but, a company officer explained, 500,000 foreign-made stoves were imported in 1978.

"It's the cheap Taiwanese imports that are hitting us. What can you do when a stove from Taiwan arrives on the dock here for $38.00?"

Buyer's Market

The glut in the number of stove manufacturers and the competition among retailers works, of course, to the advantage of the consumer. The smart stove buyer goes shopping in late winter or early spring when the sales are very slow and discounts very high. (Actually, the smart stove buyer gets a stove any way he can, rather than wait another winter.) Buy fruits and vegetables

in season, buy stoves *out* of season.

The boom in the wood stove business means that the consumer does have one immediate problem in the bewildering variety of stoves to choose from. It also means that those shopping for stoves shouldn't be overly impressed by a ''lifetime guarantee'': We sell stoves with such guarantees as well as others with no guarantee at all, and we advise our customers to buy mainly on the basis of what they see rather than what they are promised. Some manufacturers of quality stoves must inevitably fall by the wayside, regardless of guarantees.

One reason for the huge number of stoves on the market is the relative ease with which an investor can form a company to make steel — as opposed to cast-iron — stoves.

''They buy the parts shaped or pre-cut from a steel mill and simply weld them together,'' said one partner in a three-year-old company making cast-iron stoves. ''But if you want to start making cast-iron stoves, you need a lot more up-front money for patterns from which to cast that very expensive first unit.''

The question of whether steel stoves are as good as those made of cast iron is continuously debated. It is a complex subject, but as a dealer we've become well-acquainted with the chief disadvantage of cast iron: It is brittle and a poor casting will crack in use. Large cast-iron stoves frequently weigh 300 pounds or more, and no matter how well they are crated for shipping, they don't take rough handling well enough. A painfully high number of our cast-iron stoves — at least those handled by several truckers — arrive at our shop broken, apparently because they've been dropped or bounced around. We know of one high-volume dealer specializing in cast-iron Scandinavian stoves who once had freight claims totalling $10,000.

The brittleness of cast iron is a problem compounded by the fact that most mortals can't tell the difference between a good casting

and a poor one. We can all compare cast-iron stoves by inspecting the workmanship, styling, firebox configuration, door size, etc. But no consumer can make a sound judgement, based on a visual inspection, of the quality of the metal itself.

''In any foundry, a significant percentage of the castings are thrown out because they don't come out well. Quality is variable,'' said Jay Shelton in a recent conversation. Shelton, a physics professor who wrote the authoritative *Woodburners Encyclopedia*, says, ''Even the stove companies with the best reputation for quality have bad stoves come through with castings that are defective and crack in use. That's part of the ball game.''

The problem of evaluating cast-iron stoves on the basis of reputation is further muddied by Shelton's remarks on Taiwanese stoves, the latest anathema to sellers of ''quality'' heaters. (One of our distributors says he wouldn't sell Taiwanese units as a matter of conscience.) Shelton believes the Taiwanese stoves, which are considerably less expensive than comparable North American ones, should not all be painted with the same broad stroke.

''It is hard for the consumer to tell whether the one (Taiwanese stove) he's looking at is good quality or not. In talking to people in the

industry, I gather that some of them are not bad at all. It's not fair to dump on all of them. It's probably true that a lot of them are not good quality. But I don't know of any handy-dandy way for a consumer to look at one and know what he's looking at.

''A good foundry anyplace can make good castings. Some foundries there can — and do — make good products.''

In addition to our concern about the quality of the castings, we do not sell Taiwanese stoves for a variety of reasons. Mainly, we don't think it's wise to go toe-to-toe with the discount houses and chain drug stores, which sell them. When customers ask our advice on buying such units, we tell them to buy Taiwanese if money constraints force them to make a choice between a cheap Taiwanese airtight and a cheap but non-airtight domestic stove. But, since cast-iron stoves can be expected to last a lifetime, our personal choice would be to pay about $200 more for a domestically made unit, especially as their workmanship is usually far superior. In either case, if we were buying a cast-iron stove, we would not buy one via the mails (freight claims and return shipping can become the consumer's rather than the retailer's headache), and we would avoid any cast-iron stove that has a thin or invisible service organization behind it. Getting parts for a foreign-made stove can be an exasperating process.

Quality control problems are hardly limited to the casting of iron. Because the business is highly seasonal, manufacturers' payrolls see-saw with demand, and, therefore, employee turnover is high. Since most stove companies are essentially parts-assembly operations, much of the labour force — unskilled and semi-skilled — earns low wages. Low pay and high turnover means that retailers can't take quality control for granted. For this reason we usually ask our customers to inspect their new stove carefully with us at the time of delivery.

Dearth Of Information

The problem with making generalizations about wood stoves is that there's often not enough rigorous research data to back them up. Although wood is man's oldest fuel, wood heat technology is in its infancy. Before 1973, anyone who might have known about airtight stoves had a very difficult time finding one. Until late last spring, there was virtually no independent laboratory-type testing and comparison of stove performances, for example. A group at Auburn University in Auburn, Alabama, has begun testing with funds from the U.S. Department of Energy and the Fireplace Institute. In Canada, safety standards are being set by the Canadian Standards Association (CSA) and by Underwriters' Laboratory Canada (ULC). Although results still remain unpublished, the Ministry of Energy Mines and Resources has just completed testing a dozen different airtight stove designs, evaluating efficiency; data may be released in 1980. One can debate the merits of a bi-level design over a downdrafter or an S-draft stove, but there is precious little hard data to go on. That is why a deep sense of skepticism colours all our judgements about manufacturers' claims. Many dealers, too, are less than candid about this information gap. We hear an awful lot of other dealers' propaganda — admittedly second hand — that customers have picked up shopping elsewhere,

some of it simply uninformed, lots of it self-serving baloney. Last fall, we were incensed to read a local newspaper article by a normally solid reporter comparing the relative costs of energy, in which he declared — with undocumented figures — that only electric heat was more expensive than wood heat. Recently we attended an all-day, university-sponsored symposium on the energy crisis; a geologist scheduled to discuss the alternatives to oil never even mentioned wood.

In a post-lecture, corner-him-in-the-hall discussion, the geologist's remarks revealed unstated attitudes about wood that have kept it on the back burner: Wood is dirty, it's primitive and for the rural poor. These are apparently the personal attitudes of the legislators, opinion-makers and bureaucrats who make the decisions affecting energy policy. How else account for the fact that only one per cent of the U.S. Department of Energy's $8 billion budget ($8 million) is devoted to wood fuel research?

Jay Shelton has also been doing some independent research on stove performance, but he is still searching for funding that will allow him to do thorough, published comparisons of the top 10 or 20 stoves *by brand name.*

Too many consumers are under the impression that such research is already being done by groups like the International Conference of Building Officials (ICBO) or Underwriters' Laboratory. But an ''approved'' or ''listed'' stove isn't necessarily better than another one because (1) not all stoves have yet been evaluated by these groups (those that flunk aren't identified) and (2) these organizations evaluate safety, *not performance.*

Where To Buy

''Even in the area of safety,'' Shelton says, ''the standard is under active discussion within the industry. Safety is very complicated because you can do something to make a stove safe with respect to a certain conceived accident and end up having it more dangerous with respect to some other kind of accident.

''It's safer, for example, to have all stove doors welded shut so you can't have a fire in them. It's hard to know where the appropriate middle ground is.''

It is true, of course, that consumers are in little better shape when they buy dozens of other expensive goods that are complex and potentially dangerous — automobiles and oil furnaces, for example.

We have not found the perfect wood stove, probably because perfection exists only in theology and mathematics. Nor are dealers as well-informed as they should be; some are beginning to talk about dealer licensing because (1) misinformation or omissions endanger the lives and property of our customers, and (2) stove-related fires are a tremendous industry PR problem. But, until stove-shopping consumers make it their business to be well-informed, at least as well as their grandparents were, they're left to rely on their common sense and their intuition to identify a snow job.

The best approach is to visit as many stove dealers as possible, asking questions, comparing prices and services (if you drive a subcompact car and intend to buy a 400-pound firebrick-lined wood burner, delivery is something to ponder). In an area where competition is flourishing, prices will vary, sometimes substantially. Several of the stoves we sell in our own business are also handled by competitors within an uncomfortably close distance.

Although we think we give a respectable discount — 10 per cent — we can't always undersell Them. Although we have the world's lowest overhead, our biggest competitor does a higher volume of business and therefore gets a better deal at the factory; also, when the manufacturers are lopping hefty discounts from the off-season wholesale prices, Mr. Moneybags has got the capital and storage space needed to help give him a competitive advantage. On the other hand, we know a high-volume dealer who sells all his stoves at the list price *plus* shipping. So stove shoppers would be well advised to follow the cardinal rule of bargain hunters: Shop around, and don't make any strong assumptions about where you'll find the best deal or that irresistible "discontinued model."

Finally, be aware that our guardians of fire, wood stove "experts," are like rival clergy, none of whom has the Holy Book, and that, therefore, they can have only the most tenuous claim to their titles. Often the most helpful dealer will be one in an out-of-the-way country place, where the pressure to buy is low and the information dispensed comes from some one with first-hand knowledge of the stoves being sold. That, perhaps, leads us to the best shorthand sign of a good stove dealer: Unless you know exactly what you want, think twice about taking advice or buying a stove from the guy who goes home to an oil furnace every night.

— *Hal Smith*
Windsor, New York

Quest For The Magic Stove

Confusion in the airtight world

The young couple hesitated at the front door of our farmhouse, obviously wondering if they could possibly be at the right place. "Um . . . er . . . ah, do you sell — ah — sell woodburning stoves?"

It was the fall of 1977, and we had stoves set up in every spare corner of our rambling farmhouse in an Amish community near Aylmer, Ontario. I assured the couple that they had indeed found the right place and showed them every stove we had on display in the two rooms downstairs — cookstoves, downdrafters, Franklins. Nothing caught their eye.

"We know what we want," the lady finally offered. "But we don't know what you call it. It's sort of, you know, square and . . . and . . . ."

Lacking more detailed description, I led the people upstairs to show them, one by one, every stove we had in the house. At the top of the stairway the lady called out. "There it is — that's the one! That's the one we want."

She was bearing down on an Ashley cabinet model that stood with the front toward us. She reached out and touched the smooth finish, her face glowing. "We've looked all over to find a stove like this!"

"You see," her husband explained, "we don't have a chimney in our house. So we need this stove without a smoke pipe . . . ."

The sentence stopped in mid-air. The young man's eyes had followed mine to the point at the back of the cabinet where both of us could see the flue opening.

I truly felt sorry for the disappointed pair as they turned to leave. Apparently they had studied a picture of a cabinet

model stove in a newspaper ad, and since no flue opening was visible, they had concluded this was the right stove for them. As gently as I could, I explained that the stove they were seeking hadn't been invented yet.

Although stove manufacturers have not yet come up with a stackless stove, there seems to be little else they haven't thought of. Each year the rush continues as manufacturers compete with one another to put a stove on the market with a superior feature or design.

Ten years ago, a person interested in purchasing a wood burner had a hard time finding what he wanted. New woodburning stoves simply were not readily available. Today the same person may once again have a difficult time finding the stove he wants — simply because there are now so many different models and designs clamouring for his attention, each supposedly superior to the others. The variety can be confusing.

The Big Three

Let's sort the essentials from the non-essentials. Selecting a stove doesn't have to be as complicated as it may appear at first glance. There are really only three main things to keep in mind — three important qualities to insist on when buying a stove. Granted, there are several dozen other, lesser factors to take into account, but for now we will concentrate on The Big Three.

The three vital questions to ask when buying a wood burner are: Number One: Is the stove airtight? Number Two: Is the stove airtight? Number Three: Is the stove airtight?

That may seem like overstating the case. Actually, it is hard to

overemphasize the value of an airtight design in a woodburning stove. A lot of old-timers shake their heads at the current rush to put in wood burners. "Remember, Ma, how glad we were to carry that old potbelly out of the living room? And how tickled we were with our new oil furnace!" They find it difficult to understand the enthusiasm, even excitement, their grandchildren experience at lighting up a lowly wood stove.

But what Grandfather may fail to realize is that Grandson is not really going back to what the earlier generation threw out. Beyond the fact that both require some sort of chimney, there is little similarity between the potbelly Grandfather so gladly junked, and the efficient, airtight stove of today.

In fact, older people, experienced and skilled with the stoves of yesterday, sometimes have greater difficulty learning to use airtights than do the greenhorns. Not that airtights are so very complicated. It is just that these people permit what they think they know to get in the way of what they need to learn. I recall one busy Saturday morning when both my wife and I were showing customers through the store. We could not keep up, and some customers had to wait while we showed others through.

One seasoned backwoodsman, when his turn came, scoffed at the ignorance of a young man who had just purchased a stove. "Huh!" he snorted, "Some of these young fellas don't know a thing about building a fire. I'll bet when he gets ready to use that stove, he'll come back complaining that he can't locate the switch to turn it on."

His judgement of the young man's expertise in wood burning may well have been more accurate

than his opinion of his own. I ran headlong into a confrontation when I explained how to install the stovepipe on an airtight.

"Son," he said condescendingly, "I was setting up woodburning stoves long before you were born. The crimped end of the pipe always goes up — always. Common sense will tell you that — otherwise smoke leaks all over the room."

I did not argue with him. Obviously he had made up his mind, and did not care to be confused by facts. But what he failed to realize was that the user of an airtight is much more concerned about creosote leaking into the room than he is about smoke. In the days before airtights were invented, no one had a creosote problem. Having nothing more serious to worry about, people fussed about smoke leaking from pipe joints.

Smoke can leak, it is true, but the direction of the pipe ends won't stop it. If you have a good chimney draft, smoke will go up the pipe; if you don't, it won't. On the other hand, creosote *is* affected by the way the pipe is installed. If the pipes are correctly installed with the crimped ends down, and all the horizontal stretches sloping back toward the stove, excess creosote will drain back into the stove to be burned. If installed incorrectly, it will leak from the joints between sections of stovepipe, creating both mess and offensive odours.

Controlled Burn

Airtights are infinitely superior to non-airtights on two counts. First is efficiency. Some things in life are hard to measure, and the efficiency of wood stoves is one of them. Some authorities rate airtights as 60 per cent more efficient than non-airtights. Others put the figure higher, even as high as 80 or 90 per cent. Whatever the exact figure, there is no dispute that a vast difference does exist. Much less wood is required to heat the same space, due to less heat escaping up the chimney, and also because of more complete combustion. An airtight leaves only a fraction of the ash a non-airtight will leave.

Most traditional stoves were so notoriously inefficient some old-timers claim, with obvious exaggeration, that during the colder parts of winter they wouldn't get to see the wife's face for several weeks. Every time they came in the front door with an armload of wood, she hurried out the back with a panful of ashes.

The second great advantage of airtights is control. The tighter the stove, the better the control. Fire cannot burn without oxygen. Grandfather only had two recourses, beyond shutting down the stove, which on a windy night frequently had little effect. One was to shut the damper in the stovepipe. The other was to be selective in choosing the fuel being fed to the fire. During the daytime, our forebears put on only a bit of wood at a time, and added fuel frequently. During the night, unless they wanted to get up to feed the fire every two hours, they banked it. This meant guessing how much wind there would be the rest of the night, and consequently how much draft the stove would have, and then loading it with the correct proportion of green wood and dry. I recall one customer who had things all figured out. He couldn't see why he should have to add wood more than once a day. If a medium-sized stove held enough wood for a 12-hour burn, he calculated, a stove with double the capacity would heat his house for 24 hours. Once a day refueling. A great theory, and like many great theories, it doesn't work in practice.

No stove should be kept continually on a low, slow burn. Otherwise, creosote buildup can plug the stovepipes and chimney in a matter of days. There is a great deal of controversy about creosote and what causes it, and people are quick to blame the chimney, or the wood, or the stove. No doubt all three can be contributing factors, but in my opinion, the operator is more likely the villain. If you allow the fire to smoulder continuously in a low burn, you will have serious creosote problems. If, however, you open the drafts and allow a good roaring fire to burn away creosote once or twice a day, problems will be minimized.

A stove should never be criticized because it produces creosote. The ability to produce creosote is the best testimony in the world to a good stove; a non-airtight allows the wood to burn rapidly at all times, with little or no creosote formation but with poor efficiency.

If too big a stove is bad —it *must* be kept on slow burn — how about too small? Too small also presents problems. For one thing, a too-small stove won't hold enough wood for an extended burn. Also, during cold spells, you may have to push a stove very hard just to keep the room warm. Overheating a stove is not only dangerous, but doing so day after day will almost certainly shorten the life of the stove.

If you have toddlers, or often have visitors with small children, a model enclosed in a cabinet may be your "best" stove. Stove burns can be painful, even serious. Your own child will soon learn not to touch a hot stove, but it may not be so simple to train the children of all your visitors, who may have no experience whatever with furniture that is too hot to handle. Be wary of stoves with no cabinets whose manufacturers claim the exterior does not become too hot to touch. Unless there is a double wall, discount any such claim until proven otherwise.

Also, when choosing the stove "best" for you, consider where it will be located in the house. If it is to heat only one room, a radiating heater is great. If you are counting on the stove to heat several rooms, you probably need a circulating heater — especially if the stove is not centrally located. In simple words, a circulating heater is one with a cabinet, and/or fan. Many people believe a cabinet is mostly for looks, to keep a stove from looking like a stove, and to prevent burns. It does more. A cabinet, even without a fan, adds a circulating effect, pushing hot air upward, and drawing cold air from the floor. Circulation is greatly aided, of course, by a fan, which takes air in a reverse direction, pulling it from the ceiling and expelling it along the floor, resulting in a cooler ceiling and a warmer floor. (All fans require electricity).

Creosote Villain

Select a stove that is the right size for your house. The neighbour may rave about his new stove, and how well it heats all 11 rooms of his farmhouse. That's great — for him. It may be too great for you. Your house may be smaller and better insulated. The Btu output that keeps Neighbour toasty may be enough to drive you out into the snow.

But no matter how skillful they became in predicting the weather, and judging the moisture content of wood, many a night our ancestors kicked off the covers for the first half of the night, and slept chilly the second half, sweat beads having turned into goose pimples.

Today, with an airtight in the house, we light a fire in the fall, and it burns until spring. Nor do we need two wood boxes, one for green wood and one for dry. We fill the stove, and sleep comfortably all night, with no one staying awake to tend the fire. That modern little gadget, the thermostat, faithfully opens the air intake when the room gets chilly and closes it when it warms up.

Please, Grandfather, stop shaking your head.

The "Best"

One day a customer caught me alone in the store. He decided the moment of truth had arrived.

"Tell me," he said, "you have a dozen different kinds of stoves in here — tell me exactly in your honest opinion — which is the best?"

He was expecting me to say, "Ashley," or "Tempwood," or "Shenandoah," or some other brand. Unfortunately, no such answer exists. There simply is no stove that can be recommended as "best" for everyone — too much depends on where the stove will be located and what will be demanded of it.

If the primary objective is preparing meals, a cookstove is the obvious choice. If you cut your own firewood, and don't enjoy splitting wood, you should insist on a stove that features a large door and a long firebox.

If you aren't concerned about saving money, and just want a stove where you can see the fire, a Franklin type with an open, fireplace-like front may suffice. Some people still don't worry that most of the heat escapes up the chimney — they are happy enough just to see flames. Or perhaps the stove will be used just as a standby for emergency use, something to heat and cook with when the hydro fails. A common, inexpensive box stove will carry most homes through nicely, and the stove can be bought for a hundred dollars. It will keep you from freezing, heat your coffee and thaw some snow for drinking water. Why spend $500 for a stove that will be used only two days every five years?

Great Grates

Should you buy a stove with grates, or with none? For some reason most magazine articles and books on stovelore treat this subject by ignoring it. Perhaps this is so because many authors are as confused on the subject as many stove manufacturers would like all of us to be. Generally, stove manufacturers dislike grates. This is because grates make stove building more complex and also more expensive. I will admit at the outset that I am perhaps rather biased in favour of grates. They have a lot going for them, although there are disadvantages.

If the grates are shaken too frequently, or too vigorously, live coals will drop into the ash pan. This prevents maximum combustion and accordingly decreases efficiency. My solution to this problem is to make sure there is always a good buildup of ashes *above* the grate. In fact, I almost never shake the grates, even when they are shakeable, which many aren't. When the ash builds up above an acceptable level, I force some down with a poker. Also, grates may somewhat shorten the lifespan of your stove, since they tend to be the first thing to warp or break.

But grates have one big plus in their favour that cancels all the disadvantages — they make ash removal much, much easier. I would rate this especially important when heating a family dwelling. It can be a chilling experience to need to let the fire die down in January just to be able to remove ashes.

Don't be misled by promotion that promises, "Ash removal necessary only two or three times a season." In the Bahamas, perhaps. Certainly not in Canada, unless a stove is used only occasionally for supplementary heat. In the coldest part of winter, a stove that is used continually can realistically be expected to require ash removal every two or three weeks.

Of course, the no-grate fans say you don't need to let the fire go out in the stove. The recommended procedure is to remove ashes in the morning when the fire is low, scraping the live coals to the back and taking the ashes that have been uncovered. But this is nearly impossible to do without getting live coals mixed in with the ashes, and bingo, there goes all the efficiency you gained by not having grates. Anyone who has tried to shovel ashes from a stove into another container knows it can be messy — the slightest mis-move, can send clouds of dust throughout the room.

It should also be pointed out that some fuels, such as coal, do not burn well in a stove without grates. If a stove is to be used where it will not be heating continually, however, a model without grates is fine. Where the fire is permitted to die out each evening, or even each weekend, that will take care of most of the disadvantages of having no grates. Ashes can be removed when the stove is cold before kindling the new fire.

Although I cannot endorse some manufacturers' claims of ash removal being necessary only two or three times a season, it is true that airtights produce comparatively few ashes. Last winter I sold a downdraft stove to my closest neighbour and he had not used it more than a few days before he complained that, contrary to what I had led him to expect, ashes seemed to build up rapidly and he would soon need to remove them. A few days later he came over, grinning — and apologizing. "I decided to let the fire go out," he explained, "so I could empty the ashes. But the fire wouldn't go out. Twenty-four hours later it was still burning, and I hadn't added wood all that time."

Too green?

Too long?

He had made the mistake of feeding the stove too rapidly, and a deep bed of charcoal had built up. When the fire finally burned down, he went to remove the ashes, only to find there were none.

Brick vs. Cast Iron

All good stoves are lined, usually with brick or cast iron. There are people who would pay 50 dollars more for a stove with a brick lining. There are also people who would pay that much more for a stove with a cast-iron lining. I would do neither. Either one, if of a good quality and properly designed and installed, should be sufficient to do the job. Compare the height of linings in the firebox. It is true that the most intense heat is at the base of the fire, but even at that, some liners are skimpy and shallow.

If you do buy a brick liner, remember that bricks are breakable if banged with firewood when hot; with reasonable care, however, this should not be a problem.

A Touch of Magic

I have a kindly word for cookstoves any day. Our cookstove is more than a stove — it is a member of the family. In the morning I awaken it even before I call my wife. Here is where the eggs are fried, the oatmeal cooked, the bread baked, but more importantly, where our family gathers in a half circle to read aloud a book, to discuss the day's events, mend socks, do homework, or sing an evening hymn. The cookstove greets each child with a warm embrace as he scrambles from bed in the morning, and bids him goodnight in the evening as he hangs up wet mittens before retiring.

Unfortunately, the airtight revolution is only now being introduced into the cookstove world. All old cookstoves are non-airtights. In fact, only a small percentage of the new ones sold today are airtights. The airtight cookstoves that are now on the market are relatively expensive. Hopefully, as they are built in greater volume, the price will become more affordable.

Last fall I began noticing large stove ads in a weekly newspaper, with ads picturing a slant-topped stove, which the manufacturer dubbed "pyramid shaped." The stove was declared "literally phenomenal." I thought that description fitted the ads better than the stoves, but the designer, a Mr. Gatling, claimed he had been shown the stove in a dream; it was a miracle sent down from heaven. The Gatling Stove promised to "burn wood, coal, paper, pine cones, corn cobs, sawdust, bark and even peanut hulls." In fact, as the ad put it, it would handle "almost anything combustible," and managed to make it sound as though that were something unusual for stoves.

A good friend responded to the ad and ordered a stove. Upon my first visit to his house, I looked it over closely. In spite of the flamboyant ads, it wasn't a bad stove. It was well-built and reasonably airtight. I glanced up to catch my friend studying my face. He was anxious for the verdict, a bit fidgety at the thought of the price he had paid. "The dealer said it's truly a magic stove," he offered. "What do you think?"

"Well . . . ." How could I be both honest and charitable? "Maybe . . . magic is not quite the right word, but it is a good stove — a real good stove."

Later, I wasn't so sure I had done right to balk at the word magic. So what if it didn't do more than other airtights? So what if it resembled a dog house more than a pyramid? My friend had needed a stove and it would serve him well. It would add warmth and comfort to his house. It would dry his gloves and warm his feet. It would make him chuckle to himself when the fuel truck backed into the neighbour's driveway. And it would do all that on pine cones, bark, corn cobs, sawdust, newspaper logs, coal, peanut hulls — in fact, on almost anything combustible.

If that isn't magic, what is?

—Elmo Stoll
Aylmer, Ontario

(Elmo Stoll is a farmer and a leader in his Old Order Amish community.)

SPACE HEATERS

ASHLEY ONTARIO DISTRIBUTORS
3322 Dundas Street West
Toronto, Ontario M6P 2A4
(416) 762-4582
(Distributor)

MODEL: Ashley Columbian
Material: Blued steel body with cast-iron legs, top, flue collar, door frame, door
Description: Cylindrical stove with thermostatically controlled (bi-metal helix) downdraft
Airtight
Made in U.S.A.
$279

ATLANTA STOVE WORKS
6757 Northwest Drive
Mississauga, Ont. L4V 1L1
(416) 677-0144
(Distributor)

MODEL: Woodsman 24
Material: Cast iron
Description: Box stove with side baffles and upper heat chamber.

Primary and secondary air intake through fuel door.
Airtight
Made in U.S.A.
$500
Shorter model, Woodsman 20, $440

MODEL: Huntsman 30
Material: Steel with cast-iron door and firebrick lining
Description: Stepstove design. Flue extends 12″ into upper heat chamber.
Airtight
Made in U.S.A.
$450
Shorter model, Huntsman 241, $440

MODEL: Old Hickory
Material: Cast iron
Description: Box stove with draft regulator for primary and secondary air
Airtight
Made in U.S.A.
$229

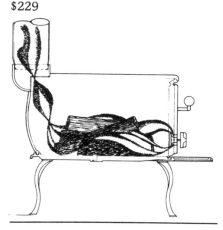

BAY BARN
Box 250
Seeleys Bay, Ontario
(613) 387-3273
(Distributor)

Reg Kumm sells a variety of wood stoves, 1850 to 1979 models. Also rebuilds antique stoves. Has over 600 stoves in stock.

BEAVER WOOD STOVES
Suite 201, 1300 Don Mills Rd.
Don Mills, Ontario M3B 2W6
(416) 487-0519
(Manufacturer)

MODEL: Beaver 24″
Material: Steel, cast-iron door
Description: Stepstove design

Larger model, Beaver 30″ available ($430)
Airtight
Made in Canada
$375

CAMAIRD PRODUCTS LTD.
Box 436
Hampton, N. B. E0G 1Z0
(506) 832-4195
(Manufacturer)

MODEL: Independence
Material: All steel
Description: Box stove with interior baffle
Not airtight
Made in Canada
Small size $310
Large size $395
Round model $285

CARMOR MFG. LIMITED
325 Hale Street
London, Ontario N5W 1G3
(519) 453-8160
(Manufacturer)

MODEL: Carmor
Material: Steel, cast-iron top, firebrick lining
Description: Top loading with downdraft burn design. Preheated air carried down to fire box through draft tubes.
Airtight
Made in Canada
$260—$500 (various models)

NORM CARTER AGENCIES
971 Bayview Square,
Coquitlam, B.C. V3J 5M6
(604) 936-3811
(Distributor)

MODEL: Mountain-Aire

Material: Steel, firebrick lined
Description: Modified box stove with curved sides. Large loading door. Thermostat.
Airtight
Made in U.S.A.
$515—$619

Mountain-Aire

MODEL: Bunn's Warmer
Material: Steel, firebrick lined
Description: Box stove with baking oven built into side. Oven temperature gauge. Fire viewing screen on freestanding fireplace model.
Airtight
Made in U.S.A.

CAWLEY STOVE CO. INC.
27 North Washington St.
Boyertown, Pennsylvania
(215) 367-2643
(Manufacturer)

MODEL: Cawley/LeMay 400
Material: Cast iron
Description: Box stove with sculptured sides. Movable baffles. Cookstove top has two lids. Adjustable feet for levelling.
Airtight
Made in U.S.A.
$550
Larger model, Cawley/LeMay 600,

$680
Canadian Distributor:
Energy Alternatives
2 Croft Street
Amherst, Nova Seotia
(902) 667-2790

CEMI PRODUCTS LTD.
Box 290
Ashland, Ohio 44805
(419) 289-2224
(Manufacturer)

MODEL: Independence
Material: Steel, cast-iron door or see-through glass door. Firebrick lined.
Description: Stepstove design. Baffle burn. Two 2'' x 4'' air ducts to circulate air from floor through stove. Twin blowers.
Airtight
Made in U.S.A.
$590
Canadian distributor:
Cemi Products Limited
Box 3580 Station C
Hamilton, Ontario L8H 7M9
(416) 561-9343

D. CHURCH & CO. LTD.
40 Trillium Park Place
Kitchener, Ontario N2E 1X1
(519) 743-9491
(Manufacturer)

MODEL: Church C
Material: Steel, steel liner
Description: Bi-metallic coil thermostat. Primary and secondary draft mix flue gases with superheated air to ''burn wood twice.''
Airtight
Made in Canada
$440
Smaller version, Church B, $390

COLE CREEK FARM-STEADING PRODUCTS
R.R.1
Verona, Ontario K0H 2W0
(613) 374-2936
(Manufacturer)

MODEL: Stove kit
Material: Cast-iron parts
Description: Parts bolt onto 45-gallon drum (not included) to make round wood heater
Made in Canada
$63—$90 (depending on style)

THE COOKSTOVE CABIN
Box 1233
Belleville, Ontario K0K 2V0
(613) 477-2684 or 962-2430
(Manufacturer)

MODEL: Little Hooter
Material: Steel, cast-iron door, firebrick lined
Description: Box stove with baffle burn design. Has 1.5-gallon humidifier. Cast-iron owl on door has tempered glass eyes.
Airtight
Made in Canada
$550

CORRIGANS WELDING & WOOD STOVE CENTRE
East Royalty, P.E.I.
(902) 892-3159
(Manufacturer)

MODEL: Patlyn
Material: Steel, cast-iron door
Description: Box stove with air jacket serving as top baffle plate. Manual or thermostatic operation.
Airtight
Made in Canada
$450

COSMAN'S WOOD HEAT UNLIMITED
327-329 Carlton Street
Winnipeg, Manitoba R3B 2K7
(207) 942-5719
(Distributor)
MODEL: Dynapac Stovaway
Material: Steel
Description: Box stove bolted together by user. Can be unbolted for storage. Supplementary or camping heater.
Not airtight
Made in U.S.A.
$200

DE LUXE EQUIPMENT INC.
8026 Jarry Street East
Ville d'Anjou, P.Q. H1J 1H5
(514) 354-1155
(Distributor)

MODEL: Jotul 118
Material: Cast iron, firebrick lining
Description: Sculpted design. Horizontal baffle with upper heat chamber. Front-end combustion. Airtight
Made in Norway
$600 (black); $700 (green)

Jotul 118

MODEL: Jotul 606
Material: Cast iron, firebrick lined
Description: Box stove with large arched heat exchanger top. Cast-iron design simulates decorative tile stoves.
Airtight
Made in Norway
$665

MODEL: Jotul 602
Material: Cast iron, firebrick lining
Description: Baffle burn design and front-end combustion. Cooking lid.
Airtight
Made in Norway
$339

Jotul 602

DE PENCIER MFG. LTD.
Box 177
Kingston, Ontario
(613) 549-8711
(Manufacturer)

MODEL: Basic
Material: Steel, cast-iron door
Description: Box heater. Sliding baffle flame control. Can be used as fireplace with screen ($45.)
Airtight
Made in Canada
$450

Dominion 001

DOMINION MFG. CO.
Bridgewater, Virginia 22812
(703) 828-6454
(Manufacturer)

MODEL: Dominion
Material: Steel, cast-iron door, firebrick lined
Description: Box stove with vertical heat retaining panel. Model 001 has air circulation tubes through stove. Model 003 has stepstove design.
Airtight
Made in U.S.A.
Model 001 $335 (U.S.)
Model 002 $280 (U.S.)
Model 003 $300 (U.S.)

EASTERN ONTARIO STOVE WORKS INC.

5 Victoria Avenue
Marmora, Ontario K0K 2M0
(613) 472-2430
(Manufacturer)

MODEL: Fisher Baby Bear, Fisher Mama Bear, Fisher Papa Bear
Material: Steel, cast-iron door, firebrick lining
Description: Stepstove burn design. Triple seal door.
Airtight
Made in Canada
Baby Bear $330
Mama Bear $410
Papa Bear $450

Fisher Mama Bear

Other Fisher stove plants in Canada:

Fisher Stove Works
2413 Hwy. 97
North Kelowna, B.C. V1X 4J2
(604) 860-8539

Lajoie Enterprises Ltd.
Box 1700
Grand Falls, N.B. E0J 1M0
(506) 473-4827

Dynes Wismer Limited
Box 36, R.R.1 Cashway Road
Barrie, Ontario L4M 4F9
(705) 726-4237

Fisher Stoves of Western Canada Limited
940 James Street
Winnipeg, Manitoba R3H 0K3
(204) 774-4804

Fisher Stove Works Ltd.
1414 Charlotte Road
N. Vancouver, B.C. V7J 1H2
(604) 985-1515

ENERCRAFT MFG. LTD.

R.R.1
Barrie, Ontario L4M 4Y8
(705) 726-3293
(Manufacturer)

MODEL: 100-201
Material: Steel, cast-iron door, firebrick lining
Description: Stepstove design with horizontal baffle. Flue extends into upper chamber. Bi-metal thermostat.
Airtight
Made in Canada
$549

ENERGY HARVESTERS CORPORATION

Box 19
Fitzwilliam, N.H. 03447
(603) 585-3300
(Manufacturer)

MODEL: Energy Harvesters
Material: Cast iron with cast-iron ribs
Description: Angled box style with sculptured motif. Interior baffle. Ribs hold wood away from sides.
Airtight
Made in U.S.A.
$448 (U.S.)
Canadian distributor:
Energy Alternatives
2 Croft Street, Box 671
Amherst, N.S. B4H 4B8
(902) 667-2790

ENHEAT LIMITED FAWCETT DIVISION

100 Main Street
Sackville, N.B. E0A 3C0
(506) 536-1520
(Manufacturer)

MODEL: Acadian
Material: Blued steel

Description: Cylindrical side loading stove. Bi-metal thermostat.
Airtight
Made in Canada
$325
MODEL: Herald 24
Material: Cast iron
Description: Box stove with sculpted designs, front damper and two stove lids
Not airtight
Made in Canada
Smaller model $225
Larger size $300

THE ENTERPRISE FOUNDRY CO. LTD.

Sackville, N.B. E0A 3C0
(506) 536-1160
(Manufacturer)

MODEL: BH25
Material: Steel
Description: Box stove suitable for camping or workshop
Not airtight
Made in Canada
$101
MODEL: Enterprise Box 25
Material: Cast iron
Description: Box stove with two stove lids. Front or top loading. Sculpted sides.
Not airtight
Made in Canada
$235

THE FARMER'S STOVE LTD.

66 Russett Avenue
Oshawa, Ont. L1G 3R5
(416) 576-6120
(Manufacturer)
MODEL: Pioneer and Cottager
Material: Steel, cast-iron door, firebrick lined
Description: Single door stepstove
Airtight
Made in Canada
Pioneer $339
Cottager $409

FERON CO. LTD.

49 Wright Avenue
Dartmouth, N.S.
(902) 463-2953
(Distributor)

MODEL: Morso 1B
Material: Cast iron, matte black enamelled finish

Description: Box stove with air circulator on inside of door. Front-end combustion.
Airtight
Made in Denmark
$495
Smaller model, Morso 2B, $365

Morso 1B

MODEL: Morso 1B0
Material: Cast iron, matte black enamelled finish
Description: Box stove with arched head exchanger top. Front-end combustion. Air circulator on inside of door.
Airtight
Made in Denmark
$695
Smaller model, Morso 2B0, $490

Morso 1B0

FINDLAY COMFORT SYSTEMS
60 Otonabee Drive
Kitchener, Ont. N2C 1L6
(519) 893-6531
(Manufacturer)

MODEL: Findlay Conestogo
Material: Steel, cast-iron doors, firebrick lined
Description: Stepstove design. Horizontal baffle. Twin draft control.
Airtight
Made in Canada
For price, contact local Findlay dealer.

FINEST STOVE IMPORTS, INC.
Box 1733
Silver Spring, Maryland 20902
(301) 946-4822
(Distributor)

MODEL: KH77 and KH56
Material: Ceramic tiles, fireclay lined, steel door
Description: Ceramic tile box stove
Airtight
Made in Germany
KH77 (three tiles high) $747
KH56 (four tiles high) $814

KH56

FRECO LIMITED
1408, 13th Avenue Ouest
Charny, Cté Lévis, P.Q.
G6W 3Z2
(418) 832-4605
(Manufacturer)

MODEL: Turtle
Material: Steel
Description: Cylindrical stove with one cooking lid. For cottages, garages, camping.
Not airtight
Made in Canada
$125

Turtle

MODEL: Poele de Camp
Material: Steel
Description: Box stove for camping, cottages, garages
Not airtight
Made in Canada
$75

FREDERICKTON JAMES STOVES LIMITED
Box 178
Niagara Falls, Ont. L2E 6T3
(416) 354-2768
(Manufacturer)

MODEL: Frederickton James
Material: Cast iron, cast-iron ribs
Description: Triangular-shaped stove with oval door, ventilated base. Horizontal baffle. Ribs hold wood away from sides.
Airtight
Made in Canada
$530

Frederickton James

HEVAC MFG. LTD.
3590 Erindale Stn. Rd.
Mississauga, Ont. L5C 2T1
(416) 275-7144
(Manufacturer)

MODEL: Wood Chief Chalet
Radiant 55
Material: Steel, cast-iron door and
flue collar, firebrick lining
Description: Box stove with
thermostatic draft control, triple
wall construction. Louvred top is
removable for cooking. Flue
baffle. Optional blower.
Airtight
Made in Canada
$249

KA-HEAT KACHELOFEN LIMITED
Box 669
Cobourg, Ont. K9A 4R5
(416) 352-2670
(Distributor)

MODEL: Kachelofen Stoves
Material: Ceramic tile, firebrick
lined

Description: Various and
attractive configurations of tile
stoves. Internal maze of firebrick
causes heat to be given up to
stove's thick tile walls. Heat is
radiated to room.
Airtight
Made in Germany

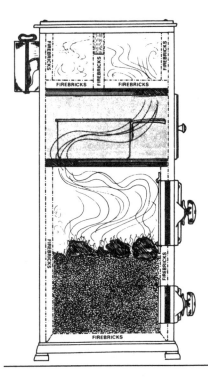

KICKAPOO STOVE WORKS LIMITED
Main Street
La Farge, Wisconsin 54639
(608) 625-4430
(Manufacturer)

MODEL: BBR-S, BBR-B, BBR-C
Material: Steel, cast-iron door,
door frame, grate. Firebrick lined.
Description: Box stoves with
inward sloping sides, double
walls. Manual draft control,
recessed flue.
Airtight
Made in U.S.A.
BBR-C $416
BBR-B $425
BBR-S $500

LAKEWOOD STOVE COMPANY LTD.
Bobcaygeon, Ontario K0M 1A0
(705) 738-3883
(Manufacturer)

MODEL: Cottager
Material: Steel, cast-iron door,
firebrick lined

Description: Box stove with
horizontal baffle. Small stove size
meant for cottages. Optional
blower and heat exchanger.
Airtight
Made in Canada
$360 (Ontario)
$400 (Ontario) with blower and
heat exchanger

Lakewood Stove distributors in
Canada:

Que-Nergie Inc.
209 Roy Street
Industrial Park
St. Eustache, Quebec J7R 4Z1

Energsave Systems Limited
R.R.3 Restigouche Rd., Dept. H
Oromocto, N.B. E2V 2G3

Fireside Conserver Products
225 Avenue D South, Dept. H
Saskatoon, Sask. S7M 1P8

Harber Mfg. (B.C.) Ltd.
Box 1238, Dept. H
Vernon, B.C. V1T 6N6

MODEL: Workhorse
Material: Steel, cast-iron door,
firebrick lined
Description: Heavy-duty box
stove, double walled. Horizontal
baffle. Blower and heat
exchanger.
Airtight
Made in Canada
$600 (Ontario)

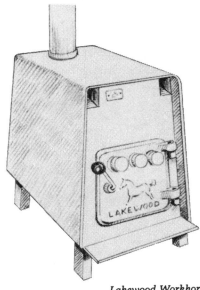
Lakewood Workhorse

MODEL: Canadian Stepstove
Material: Steel, cast-iron door, firebrick lined
Description: Stepstove design, partial horizontal baffle
Airtight
Made in Canada
$435 (Ontario)

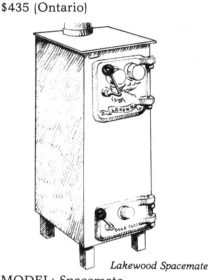

Lakewood Spacemate

MODEL: Spacemate
Material: Steel, cast-iron door, firebrick lining
Description: Narrow, tall stove that will fit into smaller areas. Baffle burn design. Optional heat shield and blower (add $65 in Ontario)
Airtight
Made in Canada
$370 (Ontario)

MODEL: Double Door and Unicorn
Material: Steel, cast-iron doors, firebrick lining
Description: Double door stepstove with horizontal baffle, heat exchanger and blower system
Airtight
Made in Canada
Double Door $695 (Ontario)
Unicorn $575 (Ontario)

Lakewood Double Door

LAFONDERIE ANTIQUE DE DAVELUYVILLE LTEE
Case Postale 69
Daveluyville, Quebec G0Z 1C0
(819) 367-2662 or 367-2663
(Manufacturer)

MODEL: Poele Abitibi
Material: Cast iron
Description: Box stoves with one to four cooking lids. One model has overhead cylindrical oven ($360.)
Not airtight
Made in Canada
$110 to $360 (various models)

MODEL: Le Bijou
Description: Box stove with heat exchanger top. Sculpted sides. Two or three level models.
Not airtight
Made in Canada
Two level $940
Three level $1,509

THE LAWSON STOVE WORKS LIMITED
11 Kent Road
Brantford, Ontario N3R 5G7
(519) 756-4154
(Manufacturer)

MODEL: Buck 1000, Buck 1500
Material: Steel, cast-iron door, firebrick lining

Description: Modified stepstove design, adjustable baffle. Optional firescreen.
Airtight
Made in Canada
Buck 1000 $330
Buck 1500 $390

LUNENBURG FOUNDRY & ENGINEERING LIMITED
16 Brook Street
Lunenburg, N.S. B0J 2C0
(902) 634-8827
(Manufacturer)

MODEL: Bluenose
Material: Cast iron
Description: Box stove with one cooking lid. Horizontal baffle. Available in several colours.
Airtight
Made in Canada
$325

MODEL: Cosy Campfire
Material: Cast iron
Description: Double door box stove. Sculpted sides. One cooking lid.
Not airtight
Made in Canada
$320

MOHAWK FABRICATORS INC.
103 Falcon Street
London, Ontario N5W 4Z2
(519) 453-1360
(Manufacturer)

MODEL: Tempwood II, Tempwood V
Material: Steel, firebrick lined, cast-iron lid in top
Description: Top-loading stove with downdraft burn design
Airtight
Made in Canada
Tempwood V $260
Tempwood II $290

NORWEGIAN WOOD STOVES
Box 219, Clarkson Post Office
Mississauga, Ontario L5J 3Y1
(416) 822-2330
(Distributor)

Lange 6303 A/B

MODEL: Lange 6303 A/B, Lange 6303
Material: Cast iron
Description: Oval-shaped stove with front-end burn design and horizontal baffle. Model 6303 has arched heat exchanger top. Sculpted sides.
Airtight
Made in Denmark
Lange 6303 A/B $567
Lange 6303 $788

Lange 6302K

MODEL: Lange 6302A, Lange 6302K
Material: Cast iron
Description: Box stove with sculpted sides. Model 6302A has cooking lid, model 6302K has upper heat chamber with oven. Front-end combustion. Horizontal baffle.
Airtight
Made in Denmark
Lange 6302A $1,022
Lange 6302K $1,399

Lange 6203BR

MODEL: Lange 6203BR, Lange 6204BR
Material: Cast iron
Description: Tall box stove uses cast iron to duplicate Kachelofen (tile) stoves. Massive radiant heat surface area. Sculpted design.
Airtight
Made in Denmark
Lange 6203BR (3 columns deep) $789
Lange 6204BR (4 columns deep) $955

Ulefos 864

MODEL: Ulefos 868, Ulefos 864, Ulefos 865
Material: Cast iron
Description: Box stove with

sculptured sides. Front-end combustion, horizontal baffle.
Airtight
Made in Norway
Ulefos 868 $275
Ulefos 864 $323
Ulefos 865 $609

MODEL: Ulefos 172
Material: Cast iron
Description: Elaborate three-tiered stove with top two tiers functioning as heat exchangers. Baffle burn design.
Airtight
Made in Norway
$1,568

Western Canada distributor:
Miles Industries Limited
Box 91686
West Vancouver, B.C. V7V 3P3

OLD TIME STOVE CO INC.
57 Edwin Street
Kitchener, Ontario N2H 4N7
(519) 742-0611
(Manufacturer)

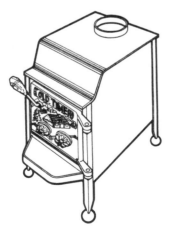

MODEL: Old Timer OTS
Material: Steel, cast-iron door, firebrick lining

Description: Single door stepstove design. Removable baffle.
Airtight
Made in Canada
$550

ONWARD HARDWARE LIMITED
932 Victoria Street North
Kitchener, Ontario N2B 1W4
(519) 578-3770
(Distributor)

MODEL: Shenandoah R-77
Material: Steel, firebrick lining
Description: Box stove with bi-metal thermostat. Optional coal grate ($50.)
Airtight
Made in U.S.A.
$399

Shenandoah R-77

MODEL: Shenandoah R-65 and R-75

Shenandoah R-65

Material: Steel, cast-iron grate, firebrick lined
Description: Cylindrical stove with large door. Bi-metal thermostat.
Airtight
Made in U.S.A.
Shenandoah R-65 $330
Shenandoah R-75 $350

PENTAGON STOVE WORKS
Box 32
Tumtum, Washington 99034
(509) 276-6660
(Manufacturer)

MODEL: Pentagon
Material: Steel, cast-iron door, refractory cement lined
Description: Twelve sided stove with fire legs. Manufacturers claim shape creates natural fire turbulence and more complete combustion. Has five legs.
Airtight
Made in U.S.A.
Pentagon 15 $425
Pentagon 18 $485
Pentagon 24 $675

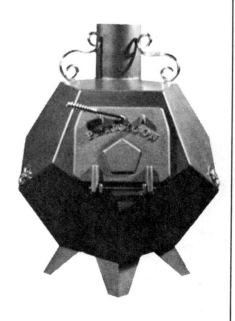

RITEWAY MFG. CO.
Box 6
Harrisonburg, Virginia 22801
(703) 434-7090
(Manufacturer)

MODEL: Riteway 2000,
Riteway 37

Riteway 2000   *Riteway 37*

Material: Steel, aluminized steel liner, grate and flue
Description: Box stove with baffled downdraft burn design. Bi-metal thermostat. Optional cabinet and blower.
Airtight
Made in U.S.A.
Model 2000 $550
Model 37 $785
Canadian distributor:
Blanche River Industries
Box 473
Belle Valley, Ontario P0J 1A0
(705) 647-7829

RSF ENERGY
Smithers, B.C.
(Manufacturer)

MODEL: H85, H35
Material: Steel
Description: Box stove with centre push loading door. Downdraft burn design. Optional hot water coil.
Airtight
Made in Canada
H35 $439
H85 $895

ERNEST SEDORE & SON
Mount Albert, Ont. L0G 1M0
(416) 473-2240
(Manufacturer)

MODEL: Sedore Stove
Material: Steel, corrugated steel

Description: Box stove with thin corrugated walls. Holes in walls cause fuel to burn from the sides inward. Flue damper installation recommended.
Not airtight
Made in Canada
Small Sedore $253
Medium Sedore $286
Large Sedore $335

SELKIRK-METALBESTOS
130 North Augusta Road
Brockville, Ontario K6V 5V3
(613) 342-6655
(Manufacturer)

MODEL: Acorn Ranger
Material: Steel, firebrick lining
Description: Stepstove design with long firebox, heat exchanger tubes and optional circulating fan
Airtight
Made in Canada
$535

SOLACE ENERGY CENTRES INC.
2425 Main Street
Vancouver, B.C. V5T 3E1
(604) 879-5258
(Distributor)
MODEL: Waterford Reginald 102
Material: Cast iron
Description: Box stove with second-level heat chamber. Baffle burn design.
Airtight
Made in Ireland
$530

MODEL: Waterford Reginald 101 and Waterford Reginald 100

Waterford Reginald 101

Material: Cast iron
Description: Box stove with baffle burn design. Model 101 comes disassembled for the do-it-yourselfer.
Airtight
Made in Ireland
Reginald 101 $350
Reginald 100 $450

Waterford distributors in Canada:

Ashley Ontario Distributors
3322 Dundas Street West
Toronto, Ontario M6P 2A4
(416) 762-4582

Conserver Society Group—One Step Ahead Energy Systems
216D Vernon Street
Nelson, B.C. V1L 4E2

Woodstoves Unlimited
R.R.1
Denman Island, B.C. V0R 1T0

The Wooden Ewe
Box 1387
Fairview, Alberta T0H 1L0

Fireside Conserver Products
225 Avenue D. South
Saskatoon, Sask. S7M 1P8

Conserver Society Products Co-op
Box 4377, Station E
109 Clarence Street
Ottawa, Ontario

Alternative Enterprises
Young's Point, Ontario

The Wood Stove Store
2623 Windsor Street,
Halifax, N.S. B3K 5C7

Sparks Conserver Products
The Boat, Charlottetown Mall
Box 1857
Charlottetown, P.E.I.

Quality Woodstoves
Box 5386, 1 Pilot's Hill
St. John's, Newfoundland

STOUFFVILLE STOVE WORKS INC.
399 Terry Drive
Newmarket, Ont. L3Y 5E6
(416) 898-4482
(Manufacturer)

MODEL: Woodcutter
Material: Steel, cast-iron door,
firebrick lining
Description: Modified box stove
with baffle burn design
Airtight
Made in Canada
Three models $340—$540

SUNSHINE PRODUCTS
Hornby Island, B.C. V0R 1Z0
(Manufacturer)

MODEL: Sunrise
Material: Steel, cast-iron front,
back, door. Firebrick lined
Description: Round stove with
outside air intake. Pipes pass
through firebox, deliver warmed
air to room. Baffle burn.
Plumbing fittings for hot water.
Airtight
Made in Canada
Three models $500 — $550

TIMBERLINE ENERGY SYSTEMS
Box 1620, 60 Shirley St. South
Timmins, Ontario P4N 7W8
(705) 267-4033 or 267-4034
(Manufacturer)

MODEL: T-18, T-24, T-33
Material: Steel, cast-iron doors
Description: Stepstove design
with horizontal baffle. Non-
asbestos door seal.

Airtight
Made in Canada
T-18 $350
T-24 $430
T-33 $480

Timberline T-18

TOWN & COUNTRY PRODUCTS
107 Telson Road
Markham, Ontario L3R 1E4
(Manufacturer)

MODEL: Heater Kit
Material: Steel parts
Description: Steel kit for
converting 45-gallon drum (not
included) to wood stove. Includes
legs, door assembly, stovepipe
flange, bolts, nuts and
instructions.
Made in Canada
$50

TROLL-AM STOVES INC.
Box 322
Newmarket, Ont. L3Y 4X7
(416) 898-2550
or
Box 3056
Halifax South, N.S. B3J 3G6
(Manufacturer)

Trolla 103

MODEL: Trolla 103, Trolla 104,
Trolla 108
Material: Cast iron
Description: Box stoves with
sculptured sides. Cooking lid in
top. Model 108 has second-level
heat chamber.
Airtight
Made in Norway
Trolla 103 $312
Trolla 104 $373
Trolla 108 $725

W.J. TULLY DISTRIBUTING
R.R.4
Tottenham, Ontario L0G 1W0
(Distributor)

MODEL: Le Petit Godin
Material: Steel, cast iron, firebrick
liner

Description: Quebec-heater style
stove with coloured enamel trim.
Fire viewing windows.
Airtight
Made in France
$400
Western Canada distributor:
Miles Industries
Box 91686
West Vancouver, B.C. V7V 3P3

ZIP-PENN CO.
188 Stronach Cres., Box 5877,
London, Ontario N6A 4L6
(519) 455-3552
(Distributor)

MODEL: Ultra Heat Mark I
Material: Steel, cast-iron top
Description: Side draft stove. Fuel
burns from top to bottom. Top
loading.
Airtight
Made in Canada
$300

CIRCULATING HEATERS

ASHLEY ONTARIO DISTRIBUTORS
3322 Dundas Street West
Toronto, Ont. M6P 2A4
(416) 762-4582
(Distributor)

MODEL: Deluxe Ashley Imperial, Deluxe Ashley Compact Console
Material: Cast-iron firebox liner, grates, flue collar, feed and ashdoors, and steel cabinet with baked enamel finish.
Description: Downdraft burn system which preheats air, and secondary air intake to increase combustion of unburned gases. Cabinet door is double-walled. Bi-metal helix thermostat; and optional automatic blower.
Airtight
Made in U.S.A.
Imperial $569
Compact Console $489

Deluxe Ashley Imperial

ATLANTA STOVE WORKS
6757 Northwest Drive
Mississauga, Ont. L4V 1L1
(416) 677-0144
(Distributor)

MODEL: Homesteader 340DG, Homesteader 2410GU, Homesteader 240C
Material: Steel and enamel cabinet, with cast-iron flue collar and firebrick liner.
Description: Thermostatically controlled. Blower circulates 150 cubic feet per minute. Side loading.

Airtight
Made in U.S.A.
340DG $430
240C (smaller version) $330
2410GU (Vycor glass windows)$530

Homesteader 340DG

AUTOCRAT CORP.
Illinois & Benton Street
New Athens, Illinois 62264
(618) 475-2121
(Manufacturer)

MODEL: Autocrat FF76
Material: Steel with cast-iron grates and liners.
Description: Has 25-inch-wide front-loading door, with full width ash pan. Heat projected to front by insulated cabinet top. Optional blower available.
Airtight
Made in U.S.A.
$530
Canadian distributor:
Cosman's Wood Htng. Unlimited
327-329 Carlton Street
Winnipeg, Manitoba R3B 2K7
(204) 942-5719

MODEL: Thermo-Wood 6724
Material: Steel cabinet with enamel finish, cast-iron lining and flue collar and grate.
Description: Side loading, with thermostatic draft control. Optional automatic blower available.
Not airtight
Made in U.S.A.
$400
Canadian distributor: (see above)

ENHEAT LIMITED FAWCETT DIVISION
100 Main Street
Sackville, N. B. E0A 3C0
(506) 536-1520
(Manufacturer)

MODEL: Fawcett CW66 Atlantic
Material: Steel with cast-iron grate, lined with firebrick.
Description: Has side loading cabinet and bi-metal thermostat. Removable top exposes cooking surface. Optional circulating fan available.
Airtight
Made in Canada
$450—$500

EVERS STOVE COMPANY
Box 1, Group F, R.R.3
Mount Hope, Ont. L0R 1W0
(416) 765-2927
(Manufacturer)

MODEL: Wood Mate North Wind
Material: Steel
Description: Curved, side loading stove. Preheated air enters through perforated tube across whole firebox. Has sloping floor, curved baffle plate. Convection channel around stove takes cool air from floor and sends it out the front of the stove.
Airtight
Made in Canada
$490

FRANCO-BELGE FOUNDRIES OF AMERICA
70 Pine Street
New York, N.Y. 10005
(212) 425-3115 or 425-3116
(Manufacturer)

MODEL: Ebene 1280, Economique 1270
Material: Cast-iron and firebrick hearth, with cast-iron cooking top and steel and porcelain cabinet.

Ebene

Economique

Description: Side loading. Top is hinged with ground hot plate for cooking. Thermostatically controlled. The Ebene has Pyrex glass windows for fireviewing.
Airtight
Made in U.S.A.
Ebene $575 (U.S.)
Economique $480 (U.S.)
Canadian distributor:
Onward Hardware Limited
932 Victoria Street
Kitchener, Ontario N2B 1W4
(519) 578-3770

MODEL: The Woodburner
Material: Has porcelain and steel exterior, with cast-iron top and firebrick lining.
Description: Top hinges up to expose a cast-iron hotplate. Side loading, with thermostat.
Airtight
Made in U.S.A.
$440 (U.S.)
Canadian distributor: (see above)

FRESH AIR FIREPLACES OF CANADA LIMITED
Box 3262
Regina, Saskatchewan
(306) 949-0868
(Manufacturer)

MODEL: Renaissance
Material: Steel with enamel finish, cast-iron grate, firebrick lined.
Description: Side loading stove with thermostatically controlled draft. Lid is louvred. Optional circulating fan available.
Airtight
Made in Canada
$400

HEVAC MFG. LIMITED
3590 Erindale Stn. Road
Mississauga, Ont. L5C 2T1
(416) 275-7144
(Manufacturer)

Wood Chief 100A

MODEL: Wood Chief 50CA Deluxe, Wood Chief 100A
Material: Steel with enamel finish, cast-iron doors, grates and flue collar. WC50CA has cast-iron liner. WC100A has firebrick liner.
Description: CSA certified stove. Louvred top lifts up for access to cooking surface. Thermostatically controlled. Optional circulating blower available.
Airtight
Made in Canada
WC50CA Deluxe $379
WC100A $329

Wood Chief Deluxe

HUNTER ENTERPRISES LIMITED

Box 400
Orillia, Ont. L3V 6K1
(705) 325-6111
(Manufacturer)

MODEL: Valley Comfort C-26
and C-31
Material: Steel with stainless steel
firebox
Description: Stove is side loading
and has preheated secondary
combustion, and automatic
thermostat.
Airtight
Made in Canada
C-26 $380, C-31 $400
Western distributor:
Valley Comfort
Winlaw, B.C. V0G 2J0
(604) 226-7221

MONT SAINT HILAIRE
STOVE WORKS LIMITED
Box 300
Beloeil, Quebec J3G 5S9
(514) 464-2169
(Manufacturer)

KONVECTOR MFG. INC.
R.R.2, Box 17, Site 209
Collingwood, Ont. L9Y 3Z1
(Manufacturer)

FREE FLOW
STOVE WORKS
South Strafford,
Vermont 05070
(802) 765-4022
(Manufacturer)

MODEL: Free Flow Circulator,
Wonder, and Furnace
Material: Steel
Description: Cylindrical stove
surrounded by hollow steel tubes
for air convection. Has interior
baffle and positive door latch.
Airtight

Made in Canada and U.S.A.
Circulator $565
Wonder $695
Furnace $820

ONWARD HARDWARE
LIMITED
932 Victoria Street North
Kitchener, Ontario N2B 1W4
(519) 578-3770
(Distributor)

MODEL: Shenandoah R-78 and
R78L
Material: Steel, with cast-iron
grate and firebrick lining
Description: R78L is same stove
as R78, only without cabinet.
Will fit into fireplace openings. Is
side loading, with primary and
secondary air intake and bi-metal
thermostat.
Airtight
Made in U.S.A.
R-78 $500
R-78L $350

FIREPLACES
& FIREVIEWERS

ANGCANAME
DISTRIBUTING LTD.
Box 292
Prince George, B.C.
(604) 562-8317
(Distributor)

MODEL: Angcaname Fireplace
Material: Stainless steel firebox,
tempered glass doors
Description: Zero clearance
fireplace insert with external air
intake, triple chamber heat
exchanger, electric blower.
Formerly the Shaw fireplace.
Airtight
Made in Canada
32" firebox $800
24" firebox $700

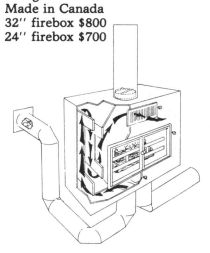

ARCTIC DISTRIBUTORS
LIMITED
12179 86th Avenue
Surrey, B.C. V3W 3H8
(604) 591-2261
(Distributor)

Efel Kamina

MODEL: Efel Kamina
Material: Steel with cast-iron grate, firebox top, lining. Porcelainized cabinet.
Description: Freestanding fireplace with baffle burn design. Hood lifts for cooking surface. Side loading.
Airtight
Made in Belgium
$700

ATLANTA STOVE WORKS
6757 Northwest Drive
Mississauga, Ont. L4V 1L1
(416) 677-0144
(Distributor)

MODEL: Franklin Line (several models)
Material: Cast iron
Description: Franklin stove with or without fireview windows
Not airtight
Made in U.S.A.
32" with windows $450

AUTOCRAT CORP.
Illinois & Benton Street
New Athens, Illinois 62264
(618) 475-2121
(Manufacturer)

MODEL: Americana 2000FH
Material: Steel, cast-iron grate and lining. Porcelainized finish.
Description: Freestanding fireplace with thermostatically controlled damper. Flue pipe has heat exchanger grilles and draft control. Removable doors, firescreen. Top and side louvres.
Airtight
Made in U.S.A.
$930
Canadian distributor:
Cosman's Wood
Heating Unlimited
327-329 Carlton Street
Winnipeg, Man. R3B 2K7
(204) 942-5719

MODEL: Americana 76FH
Material: Steel with cast-iron grate and lining
Description: Franklin-type fireplace with thermostatically controlled damper. Flue pipe has heat exchanger grilles and draft control. Removable doors, firescreen. Top and side louvres.
Airtight
Made in U.S.A.
$890
Canadian distributor: (see above)

BLAZE INDUSTRIES
50 Electronic Avenue
Port Moody, B.C. V3H 2R8
(604) 461-6611
(Manufacturer)

MODEL: Convair
Material: Steel, firebrick lined
Description: Stepstove with removable double doors and firescreen. Optional fan kit.
Airtight
Made in Canada
$575

Convair

MODEL: Firehood, Aztec, Gemini
Material: Steel. Optional porcelain finish.
Description: Acorn-style freestanding fireplaces. May be assembled by do-it-yourselfer. Pedestal stand or hearth models.
Not airtight
Made in Canada
Firehood $205—$270
Aztec $280
Gemini $350

Aztec

MODEL: Majestic
Material: Steel. Optional firebrick lining.
Description: Zero clearance fireplace with firescreen. Triple

wall design. Outside air intake.
Not airtight
Made in U.S.A.
Standard model $415
Glass doors for standard model
$230

B.T.U. MANUFACTURING OF ONTARIO LIMITED
134 Gore Street
Sault Ste. Marie, Ontario
P6A 1M1
(705) 942-3331
(Manufacturer)

MODEL: Firemate
Material: Steel
Description: Fireplace insert fits
in back corner of existing
fireplace. Blower circulates air
through unit into room.

Made in Canada
$108

CARMOR MFG. LTD.
325 Hale Street
London, Ontario N5W 1G3
(519) 453-8160
(Manufacturer)

MODEL: FireSide
Material: Steel, firebrick lined.
Vycor glass in doors.
Description: Fireviewer with

downdraft burn design. Internal
baffle. Double doors.
Airtight
Made in Canada
$450

NORM CARTER AGENCIES
971 Bayview Square,
Coquitlam, B.C. V3J 5M6
(604) 936-3811
(Distributor)

MODEL: Acme Stove
Material: Steel, firebrick lined.
Description: Single door
fireviewer with mica windows
and bulit-in firescreen.
Thermostat control. Optional hot
water coil.
Airtight
Made in U.S.A.

MODEL: Tropicana
Material: Stainless steel,
tempered glass doors.
Description: Zero clearance
fireplace with outside air intake.
Airtight
Made in U.S.A.

MODEL: Frontier
Material: Steel, firebrick lined.
Description: Stepstove design

with fireviewing double doors
and firescreen.
Airtight
Made in U.S.A.

CEMI PRODUCTS LTD.
Box 290
Ashland, Ohio 44805
(419) 289-2224
(Manufacturer)

MODEL: Colony Classic
Material: Steel, firebrick lining,
thermo-glass in doors.
Description: Double door
fireviewer with double wall
construction. Internal baffle.
Heats by convection through
double wall and by radiation.
Airtight
Made in U.S.A.
$615
Canadian distributor:
Cemi Products Limited
Box 3580, Station "C"
Hamilton, Ontario L8H 7M9
(416) 561-9343

Colony Classic

MODEL: Concept I and
Concept II
Material: Steel, mica windows.
Concept II has fireclay lining.
Description: Tubular grate
fireplace insert in combination
with double fireviewing doors.

Blower circulates air through grate.
Made in U.S.A.
Concept II $680
Canadian distributor: (see above)

Concept I

MODEL: Ultimate
Material: Steel, firebrick lined.
Description: Double door fireviewer with stepstove design. Baffle system.
Airtight
Made in U.S.A.
$580
Canadian distributor (see above)

Ultimate

MODEL: Great-O-Lator
Material: Steel
Description: Tubular grate with blower in base.
Made in U.S.A.
Canadian distributor: (see above)

CONVECT-O-HEATER LTD.
4136 South Service Road
Burlington, Ont. L7L 4X5
(416) 639-0015
(Manufacturer)

MODEL: Convect-O-Heater
Material: Steel
Description: Tubular grate with blower for fireplaces. Draws cool air in at bottom, blows warm air out top.
Made in Canada
$90—$180 (various sizes)

THE COOKSTOVE CABIN
Box 1233
Belleville, Ont. K0K 2V0
(613) 477-2684 or 962-2430
(Manufacturer)

MODEL: Sam Magee
Material: Steel, cast-iron doors, firebrick lined, tempered glass in doors.
Description: Double door fireviewer with double wall air convection and humidifier.
Airtight
Made in Canada
$640

DE LUXE EQUIPMENT INC.
8026 Jarry Street East
Ville d'Anjou, P.Q. H1J 1H5

(514) 354-1155
(Distributor)

MODEL: Jotul 4 Combi-Fire, Jotul 1 Combi-Fire
Material: Cast-iron, firebrick lined.
Description: Large front loading door swings down and slides under stove for fireviewing. Screen included. Baffle burn design.
Airtight
Made in Norway
Jotul 4 $950
Jotul 1 $750

MODEL: Jotul 6
Material: Cast iron, firebrick lined.
Description: Acorn-style freestanding fireplace with sliding doors and attached screen.
Airtight
Made in Norway
$1,200

DOMETIC CANADA INC.

Box 212
Oakville, Ontario L6J 5A2
(416) 827-9811
(Distributor)

MODEL: Nestor Martin Fireplace
Material: Steel, cast-iron firebox.
Pyrex doors.
Description: Double door
fireviewer with air convection
shell. Bronze highlights.
Airtight
Made in Belgium
$899

EARTH STOVE NORTHWEST

Box 549
Tualatin, Oregon 97062
(503) 638-8402
(Manufacturer)

MODEL: Earth Stove 3000
Material: Steel, firebrick lined.
Description: Box stove with
removable front loading door.
Firescreen included. Thermostatic
draft control.
Airtight
Made in U.S.A.
$550 (U.S.)
Compact model $490 (U.S.)

EASTERN ONTARIO STOVE WORKS INC.

5 Victoria Avenue
Marmora, Ontario K0K 2M0
(613) 472-2430
(Manufacturer)

MODEL:Fisher Grandma Bear,
Fisher Grandpa Bear
Material: Steel, cast-iron door,
firebrick lined
Description: Stepstove burn
design. Double doors open for
fireviewing. Firescreen included.
Triple seal doors.
Airtight
Made in Canada
Grandma Bear $490
Grandpa Bear $525

Fisher Grandpa Bear

ENCON

11861 Suzor Cote
Montreal, Quebec H3M 2J1
(514) 334-2915

MODEL: Better 'N Ben's 101
and 501
Material: Steel, cast-iron door,
firebrick lining.
Description: Stove fits into
existing fireplace with cover
panel to close fireplace opening.
Baffle burn design. Tempered
glass in door optional.
Airtight
Made in Canada
Model 101 $450
Model 501 $695

ENHEAT LIMITED FAWCETT DIVISION

Sackville, N.B. E0A 3C0
(506) 536-1520
(Manufacturer)

MODEL: Franklin (4 models)
Material: Steel, cast iron
Description: Franklin fireplace
with single or double doors.
Not airtight
Made in Canada
$250—$400

THE ENTERPRISE FOUNDRY CO. LTD.

Sackville, N.B. E0A 3C0
(506) 536-1160
(Manufacturer)

MODEL: Old Colony Franklin
Material: Steel, cast iron
Description: Franklin fireplace
with double doors. Firescreen
included.
Not airtight
Made in Canada
$307—$520 (various models)

THE FARMER'S STOVE LIMITED

66 Russett Avenue
Oshawa, Ontario L1G 3R5
(416) 576-6120
(Manufacturer)

MODEL: Rancher, Eastern Rancher
Material: Steel, cast-iron door, firebrick lined
Description: Stepstove design with double doors. Optional screen for fireviewing.
Airtight
Made in Canada
Rancher $485
Eastern Rancher $465

FERON COMPANY LTD.
49 Wright Avenue
Dartmouth, N.S.
(902) 463-2953
(Distributor)

MODEL: Morso 1125
Material: Cast iron, enamel finish
Description: Double door stove with firescreen. Heat retaining hood.
Airtight
Made in Denmark
$960

FINDLAY COMFORT SYSTEMS
66 Otonabee Drive
Kitchener, Ont. N2C 1L6
(519) 893-6531
(Manufacturer)

MODEL: Findlay Insert
Material: Steel, tempered glass door.

Description: Fireplace insert with heat exchanging louvres on both sides. Baffle burn design. Fireviewing door.
Airtight
Made in Canada
For price contact local Findlay dealer

Findlay Insert

MODEL: Findlay Chatelaine
Material: Steel, cast-iron doors, firebrick lined, Vycor glass in doors.
Description: Double door fireviewer with hinged, louvred top, primary and secondary baffle systems and thermostat control.
Airtight
Made in Canada
For price contact local Findlay dealer

Findlay Chatelaine

FINEST STOVE IMPORTS, INC.
Box 1733
Silver Spring,
Maryland 20902
(301) 946-4822
(Distributor)

MODEL: Koppe KK150S, Koppe KK100S
Material: Ceramic tile stove with fireclay firebox and marble top, expanded metal front screen.
Description: Tile stove with convection louvres in front and back. Thermostatic heat sensor.

Small viewing window in door. Model KK150S is 4 tiles high, model KK100S is 3 tiles high.
Airtight
Made in Germany
KK150S $1,120 (U.S.)
KK100S $1,040 (U.S.)

MODEL: Koppe KK400
Material: Ceramic tile with fireclay lining
Description: Fireviewer with thermostatic heat sensor. Flue gases pass through ducts to heat tile. Stove heats by convection and radiation.
Airtight
Made in Germany
$1,078 (U.S.)

FIRE-VIEW PRODUCTS INC.
Box 370
Rogue River, Oregon 97537
(503) 582-3351
(Manufacturer)

MODEL: Fire-View
Material: Steel, firebrick lining
Description: Cylindrical fireviewer with tempered glass door. Window vent keeps glass cool, collapsible door behind window may be closed at night. Side loading. Rear-venting fireplace model available.

Airtight
Made in U.S.A.
Standard model $420
Fireplace model $430

GERDON 1978 LIMITED
2480 Cawthra Road
Units 26 & 27
Mississauga, Ont. L5A 2X2
(416) 275-2646
(Distributor)

MODEL: Franklin
Material: Cast iron
Description: Freestanding
Franklin fireplaces. Also box
stoves and cookstoves.
Not airtight
Made in Taiwan
Franklin fireplaces $210—$245

FRECO LIMITED
1408 13th Avenue Ouest
Charny, Cte Levis
Quebec G6W 3Z2
(418) 832-4605
(Manufacturer)

Energy Efficient Fireplace

MODEL: Colonial Fireplace-Oven
Material: Steel
Description: Large fireplace insert
with baking oven and cooking
surface.

Made in Canada
$650

**FRESH AIR FIREPLACES
OF CANADA LTD.**
Box 3262
Regina, Saskatchewan
(306) 949-0868
(Manufacturer)

MODEL: Glow Boy
Material: Stainless steel firebox,
tempered glass doors. Framed in
brass or steel.
Description: Zero clearance
fireplace, outside air intake, large
warm air outlet.
Made in Canada
32" $870
28" $650

HARROWSMITH STOVES
Box 40
Harrowsmith, Ont. K0H 1V0
(613) 372-2434 and 372-2637
(Manufacturer)

MODEL: Harrowsmith
Material: Steel, cast-iron doors, firebrick lined, safety glass in doors.
Description: Fireviewer with baffle burn design, air convection around outside of stove, upper heat chamber and humidifier. Optional blower.
Airtight
Made in Canada
30'' width $650—$700
36'' width $708—$760
Not affiliated with Harrowsmith magazine.

HERITAGE STOVE CO. LIMITED
R.R.3
Collingwood, Ont. L9Y 3Z2
(705) 445-5650
(Manufacturer)

MODEL: Heritage
Material: Steel, cast-iron doors, firebrick lined
Description: Stepstove design with side draft and interior baffle. Single door on 18'' model. Double doors on larger models. Firescreen for fireviewing.
Airtight
Made in Canada
18'' width $425
24'' width $555
30'' width $625

MOHAWK FABRICATORS INC.
103 Falcon Street
London, Ont. N5W 4Z2
(519) 453-1360
(Manufacturer)

MODEL: Tempview
Material: Steel, firebrick lined
Description: Fireviewing stove with louvred top and sides. Double doors slide apart. Snap-in firescreen. Optional Vycor glass doors and blower.
Airtight
Made in Canada
$600

NORTHERN HEATLINER
Logie Road, Box 1559,
Summerland, B.C.
(604) 494-6306

MODEL: Northern Heatliner
Material: Steel
Description: Fireplace liner with outside air intake. Warm air vent across top.
Not airtight
Made in Canada
33'' model $295

NORWEGIAN WOOD STOVES
Box 219, Clarkson Post Office
Mississauga, Ont. L5J 3Y1
(416) 822-2330
(Distributor)

MODEL: Lange 61MF
Material: Cast iron, firebrick lined, Vycor glass in doors
Description: Double door fireviewer with baffle burn design and air control damper in flue collar. Glass doors are protected by cast-iron ribs. Firescreen included.
Airtight
Made in Denmark
$1,068

OLD TIME STOVE CO. INC.
57 Edwin Street
Kitchener, Ont. N2H 4N7
(519) 742-0611
(Manufacturer)

MODEL: Old Timer
Material: Steel, cast-iron door, firebrick lined
Description: Double door stepstove with removable baffle. Firescreen for fireviewing.
Airtight
Made in Canada
$650

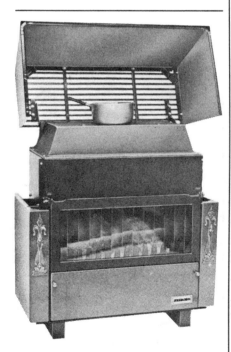

POWRMATIC OF CANADA LIMITED
709 Leveille Street
TerreBonne, P.Q. J6W 1Z9
(514) 471-6691
(Manufacturer)

MODEL: Kresno Fireplace/Stove

44

Material: Steel, cast-iron grate, top lining. Pyrex windows, enamelled cabinet.
Description: Freestanding fireplace with baffle burn design. Front or side loading. Hood lifts for cooking surface. Provision for barbecue grill.
Airtight
Made in Canada
$660
Other Powrmatic plants in Canada:
Montreal Division:
7400 — 19ie Avenue
Montreal, Quebec H2A 2L7
(514) 376-6293

Toronto Division:
1169 Caledonia Road
Toronto, Ont. M6A 2X1
(416) 781-9364

Sudbury Division:
1107 Webberwood Drive
Sudbury, Ont. P3C 3B6
(705) 674-4297

Saint John Division:
899 Ashburn Road
Saint John, N.B. E2L 4B3
(506) 696-2268

Quebec Division:
365 Rue Fortin
Ville Vanier, Quebec
G1M 1B2
(418) 683-2706

Ottawa Division:
1427 Michael Street
Ottawa, Ontario K1B 3R3
(613) 746-2140

Halifax Division:
6375 Bayne Street
Halifax, Nova Scotia B3K 2V6
(902) 454-8684

QUAKER STOVE CO.
200 West 5th Street
Lansdale, Penn. 19446
(215) 362-2019
(Manufacturer)

MODEL: Buck II, Fawn II, Doe II
Material: Steel with cast-iron door, firebrick lined. Vycor glass in door.
Description: Box stove with fireviewing door, sculpted design. Baffle burn. Window is encircled by antlers of brass-bronze deer.
Airtight
Made in U.S.A.
Buck II $595 (U.S.)
Doe II $540 (U.S.)
Fawn II $490 (U.S.)

Buck II

MODEL: Moravian Parlor Stove
Material: Steel with cast-iron and Vycor glass doors, firebrick lining.
Description: Double door fireviewer with baffle burn design. Also available as fireplace insert.
Airtight
Made in U.S.A.
$685—$775 (U.S.)
(various models)

Moravian Parlor Stove

SELKIRK-METALBESTOS
130 North Augusta Road
Brockville, Ont. K6V 5V3
(613) 342-6655
(Manufacturer)

MODEL: Acorn Olympic 2000
Material: Steel, cast-iron grate, tempered glass doors.
Description: Zero clearance fireplace insert with triple wall design, heat exchanger top, outside air intake and flexible hot air ducts.
Airtight
Made in Canada
$592

MODEL: Acorn Pyramid and Acorn Chaleur
Material: Steel, tempered glass doors
Description: Freestanding fireplace with glass doors. Pyramid has fireviewing windows all around. Chaleur is front-viewing. Various hood colours.
Made in Canada
Pyramid $822
Chaleur $620

Acorn Chaleur

STERLING INDUSTRIES
575 Bowes Road
Concord, Ontario L4K 1B6
(416) 669-9455

STERLING INDUSTRIES
Montreal North, P.Q. H1H 3C5
(514) 325-6710
(Manufacturer)

MODEL: Energy Grate
Material: Tubular steel
Description: Tubular grate for fireplace. Circulates by convection or optional blower.
Made in Canada
Grate $70
Grate with fan $180

TIMBERLINE ENERGY SYSTEMS
Box 1620, Shirley St. S.
Timmins, Ont. P4N 7W8
(705) 267-4033 or 267-4034
(Manufacturer)

MODEL: T-LF, T-SF, T-PF
Material: Steel, cast-iron doors, firebrick lining.
Description: Double door fireviewer with baffle burn design. Firescreen included. Optional pedestal, water coils, cook top.
Airtight
Made in Canada
T-PF $450
T-SF $510
T-LF $550

MODEL: TF-1
Material: Steel, Cast-iron doors, firebrick lined.
Description: Fireplace insert with double doors. Firescreen included. Baffle burn design. Optional blower.
Airtight
Made in Canada
$650
With blower $780

TROLL-AM STOVES INC.
Box 322
Newmarket, Ont. L3Y 4X7
(416) 898-2550

TROLL-AM STOVES INC.
450 Pleasant Street
Dartmouth, N.S. B2Y 3S5
(Manufacturer)

MODEL: Trolla Combi 810
Material: Cast iron
Description: Double door

fireviewer with baffle burn design. Firescreen included.
Airtight
Made in Norway
$849

MODEL: Trolla Combi 820
Material: Cast iron
Description: Double door fireviewer with baffle burn design and sculpted exterior. Includes firescreen, two cooking lids, adjustable grill unit for barbecuing.
Airtight
Made in Norway
$947

TWEED STEEL WORKS EASTERN LIMITED
Box 340
Tweed, Ontario K0K 3J0
(613) 478-2126
(Manufacturer)

MODEL: Fireplace System
Material: Steel, tempered glass doors
Description: Zero clearance fireplace with double-walled air circulation, outside air intake, tempered glass doors, optional twin fan system. Comes in various models to fit in regular fireplaces, open corners, triangular corners, see-through fireplaces.
Regular model $445—$500
Open Corner $580
Triangle Corner $502

VERMONT IRON STOVE WORKS, INC.
Warren, Vermont 05674

(802) 496-2617
(Manufacturer)

MODEL: The Elm, The Short Elm
Material: Cast iron and steel. Pyrex and Vycor glass windows. Firebrick lined.
Description: Cylindrical fireviewer with large loading door, baffled interior, cast-iron cook top.
Airtight
Made in U.S.A.
Elm $450
Short Elm $420

VERMONT CASTINGS INC.
9724 Prince Street
Randolph, Vermont 05060
(802) 728-9561
(Manufacturer)

MODEL: Vigilant
Material: Cast iron
Description: Thermostatically controlled draft, baffled interior, secondary combustion chamber. Double doors open for fireviewing. Firescreen included.
Airtight
Made in U.S.A.
$470 (U.S.)

MODEL: Defiant
Material: Cast iron
Description: Similar configuration to Vigilant model. Cast-iron cooking lid. Side and front loading.

Airtight
Made in U.S.A.
$575 (U.S.)

Airtight
Made in Canada
MK IV $475
MK V $525

WELKUM STEEL PRODUCTS LIMITED
R.R.2
Eganville, Ont. K0J 1T0
(613) 628-2528
(Manufacturer)

MODEL: Surefire MK1V, Surefire MKV
Material: Steel, firebrick lining
Description: Double door fireviewer with baffle burn design and stepstove configuration. Firescreen included.

WESTERN STOVE REPAIR AND SALES LIMITED
307-8 Avenue S.E.
Calgary, Alberta T2G 0L5
(403) 262-1580
(Manufacturer)

MODEL: Canadian Storm Warmer
Material: Steel, cast-iron doors, firebrick lined
Description: Double door stepstove with swing-out baffle. Firescreen included.
Airtight
Made in Canada

WOODKING STOVES INTERNATIONAL OF CAN. LIMITED
1458 Church Avenue
Winnipeg, Man. R2X 1G4
(204) 632-1962
(Distributor)

MODEL: Woodsman 18'', 24'', 30'', 36''
Material: Steel, cast-iron doors, firebrick lined. Nickle plated trim.
Description: Double door stepstove with twin draft control. Firescreen for fireviewing.
Airtight
Made in Canada
18'' $463
24'' $553
30'' $626
36'' $651

WOODSTOVES UNLIMITED
2110 Cliffe Avenue
Courtenay, B.C. V9N 2L4
(604) 334-4133
(Distributor)

MODEL: Olympic Crest
Material: Cast iron
Description: Double door fireviewer. Baffled interior, secondary combustion chamber. Side and front loading.
Airtight
Made in U.S.A.
$780

A man ahead of his time, J.A. Fisher in 1937 invented a double smoke chamber to extract maximum heat from his barrel stove.

FURNACES & BOILERS

AGUAHEATER CORP.
Box 815
Clark, Colorado 80428
(303) 879-3908
(Distributor)

MODEL: AguaHeater
Fuels: Wood. Fuel oil attachment optional.
Description: Cylindrical hot water heater can be used with any gravity or pressure plumbing system. Continuous hot water as long as fire is burning.
Airtight
Made in Mexico
Large $189
Regular $159
Portable $139
Freight paid to 6 Canadian cities

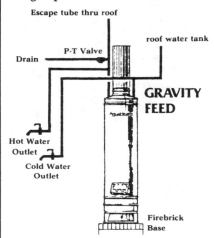

CORRIGAN'S WELDING & WOOD STOVE CENTRE
East Royalty, P.E.I.
(902) 892-3159
(Manufacturer)

MODEL: Patlyn
Fuels: Wood and coal
Description: Boiler with water

jacket at top and rear serving as baffle plate. Thermostatically controlled. Steel with cast-iron door. Steel liner. Optional hot water coil.
Airtight
Made in Canada
$750

DUO-MATIC/OLSEN
9230 Islington Avenue
Woodbridge, Ont. L4L 1B3
(416) 677-3394
(Manufacturer)

MODEL: Duo-matic CWO-B
Fuels: Coal, oil and wood
Description: Combination furnace with two thermostats. Oil burner comes on automatically when solid fuel fire burns down. Twin blowers and heat exchangers. Spun glass filters.
Airtight
Made in Canada
$1,700—$1,900

ENHEAT LIMITED FAWCETT DIVISION
100 Main Street
Sackville, N.B. E0A 3C0
(506) 536-1520
(Manufacturer)

MODEL: Fawcett WF200 Furnasaid
Fuels: Wood. Model WF200A may be installed as add-on to existing furnace.
Description: Thermostatically controlled wood burning furnace.
Airtight
Made in Canada
$575—$825

MODEL: Fawcett WB 140

Fuels: Wood. Can be used as add-on to oil, gas or electric fuel supply.
Description: Thermostatically controlled boiler with interior baffle, pressure and temperature gauges and drain-down system.
Airtight
Made in Canada
$1,087

Fawcett CWF 85

MODEL: Fawcett CWF 85
Fuels: Coal and wood
Description: Compact thermostatically controlled furnace. Dual baffle system in heat exchanger. Optional kit to hook into existing furnace. Optional fan.
Airtight
Made in Canada
$795 with fan
$675 without fan

FRANCO-BELGE FOUNDRIES OF AMERICA
70 Pine Street
New York, N.Y. 10005
(212) 425-3115 or 425-3116
(Manufacturer)

MODEL: LaForestière
Fuels: Coal, oil or wood
Description: Thermostatically controlled boiler with large loading door and secondary burn design.
Airtight
Made in U.S.A.
$1,800—$2,000 (U.S.)
Canadian distributor:
Onward Hardware Limited
932 Victoria Street
Kitchener, Ont. N2B 1W4
(519) 578-3770

MODEL: Polytherm and Polymatic
Fuels: Wood, coal, oil, gas

Description: When solid fuel runs out, unit switches directly to oil or gas. May be used as add-on to existing system.
Airtight
Made in U.S.A.
Polytherm $2,850 (U.S.)
Polymatic $2,300 (U.S.)
Canadian distributor:
(see above)

Franco-Belge Polymatic

FRECO LIMITED
1408, 13th Avenue Ouest,
Charny, Cté Lévis, P.Q.
G6W 3Z2
(418) 832-4605
(Manufacturer)

MODEL: Freco CO-20, CO-25, CO-325
Fuels: Oil, wood
Description: Boiler for domestic heating or as swimming pool heater. Optional electrical controls.
Airtight
Made in Canada
$1,412—$2,380 (various sizes)

THE G&S MILL
Otis Street
Northborough, Mass. 01532
(617) 393-9266
(Manufacturer)

MODEL: G&S Mill (5 models)
Fuels: Wood only
Description: Very large furnace, two chamber design. Firebox chamber burns at 1200 degrees F. Heat exchanger unit sends heat through forced air system.

Suitable for small companies.
Airtight
Made in U.S.A.
$6,900—$17,300

HAMPTON TECHNOLOGIES CORPORATION
Box 2277
Charlottetown, P.E.I. C1A 8B9
(902) 892-4067 or 894-8687
(Manufacturer)

MODEL: Jetstream Furnace
Fuels: Wood
Description: Wood burns in large combustion chamber at high temperatures. Tubular heat exchangers transfer heat to water in large fiberglass tank.
Airtight
Made in Canada
$2,500 (furnace plus tank)

HUNTER ENTERPRISES LIMITED
Box 400
Orillia, Ontario L3V 6K1
(705) 325-6111
(Manufacturer)

MODEL: HWO 100, HWO 125, HWO 135, HWO 150
Fuels: Wood and oil
Description: Furnace with double baffled combustion chamber and thermostatically controlled damper. Oil burning side comes on automatically when wood burns down.
Airtight
Made in Canada
$1,700—$1,750
Western Canada distributor:
Valley Comfort
Winlaw, B.C. V0G 2J0
(604) 226-7221

MODEL: RB 3D, RB 4D
Fuels: Wood

Description: Furnace with double baffled combustion chamber, cylindrical heat exchangers and electric thermostat.
Airtight
Made in Canada
$780 RB 3D
$855 RB 4D
Add $245 for blower
Western Canada distributor:
(see above)

INTER-CITY MFG. LTD.
695 Berry Street
Winnipeg, Man. R3H 0S4
(204) 786-6552
(Manufacturer)

MODEL: MFA (4 models)
Fuels: Wood and oil
Description: Furnace with twin blower assembly designed for residences and small commercial buildings. Separate thermostats for wood and oil. CSA approved.
Airtight
Made in Canada
$1,400—$1,600

KERR CONTROLS LTD.
Box 1500
Truro, Nova Scotia B2N 5V2
(902) 895-9281
(Manufacturer)

MODEL: Scotsman and Scotty
Fuels: Wood
Description: Thermostatically controlled furnace with secondary combustion and horizontal baffles. Can be used as add-on to existing furnace.
Airtight
Made in Canada
$740 Scotsman
$670 Scotty

MODEL: Titan
Fuels: Wood
Description: Thermostatically controlled boiler with tubular heat exchanger and back-up safety "blowdown" system. May be hooked up to oil fired boiler as add-on.
Airtight
Made in Canada
$1,230

KICKAPOO STOVE WORKS LIMITED
Main Street
LaFarge, Wisconsin 54639
(608) 625-4430
(Manufacturer)

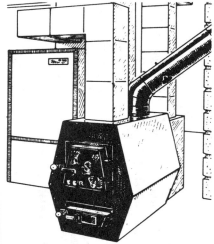

MODEL: BBR-D5
Fuels: Wood, designed as add-on to existing furnace
Description: Furnace with thermostatically controlled blower and a series of metal heat exchangers. Shares existing plenum and ductwork of your present furnace.
Airtight
Made in U.S.A.
$672 (U.S.)

MONARCH KITCHEN APPLIANCES
Beaver Dam, Wisconsin 53916
(Manufacturer)

MODEL: Add-A-Furnace AF224
Fuels: Wood. Adds on to existing furnace
Description: Thermostatically controlled blower. 10'' x 16'' rectangular duct opening in top for direct hook up to existing plenum.
Airtight
Made in U.S.A.
$700

Canadian distributor:
Cosman's Wood
Heating Unlimited
327-329 Carlton Street
Winnipeg, Man. R3B 2K7
(204) 942-5719

MULTI-FUEL ENERGY SYSTEMS
2185 North Sherman Drive
Indianapolis, Indiana 46218
(317) 542-0691
(Manufacturer)

MODEL: Multi-Fuel Energy Converter
Fuels: Wood, coal, trash
Description: Furnace which can be used alone or as add-on to existing furnace. Downdraft combustion chamber with copper finned heat exchanger.
Airtight
Made in U.S.A.
$849 (U.S.)

NEWMAC MFG. INC.
Box 545, 236 Norwich Avenue
Woodstock, Ontario N4S 7Y5
(519) 539-6147
(Manufacturer)
MODEL: WB 100, WS 100
Fuels: Wood

Description: Thermostatically controlled furnace with downdraft burn design. Can be used as add-on to existing furnace. Blower moves 1200 cubic feet per minute.
Not airtight
Made in Canada
$700

MODEL: CL-115, CL-140, CL-155, CL-170
Fuels: Wood, coal and oil
Description: Thermostatically controlled furnaces with twin blowers which move 1300 to 1900 cubic feet per minute.
Airtight
Made in Canada
$1,380—$1,450

Newmac CL-115

NORDIC ENERGY SYSTEMS LIMITED
1060 Lorne Street
Sudbury, Ontario P3C 4R9
[705] 675-3889
(Manufacturer)

MODEL: Water Furnace (4 models)
Fuels: Wood
Description: Furnace with internal baffle design, thermostatic control (non-electric) and water coil for domestic hot water.
Airtight
Made in Canada
$1,800 Mini
$1,900 Midi
$2,500 Maxi

PRACTICAL NORTHERN PRODUCTS (CANADA)
Box 1109, Station Q
Toronto, Ontario M4T 2P2
(416) 694-5455
(Manufacturer)

MODEL: Big Jim Arctic Furnace
26, 34, 40
Fuels: Wood
Description: Furnace with downdraft burn, baffle system and electric blower. Optional hot water coils and electric thermostat. Can also be used as space heater.
Airtight
Made in Canada
26 $570
34 $605
40 $635

PROCAM STEEL PRODUCTS LTD.
9 Bennett Street
Pembroke, Ont. K8A 3Y6
(613) 735-1034
(Manufacturer)

MODEL: Surefire 101CE
Fuels: Wood, electric
Description: Furnace with horizontal baffle, secondary combustion and large heat exchanger.
Airtight
Made in Canada
10 kw $1,150
20 kw $1,195

MODEL: Surefire 101CO
Fuels: Wood and oil
Description: Furnace with automatic oil start-up and shutdown. Horizontal baffles and secondary combustion. Large firebox and heat exchanger. Thermostatically controlled.
Airtight
Made in Canada
$1,400

MODEL: Surefire 101BC CSA
Fuels: Wood
Description: Thermostatically controlled furnace with large firebox and heat exchanger. Includes blower and air plenum. CSA approved.
Airtight
Made in Canada
$749

MODEL: Surefire 201A
Fuels: Wood
Description: Thermostatically controlled add-on furnace, works in conjunction with existing ductwork, chimney and fan. Horizontal baffles, secondary combustion.
Airtight
Made in Canada
$630

R.A.S. DISTRIBUTORS
228 S. McKellar Street
Thunder Bay, Ont. P7E 1H7
(807) 623-2033
(Distributor)

MODEL: SFB-3
Fuels: Wood
Description: Round boiler with thermostat, Venturi draft system and two non-concentric cylinders allowing for fully water-jacketed firebox.
Airtight
Made in U.S.A.
$949—$995

RSF ENERGY
Smithers, B.C.
(Manufacturer)

MODEL: F85
Fuels: Wood
Description: Downdraft system draws air in from back of stove. Smoke forced through fire before exiting through bottom flue. Hooks into existing ductwork. Centre push loading door.
Airtight
Made in Canada
$895

WILSON'S LIMITED (GEORGE WILSON)
27 Cumberland Street
Charlottetown, P.E.I.
(902) 894-9517
(Distributor)

MODEL: HS Tarm MB
Fuels: Wood, coal
Description: Boiler to add to existing oil or gas-fired hot water system. Thermostatic control, downdraft burn. Oil unit comes on automatically.
Airtight
Made in Denmark
$1,460—$1,980

MODEL: HS Tarm OT
Fuels: Wood, coal, coke, refuse, oil, gas, electricity
Description: Multi-fuel boiler with movable damper for baffled or downdraft burn. Tank or coil design. Two large combustion chambers, one for solid fuel, one for oil or gas. Electrical hook-ups optional.
Airtight
Made in Denmark
$2,583—$3,478

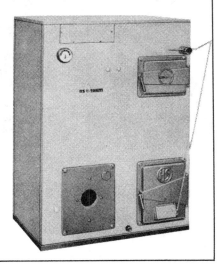

Homing In On A Range

How to find the jewel amidst the junk and bird offerings

Sandwiched between a page of card games (*Authors, Nations, Lost Heir, Old Maid* and *Snap*) and a selection of reed-bodied and parasoled high-wheel baby carriages, the 1901 Eaton's Catalogue listed its kitchen ranges. For $30, one could order the Royal Alexandra, complete with duplex grate for coal or wood burning and six cooking holes. T. Eaton & Co. did not wax ebullient in advertising the stove, but said with elegant self-assurance: "We positively guarantee this range to be perfect in every part."

Were one of these stoves to surface in a farm auction today — an occurrence that becomes ever more rare — it might fetch 10 to 20 times its original price. Less ornate models are often brought out of retirement — kitchen queens rescued from back sheds, barns and junk piles — and offered in reconditioned shape for perhaps $200 to $700 (the price will vary wildly from region to region). If you know what to look for, however, finding and fixing one up yourself can be satisfying to the wallet as well as the soul.

Spotting the jewel in the junk is not as easy as it may sound. Warm muffins and steaming chowders are hard to envision when confronted with a chipped and pitted antiquity, liberally anointed with bird offerings. Some guidelines, however, will aid in evaluating the extent and importance of defects, as well as the estimated cost of their repair.

Years of continual heat will gradually eat through predictable parts of a wood cookstove. One of the first things to go is the grate, the metal supporting structure found about halfway down the firebox. It may be a slotted cradle, a plate covered with holes or several rotating, flat-sided rods that were designed to shake down coal ash.

If the grate is burned out, badly warped or completely missing, a local welder or blacksmith can easily fashion a new one, given the dimensions of the firebox. If the coal grates don't work, or are so widely spaced as to make wood burning difficult (some cookstoves were designed only for coal use), a plate of one-half-inch steel can be placed directly on top of the old grates. The plate should have one-inch holes bored or burned through it every few inches, to allow ashes to be poked down into the ashbox.

A more difficult and potentially serious problem is a cracked or burned out firebox wall. Small cracks can be filled with stove cement, but major defects will call for firebricking or the fashioning of a new metal plate wall. Before buying a stove that needs such work, try to get an estimate on repairs. Two years ago we had a new grate and welded wall between firebox and oven done for $25. A firebox that is completely burned or rusted out is probably grounds for rejecting a stove.

Boots & Jackets

To be efficient, a cookstove must be as airtight as possible, and every pinhole and crack that sucks in unwanted air contributes to an undesirably fast burn and lack of control. The smaller perforations can be sealed up with stove cement, but beware of crevices wide enough to "bank" a coin. Carry a flashlight to check the inner surfaces of the oven, the water jacket or water reservoir, the ashbox and the back of the stove, especially where the stovepipe will connect to the stove.

The stovepipe must fit onto or into a "boot" or collar, and if this is rusted away or missing, the stove will be useless to you unless it is replaced or a new one cast.

A crack in the cast surfaces which will allow smoke to escape means automatic elimination, although marred or missing cooking plates on the stove top can be replaced. Pitting and rusting are both cosmetic blemishes, easily remedied with a wash and a good polish. Check the mechanical functions. All dampers and doors must work — or be expected to loosen up reasonably with penetrating oil. Doors should have handles and close tightly and easily.

Having decided to buy the stove, enquire about the accessories. Besides the lifter and poker of that grade school rhyme, you need the long-handled scraper used to rake ashes out from beneath the oven. If the cooker is a wood/coal combination, ask for the coal-grate crank that fits over the triangular metal stubs below the firebox. If the original extras are long gone, most hardware stores, especially in rural areas, stock them for less than five dollars apiece.

New cookstoves are worth considering if you cannot find an old model to your liking and if you have the resources and feel certain of your commitment. Sackville, New Brunswick is the home of both the Fawcett and Enterprise stoveworks, which produce enamelled wood-fired cookers retailing between $400 and $650. The Findlay Oval, once a fixture of early Ontario farm kitchens, is being produced from original moulds by the Elmira Stoveworks in Elmira, Ontario for the substantial price of $1,495. A new airtight model of this stove has become available and is selling for $1,595.

A lack of airtightness is the major drawback of traditional wood cookstoves, which cannot compare in length of burn or fuel efficiency with the current generation of airtight parlour stoves. Two European stoves, however, already offer airtight ranges: Jotul has a smallish stove that retails for approximately $800 and Waterford, an Irish firm with distributors across North America, offers the Stanley at $1,250.

It can be predicted with a reasonable degree of certainty that a number of North American stove manufacturers now have family-sized airtight ranges on the drawing boards.

Juggling the advantages of old versus new and old versus ancient ultimately becomes a purely personal decision. But, regardless of the price, a woodburning kitchen stove is guaranteed to become the most indispensable feature of your home.

—Merilyn Mohr
Astorville, Ontario

COOKSTOVES

ATLANTA STOVE WORKS
6757 Northwest Drive
Mississauga, Ontario L4V 1L1
(416) 677-0144
(Distributor)

MODEL: 15-36
Material: Cast-iron stove
Description: Stove burns wood or coal. Optional warming shelf, or range only.
Not airtight
Made in U.S.A.
$500

BAY BARN
Box 250
Seeleys Bay, Ont.
(613) 387-3273
(Distributor)

Reg Kumm has a variety of 1850-1979 models of stoves, including cookstoves. He also rebuilds antique stoves.

THE COOKSTOVE CABIN
Box 1233
Belleville, Ontario
(613) 477-2684 or 962-2430
(Distributor)
These people buy, sell and restore old and new cookstoves.

COSMAN'S WOOD HEATING UNLIMITED
327-329 Carlton Street
Winnipeg, Manitoba R3B 2K7
(204) 942-5719
(Distributor)
MODEL: Noble Steel
Material: Steel
Description: Stove built for wagon travel (for sheepmen and ranchers). Weight 100 pounds.
Not airtight
Made in U.S.A.
$250

DE LUXE EQUIPMENT INC.
8026 Jarry Street East
Ville d'Anjou, P.Q. H1J 1H5
(514) 354-1155
(Distributor)
MODEL: Jotul 404
Material: Cast iron with enamelled oven
Description: Burns coke or coal with special grates. Has adjusting damper and two or three machined lids. No high back.
Not airtight
Made in Norway
$815

ELMIRA STOVE WORKS
22 Church Street West
Elmira, Ontario
(519) 669-1281
(Manufacturer)
MODEL: Findlay Oval 9919-2 and 9919-3
Material: Cast iron with brick lined firebox, steel back and warming closet
Description: Burns coal or wood. Multiple-section cooking lid for open flame cooking, with optional water jacket. Gasketed doors and Bell dampers to control

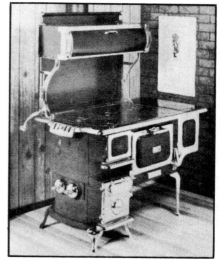

primary air supply. Porcelained framing in white or gold.
Airtight
Made in Canada
9919-2 $1,400
9919-3 $1,500
This company also stocks parts for old Findlay Ovals.

ENHEAT LIMITED FAWCETT DIVISION
100 Main Street
Sackville, N.B. E0A 3C0
(506) 536-1520
(Manufacturer)

MODEL: Fawcett Compact Charm
Material: Enamelled steel
Description: Has high back with warming shelf or closet. Optional coal grates, cast-iron water front and water reservoir.
Not airtight
Made in Canada
$500—$600

MODEL: 7-15 Dandy
Material: Blued-steel body, with cast-iron firebox, top and lids
Description: Stove is asbestos lined. No high back. Optional water front ($60) and oil retort burner ($165) available.
Not airtight
Made in Canada
$340

Fawcett 7-15 Dandy

MODEL: Fawcett Multi-Fuel Range
Material: Steel
Description: Cooks and heats with wood, oil, coal or garbage. Available with high closet or shelf.
Not airtight
Made in Canada
$600—$700

Record New Pioneer

MODEL: Record New Pioneer
Material: Cast iron and steel
Description: Heavy-duty range for camps and cottages. Has optional water reservoir.
Not airtight
Made in Canada
$400—$500

THE ENTERPRISE FOUNDRY CO. LTD.
Sackville, N.B. E0A 3C0
(506) 536-1160
(Manufacturer)

MODEL: Savoy 52DY
Material: Steel cabinet with cast-iron top and glass door
Description: Burns coal or wood. Has wood-grain facing on back-guard with aluminum trim. Has clock and minute minder.
Not airtight
Made in Canada
$626, $523 without deluxe backguard

MODEL: Woodsman 9
Material: Cast iron and steel
Description: Compact stove for camping and cottages. Five cooking lids. Ten-and-a-half-gallon copper reservoir, tinned on inside.
Not airtight
Made in Canada
$459

MODEL: Queen Cook No. 8
Material: Cast iron
Description: Elevated oven at back with swing away doors at each end. Four stove lids and two nickle-plated pot warmers. Has cast-iron rack under stove for storage and drying. Nickle-plated silhouette of Queen Victoria.
Not airtight
Made in Canada
$595

FERON COMPANY LTD.
45 Wright Avenue
Dartmouth, N.S. B3B 1H1
(902) 463-2953
(Distributor)

MODEL: Tirolia (7N)
Material: Enamelled steel
Description: Burns wood or coal. Has an extra large oven with fold down top. Optional hot water heating coil and hot water jacket available.
Not airtight
Made in Austria
$1,169

THE KROUPA STOVE
Grand Etang
Nova Scotia B0E 1L0
(902) 224-2849
(Manufacturer)

MODEL: Kroupa
Material: Steel plate with cast-iron doors
Description: Multi-functional cooker, baker, heater and fire-viewer. Oven has pyrex doors which can be left open as a heat exchanger. Firebox has Vycor glass, with a special plate cover for nighttime.
Airtight
Made in Canada
$1,000

NORWEGIAN WOOD STOVES

Box 219, Clarkson Post Office
Mississauga, Ontario L5J 3Y1
(416) 822-2330
(Distributor)

MODEL: Lange Cookstove 911W
Material: Cast iron
Description: Has dual draft control and optional enamel finish. No high back.
Airtight
Made in Denmark
$1,390

SPARKS CONSERVER PRODUCTS

Box 1857
Charlottetown, P.E.I.
(902) 892-2700
(Distributor)

MODEL: Waterford Stanley
Material: Cast iron with steel high-back and stainless steel warming shelf
Description: Has large oven and two cooking lids.
Airtight
Made in Ireland
$1,250

Random Comment

SWEET JOTUL

We have and use the Jotul cook-stove mentioned in *Sourcebook One*. The reviewer's conjecture about the small size of the firebox probably demanding the use of coal, reflects a misapprehension of the stove's sweet but specialized nature.

To follow the automotive metaphors used in the first *Sourcebook* (something that should be changed — all cars are too poorly built to compare to a good wood stove), it is as though you figured you would have to burn nitro in a moped because its engine is smaller than a Chevy's.

The Jotul cookstove is not made for supplying heat to a living space over sustained durations, but for bringing stuff to a boil. It responds with unbelievable quickness, seems to deliver all the heat to its own mass, rather than up the pipe, and cools off pretty quickly once the coals are gone.

In those respects, it is the closest thing you could get to a gas range: quick heat when and only when you want it. Rolling out of bed in the morning in our one-room geodesic hut, I can be drinking hot coffee, filter dripped, from a cold start, in 20 minutes.

The wood we use is mostly from tops of trees felled for heating wood. In tidying up the cutting mess, branches from three-quarters to two inches in diameter get sorted out to be cut into eight to 10 inch lengths and to season a bit. The resulting toy woodpile is the farthest thing you can imagine from coal. Because the Jotul burns these things rather well without splitting, a good supply is rather easy to put by. (The wood for cooking — it may be of interest to some — is from a standing dead apple tree. Our land was partially covered with orchard 40 years ago, and the dead branches of the long abandoned trees could keep us in rock-hard, clean-burning wood for many a year.)

As for coal — we tried it. It didn't seem to me that it burned very well. Maybe I didn't know how to use it correctly. Besides, we couldn't figure out what to do with the ashes.

One Drawback

The important question to be asked regarding any cookstove is how it *bakes.* (After wondering how the hell anybody can afford one of the new models.) Our Jotul bakes our bread and pies, and they're good. But you couldn't really say that baking with it is any better than "possible."

The oven is small, so some part of anything you put in is always close enough to a wall to burn. You get pretty clever about diddling aluminum foil over vulnerable spots just at the point between brown and black. They don't supply a grillwork rack for the oven, so the heat doesn't circulate as well as it might. But they do supply a roasting pan that exactly fits the oven, so you can do up a 10 or 11 pound — maximum — turkey nicely. Pictures of Jotul's older advertising material show an oven-thermometer built into the door, but our model has none. This would be worth restoring; the oven is too small to keep opening up to check and, besides, there's no place in there to put a thermometer that wouldn't be in the way.

In short, the firebox is not the limitation of this cookstove. It's a small, very efficient stove with all the advantages of smallness — quick to respond, taking little space — but with one disadvantage of smallness, in the oven. It would be a poor choice for large families and large canning operations. While baking, it puts out tremendous amounts of heat, but it shouldn't be considered as a heater, because it won't hold a fire without refuelling for more than 45 minutes or so. Those willing to develop the knack of working around its shortcomings, however, may find its advantages outweigh the limitations.

On the millionaire dream-home-stead, I would have the Jotul for routine meals in the kitchen and a great big cookstove in an adjacent, well-ventilated room for big jobs. All in all, we love our Jotul.

—Andres Ozdins
Cortland, New York

GENERAL DISTRIBUTORS

THE CHIMNEY BRUSH
R.R.1
Kinmount, Ontario K0M 2A0
(705) 488-2811

Stoves: Carmor, Enterprise, Fisher, Timberline, Tirolia. Accessories: Projet chimneys, chimney brushes, chain saws, axes, Big Joe log splitters.

CONSERVER SOCIETY PRODUCTS CO-OP INC.
Box 4377, Station E
Ottawa, Ontario K2P 1B8

Stoves: Jotul, Trolla, Valley Comfort, Morso, Enterprise, Findlay, Lakewood, Church, Free Flow, Tempwood, Le Petit Godin, Waterford. Furnaces: Valley Comfort, Furnasaid, Welkum, Newmac, Hunter. Fireplaces: Angcaname, Convect-O-Heater

COSMAN'S WOOD HEATING UNLIMITED
327 - 329 Carlton Street
Winnipeg, Manitoba R3B 2K7
(204) 942-5719, 942-1177

Stoves: Monarch, Noble cookstove, Dynapac Stovaway, Autocrat Circulator, Autocrat Americana, Autocrat Thermo-Wood.

ENERGY ALTERNATIVES
2 Croft Street, Box 671
Amherst, Nova Scotia
B4H 4B8
(902) 667-2790

Stoves: Jotul, Morso, Lakewood, Fisher, Crest, Findlay, Agua Heater, Tempwood, Reginald, Stanley, Freeflow, Bluenose, Cawley/LeMay, Energy Harvester. Furnaces: Kerr, Surefire. Accessories: Chimney brushes, Wood splitting mauls and axes

L'AUTRE SOURCE
107 Albert Street
Cowansville, Quebec J2K 2W4
(514) 263-2412

Stoves: Fisher, Tempwood, Fawcett, Stanley, Jotul, Morso, Enterprise

MILES INDUSTRIES LTD.
Box 91686
West Vancouver, B.C.
V7V 3P3
Stoves: Ulefos, Le Petit Godin, Kresno

MILLETTE STOVES
280 Grande Cote
Rosemere, Quebec
(514) 621-6631
Stoves: Findlay Oval, Stanley cookstove, Lakewood, Morso, Jotul, Trolla, Tirolia, Reginald, Cawley/LeMay, Le Petit Godin, Lange. Accessories: Insulated chimney — Selkirk and Projet

MOUNTAIN MAPLE COUNTRY STORE
R.R.1
Nipissing, Ont. P0H 1W0
(705) 729-5475
Stoves: Free Flow, Trolla, Stanley, Lakewood. Chimney brushes—rented or sold.

P.E.I. STOVE WORKS LTD.
Box 2282, Malpeque Rd.
Charlottetown, P.E.I.
(902) 892-9843
Stoves: Efel, Morso, Olympic Crest, Tirolia, Findlay, Waterford Reginald, Fawcett, Convect-O-Heater. Woodburning accessories.

THE REHILL COMPANY LIMITED
210 Wolfe St. Box 202
Peterborough, Ont. K9J 6Y8
(705) 742-5428
Stoves: Fisher, Selkirk-Metalbestos, Lakewood, Findlay Oval, Findlay Chatelaine. Fireplace accessories.

SOLACE ENERGY CENTRES INC.
2425 Main Street
Vancouver, B.C. V5T 3E1
(604) 879-5258
Stoves: Waterford Reginald, Jotul, Olympic Crest, Kresno, Waterford Stanley cookstove, Ulefos, Le Petit Godin.

WESTERN STOVE REPAIR & SALES LIMITED
307-8 Avenue S.E.
Calgary, Alberta T2G 0L5

(403) 262-1580
(Manufacturer)
Source for stove parts. Have approx. 4000 patterns for wood and coal stoves. Can cast original pieces. Cost: $3.50 per pound cast iron.

THE WOODEN EWE LTD.
Box 1387
Fairview, Alberta T0H 1L0
(403) 835-4216
Stoves: Jotul, Woodsman, Waterford, Newmac, Riteway, Morso, Fisher, Fawcett. Woodburning products and accessories

WOOD 'N' ENERGY PRODUCTS
Main Street
McDonald's Corners, Ont.
K0G 1M0
(613) 278-2023
Stoves: Lakewood, Riteway, Jotul, Free Flow, Ulefos, Findlay, Morso, Olympic Crest, Heritage, Stanley, Enterprise. Fresh air fireplaces and converters. Furnaces, boilers. Brushes, accessories.

WOOD POWER
78 Cork Street West
Guelph, Ontario
(519) 836-9990
Stoves: Fisher, Lakewood, Hunter, Waterford, Ashley, Selkirk, Carmor. Insulated chimneys: Bel Vent, Selkirk, Projet, Square A. Accessories: Kathite-H, Chimney brushes

WOODSTOVE AND SUPPLY CO.
248 Jane Street
Toronto, Ontario M6S 3Z1
(416) 767-7767
Stoves: Jotul, Tempwood, Le Petit Godin, Efel, Morso, Trolla

WOOD STOVES UNLIMITED
2110 Cliffe Avenue
Courtenay, B.C. V9N 2L4
(604) 334-4133
Stoves: Jotul, Reginald, Stanley, Mariager fireplace insert, Island Comfort. Custom fireplace inserts. Woodburning accessories

Stovepipe Oven Reincarnate

Nineteenth century design rescued from a flea market

"The wood stove served two purposes: we kept it full of jack pine logs to warm us . . . and many a meal was made with land birds stuffed and roasted in our stovepipe oven."
— A.L. Karras
North to Cree Lake

For trail-hungry trappers shooting and snaring their way through the Depression in northern Saskatchewan, the stovepipe oven was a godsend. It provided almost the same cooking and heating power of a heavyweight range for just a portion of the investment in stake money and energy. (Imagine canoeing up river with a Findlay Oval in the bow.) A trapper like A.L. Karras could double the power of his wood burner with a lightweight stovepipe oven.

Today the usefulness of a stovepipe oven is being rediscovered

by a new generation of wood burners. Compact design and moderate price make it ideal for cabin cuisine. Spliced into the six- or eight-inch stack that rises out of the mother stove, a stovepipe oven takes the heat that usually flies up the chimney and wraps it around spitting roasts, plump loaves of bread and crusty pies.

Simultaneously, door open or closed, the oven amplifies the heat produced by any space-heating stove. It adds more than 1,000 square inches of heat radiating surface to a woodburning system. I'm astounded by the increased warmth generated by my rig and am able to keep the cabin warm with about 25 per cent less firewood. And, if the craving for a midnight soufflé strikes, why not? As long as the wood stove is burning, the oven is preheated and ready to go.

Like many of the "alternative" implements appearing on the market today, the stovepipe oven is a reincarnation of a 19th century design, with an innovative twist. Manufactured by a small rural company known as Cedar Creek Homestead in Auburn, Indiana, the oven is modelled after an old cast-iron and sheet metal model unearthed at a flea market. The decorative cast ends and door, in fact, are exact replicas, joined by heavy 24-gauge sheet metal. The builders have updated the original design by adding a built-in sweep cleaner that safeguards against creosote build-up or soot jams.

Here is how it works: The oven replaces a 20-inch section of vertical stovepipe just above the wood stove. I find that locating the oven door just below eye-level works best, so that I can spy on lasagna without resorting to standing on a chair. The folks at Cedar Creek suggest that the oven be mounted at least 12 inches above the wood stove, to avoid overly hot temperatures, and they supply self-tapping metal screws to pin sections of stovepipe to the top and bottom of the oven.

Primitive Controls

When there is a fire in the stove below, heat rises through the double-wall oven, surrounding the baking chamber but not allowing smoke to come into contact with the food. Temperature depends on the fire source below, and can be closely regulated by opening and closing the oven door. At first sight, I mentally chided the makers for neglecting to inlay a door thermometer, but with the door ajar, it wouldn't make sense. A small shelf thermometer makes better sense, and works fine for me. Strangely, the soot-cleaning rod pokes out the back of the unit, making it somewhat difficult to reach in some stove installations. In a squeeze, the oven could be mounted with the door facing sideways, with the long axis of the unit parallel to the wall.

The sheet metal construction is sturdy and the cast-iron front and rear plates which clinch the oven together give the appearance of solidity. Abstract, voluptuous designs in the iron are a nice relief from the weird tableaux that live on many wood stoves.

The more *inefficient* your mother stove, the more heat that shoots up the flue, the better the oven bakes. For a while I had trouble raising baking temperatures, because I burn wood in a Free Flow stove that wicks off most heat into my house. Then I learned to cap off the Free Flow tubes while cooking, thereby "wasting" enough heat to drive the oven up to baking speed. I'm using aluminum foil caps while I wait for a local potter to turn some ceramic tube tops. I like the way the stovepipe oven mates with the Free Flow. The open oven adds what the Free Flow lacks: a hot shelf for warming coffee and cakes.

The stovepipe oven likes a chimney stack with a vertical

head about three feet above the mother stove. My setup is ideal. The oven feeds right into a metalbestos chimney that periscopes straight out of the house. Stoves that tap directly into a chimney thimble won't work.

The oven has one drawback. It damps the fire too much for open door burning. I miss the chance to transform my stove into a fireplace. Starting fires in heavy weather can be a bit tricky, too. But that's a minor trade-off in exchange for an oven, drying box, warming shelf, and a huge boost in heating efficiency — all in one. This oven looks like a wood culture pipe dream come true.

— Timothy Matson
Thetford Center, Vermont

ACCESSORIES
Log Splitters, Axes, Mauls

BARTELL INDUSTRIES LIMITED
219 Toryork Drive
Weston, Ontario M9L 1Y2
(416) 749-1253

Model: Stickler log splitter. Description: Vehicle mounted, screw-wedge splitter. $199.

BENNETT & HANSON LTD.
Hershey Drive
Smiths Falls, Ont. K7A 1L9
(613) 283-3162

Model: Big Joe wood splitters. Description: Hydraulic ram pushes wood against stationary wedge. Tractor mount model $574., P.T.O. model $995., Gas engine model $1,135.

THE BLAIRHAMPTON ALTERNATIVE
Box 748
Haliburton, Ont. K0M 1S0

Many wood-related tools including: Iltis Oxhead fuelwood splitter (7 lbs. with handle): $34.00; 10 and 20-lb. hardwood sledges: $26.00 and $34.00

C & D MARKETING INC.
342 Middlesex Turnpike
Old Saybrook, Connecticut 06475

Model: Jiffy woodsplitter. Description: Guided, forged steel wedge wood splitter.

FABSON'S ENGINEERING
Box 635, 28 View Street
Leominster, Mass. 01453
(617) 537-5174

Log splitter plans: $4.75

INTERNATIONAL IMPORTS
Box 63
Hampton, Ontario
(416) 263-8045

Brushwacker axe: 2½ to 6 pounds with German steel heads and Ontario-made handles. Wholesale prices from $9.50 to $15.00. Splitting maul: 6 pounds, under $25.00. Both products available at United Co-operatives of Ontario. International Imports will ship to other provinces.

BARBARA JOHNSON
Box 57, R.R.1
Dwight, Ont. P0A 1H0
(705) 635-2788

Model: Wedge axe. Description: Made of seven-pound, ductalloy, plough point steel on hickory handle.

LEE VALLEY TOOLS LTD.
Box 6295
Ottawa, Ontario K2A 1T4
Splitting maul (6 lbs.): $13.75.

MECHANICAL SALES CO.
1723 Lakeshore Rd. W.
Mississauga, Ont. L5J 1J4
(416) 822-5621

Model: Futura log splitter.
Description: Many models to
handle wood of different sizes.
Automatic controls, gasoline and
tractor mounted models.

METRO WOOD AND EQUIPMENT COMPANY
13 Rothsay Avenue
Toronto, Ontario M8Z 4L9
(416) 255-2225

Model: Lickity log splitter.
Description: Hydraulic log splitter
available in 15 models.

OMARK CANADA LTD.
505 Edinburgh Rd. N.
Guelph, Ontario N1H 5L4
Model: Oregon Wood Grenade.
Description: Conical-shaped wood-
splitting wedge.

ARTHUR SAGER
R.R.1 Pleasantville,
Lunenburg Cty., Nova Scotia
B0R 1G0
Model: Super-Split log splitter (not
hydraulic) and chimney brushes.

PRINCESS AUTO & MACHINERY LIMITED
Box 1005
Winnipeg, Man. R3C 2W7

Hydraulic log splitters, gas-
powered, two models: $749 and
$1,195. Log splitter kit for do-it-
yourselfers: $299.

PRO-CRAFT LIMITED
160 Don Park Road, Unit 1
Markham, Ont. L3R 1C3
(416) 495-1709

Model: Tomahawk and Tiny Tom.
Description: Hydraulic splitter
with adjustable wedge, five-
second cycle and highway wheels.
Tiny Tom does not have highway
wheels, and has fixed log length of
18 inches. Tomahawk: $1,060.
Tiny Tom: $800.

ERNEST SEDORE & SON
Mount Albert, Ont. L0G 1M0
(416) 473-2240

Model: Sedore log splitter.
Description: Splitter connects to
tractor's three point hitch: $980
With own hydraulic system:
$1,260.

SOTZ CORPORATION
Columbia Station, Ohio 44028
Twenty-pound Monster maul:
$27.95 (including shipping within
U.S.). Available in Canada from
Town & Country Products (see
below). Lift 'n' Saw Tree Lifter,
$13.95 plus shipping.

THE THACKERY CO.
1820 Frebis Avenue
Columbus, Ohio 43206
(614) 444-6882

Model: Unicorn log splitter.

Description: Screw-wedge type
splitter. $300 to $500 (various
models).

TOWN & COUNTRY PRODUCTS
107 Telson Road, Dept. H
Markham, Ont. L3R 1E4
Model: Monster maul.
Description: Twenty-pound, steel
handled, hardened head wood
splitter. $39.95.

TRANS-AMERICA POWER EQUIPMENT INC.
14801 Auburn Road
Newbury, Ohio 44065
Self-powered, Easy Split log
splitter (screw-wedge type).
Canadian distributors:

Gordon Bannerman, Ltd.
41 Kelfield Street
Rexdale, Ont. M9W 5A3

Source
R.R.1
Norbertville (Athabaska)
Quebec G0P 1B0

Maritime Farm Supply
Box 1398
Moncton, New Brunswick
E1C 8T6

VERMEER MANUFACTURING
3390 Wolfedale Road
Mississauga, Ont. L5C 1W4

Farm or commercial-scale
splitters: $1,250 and $3,100.

THE WOOD BURNING CENTRE
Box 645
North Bay, Ont. P1B 8J5
Wood processor, cuts logs to length. Gas-powered log splitters from 5 to 25 h.p. Prices on request.

WROUGHT ART MANUFACTURING
5200 Dixie Road
Mississauga, Ont. L4W 1E4
(416) 625-6209
Hit'N' Split log splitter $37.95.

Chimney Cleaning Equipment

AARAN CHIMNEY SWEEPS
206 Hodgson Drive
Newmarket, Ont. L3Y 1E2
Professionally trained chimney cleaner. Send $1.00 for catalogue.

ATLANTIC COMBUSTION PRODUCTS LIMITED
Box 84
Debert, Nova Scotia
(902) 662-2808
Co-Mate chemical chimney cleaner.

AUGUST WEST SYSTEMS, INC.
Box 603W
Westport, Connecticut 06880
All equipment necessary for chimney cleaning business. Send for free booklet.

BLACK KNIGHT COMPANY
R.R.6
Kensington, P.E.I. C0B 1M0
(902) 886-2838
Provides training for chimney sweeps.

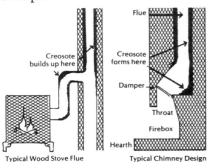

Typical Wood Stove Flue   Typical Chimney Design

BLACK MAGIC CHIMNEY SWEEPS INTL., INC.
Box 977
Stowe, Vermont
(802) 253-5990
Chimney sweeps' catalogue $1.00. Sells booklet "Chimney Sweeping and Wood Stove Cleaning." ($1.50)

CHIMNEY CARE
Box 426
Cavendish, Vermont 05142
Chimney brushes and supplies.

ENERGY ALTERNATIVES
2 Croft Street, Box 671
Amherst, Nova Scotia
Chimfex chimney-fire extinguishers (highly recommended). $26.00 for box of four.

IMPROVED COMSUMER PRODUCTS INC.
100 Towne Street
Attleboro Falls, Ma 02763
(617) 695-6841
Sells Vacu-Stack, an "automatic chimney sweep" made of heavy gauge stainless steel, which also eliminates downdrafts, puff-backs,and keeps rain, snow, leaves and birds out of chimney. $50 to $100. Will ship to Canada.

KEL KEM LIMITED
50 Hamilton Avenue
Cobourg, Ontario K9A 1W1
Glass cleaner for fireplaces and wood stoves.

KRISTIA ASSOCIATES
Box 1118
Portland, Maine 04104
Chimney brushes in all standard sizes. Booklet available, "The Chimney Brush." ($1.00)

OLD VICTORIAN PRODUCTS
R.R.1
Campbellcroft, Ontario
L0A 1B0
(416) 797-2767

Sells *Sootfoe*, a chemical chimney cleaner.

POWRMATIC OF CANADA LIMITED
1169 Caledonia Road
Toronto, Ont. M6A 2X1
Wholesale dealer only, but has many retail suppliers. Send for name of closest dealer. Stainless steel chimney brushes in all standard sizes.

SAFETY SUPPLY CO.
214 King Street East
Toronto, Ontario
Chimfex fire extinguishers. Thirty-four distributors across Canada. Price: $8.91 each.

SOOT & CINDERS
Box 1861
Peterborough, Ont. K9J 7X7
(705) 742-2911

Shaefer chimney brushes, both square and round, rods and brooms. Prices for brushes from $12.00 to $14.00.

TOP HAT CHIMNEY SWEEPS
Box 3457H, Station C
Ottawa, Ontario K1Y 4J6
Chimney cleaning accessories and instructions.

K. R. THOMPSON ENGINEERING LTD.
77 Victoria Street
Ingersoll, Ont. N5C 3K1

Kathite H chimney cleaning powder: 2 lbs./$12.50 postpaid (Ont. and N.Y. residents add 7 per cent sales tax).

TOPPER CHIMNEY SERVICE
Box 1081
Kitchener, Ont. N2G 1Y0

Provide information and supplies for those wishing to start a chimney sweeping business. Catalogue $1.00.

TORONTO CHIMNEY SERVICE LIMITED
36 Rivalda Road
Weston, Ont. M9M 2M3
(416) 742-9862

Chimney sweeping services. Information seminars.

WEBSTER INDUSTRIES LIMITED
71 Kennedy Street
Saint John, N.B.

Safe-T-Flue chimney cleaner.

WOOD-FUEL TECHNOLOGY
Box 22
La Have, N.S. B0R 1C0

Chimney brushes and fiberglass rods.

G. E. WOOD ASSOCIATES
Route 3
Gravenhurst, Ont. P0C 1G0
(705) 687-6169

Chimney brushes and chimney cleaning accessories. Send 50 cents for catalogue.

Miscellaneous

ALBION AAP INC.
2195 Ave. Ekers
Montreal, Quebec H3S 1C7
(514) 731-3241

Asbestos products for wood heaters.

ATLANTA STOVE WORKS
6757 Northwest Drive
Mississauga, Ont. L4V 1L1
(416) 677-0144

Sav-O-Heat flue pipe heat exchanger with thermostatically controlled electric fan. 6″ diameter $130.; 8″ diameter $140.

BEAVER BELLOWS
Box 585
Burks Falls, Ont. P0A 1C0
(705) 387-3382

Handcrafted bellows for starting fires.

BLAZE INDUSTRIES
50 Electronic Avenue
Port Moody, B.C. V3H 2R8
(604) 461-6611

Model: Pacific Fireplace Wyndows. Description: Outer frame is prefinished brass on steel. Tempered glass windows which open accordion style on piano hinges. Kits: $220 to $240. Assembled: $280 to $300.

BLAZING SHOWERS
Box 327
Point Arena, Ca 95468
Three models of heat exchanger, priced from $53 to $63. For more information send 25 cents.

BROOKS MFG. CO. LTD.
250 Norfinch Drive
Downsview, Ont. M3N 1Y4
(416) 661-6660

Ceramic tile-framed fireplace glass doors and metal-framed doors, up to 40 inches wide. $233.50

CEDAR CREEK HOMESTEAD
Box 666
Auburn, Indiana 46706
(219) 925-1172

Stovepipe oven made of sheet steel with cast-iron front and rear plates. $119.95 (U.S.).

THE CHIMNERY INC.
36 Rivalda Road
Weston, Ontario M9M 2M3
(416) 742-2522

Model: Bellfires. Description: Solid masonry fireplace liners.

ENCON
11861 Suzor Cote
Montreal, Quebec H3M 2J1

Model: Better'N' Ben's log lifter. Description: Made of heavy tubular steel. Self-adjusts automatically $49.95.

ENERSAVE PRODUCTS
Box 1295
Port Perry, Ontario L0B 1N0

Stovepipe heat exchanger unit.

HARBER MFG. LIMITED
7 High Street
Fort Erie, Ontario
(416) 871-4010

Model: Dumpet. Description: Fits

most pick-ups and flat bed trucks for carrying and dumping logs.

MHC MFG. LIMITED
Box 725
Tweed, Ontario K0K 3J0
(613) 478-3030

Invis-A-Glass firescreen doors.

NORWEGIAN WOOD STOVES
Box 219, Clarkson Post Office
Mississauga, Ont. L5J 3Y1
(416) 822-2330

Ceramic fire shields, supplied in kit form. Silver Seal. High-temperature resilient stove cement. Stove vent which reduces stovepipe clearance from 18 to 9 inches. Magnetic surface thermometer.

OLIVER MACLEOD LTD.
5 Edward Street
Gravenhurst, Ont. P0C 1G0
(705) 687-3421

Model: Pro-Jet. Description: Insulated chimneys and accessories.

ONE OPENING
BASE TEE
BT-1

TWO OPENING
BASE TEE
BT-2

SELKIRK METALBESTOS
130 North Augusta Road
Brockville, Ontario
Insulated chimneys and chimney accessories.

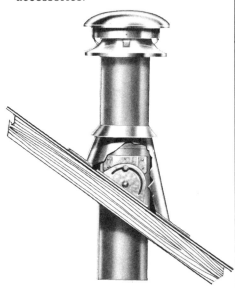

TEMPIL
2901 Hamilton Blvd.
South Plainfield, New Jersey
(201) 757-8300
Model: Pyromark 1200.
Description: Wood stove paint in several colours.

WILDERNESS WOOD-HEATING TECHNIQUES
Box 8001
Fort St. John, B.C. V1J 5E6

Thermostat draft control for wood heaters $34.95.

WROUGHT ART MFG.
5200 Dixie Road
Mississauga, Ont. L4W 1E4
(416) 625-6209

Log Lifter: $19.95.

Random Comment

THE PURIST APPROACH

We live in the sub-Arctic Boreal Forest where water is found in the solid state from mid-November to mid-May. The coming winter will be our third on wood heat.

Judging from past years here, we can count on running the house at an average of 72 Fahrenheit degrees during the day, 78 during bathing periods and coasting down to 59 to 60 degrees during night time sleeping hours. Our monetary cost of space heating, water heating and cooking is a constant: Zero.

Our house requires so little heat to stay comfortable that we can saw a day's wood in 30 to 40 minutes in the inevitable minus 40 degree cold snaps. While our friends in the big city pay to jog circles indoors and pay — in some cases — more than $1,000 per winter for electric space heating, we have exercise with a purpose and free fuel.

This is how we do it:

We are, to begin with, fortunate in living in an ''over-mature'' forest of Black Spruce and Jack Pine which contains many winters' worth of lovely, barkless, standing Jack Pine boles (barkless, limbless, dead trunks). Although some foresters refer to such forests as ''unproductive'' and ''forest slums,'' the woodland caribou, pileated woodpecker and other climax species like it as well as we do.

In the winter of 1978-79 we used five and a half cords of this wood, mostly dead pine and spruce logs, some fairly rotten. The gross heat value was perhaps 50 to 60 million Btu's. To haul this wood, we built a sort of wood-hauling rickshaw. It has two large ply-wood wheels, about three feet in diameter and constructed of double layers of thick plywood. Of course, such a cart would be useless in the bush, but we use it only in the winter and mainly over a frozen body of water. The large wheels carry the cart over bumps in the ice, and we are able to carry up to 1,100 pounds of wood at a time. So long as the surface is hard and free of snow, the hauling effort is minimal. To avoid having to trek through the bush in winter, we stack loads of wood at the shoreline during the snow-free months and leave it in readiness for winter hauling.

Small & Snug

Our house is built with logs and is fairly small, with a floor area of about 600 square feet. It has an R60 ceiling and, with insulation as well as inner walls, R20 walls. All windows are double glazed except the largest, which is triple glazed. (To reduce heat loss through the windows, we plan to install insulated exterior shutters, operable from inside and controlled by a cable like that used on manual automobile chokes.) Our house has an air-to-air heat exchanger which preheats incoming fresh, cold air with stale, warm air that is being vented outside. In total, it is the sort of house that is easy to heat.

Our wood heater is an Ashley, but don't take that as an Ashley endorsement. Purchasers of Ashleys are given a can of "furnace cement" to seal the seams. With this furnace cement, I found it impossible to seal the seams, even initially, before heating, cooling and banging the cover began.

Hence, Ashleys are not always airtight. By airtight, we mean that a firebox containing a good bed of coals can be filled with dry kindling and then, just as she starts to roar, the throttle can be closed and in 10 minutes the fire will be dead. That's airtight.

The standard Ashley, packed with logs for the night, can cook all the moisture out of the wood and then burn so hot and leak enough air in to undergo a literal "reactor melt-down," with the inner of the two sheet metal walls being damaged by the heat.

We recommend that anyone buying an Ashley-type heater (the price is substantially less than many other airtights) have all seams brazed (sheet metal to cast iron). The asbestos-rimmed front door on the Ashley is also an

Heavily insulated, the Jeffries' log home in the Boreal Forest of northern Saskatchewan is heated solely with hand cut wood, much of it poor quality.

excellent potential leak source. We've never opened it, using the top-loading door, hoping to avoid abrading the asbestos rope and degrading the seal (not to mention broadcasting asbestos particles).

The air intakes of the Ashley and our kitchen wood stove have been reworked to draw outside air through vents in the floor and crawl space. The cookstove is an old McClary "Royal Charm," never intended to be airtight. However, a little sheet metal here and there has improved that leak situation.

Because the kitchen stove can be a major funnel for warm air to escape the house at night, once the fire dies out, we have devised a method of sealing off the stove's flue before going to bed. Inside the house, the stove has a clean-out tee (see diagram), in which we

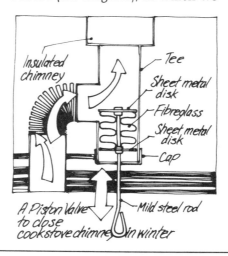

Insulated chimney — Tee — Sheet metal disk — Fibreglass — Sheet metal disk — Cap — A Piston Valve to close cookstove chimney in winter — Mild steel rod

have installed a primitive piston valve. At night in winter, after all the coals in the cookstove are dead, the chimney piston valve is closed, along with the air intake valve. This effectively blocks the escape of warm air from the house and cuts our fuel needs substantially.

Woodcutter Unchained

Perhaps the most pleasant aspect of heating with wood is sawing the fuel. For fifteen 1975 dollars we bought a 60-inch crosscut saw from Mr. S. Goldman, proprietor of Canada Metal in Regina. Despite its length, the saw is stiff enough to be used by one person.

Such a saw, with a little practice, can be made to sail through a seasoned eight-inch spruce log in 45 stroke cycles or less than a minute. This is twice as fast as is possible with a large (30-inch) Swede saw. The crosscut saw sends out chips, not dust.

Of course, the saw must be sharp and set. A standard saw file with a handle will sharpen a big cross-cut saw. The correct angles of the cutter surfaces can be determined from the virgin surface near the handle of the saw. The rakers (see diagram) should be filed to a point and then tapped with a hammer to form a barb, as shown. It is crucial that the overall profile of the blade conform to the diagram. Rakers should be about 1 milli-metre — "the thickness of a dime,'' as an elderly professional sawright told me — shorter than the adjacent two cutters.

If the saw binds, then it probably needs to be set. This can be done with minimal risk of breaking a cutter by clamping the back of the saw in a vise and clamping the cutter with an adjustable spanner (wrench). Each cutter is pulled so that its sharp tip, which lies out of the plane of the saw, will lie further out of the plane. Pull the end of the spanner with a spring scale, starting with only five or six pounds showing on the scale. After going over all the teeth, try cutting again. If the saw still binds, try a bit more force. Ours took 13 pounds. Doubtless, a professional could do a better job with a jig, but ours has never been set since.

We don't own any petroleum-powered engines except that in our 1967 half-ton truck kept at the nearest town and road, 20 miles south. Specifically, we don't have a chain saw. Chain saws make some aspects of wood management much easier, but they also offer lead pollution, carbon monoxide, noise and vibration. Eschewing petroleum motors is also partly in deference to the local woodland caribou and nesting bald eagles. But mostly we don't use a chain saw because the house we live in has such a high insulation level that the modest amount of wood management required is a work-able daily chore, not a burden faced with regret. We feel a thermally efficient house is the key to wood heat.

Wood heat fits well into our lives. The snow outside is pure and edible right through winter in contrast to snow around oil-heated buildings. At the risk of offending vegetarians we might add that a wood heater is a good disposer of fish and hare offal in winter. Wood ashes are important

phosphorus and potassium sources for our garden, and the animal nutrients in the ashes find their way back into the biosphere quickly that way. Wood ashes and nitrogen-containing compost from our composting toilet have enabled us to grow respectable cool-weather crops in an area characterized by acidic, nutrient-deficient soils.

Wood heat is, in the north woods, part of the way to live rationally and properly, with solid exercise but rewarding comfort and security.

—*Charles Jeffries*
and Ann R. Jeffries
LaRonge, Saskatchewan

SPLITTING HEADACHES

Beware the ''Hit'N'Split'' from Wrought Art Mfg. in Mississauga, Ontario. The principle of the thing is fine, but it is constructed of lightweight or poor quality metal which is totally inadequate for the advertised task.

Six good whacks with a 12-pound sledge on a single log and I was left with a twisted mess of useless metal. The log is still not split, and I am out $40. It might work on dry soft pine or cedar.

I can recommend the Mini-Winch (306 Norton Building, Seattle, Washington 98104). This is an attachment which fits on a chain saw and which consists of a sturdy 180:1 reduction gear and capstan.

Fitted to a good chain saw, it gives a pretty fair source of power for pulling logs, raising logs or getting vehicles out of the mud. It really requires two people to operate the thing, but it is the only portable power winch I know of, and it is not widely advertised.

— *Nyla N. Maurer*
Bolton, Ontario

WEDGING MAUL

The Monster Maul is, as advertised, a super tool, and the chief wood splitter in our house says he wouldn't be without it. One blow usually suffices to split straight-grained pieces, even very large ones, though several chops are often necessary for our crooked, knotty yellow birch.

The advertisement says, ''Split enough in five minutes for all day.'' Well . . . . No, not enough to feed our stove and furnace, but I don't find much else to fault in the claims. The price (including shipping) is $27.95 in the U.S. and $39.95 in Canada. I suggest, with all due respect to tariff and transfer regulations, that prospective purchasers on this side of the border invite a friend from the U.S. to bring it up as a birthday present.

From the time we first saw the Monster Maul advertisement, the person in their photograph has changed from a thin girl (mauling stove wood) to a man. Not to precipitate a sexist dispute, but a 20-pound wedging maul is a heavy-weight tool, too heavy for most women. I, weighing 10 stone and fairly strong, can use it but cannot swing it in a good arc. In fact, I tend to topple over backward if I raise it past my balance point. The maul is heavy enough, though, to be effective just dropped on a stump, from eye level.

I don't know about the cute line that says ''Healthful . . . split instead of jog,'' but I do feel like Wonder Woman when I pick up an ordinary axe after mauling four or five big blocks. Whack. Whop. It feels light as a fly swatter.

—*Molly Miron*
Upper Kennetcook, Nova Scotia

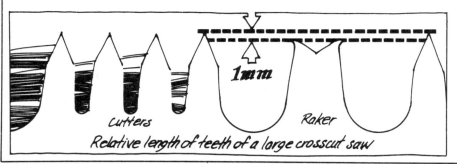

Cutters   Raker

Relative length of teeth of a large crosscut saw

1mm

THE BAY BARN

Reg Kumm bills it as "The World's Largest Collection of Recycled Stoves," and no one has yet come forward with a challenge. This out-of-the-way place has nearly 900 assorted wood stoves in stock, ranging in price from $10 to $2,000, with corresponding levels of condition, beauty and rarity. Kumm likes to give tours, even if you aren't buying, and it's well worth the trip if you happen to be in Eastern Ontario (north of Kingston). No mail order sales.

The Bay Barn
Box 250
Seeley's Bay, Ontario K0H 2N0
(613) 387-3273
—David Creighton
Maberly, Ontario

TOO GOOD TO BE TRUE DEPARTMENT

Now that a hundred different kinds of "airtight" wood stoves have pretty well outdated their leaky predecessors, a new generation of wood burners is on the verge of entering the market. They are designed to eliminate all creosoting, reduce the amount of watching and tending to a once-a-day maximum and give a much more convenient distribution of heat.

These are the stored heat, complete combustion furnaces, first developed at the University of Maine three years ago and brought to the production stage in Prince Edward Island. Hampton Technology's "Jetstream" is the first of its kind on the market in Canada, but is thus far offered only in the Halifax-Dartmouth area in a marketing test begun in the fall of 1979.

The principle was originally conceived by Dick Hill under a U.S. Department of Energy grant to overcome some of the short-comings of the airtights, most notably their inconvenience, their serious creosoting during slow burning and smoke production whenever they are fuelled.

The improvements have been achieved by carefully engineering the combustion chamber so that, with the addition of pressurized air from a blower, very high temperatures necessary for the complete combustion of all the volatile gases is achieved within six minutes of lighting the fire. "There is no smoke whatsoever and the furnace achieves an unheard of 84 per cent efficiency," claims developer Dennis Edell. The heat is then transferred to an insulated hot water storage tank and can be redistributed wherever needed in the house by either a hot water or forced air distribution system. It provides domestic hot water as well.

The domestic furnace measures 41 by 24 by 41 inches. It is loaded vertically with generally unsplit wood up to 33 inches long and 12 inches in diameter and because of the forced air system, "lights very easily."

The single load of wood burns "at full blast," without noticeable emissions, heats up the water and dies out. Then the householder draws his/her heat and hot water from the storage, over the next 24 hours during the coldest part of winter. During summer it will provide hot water for about five days between firings.

The insulated storage tanks come in 625 and 1,250 gallon sizes and only lose heat at about 600 Btu's per hour — less than a refrigerator. So a bungalow of 1,200 square feet can get all its hot water plus space heating for the year on only six to seven cords of wood.

If this isn't convenient enough, a back-up oil heat unit is available which will keep the storage tank at 120 degrees F minimum. Edell says, with an ironic grin, that they hope to replace this with an electric emersion back-up so that people who don't stoke their fires will be forced to pay a more palpable penalty.

The furnace will cost about $1,600, with the storage tanks running around $1,200 to $1,500 installed.

Hampton Technology, Inc.
West Royalty, P.E.I.
Dennis Edell (902)892-4067
Dave Murray (902)658-2233
—David Creighton
Maberly, Ontario

CUTTING THROUGH THE BAFFLEMENT

All of this talk about exotic, *scientific* wood stove design reminds me of the centipede which someone talked into thinking about how it managed to decide which foot to move. Suddenly, the centipede couldn't move at all.

Science has pointed out that the combustion of wood is very complicated. All the vapours and gases and stages of primary and secondary this and that make it sound as if you really need some incredible apparatus to pull it off. The fact is that we can't do a damn thing about most of those stages and phases. All we can do is start the fire and feel good in its warmth.

We bought a Fisher Baby Bear several years ago — when the choice of stoves was a fraction of that today — and I think this small stove has taught me well about stoves. It doesn't matter what gadgets, labyrinths, baffles or refinements a stove has as long as you have reasonable control over the draft and you don't have to worry about the metal burning through.

If the Fisher works, *anything* will work. The nature of burning wood seems to be that if you provide a steady supply of air, it keeps a steady burn. The Fisher does this. With the Ashley I once used, I had trouble supplying a steady amount of air — its thermostat had a mind of its own, sometimes sucking in cold air so fast that the thermostat (caught in its own breeze) thought it was cool, despite the fact that the stove was getting hotter and hotter.

Not so the Fisher (or anything like it). I set the draft control (a simple spin cap) and get a steady output of heat until the wood is gone. This wouldn't have come as a surprising discovery to me if I hadn't started out brainwashed into thinking people need thermostats to survive.

The famous Scandinavian cigar burn? I started out treating our Fisher like a campfire, constantly throwing on more wood and, of course, it was always full of a mess of coals, charcoal and unburned wood. But when I calmed down and let it do its stuff, I noticed that the fire worked from the front — where I started it — to the back. *Ja!* Cigar burn, North American style.

Of course, the Fisher is pretty homely. If I had to do it today, I would try to buy a stove that shows more reverence in its craftsmanship, that goes a bit beyond the pure materialism of utility. North America is finally, again, producing stoves that show some love for being alive.

But it is a good stove. It works. Burning wood makes heat, and the Fisher enables you to burn it in a controlled way. Asbestos gaskets, bimetal strips, baffles and reindeer on the sides can't help.

Some of the heat, of course, is going up the chimney and we have to accept that fact. It's probably a very good lesson for us all — everything has a cost and our mastery over things is never all that complete.

—*Andrejs Ozdins*
Cortland, New York

WOOD FIRED ODYSSEY

My husband and I have relied solely on wood heat for the past five years, starting as complete innocents and ending up with some experiences which may be instructive to anyone thinking about buying a stove for the first time.

Our first stove was a cute little number we came across in a junk store. It was an old-fashioned cookstove, with several parts missing from the firebox, and we bought it for $50. It seemed a bargain. My husband put the firebox back into working order with parts found on an old farm

nearby, and he even improved the stove by adding a water jacket.

Everything worked fine — we had hot water, a place to cook and warmth on chilly evenings and mornings. Then October arrived and the weather turned cold. We found that the stove would hold a fire for only a short time and needed constant refilling to keep the house warm. At first my husband and I took turns getting up in the night to feed the fire, but sometime in November domestic tensions started to build and — with the first threatening trickles of snow falling — we decided to invest in a back-up stove.

Our next heater came fully recommended by a used-to-be-friend of ours. "Cheap and efficient," he said. Cheap, yes: $18. Efficient, no. It was a round tin stove with a tin liner inside; both layers of metal were very thin and we were afraid to leave the thing burning without one of us being there to watch it. The stove would heat up very quickly — the one good trait of cheap tin

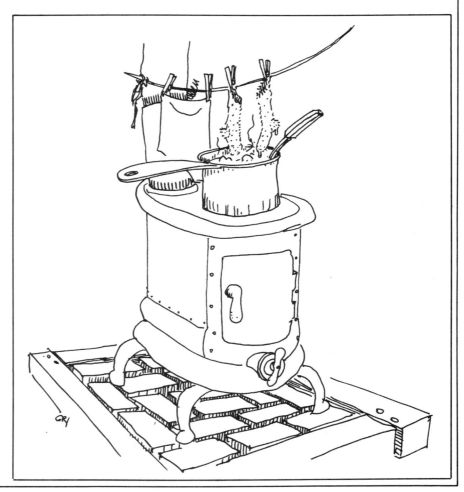

BIOMASS 67

stoves — but then the metal would become bright red and the whole unit would start dancing around on the floor. After an episode in which we thought the thing was about to explode, we decided — after running for cover — that the stove had to go.

Our next purchase was an auction special which lasted at least a month before it got the heave-ho. This one was very similar to its predecessor, but with a cast-iron top and legs. This prevented the stove from dancing around, but, again, the stove was not airtight, although occasionally we did get up early enough in the morning to see a few red coals in the bottom of the stove.

By this time our nerves were thinning and the arguments were turning into rolling-on-the-floor battles. We decided to go all out, and purchased a fine-looking, thermostatically controlled, airtight, cabinet model wood heater. We paid $400 for this stove, and it's been worth every cent. We don't have to worry about sitting up all night watching the fire. It has its own little thermostat to do the watching for us.

Buying a good stove saved our sanity, not to mention our marriage.

—Margaret Coulter,
Quadra Island, British Columbia

URBAN WOOD FUEL

True burners of wood have only scorn for the packaged ''fire logs'' now sold in every chain drug store and discount centre in the country. Expensive — 99 cents per stick is common today — and often laced with petroleum additives to promote the burn, these pseudo-logs are offensive both aesthetically and economically.

A more acceptable form of packaged wood, however, may be on the way. A plant in Brownsville, Oregon is now producing more than 250 tons of pelletized wood each day, and the concept is coming to Canada. Shell recently began investigating the process, which takes wood and chops, shreds and then heats it at 200 degrees Fahrenheit.

At this temperature it becomes

''paste-like,'' according to Paul Bakker, an advisor to the Ontario Ministry of Energy,

''You can pass it through an extrusion machine like spaghetti,'' says Bakker, an expert in biomass energy. ''It lubricates itself. Then it is chopped into pellets.''

These heavy, dense pellets compare very favourably with coal in their heating value. Eight to nine thousand Btu's per pound is the current figure for the concentrated wood. Good coal yields 12,000 Btu's.

Shell's projections show that a single plant, employing 18 persons, could turn out 100,000 tons of pellets annually, as much energy as contained in 230,000 barrels of oil.

''The advantage,'' says Bakker, ''is that it is virtually ash-free. Moreover, it allows for uniform feed (in large-scale energy systems) and has a large specific surface area.''

Pelletized wood may have the ability to satisfy the needs of industrial energy users — as well as city-bound homeowners pining for a wood stove or furnace.

—Michael Asti-Rose
Toronto, Ontario

REPLACEMENT MICA

When I bought my pretty little cast-iron parlour stove, it was missing the mica 'windows' that fold open at the front, allowing either the wood or coal to be inserted; closed, the flickers of flame could be seen. But where to find mica sheets in this day and age?

Fortunately I discovered Y. Franks' store in Vancouver, where all sorts of spare parts for cast-iron stoves are available — including 4''by 6''mica sheets for $3.00 each.

Now the stove not only looks pretty but is functional, living up to the name emblazoned on the front — ''Good Cheer''!

Y. Franks Limited
1490 Kingsway
Vancouver, B.C.
Phone (604)879-9407

—Paula Gustafson,
Yarrow, British Columbia

KETTLE VS. HOTPLATE

Abstract: An electric kettle beats hell out of a hotplate for boiling water.

Introduction: Power rates have more than doubled in Nova Scotia in the last few years. In the summer, when not using his wood stove, the experimenter had been using an electric hotplate to heat water. This seemed slow and inefficient due to the fact that the heating element is external to the water being heated.

Thus, heat is lost (1) by radiation from the element in directions other than the kettle of water, (2) by conduction through the metal surfaces of the hotplate and kettle and (3) by convection of the warmed air surrounding the hotplate and kettle. An electric kettle, wherein the heating element is completely surrounded by water, should minimize heat loss and maximize efficiency. Despite this obvious logic, the experimenter was subjected to considerable abuse by skeptics and nay-sayers, whereupon he resorted to empirical methods to prove his point.

Subjects: One Force Model 866D Electric Hotplate and one General

Electric Model K49HS Electric Kettle, each with identical power rating of 1500 watts.

Procedure: 1500 ml of water at 36 degrees F was placed in the Electric Kettle. 1500 ml of water at 36 degrees F was placed in a kettle on the Hotplate. This second kettle completely covered the Hotplate element for maximum efficiency of heat transfer.

Both kettles were at room temperature when the water was added. Both appliances were switched on at the same moment, and the time it took for the water in each to come to a rolling boil was observed.

Observations: Boiling time for the kettle on the Hotplate was 16.75 minutes. Boiling time for the Electric Kettle was 6.5 minutes.

Conclusions: The relative efficiencies of the two appliances can be expressed in terms of a simple ratio:

$$\frac{Bh}{Bk}$$

where Bh is the boiling time for the Hotplate and Bk is the boiling time for the Kettle. Using the above data, it is clear that the Kettle is 2.6 times faster, and therefore more efficient, than the Hotplate. Moreover, one can estimate the savings due to the use of this more efficient unit. If the Kettle were used one hour per day at $.03 per kilowatt-hour, the cost of power for a year of use would be:

$$1.5 \text{ kwh} \times \$.03/\text{kwh}$$
$$\times 365 \text{ days} = \$16.42$$

If the Hotplate were used to heat the equivalent amount of water, the cost would obviously be the above amount times the efficiency factor of 2.6:

$$\$16.42 \times 2.6 = \$42.69$$

Assuming power rates of $.03 per kwh, the amount saved by using the Kettle instead of the Hotplate for one year would be $26.27, which is the approximate cost of the Kettle. At $.04 per kwh the saving would be $35.04, and at $.05 per kwh, the saving would be $43.80.

Thus, depending on the power rates, the Electric Kettle pays for itself within a year or less, and besides, *Ya don't hafta sit around and twiddle yer thumbs while ya wait fer the goddam water ta boil.*

—*Andrew D. Terris*
Red River, Nova Scotia

BEATING THE DRUM FOR KROUPA

Anyone thinking of buying a new wood burner should know about the Kroupa Stove which has just appeared on the market. The term unique can accurately be applied to this fine stove, which uses one fire to accomplish various functions (space heating, cooking, baking, warming domestic water and allowing a nice view of the fire). The Kroupa does them all remarkably well.

The stove is airtight, with firebrick lining and a Corning glass window in the doors of both the large firebox and the oven. Heat surrounds the baking chamber, allowing bread to bake very evenly and we've found that it isn't difficult to maintain a temperature of 350 degrees in the oven without roasting everyone in the house at the same time.

This stove is a real gem and is a big step toward combining various woodburning functions into a single unit.

—*Nicole Webb*
Grand Etang, Nova Scotia

THE DEFIANT STOVE

For anyone truly serious about heating with wood, the selection of a stove is a momentous decision — perhaps because making the right choice involves not just our sense of economy, but our sense of virtue as well.

I deliberated a long time before making my choice, but in the end the decision became quite simple: I listed what I wanted in a wood burner roughly in order of importance, then bought the stove that came closest — a Defiant from Vermont Castings. That was three years ago, and I've since bought the slightly smaller Vigilant as well. I'm delighted with both.

First, the stove had to be big enough to be the main source of heat for our medium-sized, well-insulated house. I wanted both *radiant* (direct) heat and *convected* (airborne) heat. That eliminated the wood furnaces and the jacketed air-circulating heaters. Next, I wanted a unit that had primary and secondary air systems — a crucial factor in efficiency. My stove had to be long-burning (overnight) and self-regulating; that meant a thermostat. I hoped to find a stove which, along with all of these things, could also be operated with the fire visible if I wanted; an open fire adds cheer and comfort to a place like nothing else. Being an old-time romantic, I wanted it in cast iron rather than sheet metal. And I wanted it to be well made of good materials.

Classic Lines

The Defiant had all these features and more I hadn't thought of. It has a five-foot-long system of baffles that gives the stove its high efficiency. (Laboratory tests, I hear, have shown the Defiant to be one of the most efficient wood burners on the market.) It can be operated either as an efficient airtight heater or with the fire visible through opened doors, Franklin-style. It has a draft control that lets you burn off creosote periodically with a hot fire and a cooking surface on top. And it can be purchased with either a top-exit or a rear-exit flue collar. The one thing that might be a drawback for a few people is the location of the door at the left end — the stove cannot be installed with that end in a corner. Clearly, its design is technically sophisticated but free of unnecessary gimmickry. Because the Defiant is a large and efficient stove, it should be considered seriously only where a lot of heat is needed. It can't work properly if you run it damped down to heat a small space.

Beyond all of these practical

features, there is a grace to its design that makes it easy to be proud of — it is a handsome, pleasing piece of furniture. (Its classic lines have already been copied by several manufacturers.)

There is something else that makes it a fine stove, too: quality of materials and workmanship. The castings are superbly made, and they are well put together. In watching the stoves being made at the factory (when I picked mine up) and in dealing with company staff, it was quite clear that they all really care about the product and service they sell. They were most helpful, too, in arranging shipping and advising on customs procedures. Included with every stove is an ash shovel, a lovely fire screen and a can of touch-up paint. I strongly recommend getting the optional heat shield and andirons as well. They improve safety and performance.

By the time it was set up in our Ottawa Valley home, the Defiant wasn't cheap — we Canadians have to pay 20 per cent duty on top of the currency differential on top of the U.S. price of $575, as well as shipping. But the Defiant, in my experience, offers excellent value for money. I expect it will be warming me well when I'm an old man, and with care could easily be giving warmth and pleasure to my children long after I'm gone. Although they haven't set a firm date yet, Vermont Castings, Inc. hopes to start direct distribution in Canada in the future.

The information package that Vermont Castings, Inc. sends (for $1) to inquirers includes a copy of the stove operation manual for both the Defiant and the Vigilant. It's a useful document even if you don't buy a stove.

—Paul Reed
Stittsville, Ontario

A SECOND OPINION

A Defiant wood stove has taken us through two northern Wisconsin winters, heating what used to be a church (with 14-foot ceilings and 1,000 square feet of floor space) with roughly 10 face cords of wood.

It is a beautiful stove, holds a fire

well, and the front doors open in the fall and spring to give us a cozy fireplace. We found the workmanship on our particular stove somewhat shoddy, however; the stove arrived with furnace cement spattered on the finish and half-filling the secondary air channel. Like most airtights, it is subject to creosote build-up and occasional fits of back-puffing.

I highly recommend it, though I'm not ready to call it the "Rolls Royce" of wood stoves.

—Ken Parejko
Holcombe, Wisconsin

HURRICANE FISHER

Fisher Stoves claims that their open-door models — the Grandpa and Grandma Bears — are airtight should not be accepted at face value.

I bought a Grandma last fall and found that, with both draft controllers shut tight and the doors locked closed, the draft being sucked between the doors sounded like a veritable hurricane.

Even with the chimney draft closed, I have never had a stove full of *dry apple wood* burn for more than three or four hours. I've had to install an asbestos gasket to slow the air leak. Incidentally, the Fisher dealer assured me that the stove was so airtight that I wouldn't need a chimney draft.

—Douglas Steele

DITTO

We heated *Harrowsmith's* editorial offices for two winters with a bartered Fisher "Papa," which was as airtight as they come and did a yeoman's job.

A second Fisher, this with double doors, was installed at home, and the first heavy loading of hard maple resulted in a completely uncontrolled burn and a sleepless night. Even with the dampers screwed tight and the doors shut, the fire roared on.

Fisher says it has since improved the design. Anyone buying a used open-door stove would be well-advised to avoid Fisher if airtightness is a deciding factor.

—JL

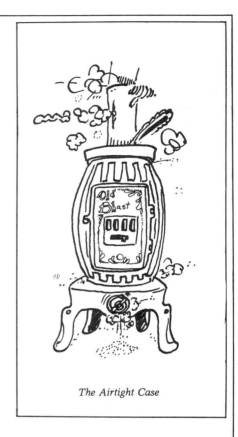

The Airtight Case

"BURNING ENTHUSIASM"

The most complete line of wood-burning equipment in fabled Lanark County is on display in the renovated casket factory in MacDonald's Corners known as "Wood 'n' Energy."

Spawned by Cal Wallis last year in a log pig barn up near Watson's Corners to supply wood stoves and hard-to-get items for the many "back-to-the-land" folks in the area the business has quickly caught on and has had to move to larger, more accessible quarters.

The present store contains 30 to 40 different stoves to suit every need plus "virtually every conceivable accessory" from log splitters, chain saws, splitting mauls and lifetime axe handles to insulated chimneys, efficient fireplaces, water heaters and furnaces. The proudest corner is the cookstove room where Cal boasts "the best collection available in Ontario." He has the Godin (which makes 35 different models) from France, Tirolia from Austria, Stanley from Ireland as well as the Canadian Findlay (most expensive at $1,500 to $1,600) and Enterprise (cheapest at $530 to $680).

But hardware is only part of what Wood 'n' Energy offers; for Cal has a self-confessed "burning enthusiasm for wood heat" and all matters pertaining to it. He immediately loves anyone with an intelligent question or a strong opinion on the subject and will quickly burst into one of his famous "heated arguments" with the slightest crank of the grate. His enthusiasm is matched by his stubborn integrity, from an unwillingness to sell something to someone who doesn't need it, to a refusal to carry items that are commonly available elsewhere.

The whole idea for the business blossomed from a summer spent in the Community Conservation Centre in Smiths Falls where Cal quickly took over the wood heating department, filling the large showroom with local merchants' stoves and his head with the thermodynamics of wood combustion and everything related. Since then he has broadened into other areas besides — solar hot water panels, organic gardening tools (no seeds) such as Mainline tillers, composters, diatomaceous earth, solar and electric food dryers, etc., and a very good line of how-to books and periodicals.

Wood 'n' Energy will ship anywhere in North America by either the cheapest or the fastest route, whichever is specified. And they will order anything they don't have in stock, if they like it enough.

—*David Creighton*
Maberly, Ontario

POOR COMBINATION

A word of caution to would-be-owners of Newmac "combination" furnaces: The claims made in this company's sales literature, are, in my opinion, stretching the truth.

During cold temperatures, the six to eight hour filling periods shrink to two to three hours. Even at that, the oil part of the furnace has to "kick-in" occasionally to provide enough heat. Also, after one year of use, the wood box in this particular furnace has become so warped that the liner has separated from the inside of the furnace and thereby created even more problems.

For all intents and purposes, the woodburning part of the furnace has become an emergency back-up system should the oil-fired part become inoperative. When the Newmac distributor was contacted about this hazard, I was assured that the problem would be rectified — at my cost! After one year of use, the Newmac — in my estimation — has become too unsafe to use.

—*Norbert Hirschkorn,*
Duck Lake, Saskatchewan

STOVE BUYER'S CHECKLIST

☐ Is it airtight?
☐ Is it the right size for your particular situation?
☐ Does the stove do everything you want it to? (Can the fire be viewed, if that is an important consideration? Does it have a cooking surface? Is it enclosed in a cabinet if young children are a concern?)
☐ Is the overall quality good? (Do doors close easily and with a tight fit? Are all seams well sealed? Are the welds properly done? Are the draft controls precise and easy to operate? Has the stove cracked in shipping?)
☐ Does it have a good lining? (Firebrick or metal liners. Liners that bolt on may be impossible to remove and replace in later years.)

☐ How big is the fuelling door and the firebox? (Those who prefer not to spend inordinate amounts of time making small pieces of wood out of larger ones, just so they will fit into the stove, should think seriously about this. Try putting a few pieces of wood into a stove in the showroom.)

☐ Is the stove easy to clean? (Ash removal will be a frequent chore. Does the stove require contortionist manoeuvres to clean?)

☐ Does the stove carry a guarantee? (Because of the weight of most airtight stoves, it is unlikely you will ever want to ship it back to the factory for repairs, but a good guarantee is an indication of a conscientious manufacturer. More important; is the dealer reputable and will he correct problems that arise?)

☐ Does the flue exit from the top or back? (A rear-exiting flue forces the stove to be positioned further from the wall and may take up too much space in a small home.)

☐ Will the dealer deliver the stove, if you are unable to transport it yourself? Will he install it and check the chimney?

Books

WOOD STOVE HANDBOOK
By Wilburn W. Newcomb
Theodore Audel & Co.
4300 West 62nd Street
Indianapolis, Indiana 46268
128 pages, $9.25

REDISCOVERING THE WOODBURNING COOKSTOVE
By Robert Bobrowski
The Chatham Press
Old Greenwich, Connecticut
95 pages, $5.95

THE WOOD STOVE AND FIREPLACE BOOK
By Steve Sherman
Thomas Nelson & Sons Ltd.
81 Curlew Drive,
Don Mills, Ontario M3A 2R1
128 pages, $4.95

WOODSTOVE COOKERY

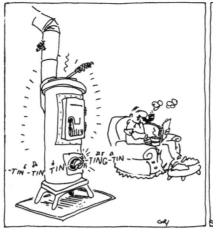 

By Jane Cooper
Garden Way Publishing
Charlotte, Vermont 05445
196 pages, $5.95

WOOD HEAT
By John Vivian
Rodale Press, Inc.
Emmaus, Pennsylvania
320 pages, $8.95

THE COMPLETE BOOK OF HEATING WITH WOOD
By Larry Gay
Garden Way Publishing
Charlotte, Vermont 05445
128 pages, $4.25

WOOD ENERGY
By Mary Twitchell
Garden Way Publishing
Charlotte, Vermont 05445
170 pages, $7.95

THE CANADIAN WOOD HEAT BOOK
By Gordon Flagler
Deneau & Greenberg
Publishers Limited
295 pages

WOODBURNER'S ENCYCLOPEDIA
By Jay Shelton and
Andrew B. Shapiro
Vermont Crossroads Press
Waitsfield, Vermont
155 pages, $7.95

HEATING WITH WOOD —SAFELY
Central Mortgage & Housing Corporation
Montreal Road
Ottawa, Ontario K1A 0P7

NATIONAL WOOD STOVE & FIREPLACE JOURNAL
Box 8006
Fountain Valley, Ca 92708
(714) 962-9321
Canadian subscriptions:
$21.00/yr., $35.00/2 yrs.

FIREPLACE REPORT
By H. Morstead and
O. Knudsen
Atlantic Masonry Association
470 York Street
Fredericton, N.B. E3B 3P7
52 pages

HEATING WITH WOOD
The Institute of Man and Resources
50 Water Street, Box 2008
Charlottetown, P.E.I. C1A 1A4
11 pages, $2,00

Organizations

CANADIAN WOOD ENERGY INSTITUTE
49 Gloucester Street
Toronto, Ontario M4Y 1L8
(416) 967-5760

SOLID FUEL ADVISORY SERVICE
Hobart House
Grosvenor Place
London, England SW1X 7AE
01-235-2020
A clearinghouse of information about British-made open fireplaces with water-filled jackets that serve as the core of wood-fired central heating systems. Export to North America can be arranged.

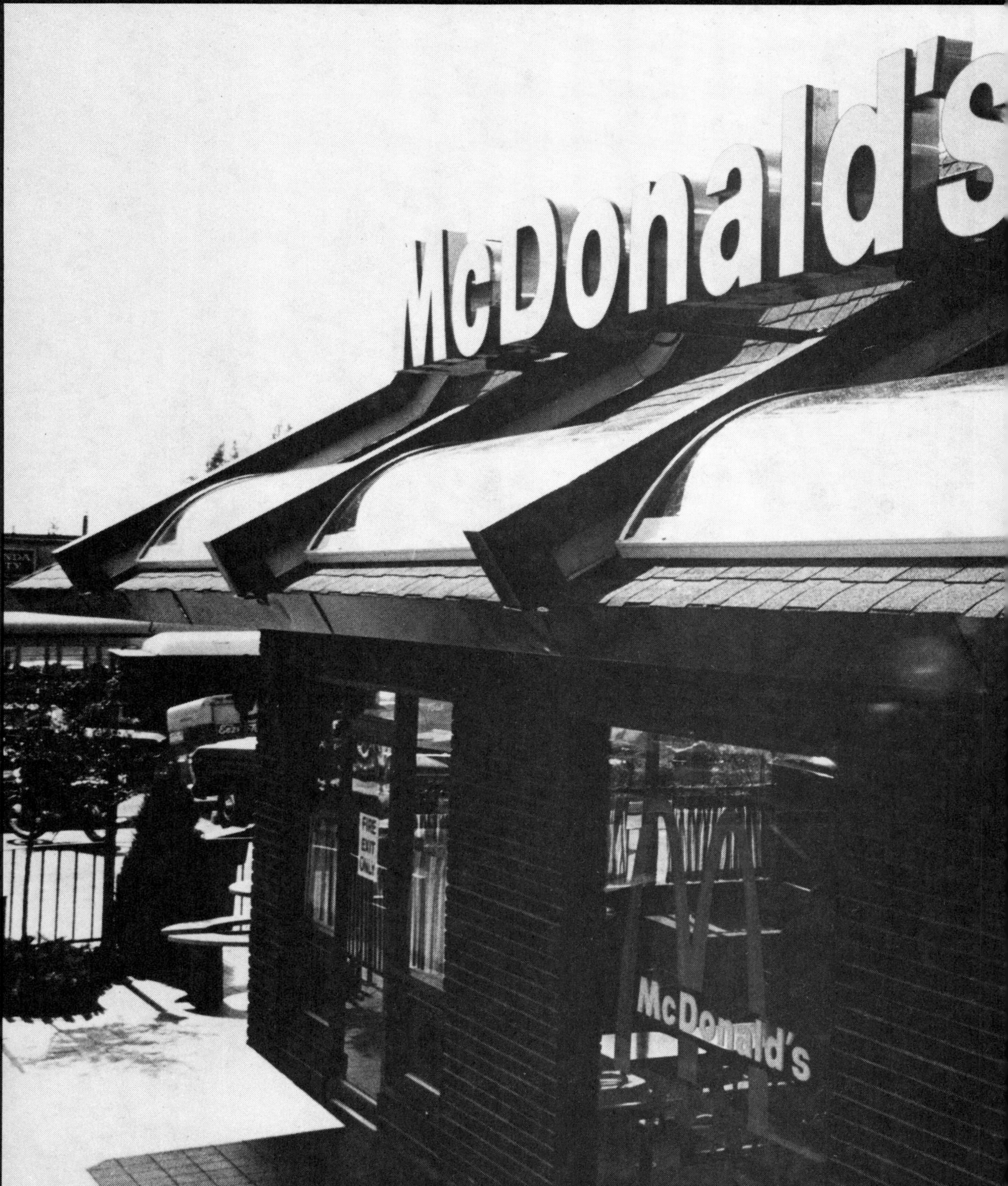
McDonald's
FIRE EXIT ONLY
McDonald's

Solar

Nick Nicholson's Solar X, Ayer's Cliff, Quebec

Buying Into The Sun

A pragmatist's guide to contemporary solar hardware

It seemed, they now say, the perfect idea at the time. Canada's most promising young solar panel manufacturer bartering its own product for an ad in Canada's fastest growing country living/ alternative energy/back-to-the-land magazine. The response, by any standard, was overwhelming: several thousand requests from readers for more information about the solar company and its products.

For Amherst Renewable Energies Ltd., now located in the small town of Perth, Ontario, it was a mixed blessing. Remembering the fiasco, company President Richard Davies is rueful. ''We tried to answer all the letters, but it cost us a minimum of a dollar

to respond to each, even if it just meant sending a brochure. That was a lot of wasted effort and a major expense for a struggling company. We ended up with one or two sales.''

Amherst, with no sales staff and a mailing brochure rich in technical data but almost devoid of description or explanation understandable by the average university-educated layman, had expected the public to be overwhelmed by the performance data and reasonable price of their panels. Amherst's experience points up the most fundamental problems in Canada's solar industry today. The people, even those people genuinely sympathetic to the idea of solar

energy, are wary of the cost when returns seem vague, or even unattainable. Reading Amherst's brochure, one respondent put it aside and said, ''O.K., they can sell me a solar panel for less than $400. What do I do with it?'' With the would-be purchaser unsure of how to buy a solar system and the would-be seller equally unsure of how to sell it, the results should have been predictable.

Until very recently, the solar industry in Canada had consisted of not much more than a handful of small firms, mostly one-man operations, surviving on government demonstration project money and occasional jobs for friends. All too often, the panels and systems they created failed to perform or broke down completely. The public, if confused, was at least correct in assuming that buying into solar systems was a risky investment.

Costs have been, and still are, high for active solar systems. There is little way you can make a mechanical solar space heating system, for example, pay for itself, unless you happen to be a keen and knowledgeable solar enthusiast who can design and install everything yourself. (It is interesting to note that two of Amherst's key people, those who originally designed the panels, left the firm and have concentrated on less expensive, more reliable passive solar designs.)

All of this may be changing, however, mainly because the federal government has entered the fray with large—by Canadian solar standards—amounts of money to spend. In July, 1978 Minister of Energy, Mines and Resources, Alastair Gillespie announced that Ottawa would spend $380 million over the next five years to develop solar and biomass energy.

The federal programme was designed to encourage existing manufacturers with research grants and to create a guaranteed market for Canadian solar companies with government purchases of solar heating systems.

The PUSH and PASEM programmes got underway with the objective of establishing a viable solar heating industry in this country by 1985. The PUSH programme provides a guaranteed market of $125 million for solar heating equipment; the PASEM project gives out up to $300,000 for research and development which has to be matched in part by each manufacturer—the exact amount depending on a complicated government formula. To assure that small firms could compete for a PASEM grant, initial grants of $10,000 were given out to help them produce well-researched and documented applications for the big money.

Survival Games

The idea was to find the 10 solar firms most likely to succeed in this country and allow them to become competitive enough to hold their own against imported equipment from the United States. The PASEM winners, then, were to be the cream of the crop—the companies who would use the large infusion of capital to the fullest.

Some manufacturers, however, could not be bothered with the hassles of dealing with the government and did not participate in the PASEM programme at all. Two of the companies who didn't even apply for PASEM grants were Imperial Oil and Philips—companies big enough to make it on their own.

Guildcraft, an Ontario firm that produces hot water and pool heating systems, applied for a PASEM grant but was turned down. Now, President Ron Webb is not sure he wants to bother with the government any more.

"I don't agree with the way the government is going about it . . . . Frankly, we've found it is just as good to go ahead ourselves."

His company went to the government with several other companies, as a consortium, with an idea for a "total integrated system" that would incorporate solar with the entire design and structure of the building. Webb says now that he thinks the government would rather keep manufacturers working in

isolation from each other and the rest of the building industry.

The PASEM winners represent a real cross-section. Some of them, firms such as Temspec and GSW, are established in the heating and air conditioning industry. Others, such as Solatherm and Solartech, were originally small operations but now have large Canadian corporations as the major shareholders.

Small But Independent

There are also a few small firms, such as Amherst, Watershed and Solartronics which are struggling to survive independently and have not yet become part of the corporate infrastructure. These smaller outfits, however, still have to provide their contribution to the PASEM programme (up to $100,000) and it's not likely they will survive indefinitely without major capital input.

Although there is a great deal of talk about solar heating being a "small is beautiful" technology, it looks more and more like only the large existing industrial corporations can afford to develop and refine the product, and then wait for the market to develop in the 1980s.

Because the market is still small, some firms are more interested in sales than profits. Right now, most solar companies are being subsidized by parent corporations and this further reduces the chances of survival for the small and independent solar company. (Pragmatic observers feel, however, that if the large solar companies are successful in developing durable, reliable hardware they will contribute, in the end, to the "small is beautiful" goal of energy independence for individual households and communities.)

Solar heating can be anything from windows facing south to catch whatever heat they can, to extremely complex mechanical systems that convert the sun's rays to space or water heating. Passive and active systems, as they are called, have their own advantages and drawbacks; there are supporters in both camps.

Bruce Gough, an Ottawa consultant who has recently

completed a study on passive solar heating for the Department of Energy, Mines and Resources, says, "Active solar systems have two Achilles' Heels: cost and reliability. An active system can cost between $10,000 and $20,000, with no guarantee that it will last 20 years. Most people aren't gamblers."

For retrofit applications, the trade-off between active and passive systems is not so clear cut, Gough says. When extensive renovations are being made to older homes, it is possible to install passive solar economically if the house has a southern orientation.

Richard Davies, who is also president of the Canadian Solar Industries Association, recommends that new houses be constructed so that they are "solar ready"—allowing entire systems to be retrofitted at a later date.

He says that one reason active solar systems are so expensive is that they are overdesigned. Solar energy is a low-intensity and intermittent energy source. It requires exceptional engineering skill to capture it economically year after year, Davies explains. Using traditional design formulas, you end up with something that costs too much.

Consultants hired by the government do not have any real incentive to reduce the total cost of the system, Davies says, but with greater attention to detail, costs can be reduced.

Present government estimates indicate that 75 per cent of the houses that we will be living in by the year 2000 have already been built. Davies claims that retrofitting these existing houses with solar will be where the major active solar market lies.

Affordable Approaches

Pure passive solar design, in which no panels are used, requires a minimum of financial gamble, but a maximum of insulation and south-facing window glass. The key is to reduce heat loss to a minimum, weathersealing all doors and windows and insulating walls and

roof to R40 and R60, respectively. There is, in this, an analogy to the wood stove industry. The more airtight the house, the better the efficiency. Heavy insulation is gratifying in the immediacy of its returns—heating bills are cut drastically and forever. South-facing windows —passive solar collectors—can look after as much as half of the total remaining energy bill. With careful design and construction, it is possible to build solar-panelless homes with heating bills of less than $100 per winter (1979-80 dollars)—even in extreme northern Canadian locations.

Super-insulated homes may be inexpensive in the long run, but, with all the trimmings such as heat recovery systems (to strip warmth from stale air being ventilated outdoors), their construction price can rise as much as $5,000 over conventional frame homes of the same size. The figure need not be that high, of course, it takes very little to build a house vastly superior to the standard, two-by-four, frame buildings that are still proliferating.

While passive design is almost fail-safe, the goal of 100 per cent solar homes will probably only be achieved with the aid of active solar collectors. Until a major technological breakthrough occurs or until mass production brings down the prices, active solar

systems designed for space heating will remain out of financial reach for most homeowners.

On the other hand, active systems used to heat domestic hot water are already working well for many people, and they become especially price-competitive if you can install the system yourself or have a friend in the plumbing business.

"If I was going to do it, I'd build my own system from soup to nuts," is the way Michael Bell, an engineer with Ontario Hydro's Research Division, puts it. Most people would agree with him—to keep costs reasonable, you should put in your own system.

If you are at all practical and you read up on the subject, it is possible to build yourself a reasonably reliable water-heating system for less than $1,000, and less than $500 if you're willing to cut a few corners.

For those who want to build a homemade solar hot water system; about the best source of information is *Solar Systems in British Columbia: A step by step guide to help build your own solar water heater.* The book, based on a workshop course held in communities throughout B.C. and Alberta, is published by the Energy Conservation Division of B.C. Hydro and was prepared by Chris Mattock and friends, under

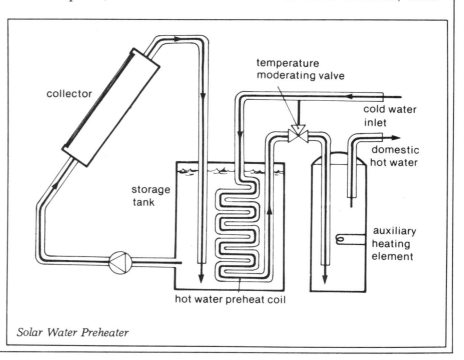

Solar Water Preheater

problem, some manufacturers, such as Nortec, have deliberately designed their water heating systems so that you *can* buy many of the components from Canadian Tire. In this case, only the specialized parts have to be purchased from the manufacturer.

In the solar business, as in anything else, the fewer links in the distribution chain the better. Most of the manufacturers do not mind dealing directly with consumers—if they have done their homework and are ready to buy. On the other hand, manufacturers are in business to make a living and cannot come running out to individuals' homes or give a lot of free advice. Most don't want to see you until you know in your own mind that you want to go solar.

Dealing with uncertain buyers, in fact, has soured some manufacturers on a consumer market that requires a great deal of marketing effort and may produce few sales. Some now concentrate their efforts on government and industrial-scale projects.

Most, though, are still selling solar products to you and me. Swimming pool heating systems are already a well-established item on the Canadian solar market, and domestic hot water systems will likely be the next up-and-coming big seller.

Design Quandaries

Domestic hot water systems have one design problem to overcome: the possibility of freeze-up in the winter. How various systems deal with this problem distinguishes one from another. The four major systems on the market— thermosyphon, drain-down, closed loop and drain-back—all have special selling points and drawbacks.

The **thermosyphon system** relies on natural convection flow to move the water through the collector to the storage tank. Because there are no pumps or electronic controls, the bottom of the storage tank has to be at least a foot above the collector, in order to assure that the natural tendency of hot water to rise can work effectively.

the name of Solar Applications and Research Ltd.

If you are leery about starting from scratch, there are many sources of solar conversion kits, consisting of all necessary components and usually easy to construct and install. The other route, of course, is to make a telephone call and write a cheque: some companies are now prepared to sell off-the-shelf water heating systems and have them professionally installed for you.

Which brings us to the first fact any solar buyer will encounter— you cannot walk into Canadian Tire or Sears and buy a solar system and the local heating/ plumbing experts are unlikely even to have touched a solar panel. In fact, with the possible

exception of Petro-Sun (alias Thermo-Solar), none of the Canadian manufacturers has set up anything resembling a national distribution system.

Most operate only in the region where their plant is located and, at present, no collector is outstanding enough to warrant shipping it across the country. As Michael Bell says, "In general, the difference in performance among collectors is not all that great. Most work fairly well and most work about the same." The localized nature of the solar industry does have one advantage. With the manufacturer reasonably close, you will be able to get in touch should something go wrong and your collector need repair work.

To get around the distribution

To achieve thermosyphoning, the tank must usually be put in the roof area, often in an unheated attic, which can mean serious problems with freeze-up during the winter. At the moment, the only manufacturer who offers an off-the-shelf thermosyphon package is Solatherm, and its package is meant for summer cottages only, not for year-round use.

Thermosyphons have a reputation for being temperamental and in our view may not be worth the trouble, unless you don't have electricity.

Ron White, an enthusiastic Sunday-afternoon solar experimenter from Ottawa who calls himself a "rank amateur," has had a love-hate relationship with thermosyphon. He installed a thermosyphon system in his home but found that it just wouldn't work all the time.

The "ultimate system," he says, is a thermosyphon with a pump to fall back on.

"I would like to go thermosyphon, because it's nice to get something for nothing. But the fact is you have to pay for everything in this world, and the $75 you pay for a pump pays for itself over and over again."

He says air getting trapped in the nooks and crannies of a thermosyphon system will stop it from working and that the fall-back pump is needed to get water circulating again.

To anyone who argues in favour of a thermosyphon system alone, White simply states, "I dare say they haven't had one running all through the winter or even a nippy fall."

In contrast, Ontario Hydro's Michael Bell recommends thermosyphon.

"Get a thermosyphon and run it only in the summer. There's little cost because there is no pump involved, no electricity." The technology is so simple, he says, that you can do it all yourself and avoid the "uneconomical" cost of installation by a contractor.

Bell is speaking from personal experience. He has installed a thermosyphon system in his back garden and it's working just fine.

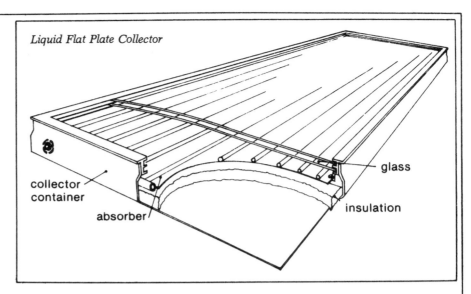

Liquid Flat Plate Collector

collector container

absorber

glass

insulation

The other systems, drain-down, closed loop and drain-back, are pumping systems. The main difference is how each resolves the freeze-up problem.

The **closed loop system** uses antifreeze to keep the collectors and the tubes inside them from freezing up on cold winter nights, but the ethylene glycol used in the solution is poisonous and must not contaminate the drinking water. The antifreeze is contained in a "closed loop" and a heat exchanger is used to heat the water in the tank.

To ensure that there is no possibility of ethylene glycol getting into the water supply, there has to be "double-wall" protection. Although they counter the problem of contamination, double walls are inefficient with a great deal of heat lost in the heat transfer process.

There are non-toxic antifreezes such as propylene glycol which, if used, eliminate the need for the inefficient double-wall heat exchanger. But this is not good enough, building code officials argue, because there is no guarantee against a householder, through ignorance, replacing propylene glycol with ethylene glycol in the future and creating a health hazard. This issue is still under consideration and will not be resolved until the new Canadian Standards Association (CSA) standard is issued.

Right now, you can get double-wall protection in a variety of ways: "wrap around" heat exchangers fixed to the outside of

the tank; double-wall coil heat exchangers installed as an element within the tank; and two pump systems, with a separate heat exchanger tank (heated by a closed loop circuit from the collectors with a second circuit preheating the tank).

A **drain-down system** avoids the problem of using antifreeze. When the outside temperature is near freezing, the water in the system drains down to the tank in the basement.

This system does not require a complicated heat exchanger and operates at high efficiency. The only drawback is the disastrous consequence of system failure—if a valve sticks or the controls do not work the collector can freeze up and very expensive parts can be ruined.

Most manufacturers are unwilling to provide an extended warranty on drain-down systems. They may also insist that they be responsible for installation, because, if errors are made, the system may not drain down correctly.

The **drain-back system** is similar to the closed loop but uses water instead of antifreeze. When the temperature drops, the water drains back but does not mix with the drinking water. One advantage of this system is that hard water will not form deposits on the collectors. For evacuated tube technology this is essential and, in those systems, ionized water is used to prevent scaly build-up.

Once the water is heated, there are two main options for storing it: single or double tanks.

Most manufacturers offer a two-tank system which consists of a standard hot water tank and a solar pre-heating tank. The solar system heats the water in the tank which then flows into a standard domestic hot water tank.

Solarsystems in Vancouver is developing a single tank system; company president E.W. Hoffmann claims the advantage to this approach is that the electrical preheater is not used to make up for the heat loss from the stored water.

The system relies on heat stratification, taking cold water from the bottom of the tank directly to the collectors, says Hoffmann. The disadvantage is that the water circulating through the system is generally at a higher temperature, so overall collector efficiency is lower. In time, the back-up electrical heater warms up the water in the bottom of the tank, and so the solar collectors are prevented from providing their full contribution.

Ontario Hydro has evaluated different types of hot water systems at its testing facility in Toronto and researcher Michael Bell says he found that the single most important factor is the size of the collector array: by doubling the collector, it is possible to double the efficiency of the system.

The study also found that collector efficiency is important, although the performance of the high efficiency collector tested deteriorated rapidly. After a few weeks, its performance was no better than a typical collector.

Perhaps surprisingly, heat exchanger efficiency was found not to be that important. A drain-down system was found to be only 10 per cent more efficient than a closed loop system with a wrap-around heat exchanger.

The size of the storage tank was also not crucial. Most manufacturers offer a 100-gallon tank, although Bell found that a 50-gallon tank would be adequate.

The study also found that heat loss from the storage tank is quite significant and Bell suggests that manufacturers come up with a system where the two tanks are combined in a single unit.

What *does* alter the economics of solar hot water heating is life style and living habits. In its experiment, Ontario Hydro simulated in-use performance by linking the systems in their labs with private homes, via a telephone hook-up. Whenever somebody turned on the tap in any of the homes, hot water was

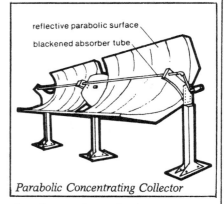

Parabolic Concentrating Collector

reflective parabolic surface

blackened absorber tube

also drawn from the test systems at Hydro.

So far, no definitive consumption patterns have emerged, but it is clear that solar systems are sized to meet fairly typical family needs. Because most are meant to provide 15 gallons per person per day, if you are an intermittent water user and go from using a lot one day to none the next, you may find that solar water heating is not for you.

The economics of solar favour households that use fairly large batches of hot water a few hours apart throughout the day and, if you don't fit that mould, you may find your system being over- or under-utilized.

Collector Basics

Because the collector is one of the most important components of the system, choosing the right one for your purposes is a key decision. The technology is evolving rapidly, so before you buy, know the options.

In the solar collector competition, where the main events are cost and reliability, there are several contenders ranging from flat plat collectors, which are the type most Canadian manufacturers produce, to the newer evacuated tube type, which have yet to live up to their promise.

Flat plates, the slow and steady tortoises in the race, are heavy, bulky, difficult to ship and limited to low temperature heat production. They consist basically of a sandwich box of glazing, absorber and insulation packaged in a flat container.

Concentrating collectors, the high performance hares, are used for high temperature hot water.

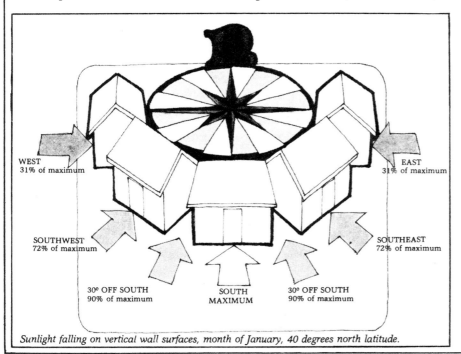

WEST
31% of maximum

EAST
31% of maximum

SOUTHWEST
72% of maximum

SOUTHEAST
72% of maximum

30° OFF SOUTH
90% of maximum

SOUTH
MAXIMUM

30° OFF SOUTH
90% of maximum

Sunlight falling on vertical wall surfaces, month of January, 40 degrees north latitude.

They use reflective surfaces, lenses or other optical devices to concentrate the sun's rays onto a small area, creating a large amount of heat.

Tracking collectors, such as the trough or parabolic dish, track the sun as it moves across the sky and concentrate its rays on a focal line or point. Non-tracking collectors trap the sun's rays in a deep curved V-shaped trough and then funnel them to the absorber at the bottom.

Evacuated tube collectors are the dark horses of the big league solar business. There are at least six multi-national corporations in the business, although only Owens-Illinois actively markets in Canada (through its distributor, Solartech).

It is the claim of Amherst President Richard Davies that evacuated tube technology makes flat plates obsolete.

"Flat plates are like kerosene lamps," he says. "Evacuated tubes are the light bulbs."

What excites Davies is that the thin glass tube used in the new technology can be produced, if it is produced in quantity, very cheaply. He compares it to the mass production of automobiles at the turn of the century, when the number of cars made jumped to 1.5 million in 1916 from 200,000 in 1910. Since assembly-line production of gasoline engines began, the automobile industry has never looked back.

Davies predicts that, with large-scale manufacturing, collector costs could be as low as seven dollars a square foot as compared to current costs of about $15.

Evacuated tubes are also highly efficient, because a vacuum is created around the tube and, without air around the absorber, heat loss is greatly reduced. Special coatings can be applied to the tube to further improve its efficiency. Because heat loss is reduced to a minimum, evacuated tube collectors could be well-suited to our cold Canadian climate. Used in combination with non-tracking compound parabolic reflectors, temperatures high enough to boil water can be generated.

Whatever the long-term potential of evacuated tubes may be, at the moment they are not mass-produced and flat plate collectors continue to compete favourably with them.

Even with mass production, the cost of most flat plate collectors will not come down as they are made from heavy and expensive materials like copper and aluminum. To stay competitive, manufacturers are experimenting with low cost materials like plastics. The best example is SolaRoll, an American product which uses a rubbery material known as EPDM. The product is a pliable extrusion which can be rolled up into a convenient package so shipping and distribution costs are minimal. The collector is site assembled with the glazing and rigid insulation being purchased locally. Installation is simple as you only need to glue the collectors to the roof. Another big advantage is that you do not have to worry about freeze protection. If ice forms, the rubbery material expands and so, in theory, there should be no problem with broken pipes. EPDM is not a new material and has a good track record for durability. The manufacturer, Bio-Energy Systems, is confident enough to give the product a 15 year guarantee. In the States, the product retails at six dollars a square foot for do-it-yourself installation, and nine dollars a square foot for professional installation. This is less than half the cost of conventional low temperature flat plate collectors.

Specifics

Once aware of the general types of equipment on the market, you are ready to start looking at specific collectors. Be prepared to be a little overwhelmed; solar heating involves a maze of technical jargon that can and does confuse most non-experts.

Honeycomb suppressors, matrix absorbers, selective surfaces are all terms that won't mean much to most people. Fortunately, from the consumers' point of view, it is not necessary to know the technical refinements and details of various features. What you do have to know is how efficient the collector is, how long it will function effectively and how much it's going to cost. You can learn these things by looking at testing results.

Most collectors produced by Canadian manufacturers have been tested according to ASHRAE

93-77. This is a testing procedure involving measurement of the solar energy which falls on the collector and the amount of energy that is picked up by the collector. The results are plotted on a graph, according to a fairly complicated formula.

Without going into all the details, what is important is the slope of the curve and where the curve intersects with the vertical Y-axis.

In general, the higher the Y-intercept (see point A), the more efficient the collector is during the summer months. The flatter the curve, the more efficient the collector is in the winter. (See sample graphs.)

Most manufacturers will include efficiency data in their literature and you should be wary of anyone whose product has not been tested.

The federal government, through the National Research Council, pays half the testing costs and will also pay to have the equipment shipped to the Ontario Research Foundation, where the tests are done. Any manufacturer who is serious about solar will have had his product tested, but the procedure is difficult and the results not always reliable.

Still, with the government willing to help foot the bill, there is no reason for someone not to have the tests done, so you should use extreme caution in dealing with anyone who has only tested his product himself or who presents a purely theoretical performance curve. Remember, too, that data can always be manipulated to make the results look impressive—it happens in solar too—so the best thing to do is ask to see the original testing report.

Although it is an important consideration, the efficiency curve should not be thought of as the be-all and end-all. It is only 90 per cent accurate and often bears little resemblance to on-the-job performance.

Efficiency tests are misleading, simply because of the artificial conditions of the lab, although compensating tests have been developed to help you evaluate the efficiency curves. One such test is the **incident angle modifier** which will give some idea how well your collector will work at the various angles at which the sun's rays strike it. By knowing the collector's efficiency when the sun hits at a 90-degree angle, you will be able to figure out its efficiency at different times of the day and year.

ASHRAE regulations also say the collector has to be tested when there is not a cloud in the sky. Because this is a bit optimistic in the Canadian climate, the compensating ''time constant'' factor is needed. This will tell you how quickly the collector will respond to changes in the sky and it should, allowing for the way the measurement is taken, be as low as possible—seconds rather than minutes.

It's important to know how to apply the efficiency data, because choosing the best heating system depends on its intended use.

If you're looking for a swimming-pool heating system, the only thing that matters is how high the Y-intercept is. The wintertime efficiency is not important. For space heating, on the other hand, a flat curve (winter efficiency) is what you want. (See sample graph.)

Water heating is a little more tricky. You can go for a low cost system that will provide most of the hot water in the summer, some in the spring and autumn, and virtually none in the winter.

Fallibility

On the other hand, you can opt for a more expensive collector system and try to get year-round water heating. Of course, the winter months in Canada are not particularly sunny, and—in our view—it's questionable whether you would get your money's worth out of more expensive equipment.

As Michael Bell points out, if you have your summer-only systems working for 50 per cent of the year, you will definitely be getting most of the sunshine the country has to offer and, at the lower price, it may be your best bet with the hardware available today.

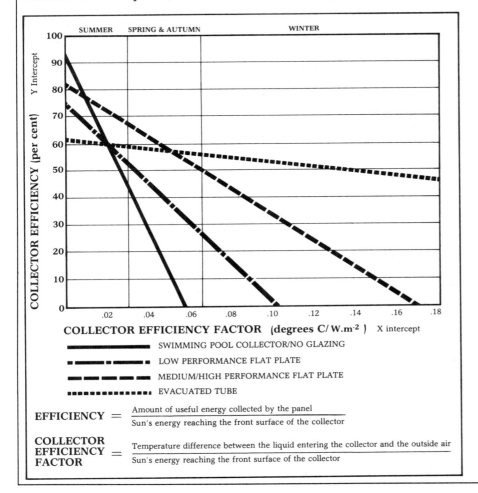

COLLECTOR EFFICIENCY FACTOR (degrees C/ W.m⁻²)   X intercept

————————— SWIMMING POOL COLLECTOR/NO GLAZING
—·—·—·—·— LOW PERFORMANCE FLAT PLATE
— — — — — MEDIUM/HIGH PERFORMANCE FLAT PLATE
■■■■■■■■■ EVACUATED TUBE

$$\text{EFFICIENCY} = \frac{\text{Amount of useful energy collected by the panel}}{\text{Sun's energy reaching the front surface of the collector}}$$

$$\text{COLLECTOR EFFICIENCY FACTOR} = \frac{\text{Temperature difference between the liquid entering the collector and the outside air}}{\text{Sun's energy reaching the front surface of the collector}}$$

Some solar heating systems have been spectacular in their total and rapid failure: collectors freeze, break, fall apart; glazing fogs or pops out of its framing. Buyers need to know that their equipment will not fall apart within a year or two, and the best way to avoid that is to check the track record of the collector you want to buy. Learn where the collector was first installed, what the problems were and what repairs if any had to be made.

The only way to assess a collector that is too new to have much of a record is to analyse its components. When conventional materials such as copper or glass are used, there should be no problem, but plastic glazings and specialized absorber coatings should be checked more carefully.

The standard claim of most manufacturers is that their equipment will last 20 years. It sounds great, but in fact is unlikely to be the case. Repairs will almost inevitably be needed and it will help to know how to go about looking after your system. Knowing how to remove single collectors from an array, how to replace glazing and how to install sensors will come in handy.

Canadian solar manufacturers have had to learn on the job, marketing their products before all the technical riddles have been solved. Their mistakes have been painful and costly. Don't dismiss any firm out of hand for past problems; if the company dealt with complaints quickly and efficiently they are probably worthy of consideration.

Finally, don't be too hard on the solar industry. It is in its infancy and it is no wonder that many of the early models did not function properly and that many of the bugs are still being ironed out. While some people have had trouble with their systems, others have been completely satisfied and will swear by solar.

If, after reading to this point, you are still interested in solar systems, it helps to know where to start looking. The following list shows solar manufacturers and

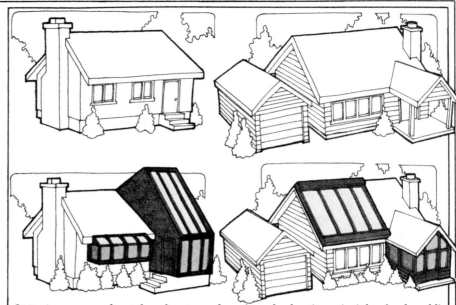

Older homes can often take advantage of passive solar heating principles, by the addition of solar greenhouses, glassed-in porches and entry foyers and the mounting of skylights that face toward the sun. Additional shrubbery plantings help prevent foundation heat loss. A highly recommended new "kit" of such ideas is available for $3.75, postpaid, from Total Environmental Action, Church Hill, Harrisville, New Hampshire 03450.

distributors throughout the country. The list is broken down by region and our emphasis has been on the PASEM grant winners, although some non-winners who are also reliable companies have been mentioned. Because only the bigger firms are on this list, a number of areas in the country seem under-represented. That shouldn't discourage you, though, because chances are good you'll find someone in your area who knows about solar and can help.

As Tang Lee, with the Faculty of Environmental Design at the University of Calgary, says about the solar industry in the Prairies, "It's a cottage-type industry. Knowledge about it passes by word of mouth."

If you want to find out about solar, just start asking around. We don't think you'll be disappointed.

MARITIMES

There were no PASEM winners in the Maritimes, although a few firms applied. According to Martha Musgrove-Pratt at the Institute of Man and Resources in Charlottetown, a local company called **Renewable Energy**

Systems Ltd. is hoping to begin solar construction soon and has completed some designs. She says Kerr Furnaces (see BIOMASS) of Nova Scotia is looking into solar as well, although that company has not made any definite plans.

With high energy prices in the Maritimes, solar hot water heating is cost-effective, but the most prevalent alternative energy in that region is wood heating. There are, however, a small number of solar heating equipment distributors.

The Charlottetown Institute, which is monitoring a number of solar heating systems in the area, is working to make the public more aware of solar energy.

"We're looking at how well various systems work and trying to reduce installation costs," says Musgrove-Pratt. "First-time (installation) costs are horrendous. We've reduced that quite a bit and are now trying to introduce tradesmen to the various systems."

QUEBEC
Petro-Sun, alias Thermo-Solar, is the front runner in the Canadian solar industry. The new firm is the result of a merger between a Quebec-based gas exploration

company, Quebec Manitou, and Thermo-Solar. Petro-Sun has developed a wide distribution network, particularly in Ontario and Quebec, and significant sales in the pool collector market.

Petro-Sun's competitors complain that its flying start is a result of the fact that the firm did not develop its own liquid collector but only manufactured (under licence) the Sunworks Collector produced by the Enthone Corp. in the United States. Some of the parts of the collector, such as the selective surface absorber coating, are fabricated by Enthone.

Michael Sicotte of Petro-Sun says the company is working on a selective coating facility in Quebec so that it will no longer have to ship the absorbers to the U.S.

The performance of the collector is solid but not dramatic. Its main selling point is that it has a long track record—the first system in the United States was installed seven years ago.

The firm markets a drain-down and closed-loop hot water system but it does not push the drain-down because it is concerned about freeze protection problems. It only provides a two-year warranty for the drain-down, compared to five for the closed-loop. That system uses an internal heat exchanger imported from the U.S.

The non-PASEM winner, **Fibratech,** which produces a collector, is struggling to build up a reputation.

There are also two major solar equipment distributors in Quebec: Solerco and Atelier Solaire.

Solerco is headed up by the aggressive Pat Soler, whose distribution house stocks a number of specialized solar components and parts, all listed in his company's catalogue.

Atelier Solaire last year joined forces with **DeLuxe Co.,** the company responsible for distributing Jotul stoves in Canada, and the two are now setting up a strong distribution network. The main product line is SEP, from a major American solar manufacturer, but the firm carries a number of solar components and parts as well.

ONTARIO
The majority of solar firms in Canada are located in Ontario. Out of the 10 PASEM grants awarded, eight were to Ontario firms. Listed below in alphabetical order are the products and manufacturers. **Amherst Renewable Energy Ltd.** is a small company with a high profile, thanks to President

Grumman installation, Vermont, U.S.A.

Richard Davies, manufactures air and liquid collectors that are generally acknowledged to be above average, with interesting design features and good efficiency curves.

Musgrove-Pratt in Charlottetown says Amherst collectors are the best the Institute has in operation with its own water heating package right now.

"Each system is providing 70 to 75 per cent of the domestic hot water requirements over a one-year period," agrees IMR solar field technician Roland MacKinnon.

Amherst is planning to market its air collectors, which are bulky and not worth shipping long distances, in kit form so that they can be assembled locally by sheet metal fabricators. Amherst is also the exclusive Canadian distributor for Philips evacuated tube and photovoltaic products.

Although Amherst plays with this more advanced technology, it has not forsaken its "hippie" roots and is happy to put up with the exigencies of the do-it-yourself market. If you live within a 50 mile radius of the factory, the company will send along a supervisor to help you install your system.

Nortec Solar Industries produces a low cost liquid collector known as the "Hi-Y" because it has a good summer efficiency rating but doesn't do so well in the winter. The solar hot water heating package put together by the company comes in kit form and features a two pump heat exchanger.

At the moment, Nortec general manager James Ramsden says the company is only marketing the system "half-heartedly." Nortec is concentrating instead on industrial applications and developing a high temperature collector using heat pipe technology.

GSW Ltd. of Mississauga, became a PASEM winner when a Manitoba firm backed out. The company's solar programme includes domestic and light commercial water heating applications. The collector is a non-corrosive type with selective absorber coating and single glazing.

Solartech was not technically a PASEM winner. The government contract was actually awarded to Electrohome Ltd.—a major television manufacturing company that withdrew after making the PASEM short list. Solartech, wanting the glory (and money) of being a PASEM recipient, bought out Electrohome's Solar Division and is now working on that company's proposal for an air collector.

Solartech also distributes Owen-Corning's evacuated tube collector and is planning to manufacture the module assembly in Canada. The system is a unique drain-back set-up using ionized water as the heat transfer fluid.

Solartronics produces a glazed pool collector which is really only worth the extra cost (an unglazed black collector is less expensive) if you're interested in early spring or autumn pool dips.

The company is also developing a low-cost plastic collector for use in hot water systems.

Solatherm, in Mississauga, produces a medium performance liquid flat plate collector. It has a reasonable efficiency although there have been problems.

Solathern equipment installed by the Institute of Man and Resources in P.E.I. was removed from the project after serious trouble cropped up.

"The main problem was that we couldn't get it working . . . . We couldn't afford to put any more time or effort into the system," says Roland MacKinnon.

An Ottawa housing project in the city's west end—Heron Gate—also had difficulties with the Solatherm equipment installed by Davis, Eryou, and Associates. In this case, though, the problems were solved and the system has been working since June.

"The problems were fixed over the winter," says company president W.R. Davis. "The system is in place and working and we are confident the former problem will not recur." John Atkinson, president of Solatherm, dismissed the difficulties as "early teething problems." He pointed out that the collectors at Heron Gate were repaired under warranty.

Solatherm also produces a closed-loop hot water system and a low-cost thermosyphon kit which can be site-assembled by the homeowner.

Temperature Specialties in Downsview is a heating and ventilation equipment manufacturer that sells directly to wholesalers and is not directly involved with the retail consumer market at this time.

The company's collector design has evolved from one developed by University of Toronto Professor Frank Hooper which was first used on Provident House, Ontario.

Solar heated water at this Gunton, Manitoba fish hatchery spurs the growth rate of breeding trout. The 48-panel system, installed by hatchery staff, uses Amherst panels.

There is no such thing as a stereotypic passive solar design, as this Toronto-area home by architect John Hix demonstrates.

Watershed Energy Systems is a small manufacturing firm which produces a site-assembled air collector. The Teflon honeycomb convection suppressor, which is installed between two layers of glass, breaks up the air circulation currents between these two layers and works effectively to decrease heat loss. The glazing unit can be installed by itself in buildings as a very efficient form of window glazing.

Because the honeycomb is complex to manufacture, it seems unlikely that it will compete with evacuated tube technology in the long run. Watershed also plans to offer a solar hot water heating system, once development work is complete.

Envirogetics, an air and liquid collector manufacturer that did not get a PASEM grant, deserves to be considered. The company is alive and well and its equipment is among that being used by the Institute of Man and Resources.

The Envirogetics collector, like Temspec's, draws its inspiration from Professor Hooper's original design. The company has also developed a single-tank drain-down system which uses compressed air to ensure that there is no liquid left in the collector.

One satisfied Envirogetics

customer is R.J. Newburg of Kettleby, Ontario.

''It works, there's no doubt that it works, but whether there is a payback or not is another question . . . Quite honestly, I'd rather piss my money down the drain than give it to Hydro.''

Although it has meant some adjustments for his family, he says they have never run out of hot water and it really hasn't demanded much change in water use habits.

Solcan is another small firm, long established, which missed out on the PASEM hand-outs. The firm produces a closed-loop solar hot water package which incorporates a thermosyphon heat exchanger.

Jim Bolton, chairman of the Solar Energy Society of Canada (SESCI), has installed a Solcan system that preheats water before it goes to an oil water heater in his own home. This system, he says, is an experiment.

''We're not looking at this system as an economically viable set-up. After about a year, we'll be able to see how well it's working . . . . So far it seems to be giving lots of hot water and the amount of oil used this summer will be lower.''

PRAIRIES
The Prairies and solar energy are not mixing very well right now.

Whether it's because of the cheap price of natural gas or the long-standing problem of freight rates through the Rockies, there are at the moment no major manufacturers in the Prairie Provinces.

Although solar conditions are ideal, there is not much being done in Manitoba to encourage solar.

E.M. Price of Winnipeg was awarded a PASEM grant but the firm dropped out so that it could concentrate its resources on developing an integrated low-energy ceiling system.

Saskatchewan has gained world-wide attention for its passive solar homes. There are several small companies in the province manufacturing specialized passive components: air-to-air heat exchangers, insulated shutters and the like.

Mechanical solar systems have not been forgotten either. Research and development is being carried out by **Saskatchewan Minerals** to develop a sodium sulphate phase-change material which will provide a very compact way of storing solar heat.

One firm that is using eutectic salt heat storage is **Solar Heating Ltd.** which has built several solar houses incorporating site-built air collectors.

Government policy is not helping the solar industry in Alberta, according to Tang Lee at the University of Calgary. Despite provincial legislation that is supposed to encourage development in the renewables area, most energy money is poured back into oil, gas and non-renewables.

"Less than 10 per cent (of the energy development budget) goes to renewables," he says, and most of that ends up at the Alberta Research Council.

That doesn't mean everyone has given up, though.

Lee says there are a number of small companies producing collectors, some of them making only a dozen a year or so. Knowledge of these builders passes by word of mouth among people interested in solar in Alberta.

Often the homeowners help build and install the collectors and many of the manufacturers are individuals who hold other full-time jobs. One Alberta manufacturing company is **Sunergy Systems** in Edmonton, a firm that has been involved in solar greenhouse construction.

BRITISH COLUMBIA

The only PASEM winner in British Columbia is **Solarsystems Industries.** This firm is credited with building the first solar-heated home in Canada in 1971. Solarsystems produces a liquid collector which can be purchased in component form or site-assembled. The collector, as tested, has a poor efficiency and it is a bit tacky in appearance. The durability of the plastic glazing is also open to question.

Like all other PASEM winners, Solarsystems is hard at work trying to improve their product. E.W. Hoffman expects that their new collector will have greatly improved performance.

The company also produces a drain-down hot water system that could be used anywhere in Canada, says Hoffman.

Ark Solar Products is a B.C. dealer that uses Solarsystems

collectors in the domestic hot water systems it puts together.

Company president Gil Parker, who has installed a system in a home he owns, says, "We're really pleased with it. We've saved a lot of electricity."

The firm has been in operation for two years, Parker says. Business has been good—he has installed close to 20 pool, domestic hot water and space heating systems—and "we'll really be doing business next year."

His company supplied Dr. and Mrs. Charles Clayton with a domestic hot water system at the beginning of the summer. The family is getting lots of hot water, Mrs. Clayton says, and she is "very happy with the way the system is working."

There are several other small solar collector manufacturers tinkering away on the west coast. **Sol-Way** stands out as a good example. That company produces both a drain-down and a thermosyphon hot water package; its collectors were used on the Kitsilano Solar Townhouses designed by Solar Applications and Research.

— Michael Glover and Kathryn Fournier Ottawa, Ontario

The following directory of solar manufacturers, suppliers, designers and information sources has been compiled with the assistance of the Department of Energy, Mines and Resources and excerpted in part from their *Solar Heating Catalogue No. 2*, a highly recommended guide to the Canadian solar establishment.

ONTARIO
Manufacturers

STREAMLINE COPPER & BRASS LIMITED
290 Ellor Street
Strathroy, Ont. N7G 3J3
D.W. Graham (519) 245-0800

Manufacture copper tubes for solar application, including: D shaped tube, serpentine grid, helical coil and double tube, as well as headers.

SUN TEMP SOLAR SYSTEMS LIMITED
1110 Brydges Street
London, Ont. N5W 2B6
Brian Maguire (519) 453-4325

Manufacture the Sun Temp Collector (liquid type), which measures four by eight feet and is double glazed with Sundex glass. Tightly serpentined copper tubing serves as the absorber and the frame is anodized aluminum. Ten year guarantee.
Sun Temp Collector: $350 to $450 per panel.
This company also supplies controls, pumps and storage tanks.

SOLATHERM ENERGY SYSTEMS LIMITED
1711 Mattawa Avenue
Mississauga, Ont. L4X 1K5
John Atkinson (416) 275-2177

Produces solar water heating system with three collectors totalling 60 square feet, along with pump, controls and tank. Approx. $1,095 for basic system. Kits available.

SUNTRON MFG.
390 Dennison Street
Markham, Ont. L3R 1B9
(416) 495-6898

Manufacturers of the Wilson "crab-eye" type concentrating collector, which measures 81 by 31 inches and markets for $995 with single glazing or $1,195 for a double-glazed model.

SOLARFIN PRODUCTS
108 Ottawa St. North
Hamilton, Ont. L8H 3Z1
(416) 544-0491

Makers of Solarfin Venus flat plate water heating collector glazed with acrylic and Tedlar and either aluminum or copper as the absorber material. Also manufacture the Mercury Concentrating Collector which produces high-temperature water, is covered by a convex sheet of Tedlar, and consists of 6.5 foot long aluminum reflector positioned on a 90-degree angle from a copper tube and aluminum fin absorber. Prices on request.

RAYPACK
B.R. Watkin
120-124 Skyway Avenue
Rexdale, Ont. M9W 4Y9
(416) 675-1262

The widely available Raypack collector, of American design, is now being produced in Canada. Glazed with glass, aluminum absorber bonded to copper tubing. Price on request.

TEMPERATURE SPECIALTIES MFG. LTD.
585 Canarctic Drive
Downsview, Ont. M3J 2P9
Jim Rawes (416) 661-0535

Manufacture/supply the Temspec liquid collector specially designed for Canadian climate. May be single or double glazed with white water crystal tempered glass. Copper absorber plate backed with degassed fibreglass insulation. Temspec Collectors approx. $16.50/sq. ft.

NORTEC AIR CONDITIONING IND. LTD.
Box 1263, Station B
Ottawa, Ontario K1P 5R3
Jim Ramsden (613) 822-0335

Manufacture the widely distributed Nortec liquid flat plate, "High-Y" collector. Single glazed with glass, aluminum extrusion frame and copper absorber sheet. Also distribute heat pumps in Ontario.
Nortec Liquid Collector Suggested Retail Price: Approx. $12 to $14.50 per square foot.

ENVIROGETICS LTD.
195 Milner Avenue
Scarborough, Ont. M1S 3P7
(416) 291-1657

Makers of the all-Canadian Suntrap liquid type collector, featuring single, pebbled glass glazing, galvanized steel frame and copper absorber tubes and plate.
Suntrap Collector (22 sq. ft.) $330.00 (Discount on 20 panels or more.)

GUILDCRAFT (1978) LTD.
130 Esna Park Drive
Markham, Ont. L3R 1E3
R.P. Webb (416) 495-0086

Manufacture Sunmaster liquid collector; distributors of Solar Systems International Inc., Mr. Sun liquid collector.
Sunmaster suggested retail price: Approx $11.00/sq. ft.

MURFIN HEATING & COOLING LIMITED
55 Torbarrie Road
Downsview, Ont. M3L 1G5
L.H. Hustler (416) 249-7991

Manufacture Murfin air collectors; design, fabrication and installation of air type solar systems for space heating or domestic hot water.
Murfin panels approx. $9.00—$14.00 per sq. ft.

ENERGY FARMS LTD.
Westbrook, Ont. K0H 2X0
Harry Nybom (613) 389-5006
Manufacture and supply Unisol 77 energy system and Unisol 3 air-media solar collector.

SOLARTECH LIMITED
21 Prince Andrew Place
Don Mills, Ontario M3C 2H2
David Wood (416) 449-4415

Solartech has now entered into manufacturing two lines of collectors, the Solair curved cover plate hot air panel and a new evacuated tube, drainable unit. This is considered by Solartech to be a major advance, especially for cold climates, as the collector reportedly loses much less heat than a flat plate unit and will operate on grim winter days when other units are ineffectual. Solartech also supplies various component parts, including pumps, controls and gravel bed storage unit plans.

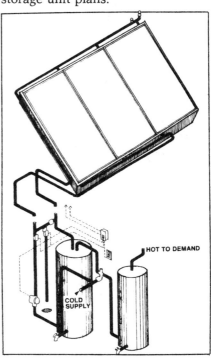

Evacuated Tube Collector (4 x 4½ ft.) $425
Evacuated Tube Hot Water Package (complete with three panels, controls, pump and storage tank) $2,850
Solar Air Movers $1,795—$1,995
Solair Air-Type Collectors $8.50/sq. ft.
$10.50/sq. ft. installed
Thermo-solar Hot Water Packages $1,575—$2,675

IMP-SOL PRODUCTS INC.
22 Aloma Cres.
Bramalea, Ont. L6T 2N9
Paul Brafield (416) 451-1121

Manufacture Imp-Sol liquid collector.

ENERGY TECH
Box 1094, Station B
341 Durham Street
Ottawa, Ont. L1J 5Y9
R. Bilsky (613) 579-1433

Manufactures Energy Tech solar panels and supplies Fafco and Solatherm solar panels through retail solar energy store.

K.R. THOMPSON ENGINEERING LTD.
Box 34
Ingersoll, Ont. N5C 3K1
J. Thompson (519) 485-5161

Developers of Blacklite plastic water collector panels.

SOLARTRONICS
9 Hershey Dr. Box 850
Smiths Falls, Ont. K7A 4W7
(613) 283-6666

Aquasol solar pool heating systems at $1,500 to $3,000 per system.

TARGET CONSTRUCTION & SUPPLY LIMITED
2476 Beryl Road, R.R.1
Oakville, Ont. L6J 4Z2
Norm Wright (416) 845-3701

Residential construction company; manufacture, supply and install liquid flat-plate collectors and poured-in-place concrete storage tanks.

EILEETO IND. LIMITED
68 Kent Avenue
Kitchener, Ont. N2G 3R1
J. Thomas Danberger
(519) 576-8215

Manufacture Eileeto fibreglass solar heat panels—liquid and air collectors.

GRAHAM PROD. LTD.
Box 2000
Inglewood, Ont. L0N 1K0

Manufacture Excelite flat and corrugated fibreglass reinforced plastic panels.

C.D. JOHNSON & ASSOCIATES LTD.
Suite 100, 56 Sparks St.
Ottawa, Ont. K1P 5A9
(613) 238-6069

Developers of Simi-System solar panel water heating device.

PHILIPS ELECTRONICS LIMITED
601 Milner Avenue
Scarborough, Ont. M1B 1M8
(416) 292-5161

Dutch-design evacuated tube collectors for hot water and space heating. Also offers solar components. Philips Collector: Approx. $22/sq. ft.

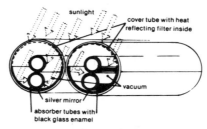

Evacuated Tube

S.A. ARMSTRONG LTD.
1400 O'Connor Drive
Toronto, Ont. M4B 2T9
Head Office (416) 755-2291

Manufacture, market and service Armstrong Circulators (pumps) and heat transfer products.

CLEMMER IND. LIMITED
446 Albert Street
Waterloo, Ont. N2J 4A1
Custom Sales (519) 884-4320

Manufacture Clemmer metal storage tanks and linings for hot water, flammable liquid etc. Metal fabrication.

COUNSOL
R.R.1
Grand Valley, Ont. L0N 1G0
Rodney Graves (416) 667-3356

Sizing calculations for residential solar heating systems; testing solar collectors.

DANFOSS MFG. COMPANY LIMITED
1230 Lakeshore Road E.
Mississauga, Ont. L5E 1E9
Order Desk (416) 274-2311

Manufacture Danfoss differential temperature controlled valve for solar heating systems.

HOTHFIELD SYSTEMS INC.
65 King Street
Lindsay, Ont. K9V 1C4
D.J. Steel (705) 324-4110

Manufacture solar-heated

greenhouses, domestic and commercial.

RHEEM CANADA LTD.
Solar Products Division
Box 846, 128 Barton St.
Hamilton, Ont. L8N 3P3
(519) 527-9194

Solar hot water heaters.

ROBERTSHAW CONTROLS (CANADA) LTD.
41 Medulla Avenue
Toronto, Ont. M8Z 5W1
E.A. Pike (416) 233-5831

Manufacture SD10 Solar Commander; solid state pump switching, thermistor sensors and encapsulated circuits.

A.O. SMITH CORP.
738 Erie Street
Stratford, Ont. N5A 6T3
George Pick (519) 271-5800

Storage tanks and heat exchangers.

VAPOR CANADA LTD.
9 Royal Crest Road
Rexdale, Ont. M9V 2L6
Lloyd Algie (416) 743-7200

Manufacture and supply Magatherm thermal storage systems for domestic water or water-source heat-pump systems; supply heat exchangers, valves and valve parts.

LOW SILHOUETTE SKYLIGHTS
Type LSF — Single Dome
Type LSFD — Double Dome

ALLIED PLASTIC FABRICATORS
4461A Chesswood Drive
Downsview, Ont.
(416) 630-5600

Makers of reasonably-priced double panel skylights which resemble solar panels and can be incorporated in passive heating designs.

KUNTZ ELECTROPLATING LTD.

851 Wilson Avenue
Kitchener, Ont. N2C 1J1
Jack Karne (519) 579-6440

Electroplate selective black
chrome surface on copper,
aluminum or steel solar absorber
panels.

CLARE MOORE LTD.

400 Cannon St. E.
Hamilton, Ont. L8L 2C8
Robert Moore (416) 522-3576

Refrigeration and air-conditioning
contractor developing and design-
testing a solar collector.

NIXON PLATE COILS LTD.

R.R.1
Gormley, Ont. L0H 1G0
C.R. Patel (416) 923-3746

Manufacture steel and stainless
steel flat plate absorbers.

SOLCAN LTD.

R.R.3
London, Ont. N6A 4B7
Robert K. Swartman
(519) 473-0501

Manufacturers of the Solcan line
of air, water and pool heating
collectors, featuring plywood
frames, double reinforced
fibreglass glazing and aluminum
absorber plate. Hot water systems
and solar greenhouse kits.
Solcan Air or Water Collector:
Approx. $12.00/sq. ft.

SOLCO ENERGY SYSTEMS LIMITED

Suite 606, 61 Waterford Dr.
Weston, Ont. M9R 2N7
George Clayton (416) 247-4110

Developers of the Solco liquid flat
plate collectors, either assembled
or in kit form. Collector measures
three by seven feet, with extruded
aluminum frame, black painted
aluminum absorber plate and
single layer of tempered glass for
the cover.
Solco Collectors: $375 each

A.S. SEED

Box 364
Thunder Bay, Ont. P7C 4V9
Jerrold Burns (807) 622-4411

Design and develop Sunrunner
solar product line; supply and
install ILSE panels, collectors, etc.

Solar demonstration shows, from front to back, Watershed air-type collectors, Solartech evacuated tubes and Amherst flat plate liquid panels.

SOLARFOIL HEATING SYSTEMS

"Solar Manor"
R.R.1
Smithville, Ont. L0R 2A0
Neil Switzer (416) 957-2163

Design, construction and
maintenance of the "Solarfoil" hot
air/rock heating system for
residential, commercial, industrial
or agricultural purposes; also
environmental planning and
design.

Package price(Installed):
$19.80/sq. ft.

SUNGLO SOLAR LTD.

1081 Alness Street
Downsview, Ont. M3J 2S1
Joe Sherman (416) 661-2560

Manufacture Sunglo solar pool
heater, also automatic and manual
control systems for solar pool
heating systems.

SOLARIS ENERGY PROD.

11 Alderbrook Drive
Ottawa, Ontario K2H 5W4
Kreso P. Perovic
(613) 828-7431

Manufacture and supply Solar-
Panel floating solar swimming
pool panels.

PROVINCIAL PLASTICS LIMITED

54 Guelph Avenue
Cambridge, Ont. N3C 1A3

Doug Mitten (519) 659-9711
Manufacture solar panels for
pools.

WATERSHED ENERGY SYSTEMS LIMITED

108 Liberty St. W.
Toronto, Ont. M6K 3C4
Doug Hart (416) 536-6884

Doug Hart appears to be making
the transition from basement-
inventor to successful solar
manufacturer, but with a goal of
keeping Watershed a small
company providing personal
service. The company specializes
in air collector panels with a
honeycomb convection suppressor
built in to prevent heat loss.
According to Hart, "The
honeycomb collector developed at
the University of Waterloo by
Terry Hollands may be Canada's
most efficient flat plate collector.
In fact, independent tests even
rank it ahead of the evacuated
tube collectors."

Watershed has North America's
first solar-heated car dealership to
its credit (Toronto's new Lada
showrooms), and now offers a
new "honeycomb window" for
passive solar designs (lets light in,
but has insulating value equal to
thermopane glass plus an R12
shutter). Ten year guarantee on
products.

Watershed Air Collectors:
$15.80/sq. ft.
Space Heating Systems, Complete:
$8,000—$8,500 for average house

AMHERST RENEWABLE ENERGY LIMITED

Box 387
Perth, Ont. K7H 3G1
Richard Davies (613) 267-6060

Several of Amherst's founding partners have left and become passive-solar converts, but the company continues to produce one of the most-praised Canadian line of panels. Evacuated tube collectors will soon be marketed by Amherst, but the basic panels (both air and liquid) are available in various glazings (Tedlar, Teflon, Glass/Teflon). The absorber itself is a series of flattened, rectangular copper/brass tubes which provide a fully-wetted absorber surface in the liquid collector. The air collector has an absorber back composed of fibreglass matrix painted black. One year warranty.

Amherst 100 (liquid type) $13.50/sq. ft. approx.

Amherst 200 (air type) $9.00/sq. ft. approx.

MIROMIT SOLAR CORP.

271 Glidden Rd. Unit 6
Brampton, Ont. L6W 1H9
(416) 457-1961

Solar collectors, solar hot water system. Made since 1958 in Israel, Miromit now has a manufacturing plant in Canada. Prices on request.

CAN-SOLAR HEAT

1856 Hardick Drive
Sarnia, Ont.
(519) 336-3650

Trickle-Type solar panels for heating swimming pools. Can-Solar panel $105/ea.

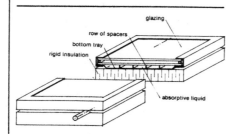

MARKKO CONSTRUCTION

Suite 309
195 Kennedy Road S.
Brampton, Ont. L6W 3H2
R. Cairemus (416) 453-4325

Makers of Suncatcher collectors, available only as part of complete

hot water system. Prices on request.

TRIODETIC BUILDING PRODUCTS LIMITED

335 Roosevelt Avenue
Ottawa, Ont. K2A 1Z2
H.G. Fentiman (613) 725-2181

Space frame structures for supporting solar collector panels.

SUNPOWER SOLAR SYSTEMS

Box 791
Cornwall, Ont. K6H 5T7
Walter Powell (613) 938-2402

Sunpower Mark IV swimming pool heaters.

Suppliers

ALTERNATE ENERGY SYSTEMS

203 King Street South
Waterloo, Ont. N2J 1R1
David Paduck (519) 745-2861

Distributors of Thermo Solar's Solector line of air and liquid collectors, drain-down and closed loop systems.

JOHN HOYLE SALES

699 Central Avenue
London, Ont. N5W 3P9
Jim Hoyle (519) 672-0111

Distribute Nortec collectors and components.

INDUSCO SALES LTD.

48 Chauncey Avenue
Toronto, Ont. M8Z 2Z4
Tom Kilmer (416) 231-9377

Distribute Nortec collectors and components.

CANADIAN SOLAR SYSTEMS

2672 Hayford Court
Mississauga, Ont. L5K 1P7

Distributor of Grumman collectors and domestic hot water systems and components.

CANADIAN SOLAR

1810 Bank Street
Ottawa, Ontario K1V 7Y6
Bruce Benson (613) 733-0332

Suppliers and installers of Solar Industries Solar Energy flat plate collector panels with related accessories and controls for heating swimming pool water.

FUTURE RESOURCES & ENERGY LIMITED

Box 1358, Station B
Downsview, Ont. M3H 5W3
(416) 630-8343

British-made Redpoint solar panels, glazed with float glass with vacuum tube transfer pipes. Prices on request.

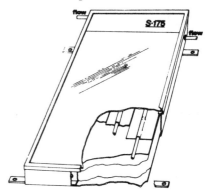

INTERSOLAR CORP.

85 Valleybrook Drive
Don Mills, Ont. M3B 2S6
J.D. Crang (416) 449-1203

Distribute Contraves Multi-purpose collector.

NATURAL POWER SYSTEM

28 - 1730 McPherson Court
Pickering, Ont. L1W 3E6
Mike Clayton (416) 839-8070

Distribute Suntron Mfg. Wilson collector.

PAYNE INDUSTRIAL SALES LIMITED

519 Fountain St. S.
Cambridge, Ont. N3H 1J2

Distribute Nortec collectors and components.

PERRIN-TURNER LTD.

34 Mendota Road
Toronto, Ont. M8Y 1E8
A.J.LaPrairie (416) 252-6213

Supply and install Grumman Sunstream collectors and systems.

SOLAR

Main Street
Atwood, Ontario N0G 1B0

Supply and install domestic, industrial and agricultural systems. Equipment lines carried: Grumman liquid collectors, Eileeto air collectors, Excelite glazing, Dynesco pumps.

SOLAR CANADA
4776 Wyandotte St. E.
Windsor, Ont.. N8Y 1H7
Roland Demers (519) 945-6322
Representative and distributor for
U.S. firms: Sol-Ar-Tile Inc.,
Solartor, Helio-Thermus, Crystal
Solar Energies, Solar Usage Now.
Also these Canadian firms:
Watershed Energy Systems,
Future Resources and Energy Ltd.

SOLAR CENTRE CANADA
47 John Cabot Way
Toronto, Ont. M3N 2T5
(416) 743-3361
Suppliers of Champion solar
furnace.

HARNETT & NORTH
Box 2952, 504 - 16th St.
Thunder Bay, Ont. P7B 2R8
Jim Harnett (807) 344-9601
Distributes Nortec collectors and
components.

**HALTON SOLAR
STRUCTURES LIMITED**
R.R.2, Trafalgar Road
Georgetown, Ont. L7G 4S5
Wray Gibson (416) 877-3859
Heating, plumbing and electrical
contractors. Supply Lennox water
heaters, Champion solar furnaces,
Raypak pool and domestic water
heaters.

ENERGY TECHNIQUES
Box 381, Station A
Rexdale, Ont. M6W 5L4
W.J. McKenna (416) 675-1062
Supply solar equipment for pool
hot water, space heating; solar
heat pumps; Raypak products.

EFSTONLINE INC.
3500 Bathurst Street
Toronto, Ont. M6A 2C6
Evan Efston (416) 787-4584
Supplier of Silicon solar panels
and Solarex products. Literature
on solar projects available.

GO SOLAR SERVICES
3258 Flanagan Cres.
Mississauga, Ont. L5C 2M5
John Guttridge (416) 276-2485
Supply and install Fafco
swimming pool solar heating
system. Manufacture and install
Solarcraft control and monitoring
devices.

SUNWORKS
Box 547
Hawkesbury, Ont. K6A 2Y2
Denis Fortin (613) 632-6777
General contractor, sales and
installation of complete systems
for pool, domestic hot water and
space heating. Sales of solar
panels, pumps, controls, etc.

TRANTER CANADA
6700 Finch Avenue West
Rexdale, Ont. M9W 5P5
Sales Dept. (416) 675-1210
Distribute Tranter Inc. absorber
plates.

HOKE CONTROLS LTD.
2240 Speers Road
Oakville, Ont. L6L 2X8
Sales Dept. (416) 827-9807
Supply Gyrolok flareless tube
fittings.

NORDEL INTERIORS LTD.
336 Wellington Rd. S.
London, Ont. N6C 4P7
J.G. Norris (519) 672-3440
Supply and install Solar-X
reflective film for windows.

**TORONTO SOLAR
ENERGY LIMITED**
2411 Dundas St. West
Toronto, Ont. M6P 1X3
(416) 536-7882
Multi-purpose source, offering
various types of wood stoves,
energy saving heat controls, hot
water radiators and liquid and air
type collectors, as well as storage
systems. Retail store.

**BENNET & WRIGHT
(EASTERN) LIMITED**
47 Cranfield Road
Toronto, Ont. M4B 3H7
John Hutt (416) 751-5111
Mechanical contractors providing
multi-trade installations for
domestic and industrial
commercial sectors.

**HOLMES & HOLMES
ASSOCIATES LIMITED**
79 Mercer Street
Chatham, Ont. N7M 4A9
Ken Holmes (519) 351-2057
Trained electrician specializing in
the installation of solar collectors.

**WESRON MECHANICAL
LIMITED**
Box 185
Sarnia, Ont. N7T 7H9
Ron Latta (519) 337-2691
Install Lennox equipment.

**ENERGY CONVERSIONS
COMPANY**
216 Albany Avenue
Toronto, Ont. M5R 3C6
Arthur Jacobs (416) 535-1550
Install energy saving devices in
heating/ventilation and
refrigeration/heat pump systems
for industrial and commercial
sector; development of solar
energy hardware.

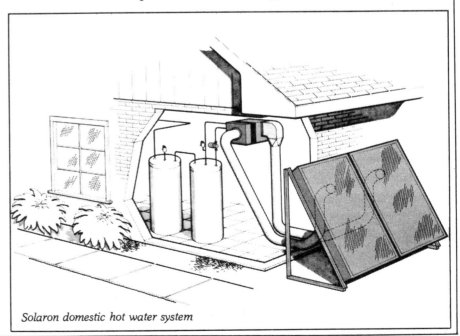

Solaron domestic hot water system

AIRFLOW DEVELOPMENT (CANADA) LTD.
376 Enford Road
Richmond Hill, Ont. L4C 3G1
Brian Cornwall (416) 884-1191

Source for supply/testing equipment, including solarimeters, radiometers and sunshine recorders.

DOUGLAS ENGINEERING COMPANY
Box 5500
Don Mills, Ont. M3C 2X2
J. Whiteside (416) 495-1400

Distributors of the British-made Myson circulator pump ($120—$200).

CONSERVAL ENGINEERING INC.
364 Supertest Road
Downsview, Ont. M3J 2M2
John Hollick (416) 661-7057

Solaron (from Colorado) and Suntrac air collectors.

CHEMPLAST INC.
2450 Dunwin Drive
Mississauga, Ont. L5L 1J9
Bob Bowman (416) 828-2100

Supply greenhouse and solar collector glazing, including: DuPont, Teflon and Martin Processing Lumar film.

H.G. FRANCIS & SONS LIMITED
508 Gladstone Avenue
Ottawa, Ontario K1R 5P1
Bill Francis (613) 232-2601

Mechanical contractors install solar systems and components. Lines carried: Lennox Solar collectors, Lennox Solarmute domestic hot water systems; Solaron collectors and systems; swimming pool systems.

FIRST CO-OPERATIVE SOLAR CO. LIMITED
R.R.2
Peterborough, Ont. K9J 6X3
Ernie Jenkins (705) 745-9480

Facilitates applications of solar heating through workshops, technical advice, materials, procurement and skills exchange and advice. Solar heating kit for swimming pools. Initiation fee of $1.00. Shares available for $10 which must be purchased before an individual can buy materials.

EDMUND SCIENTIFIC PRODUCTS
3500 Bathurst St.
Toronto, Ont. M6A 2C6
(416) 787-4584

Source of components and kits for solar demonstration experiments, as well as small size panels, books and an array of photovoltaic gadgetry.

HABITAT RESOURCES
2500 Princess Street
Kingston, Ont. K7L 4W2
(613) 542-1134

Grumman and Solex solar lines. Sells systems and components. Domestic hot water heaters, as well as industrial components for space heating.

ENVIROTRON SOLAR LIMITED
7290 Torbram Road
Rexdale, Ont. L4T 3T8
(416) 677-7762

Primarily concerned with swimming pool heating (Fafco components) but also offering domestic water and space heating systems.

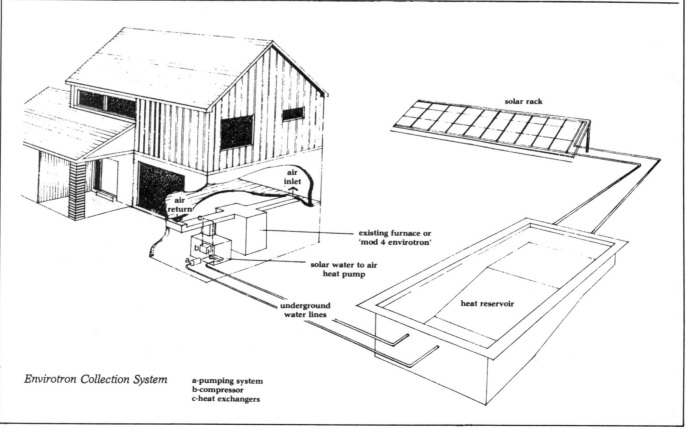

Envirotron Collection System

a-pumping system
b-compressor
c-heat exchangers

Designers

CONSERVAL ENGINEERING INC.
364 Supertest Road
Downsview, Ont. M3J 2M2
(416) 661-7057

Solar designs—residential and commercial do-it-yourself designs.

ALLEN DRERUP WHITE
334 King Street E. Studio 505
Toronto, Ont. M5A 1L7
(416) 368-2821

Designers-builders, consultants, energy conservation and solar heating. Active and passive solar energy. Industrial, commercial and domestic.

HIGHLANDS ENERGY CENTRE
R.R.5
Orangeville, Ont. L9W 2Z2

Engineering, design and marketing services in all areas of renewable energy and energy conservation equipment.

EXPERIMENTAL ENGINEERING EQUIPMENT LTD.
Box 880, 8 Centre Street
Niagara-on-the-Lake, Ont.
L0S 1J0
W.E. Jones (416) 468-7560

Consulting engineers for total energy systems, especially in northern latitudes. This firm also offers an educational demonstration flat plate collector.

SUN-SENSE
348 Piccadilly Street
London, Ontario N6A 1S7
Bill Smith (519) 438-8559

Design and installation of solar heating systems and components.

STONEYBROOKE SOLAR SYSTEMS LIMITED
239 Lisgar Avenue
Tillsonburg, Ont. N4G 4N3
George Balpatoky
(519) 842-8080

Design and construction of solar heated homes. Supply services and equipment for solar hot water heating and solar heated swimming pools.

Conserval Engineering

CLEMANN, LARGE, PATTERSON & ASSOC.
1770 Courtwood Cres.
Ottawa, Ontario K2C 2B5
John Bekolay (613) 224-8090

Mechanical and electrical engineers with in-house computer-aided design.

VERNON CLARK
551 Knights Hill Road
London, Ontario N6J 3A1
(519) 686-9701

Construction, life cycle and maintenance cost consultant.

CHORLEY & BISSET LTD.
Box 428
London, Ontario N6A 4W1
Paul Monaghan (519) 679-8660

Consulting engineer doing analysis and design of solar heating and cooling systems. Energy management studies.

CHAPPLE ENGINEERING LIMITED
Box 623
Haliburton, Ontario K0M 1S0
W.C. Stetham (705) 457-1473

Consulting mechanical engineers —retrofitting of existing systems with solar systems.

CHAPMAN AND WALKER, ARCHITECTS
416 Moore Avenue
Toronto, Ontario M4G 1C8
(416) 425-1223

Design of buildings which incorporate passive and active solar systems.

CANADIAN ASTRONAUTICS LTD.
Suite 201, 1024 Morrison Dr.
Ottawa, Ont. K2H 8K7
Ronald Buckingham
(613) 820-8280

Solar system design and performance analysis.

CAIREMUS MARKUS, ARCHITECT/PLANNER
Suite 309, 195 Kennedy Rd. S.
Brampton, Ontario L6W 3H2
(416) 453-4325

Design and engineering of liquid type solar systems, retrofitting included.

BOLGON & ARMSTRONG ARCHITECTS
61 Curlew Drive
Don Mills, Ont. M3A 2P8
G.W. Armstrong (416) 445-6840

Design, planning and co-ordination of buildings with solar heating systems.

S.B. BERTLES
2050 Naskapi Drive
Ottawa, Ont. K1J 8M3
(613) 741-5037

Design of heating systems for retrofitting, new domestic systems and swimming pool systems.

BEINHAKER/IRWIN ASSOCIATES
6th Floor, 40 University Ave.
Toronto, Ont. M5J 1T1
Alan Seymour (416) 862-0450

Architecture, engineering, planning consultants.

ALLIED MECHANICAL
331 Elgin Street
Ottawa, Ontario K2P 1M5
John Rasmussen (613) 234-7117

Design and installation of solar heating systems.

JOE SOMFAY, ARCHITECT
480 Washington St.
Salem, Ontario N0B 1S0
(519) 846-0251

Professor of architecture at University of Waterloo. Designer of low-cost solar residences.

SOLSAVE INC.
33 Lincoln Green Drive
Markham, Ont. L3P 1R6
Jeff Hapson (416) 294-9366

Computerized design services.

SOLAR ENERGY STRUCTURES
279 Eglinton Avenue East
Toronto, Ontario M4P 1L3
A.A. Goldes (416) 486-0911

Engineers offering custom plans for new and retrofitted residential solar systems; energy library open to public.

SOLAR CONSTRUCTION LIMITED
Hazelglen Plaza
Kitchener, Ontario N5M 2A2
Gary MacKinnon (519) 743-1483

Designs and constructs solar buildings.

WESLEY SWIFT
Apt. 2, 157 Second Avenue
Ottawa, Ontario K1S 2H6
(613) 238-2578

Consultant to architects and builders of active, passive and hybrid domestic systems. Systems analysis.

TOWNSEND, STEFURA AND BALESHTA
255 Larch Street
Sudbury, Ont. P3B 1M2
O.J. Baleshta (705) 675-3383

Architects.

TILLMANN AND LAMB, ARCHITECTS/PLANNERS
318 Wolfe Street
London, Ontario N6B 2C5
Wilfrid B. Lamb (519) 672-1440

Design of buildings integrating solar collectors and energy storage components.

TAYLOR, RONEY KAMERMANS
Box 500
Gilmour, Ont. K0L 1W0
(613) 474-2302

General building service—passive solar and energy conserving designs. Also simple active air systems using rock storage.

SOLARCH
22 John Street
Willowdale, Ont. M2P 1H2
T. MacSweeney (416) 225-2820

Contractors offering architectural design and installation service.

SOLAR CENTURY SALES INC.
53 Big Red Avenue
Agincourt, Ont. M1V 1N8
V. Lasch (416) 292-9400

Design and install Aquasol solar swimming pool systems.

SHELTER CONSTRUCTION AND DESIGN LIMITED
R.R.1
Glencairn, Ont. L0M 1K0
Jeremy Jenkins (705) 466-5721
or (416) 251-2115

Design of energy-efficient houses, design and install large-scale storage tanks. Specialized insulation installer—urethane foam.

SCANADA CONSULTANTS
436 MacLaren Street
Ottawa, Ont. K2P 0M8
Chris Milne (613) 236-7179

Residential solar design and applications; feasibility and cost-benefit engineering on active and passive systems.

TYMURA SOLARDESIGNERS
Hilldale Road
Thunder Bay, Ont. P7B 5N1
(807) 767-8254

Designers of passive, active and hybrid solar buildings.

Northern solar home by Tymura design, showing a hybrid system of active panels and passive solar collection via south-facing windows.

PROCTOR AND REDFERN LTD.
75 Eglinton Ave. E.
Toronto, Ont. M4P 1H3
Allan Brass (416) 486-5225

Mechanical, electrical, structural and architectural services for use in design of solar heating or cooling installations.

PIATROWSKI ENGINEERING LTD.
Box 524, 1281 Cassells St.
North Bay, Ont. P1B 4B8
(705) 472-2536

Mechanical/electrical design for solar heating.

OTTAWA VALLEY CEDAR HOMES LTD.
1581 Carling Avenue
Ottawa, Ont. K1Z 7M3
D. Ryan (613) 725-3177

Custom-designed homes with solar heating systems, plus system design and retrofit installation; suppliers for Solector and Solartech systems.

REID, CROWTHER AND PARTNERS LTD.
220 Duncan Mill Road
Don Mills, Ont. M3B 3J5
E.B. Wong (416) 445-2004

Consulting engineers offering computerized modelling for energy conservation in HVAC systems.

DFA ENGINEERING LTD.
200 Adelaide St. W.
Toronto, Ont. M5H 1W7
W.D. Aitken (416) 361-1588

Mechanical/electrical consulting engineers offering solar engineering design and installation.

MIDDLETON ASSOCIATES
Suite 404, 980 Yonge St.
Toronto, Ont. M4W 2J9
Joan Hayes (416) 961-5136

Consulting services in solar energy including market surveys, economic analyses and industrial development.

GORD MEUSER DESIGN
R.R. 3
Wheatley, Ont. N0P 2P0
(519) 825-4630

Design and construction of solar homes.

MECHANICAL CONSULTANTS WESTERN LTD.
Suite 516
207 Queens Quay West
Toronto, Ont. M5J 1A7
G.C. Bellamy (416) 363-2448

Consulting engineers offering services in mechanical and electrical building systems designs.

KINGSTON SOLAR SYSTEMS LIMITED
1085 Princess St.
Kingston, Ont. K7L 1H3
Don Sleeth (613) 549-4041

Design and installation of solar systems. Fafco pool collectors, Solaron air collectors.

WILSON H. KERR
Apt. 807, 150 Mary Street
Chatham, Ont. N7L 4V2
(519) 354-4127

Solar heating system design.

E. JENKINS
R.R. 2
Peterborough, Ont. K9J 6X3
(705) 745-9480

Architectural technologist/ interior designer providing construction details for space and water heating systems.

HORVATH AND ASSOCIATION
11 Laurie Shepway
Willowdale, Ont. M2J 1X7
John A. Horvath (416) 497-9761

Designers and developers of solar-assisted heat pump systems (air and water source), and associated hardware etc. Building designs for passive systems.

HOOPER AND ANGUS ASSOCIATES LIMITED
Suite 402, 980 Yonge Street
Toronto, Ont. M4W 2J9
Stuart Angus (416) 961-4151

Consulting mechanical engineers specializing in cost-effective energy conserving designs and computer simulation programmes for system performance.

ECE GROUP
205 Lesmill Road

Don Mills, Ont. M3B 2V1
Jack Chisvin (416) 449-1030
Solar system design and energy conservation studies.

SUNDANCE CONTRACTING
R.R.3 Yarker, Ont. K0K 3N0
David O'Connell (613) 358-2906
Solar design services, installation and energy-efficiency consultation.

JOHN HIX, ARCHITECTS AND PLANNERS
207 Queen's Quay W.
Toronto, Ont. M5J 1A7
(416) 861-1085

Design of energy-conserving, active, passive and hybrid solar housing and buildings, solar greenhouses. Some experience with underground design.

HIGHLANDS ENERGY SYSTEMS LIMITED
70 First Street
Orangeville, Ont. L9W 2E5
Ben Tripp (519) 941-5041

Engineering design and supply of energy-efficient houses, including solar heating systems.

HELIX
7 Whiteburn Cres.
Ottawa, Ont. K2H 5K5
Ron White (613) 829-0798

Design and supply passive and active solar systems, especially hot water and pool heating.

BRUCE D. GOUGH
20 Rupert Street
Ottawa, Ont. K1S 3S3
(613) 235-6865

Passive solar advocate/design.

ENERGY NORTH INTERNATIONAL LTD.
1570 Liverpool Court
Ottawa, Ont. K1B 4L2
Jay Jayaraman (613) 731-1084
Design and installation of solar systems and components.

ECODOMUS DEVELOPMENTS
Box 4061, Station E
Ottawa, Ont. K1S 2L0
Rein Soosaw (613) 238-2243
Passive solar design and construction services.

DSMA ATCON LIMITED
4195 Dundas St. West
Toronto, Ontario M8X 1V4
Jim White (416) 239-3011

Offers systems analysis,
component design and
development and solar system
computer models.

**RAYMOND MORIYAMA
ARCHITECTS & PLANNERS**
32 Davenport Road
Toronto, Ont. M5R 1H3
Doug Lorriman (416) 925-4484

Architectural and planning
services.

FOG-RUN DESIGN
Burnstown, Ont. K0J 1G0
(613) 432-3901

Architectural and design service
oriented toward smallness,
appropriate technology and
alternate energy systems.

**ADVANCED IDEAS
MECHANICS**
Box 48
Hyde Park, Ont. N0M 1Z0
Gary Johnson (519) 473-0638

Design and installation of solar
greenhouses, energy efficient
swimming pool enclosures,
custom designed solar houses.

CYTECHNICS LTD.
41 Ridgefield Cres.
Ottawa, Ont. K2H 6S3
H.D. Halverson (613) 828-4277

Design and modification of solar
systems and equipment.

**COWLEY CONSULTANTS
LIMITED**
Suite 5, 4480 Chesswood Dr.
Downsview, Ont. M3J 2B9
J. Cowley (416) 635-1678

Design of complete solar systems.

**UNIVERSITY OF WESTERN
ONTARIO**
Faculty of
Engineering Science
London, Ont. N6A 5B9
R.K. Swartman (519) 679-3332

Engineering design and analysis of
solar heating systems.

AMHERST II
R.R. 4
Perth, Ont.

Hans Simms
Energy efficient housing.

Contact

SESCI Barrie Chapter
Technology Division
Georgian College
401 Duckworth Street
Barrie, Ontario L4M 3X9
Margaret Arthur (705) 737-4336

SESCI Kent Chapter
Apt. 807, 150 Mary Street
Chatham, Ont. N7L 4V2
W. Kerr (519) 354-4127

SESCI Kingston Chapter
Box 153, Station A
Kingston, Ont. K7M 6R1
Don Sleeth (613) 549-4040

SESCI Mississauga Chapter
2222 Belfast Cr.
Mississauga, Ont. L5K 1N9
T. Gruner (416) 822-4111

SESCI London Chapter
Box 2220, Station A
London, Ont. M6A 4E3
Peter Shaw (519) 433-3418

SESCI Ottawa Chapter
Physics Dept.
Algonquin College
Lees Avenue Campus
Ottawa, Ont. K1S 0C5
Wes Swift (613) 237-8142

SESCI Peterborough Chapter
250 Aberdeen Avenue
Peterborough, Ont. K9H 2W9
E. Jenkins (416) 360-1700

SESCI Sarnia Chapter
1934 Lombardy Drive
Sarnia, Ont. N7S 2E2
Nick Wistinghause (519) 542-2229

**SESCI
Thunder Bay Chapter**
Hilldale Road
Thunder Bay, Ont. P7B 5N1
Robert Jones (807) 577-4868

SESCI Toronto Chapter
Box 396, Station D
Toronto, Ont. M6P 3J9
Bob Argue (416) 762-8616

SESCI Windsor-Essex Chapter
Dept. of Chemical Engineering
University of Windsor
Windsor, Ont. N9B 3P7
Ronald DeMers (519) 945-6322

SOLAR ENERGY STRUCTURES
279 Eglinton Ave. E.
Toronto, Ont. M4P 1L3
A.A. Goldes (416) 486-0911

**RYERSON POLYTECHNICAL
INSTITUTE**
50 Gould Street
Toronto, Ont. M5B 1E8
H. (Ken) Burkhardt
(416) 595-5071

Literature, information and education
on solar; research on absorbing
surfaces; courses on collector design;
library contains books, journals,
pamphlets.

**ALTERNATIVE ENERGY
RESOURCE CENTRE**
Sheridan College
Box 7500
Brampton, Ont. L6V 2M7
A.J. McKegney (416) 459-7533

Information and education on
alternative energy sources.

**ALTERNATE FORMS
OF ENERGY**
IBM Country Club
Box 245
Markham, Ont. L3P 3J7
Serge Tenthorey (416) 443-4184

Research and evaluation of alternative
forms of energy including solar.

CALIENTE SUN SYSTEMS
140 Stewart Street
Ottawa, Ont. K1N 6J5
Geoff Chrysler (613) 235-7805

Information and education on
available solar equipment.

**CANADIAN SOLAR
INDUSTRIES ASSOCIATON**
601 Milner Avenue
Scarborough, Ont. M1B 1M8
F. Snape (416) 292-5161

Newsletter: Government lobby.

ENERGY PROBE
43 Queens Park Cres. E.
Toronto, Ont. M5C 2C3
Jan Marmorek (416) 978-7014

Lobbyists and activists in the field of
renewable energy, including solar.
Publish "Renewable Energy
Handbook." Energy library open to
public.

MICHAEL GLOVER
Renewable Energy Consultant
44 Dufferin Road

Ottawa, Ont. K1M 2A8
(613) 741-3304

Consultant on renewable energy.

ENERGY RESEARCH GROUP
Room 218
C.J. MacKenzie Building
Carleton University
Colonel By Drive
Ottawa, Ontario K1S 5B6
J.T. Rogers or J. Lukasiewicz
(613) 231-2652

Carleton faculty members co-ordinating research on energy utilization in Canada.

ESM ENERGY SYSTEMS MANAGEMENT LIMITED
9 Runnymede Cr.
London, Ont. N6G 1Z7
M.J. Ash (519) 471-4463

Research, development, design and evaluation for solar heating.

GIFFELS ASSOCIATES LTD.
30 International Blvd.
Rexdale, Ont. M9W 5P3
Eric Hoel (416) 675-5950

Engineering studies, research, design of solar space and water heating systems, energy analyses.

PROF. F.H. THEAKSTON
School of Engineering
University of Guelph
Guelph, Ontario
Lucy McNally (519) 824-4120

Research to determine potential of solar in agriculture: space heating, grain drying, hot water heating, etc.

HUMBER COLLEGE OF APPLIED ARTS AND TECHNOLOGY
Box 1900
Rexdale, Ont. M9Z 5L7
Ken Cohen (416) 675-3111

Research and development in energy conservation and solar.

HARRISON DESIGN RESEARCH CORP.
Cavell School
R.R.2
Owen Sound, Ont. N4K 5N4
J.A. Harrison (519) 371-2002

Research and development of solar heating systems.

MIROTEK INTERNATIONAL LIMITED
932 McGowan Road
Scarborough, Ont. M1P 3H6

Advisory service on solar heating systems.

WATERLOO RESEARCH INSTITUTE
University of Waterloo
Waterloo, Ont. N2L 3G1

Research and development of flat-plate collectors and packed bed low-temperature storage systems; testing of absorptivity and emissivity of collector surfaces.

THE CARDIC PROJECT
56 Queen St., Box 310
St. Catharines, Ont. L2R 6V3
(416) 685-4211

Conservation and alternate resource development in Canada. Designed and constructed a passively heated solar home at Port Severn, Ont. Public viewing.

DAVIS, ERYOU & ASSOCIATES LTD.
2540 Sheffield Road

Proof that solar design can be accomplished by amateurs, this residence was constructed as a YMCA project and is open to the public in Port Severn, Ontario.

Ottawa, Ont. K1B 3V7
W.R. Davis (613) 746-3760

Research, development, design and installation of solar systems; system monitoring and computer simulation.

SAULT COLLEGE OF APPLIED ARTS AND TECHNOLOGY
443 Northern Avenue
Sault Ste. Marie, Ont. P6B 4J3
P. Hryhorchuk (703) 949-2050

Research on solar domestic hot water heating.

DR. J.K.S. WAN
Department of Chemistry
Queen's University
Kingston, Ont. K7L 3N6
(613) 547-2661

Research into low-temperature solar heat storage.

TRENDSEEKER ASSOCIATES
Box 13024
Kanata, Ontario K2K 1X3
E. Billowes (613) 592-4206

Engineering consultants doing research and development in low-cost solar panel production.

CANADIAN SUN SYSTEMS LIMITED
R.R.1
Campbellville, Ont. L0P 1B0
Leo R. Dorbeck (416) 854-2178

Engineering company developing evacuated concentrating collector.

ONTARIO RESEARCH FOUNDATION
Sheridan Park
Mississauga, Ont. L5K 1B3
Graham Northgate (416) 822-4111

A research laboratory for testing solar collectors, designing solar products, evaluating materials and monitoring systems.

ACRES CONSULTING SERVICES LIMITED
5259 Dorchester Road
Niagara Falls, Ont. L2E 6W1
D.L.R. Cronin (416) 354-3831

Feasibility studies, design, construction supervision, project management, research and development on solar systems.

OKINS, LEIPCIGER, CUPLINSKAS, KAMINKER AND ASSOCIATES LIMITED
1 Valleybrook Drive
Don Mills, Ont. M3B 2S7
E.L. Cuplinskas (416) 445-8255
Consulting engineers offering computing services, including complete in-house solar software,

design of solar systems, feasibility studies, research studies and reports.

LEE ELKEN BECKSTEAD FAIR, ARCHITECTS
207 Queen's Quay West
Toronto, Ont. M5J 1A7
(416) 364-9458

Research and design of solar heating systems.

BRITISH COLUMBIA Manufacturers

SOLARSYSTEMS INDUSTRIES LTD.
1177 N. Horseshoe Way
Richmond, B.C. V7A 4S5
(604) 271-2621

E.W. Hoffman runs one of Canada's most reputable solar companies, producing flat plate collectors (water type), storage tanks and differential thermostats. Hoffman says that Solarsystems is about to introduce a "state of the art" collector, "using low iron-content glass, aluminum frame, copper absorber and black chrome selective coating.

Solarsystems collectors are noteworthy for their size (the largest being 4 by 24 feet) and the comparatively low cost per square foot. Prices run from $14.90 to $18.60 per square foot. To augment solar space and water heating systems, Solarsystems also manufactures a Watergrate, for replacement in a fireplace. The water is circulated through the grate's steel tubular frame and piped to storage or through heating radiators elsewhere in the house. Various size models range in price from $148 to $479, with custom designed units available upon request. Send $2.00 for Canada's most comprehensive solar and alternative energy catalogue.

Watergrate fireplace grate in your fireplace will double the efficiency of your fireplace and augment your conventional heating system. It will distribute your fireplace heat throughout your entire home and reduce your heating costs. It will store the surplus heat from your fireplace for use during the night or the next day.

The Watergrate Fireplace Water Heating System is an efficient energy

recovery, storage and utilization system. This system makes new fireplaces and converted old fireplaces into efficient energy contributors rather than energy wasters.

The Watergrate unit can be used with water or air house heating system. If used with a storage tank the surplus heat can be stored for use during the night. The Watergrate is ideal for use with Solar Heating Systems. It will provide supplementary heat during periods of poor weather and could replace the conventional furnace.

How Is The Watergrate Installed? The Watergrate can be installed in new or existing steel or masonry fireplaces. It can be supported from the side walls by means of pipe sleeves provided, and the supply and return piping can be hidden in the masonry. In existing fireplaces the Watergrate can be standing on the hearth on the legs provided.

Can The Watergrate Be Used As A Sole Source Of Heat? The Watergrate can be the ideal heating system for well insulated small homes or vacation cottages. Permanent-type antifreeze should be added to systems in homes that are left unused for extended periods.

What If Water Circulation Fails? If water fails to circulate due to equipment failure, the water in Watergrate will boil out and is taken up in the storage expansion space. In pressurized (closed) systems, a relief valve insures against overpressure; non-pressurized (open) systems require no relief valve since they are vented. Care must be taken not to install shut off valves which, if accidentally closed, would lock the pressure in the Watergrate.

Where Can The Necessary Components Be Obtained To Complete The System? Solarsystems Industries Limited stocks all components, such as storage tanks, pumps, differential thermostats, and electric valves which are required for a complete system, and is also the major Canadian supplier of solar heating equipment. Send us a sketch of your present heating systems; we will be glad to advise the best system and quote on all components.

Water Storage Tanks (Fibreglass)
560 U.S. gallons $765
1,028 U.S. gallons $1,148

Differential Thermostats $69 to $98
25,000 Btu Finned Heat Exchanger $359.00

SOL-EN SYSTEMS
28 - 11 Avenue S.
Cranbrook, B.C. V1C 2P1
(604) 426-4621

Manufacturers of the "Heatblaster" flat plate air collector, which measures 30 by 80 inches and sells for $445. This collector is designed specifically for installation in new buildings during roof construction, and the unit has a self contained fan and thermostat. Sol-En is currently designing a hot water collector and, in addition to consulting services, offers a kit for a year-round, double-glazed solar greenhouse. Known as the "Evergreen," the greenhouse comes in two models, priced at $1,200 and $1,500 and measuring 8 by 8 feet and 8 by 12 feet, respectively. Unfortunately, company literature is vague in describing the contents of the kit. Blueprints are available for $8 per set.

ISLAND SOLAR SUPPLY LTD.
2915 Prior Street
Victoria, B.C. V8T 3Y4
(604) 384-0106

New entry in the panel manufacturing business, with what appear to be very low priced collector kits.
Island Solar Supply Panel (4' by 6½') $350
Island Solar Supply Panel Kit $75
Control package: U.L. approved differential thermostats, control valve module, thermistors, pump and air vent-vacuum breaker. $350

HYBRID ENERGY SYSTEMS INC.
Suite 314, 2902 W. Broadway
Vancouver, B.C. V6K 2G8
Michael Davies (604) 734-2375

Manufacturer of the new Hybrid solar panel with aluminum absorber; supply water pumps and assorted hardware.

D.I. KNIGHT & ASSOCIATES LIMITED
Box 583
Barriere, B.C. V0E 1E0
(604) 672-5831

Manufacture and installation of Sun Arch swimming pool enclosure and Sun-Heat collector panels.

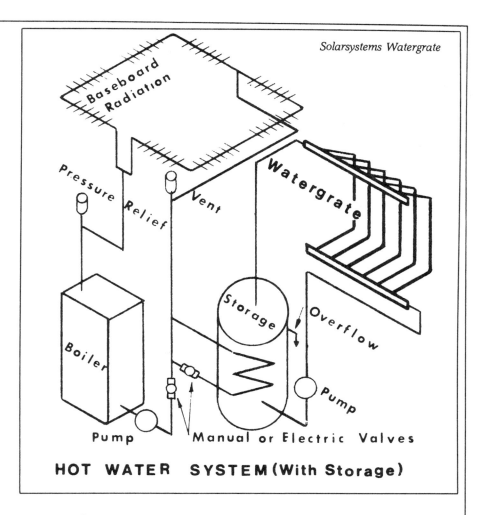

Solarsystems Watergrate

HOT WATER SYSTEM (With Storage)

Suppliers

AIRCON
20273 Industrial Avenue
Langley, B.C. V3A 4K6
Dennis O'Brien (604) 530-2371

Distributes Thermo Solar Solector line of air and liquid collectors, drain-down and closed loop systems.

BARTLE & GIBSON CO. LIMITED
30 Ovens Avenue
New Westminster, B.C. V3L 1Y9
Sales Dept. (604) 522-0631

Grumman collectors and domestic hot water systems and components.

BARTLE & GIBSON CO. LIMITED
960 Yates Street
Victoria, B.C. V8V 3M2
Sales Dept. (604) 382-9218

Grumman collectors and domestic hot water systems and components.

INTERIOR SOLAR ENERGY SYSTEMS INC.
2482 Ross Road
Kelowna, B.C. V1Z 1M1
Sales Dept. (604) 769-4023

Distribute Solarsystems Industries products.

MIROMIT
12280 Vickers Way
Richmond, B.C. V6V 1H9
(604) 278-4119

B.C. firm offering a line of Israeli panels—will ship outside British Columbia.

PACIFIC SOLARTECH
1006-A Victoria Street
Kamloops, B.C. V2C 2C4
(604) 372-7336

Supply and install air solar systems with eutectic salt storage trays.

PATES SUPPLY LIMITED
140 Terminal Avenue
Nanaimo, B.C. V9R 5C5
(604) 754-3311

Supplier of Sunpower Kitset solar water heater and Sunpower swimming pool solar panels.

SUN-TEX INDUSTRIES LTD.
726 Richards Street
Vancouver, B.C. V6B 3A4
(604) 733-6624
Solar-X reflective film for windows.

SOLAIR SYSTEMS INC.
Box 508
Vernon, B.C. V1T 6M4
(604) 545-7982
Distributors and installers of solar systems and components (Fafco, Sunspot, Sunworks, Solaron)

COSY SOLAR PRODUCTS
Box 150
Peachland, B.C. V0H 1X0
Ken Davis (604) 767-9408
Fafco solar heat exchangers for heating swimming pools; heating systems; solar blankets.

INSULATION CITY
4375 Canada Way
Burnaby, B.C. V5G 1J3
Ian Fleming (604) 430-2292
Supply and install systems and components, including Raypak, Fafco, Solarsystems.

SOL-RAY CORP. LTD.
Suite 4, 636 W. Broadway
Vancouver, B.C. V5Z 1G1
(604) 873-1735
Miromit flat plate collectors and domestic hot water systems.

WARCO SPECIALTIES
5057 Regent Street
Burnaby, B.C. V5C 4H4
Nortec collectors and components.

BANTING AND ROSSL ENGINEERED ENERGY SYSTEMS LIMITED
19 - 9th Avenue S.
Cranbrook, B.C. V1C 2L9
Bob Banting (604) 489-4913
Install Solarsystems water systems and Kooten-Air air systems.

CAREFUL ECO SYSTEMS LIMITED
R.R.2
Gibsons, B.C. V0N 1V0
(604) 886-7336
Solarsystems collector panels.

ARK SOLAR PRODUCTS
2666 Quadra St.
Victoria, B.C. V8T 4E4
Solarsystems panels and Fafco pool panels, as well as design advice and installation services.

SOLACE ENERGY CENTRES INC.
2425 Main Street
Vancouver, B.C. V5T 3E1
(604) 879-5258
This retail store is unique in Canada, resembling an alternative energy fair in the variety of offerings (see Biomass, Wind and Waste Lines chapters). In the solar department, Solace offers Thermo-Solar, Fafco, Sol-Way collectors and components, as well as photovoltaic panels, insulating shades and consulting services for using the products they sell.

Thermo-Solar Domestic Hot Water Package $1,599.
Sol-Way Panels $11.75/sq. ft.

The IS High "R" Shade: The IS High "R" Shade has been developed to meet the need for window insulation. It is economical and easily adaptable to a variety of window sizes in new and existing buildings. Resembling an ordinary window shade in appearance, the IS Shade can be used in residential or commercial buildings.
The IS Shade is made up of five layers of plastic film and is installed on the interior side of windows. It rolls up and down in the same way as a regular window shade and is very compact when rolled up. When the shade is pulled down, the five layers separate to form a series of dead air spaces. A unique spacer is used to separate the layers of shade material. The interior layers of the shade are made of metallized film. The room side layer is made of vinyl. This assembly develops a high resistance to heat flow through the shade.
The sides of the IS Shade must be contained in a guide frame made of wood or plastic extrusion. Special seals are used to reduce air movement past the IS Shade.
For IS Shades to be effective, they must be fully drawn every night during the heating season to trap heat energy in the house. By opening them during the day, you

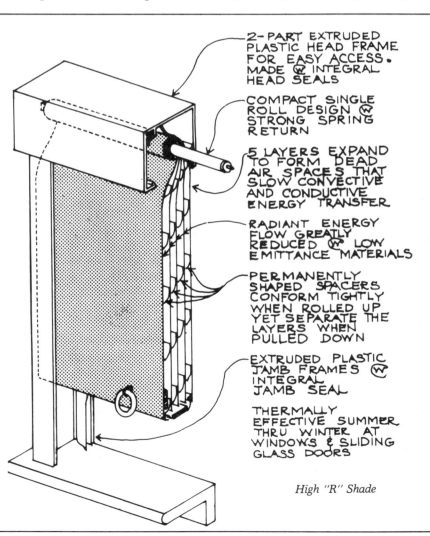

2-PART EXTRUDED PLASTIC HEAD FRAME FOR EASY ACCESS. MADE W INTEGRAL HEAD SEALS

COMPACT SINGLE ROLL DESIGN W STRONG SPRING RETURN

5 LAYERS EXPAND TO FORM DEAD AIR SPACES THAT SLOW CONVECTIVE AND CONDUCTIVE ENERGY TRANSFER

RADIANT ENERGY FLOW GREATLY REDUCED W LOW EMITTANCE MATERIALS

PERMANENTLY SHAPED SPACERS CONFORM TIGHTLY WHEN ROLLED UP YET SEPARATE THE LAYERS WHEN PULLED DOWN

EXTRUDED PLASTIC JAMB FRAMES W INTEGRAL JAMB SEAL

THERMALLY EFFECTIVE SUMMER THRU WINTER AT WINDOWS & SLIDING GLASS DOORS

High "R" Shade

allow the windows that receive sunlight to gain solar energy passively. For new construction large south-facing windows are becoming more common because they collect more free energy than windows in other orientations. During the air conditioning season the IS Shades may be partially or fully drawn in order to reduce direct solar gain.

Insulating Value of the IS High "R" Shade: Although heat loss can never be stopped altogether, it can be slowed down with insulation, which resists heat transfer. The higher the resistance (R) of a material, the slower the heat transfer. Resistance values are additive; if one inch of an insulating material has an R 3, then a two-inch thickness has an R 6.
Dynatech R/D Company has recently performed air-to-air thermal transmittance tests which show that a five-layer IS High "R" Shade in combination with two sheets of glass has an R 15 or better. With one sheet of glass, the overall resistance drops by less than R 1.
This value R 15 may be compared with R 11 for 3½" thickness of glass fiber insulation, R 4 for 3½" of wood, and R 12 for 3" of foam beadboard. The average insulated wall of a wood frame house has an R 14.4; therefore the IS Shade compares in insulating value to a wall.
If you decide to use the IS Shade and your home is heated with oil, your payback could be in two to five years, comparable to the expected payback when adding insulation to your roof. If you have electric heat, payback could be in one to three years because of the higher costs of this form of energy.
$2.75/square foot

High Density Unipanels:
These revolutionary new Solarvoltaic panels mark the dawn of a new era in photovoltaic power. Years ahead of U.S. Department of Energy power-density goals, they are the most efficient and—per unit of surface area—the most powerful terrestrial solar panels ever manufactured. In fact, their power parameters (13 per cent overall conversion efficiency, almost 12 W/ft^2 power density are approximately double what was previously accepted as state-of-the-art. They deliver over a kilowatt-hour per week when installed at a site receiving average U.S. insolation.

These industry-leading Unipanels depart radically from traditional panel construction practices, most obviously in their cell shape: basically, square. Packed densely on the panel substrate, they eliminate the space wasted by traditional round cells and make essentially the entire panel surface active photovoltaic area. In addition, their remarkable 14 to 16 per cent conversion efficiency, achieved by the most advanced Solarex proprietary processes, far surpasses that of cells in previous commercial solar panels.

Features
12- or 24-volt (nominal) output, customer-selectable at panel junction box
Rugged anodized aluminum mounting frame with UL-approved weatherproof junction box
Excellent safety parameters: at least 100 megohms isolation from ground, tested at 1500V
64 computer-designed high-efficiency solar cells series-connected in two twelve-volt strings with:
patented corrosion-resistant Trimet electrodes
photolithographically applied redundant fine-line current collector pattern for enhanced reliability and efficiency
Solarex proprietary tantalum oxide anti-reflective coating
redundant stress-relieved interconnections
P plus back surface field for maximum output voltage
$1,450.00

Designers

THE SOLAR GROUP ARCHITECTS
2425 Main Street
Vancouver, B.C. V5T 3E1

Architect Robert Isaac-Renton and his associate Joan Stapleton offer design services through Vancouver's Solace Energy Centres.

SOLAR APPLICATIONS AND RESEARCH LTD.
3356 West 13th Street
Vancouver, B.C. V6K 2R9
Chris Mattock (604) 733-5631

Consultants offering design and analysis services for active and passive space/water heating systems; photovoltaic systems design; courses and seminars on solar systems design.

CHARLES HAYNES
Suite 6, 765 W. Broadway
Vancouver, B.C. V5J 1J5
(604) 876-9958

Architect specializing in self-help, low-cost solar designs.

DRAWING-ROOM GRAPHIC SERVICES LTD.
Box 86627
North Vancouver, B.C.
V7L 4L2
(604) 689-1841

Authors of Solplan I and Solplan II: catalogues of solar house plans, including design considerations and site selection factors. (See Books)

WARMHOUSE DESIGNS
2808 Graham Street
Victoria, B.C. V8T 3Z4
(604) 382-3464

Conserver building and heating system design and consulting; both passive and active solar heating and wood/solar integration. Solar greenhouses. Offers community solar do-it-yourself workshops in B.C.

JOHN E. STEGMAN
Box 205
Nelson, B.C. V1L 5P9
(604) 352-7646

Design of hot water heating systems, space heating systems and greenhouses—active, passive or hybrid options.

TRIMBLE'S SOLAR HEATING LIMITED
361 - 4th Avenue
Campbell River, B.C.
V9W 3W7
Sales Dept. (604) 287-9674

Design and consulting services; manufacture of solar collectors; component sales.

VICTORIA SOLAR DESIGN CONSULTANTS
2808 Graham Street
Victoria, B.C. V8T 3Z4
Bruce McAllister (604) 382-3464

Residential and small commercial building design utilizing active, passive and hybrid solar systems; exclusive design rights for JB248 Solar Heat System.

JOSEPH ANTHONY LANDSCAPE DESIGNERS
2864 Venables Street
Vancouver, B.C. V5K 2R3
Tony Graziani (604) 251-1447

Consultation and design for active and passive solar units, greenhouses and underground houses.

ROGER W. BRYENTON
956 East 16th Avenue
Vancouver, B.C. V5T 2V9
(604) 873-6080

Consulting engineer offering technical and design service for active and passive systems, greenhouses, heat recovery systems, educational programmes.

THE DESIGN CENTRE
22550 Lougheed Highway
Maple Ridge, B.C. V2X 2V1
Jan T. Virding (604) 467-1612

Architectural technologist designing active and passive solar-heated houses.

DARREL JENSEN ARCHITECT
235 Wilson Street
Victoria, B.C. V9A 3G1
(604) 385-1958

Research, design and practical installations of solar systems.

MARK MAYALL, ARCHITECT
236 East 4th Street
North Vancouver, B.C.
V7L 1H9
(604) 985-7252

Energy conservation including site planning, compact shelter design and passive systems.

ORME AND LEVINSON ARCHITECTS AND PLANNERS
1043 Johnson St.
Victoria, B.C. V8V 3N6
Ben Levinson (604) 382-5125

Design for active and passive solar-heated houses.

H.J. SAALTINK AND ASSOCIATES LTD.
27961 McTavish Road
Mt. Lehman, B.C. V0X 1V0
(604) 856-4982

Engineers specializing in energy-efficient dwellings and solar design.

SKRDLA DESIGN LTD.
13830 - 79th Avenue
Surrey, B.C. V3W 2Y9
Josef Skrdla (604) 594-6562

Design and develop solar systems and components, holding tanks and heat collectors.

BYDAND SOLAR CENTRE LIMITED
Box 33744, Station D
Vancouver, B.C. V6J 4L6
Douglas R. Gordon
(604) 731-4171

Design and install active and passive solar systems, including Fafco Inc. pool heating systems. Computerized thermal and economic analysis.

SOLSTICE DESIGN & CONSTRUCTION LTD.
9191 Ardmore Drive
R.R.2
Sidney, B.C. V8L 3S1
Donald Thompson
(604) 656-1260

Information, installation and design for solar heating of new and existing buildings.

CARLOS A. CASTELLON
1151 Lillooet Road
N. Vancouver, B.C.
V7J 3H7
(604) 988-7342

Building design and retrofit design services.

Contact

SESCI VANCOUVER CHAPTER
504 Davie Street
Vancouver, B.C. V6B 2G4
Terry Lister (604) 591-4412

SESCI VICTORIA CHAPTER
Environmental Centre
Suite 101, 645 Fort St.
Victoria, B.C. V8W 1G2
D. Jensen (604) 388-3103

ECON
1751 Nanaimo Street
Vancouver, B.C. V5N 5C1
Ken Cooper (604) 253-8380

Information and education for public and professional groups.

NORTHERN LIGHTS MAGAZINE
4256 Melrose Street
Port Alberni, B.C. V9Y 1V4

Periodical covering all areas of alternative energy and energy conservation in layman's terms with plans and descriptions for do-it-yourselfers. Write for sample copy.

QUEBEC Manufacturers

NORTHERN SOLAR HEAT
1553 Leprohon Street
Montreal, Quebec H4E 1P1
M. Johnston (514) 769-5806

Source of Nor-Sol liquid collector panels, heat exchangers and storage tanks. Nor-Sol offers solar kits (ask for price list). Double-glazed Twindow glass cover, copper absorber plate.

FIBRATECH INC.
5 Montee des Arsenaux
Box 100
St. Paul l'Hermite, Quebec
J5Z 2N4

Flat plate liquid heating collectors ranging in price from $250 to $400 each, depending on materials used. Glazings offered are glass, acrylic, fibreglass or reinforced plastic. Copper absorber sheet with fibreglass frame and case.

ATLAS ASBESTOS CO.
5600 Hochelaga
Montreal, Quebec H1N 1W1
(514) 259-2531

This firm turns out a panel glazing material known as Filon, consisting of acrylic/polyester resin reinforced with fibreglass and coated with Tedlar film to retard ultraviolet degradation. The material is also sold as Clearlite and promoted as a greenhouse glazing. Company claims 92 per cent light transmittance and long life.

THERMO SOLAR INC.
Div. of Magnetics Intl. Ltd.
2915 Boul. Pitfield
St. Laurent, Quebec H4S 1L6
(514) 337-2264

Producers of the Solector line of liquid heating collectors, priced in the range of $148 for 11 square feet of collector. Glazed with glass, copper absorber plate and extruded aluminum frame. Thermo-Solar says its collectors are designed for producing heat up to 240 degrees (F), and can be employed for water heating, space heating, low temperature steam

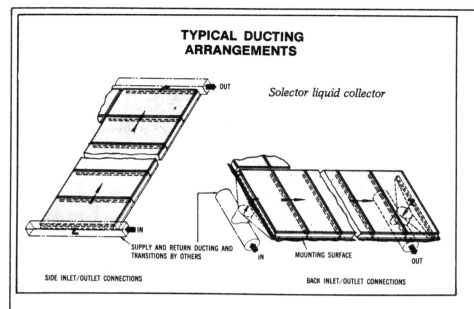

TYPICAL DUCTING ARRANGEMENTS

Solector liquid collector

SUPPLY AND RETURN DUCTING AND TRANSITIONS BY OTHERS

SIDE INLET/OUTLET CONNECTIONS

OUT

IN

MOUNTING SURFACE

IN

OUT

BACK INLET/OUTLET CONNECTIONS

production and distillation. Information available in both French and English.
Also offered: Solector Pak 1000 (Complete domestic hot water system to preheat water for conventional heater. Basic system sells for about $1,500.)
Solector Air-Cooled Panels (Prices on request.)

THERMAX CORPORATION
Box 968, Station B
Montreal, Quebec H3B 3K5
Colin Kerr (514) 284-9230

Developers of high efficiency flat plate collector.

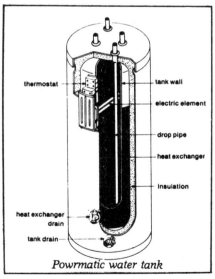

thermostat

tank wall

electric element

drop pipe

heat exchanger

insulation

heat exchanger drain

tank drain

Powrmatic water tank

POWRMATIC OF CANADA LIMITED
709 Leveille Street
Terrebonne, Quebec J6W 1Z9
N. Fleisler (514) 471-6691

Manufacturers of Powrmatic stone-lined, heavily insulated water tanks for storing solar-heated domestic water. Each comes with built-in copper heat exchanger and thermostatically controlled back-up heating element (electric). Tank sizes from 48 to 144 gallons.

Suppliers

MARCEL & HUBERT DUFRESNE INC.
1150 Galt East
Sherbrooke, Quebec J1G 1Y5
Marcel Dufresne (819) 563-5310

Manufacturers of the new Air Sopak 77 Solar Furnace, which serves to handle heated air supplied by air heating panels. Unit comes assembled, wired and ready for installation. Price: $1,980. This firm also offers design consultation and serves as a distributor for domestic hot water systems, pool heaters and other goods.

SOLERCO LIMITED
Box 211
Ayer's Cliff, Quebec J0B 1C0
(819) 836-5935

One of the country's largest suppliers of solar components, including all necessary parts for the construction of air or water heating systems. Solerco also offers glazings for greenhouses, along with necessary neoprene-ringed sealing screws for installation. Send $2.00 for 48-page catalogue (refundable with first purchase).

SOLAR WATER HEATER TANKS
65 gal. $416.41
80 gal. $526.58
120 gal. $658.38
(Add $37.63 for electric back-up element.)

AIR-SO-PAK SOLAR AIR HANDLER
$1,500

KALWALL SUN-LITE GLAZING
Fibreglass reinforced polymer sheet for collector covers. Priced as follows:

Regular	1 to 199 sq. ft.
.025" Thickness	.83/sq. ft.
.040"	.91/sq. ft.
Premium	
0.25" Thickness	.93/sq. ft.
.040"	1.12/sq. ft.
.060"	1.30/sq. ft.

SUN-LITE GLAZING PANELS

Sun-Lite Glazing Panels consist of two flat sheets of .040 Sun-Lite Premium II bonded together under controlled heat and pressure to an extruded I-beam spacer. This spacer is utilized for the perimeter frame as well as the internal cross support. The panels come in three sizes:

Panel A
½" x 23-9/16" x 95½" $57.21
Panel B
½" x 33¾" x 75-5/8" $65.19
Panel C
1½" x 47-3/8" x 95½" $129.57

ATELIER SOLAIRE ENR.
Div. of De Luxe Equipment
8010 Jarry St. E.
Anjou, Quebec H1J 1H5
Michel Lesperance (514) 354-1155

Suppliers and installers of a wide range of solar systems and components. Lines carried include: Solar Industries Aqua-thermal Accumulator; Solar Energy Products flat plate collector and components, Sunfired open/closed hot water systems and solar pool heating systems; greenhouses also available.

W.G. McDONALD CONSTRUCTION CO. LTD.
Parc Industrial Richelieu
133 Jean Proulx
Hull, Quebec J8Z 1T4
W.G. McDonald (819) 770-9627

Supply and installation of Watershed air collectors.

PLASTISER INC.
4171 rang Ste-Rose
Lourdes de Joliette, Quebec
J0K 1K0
J.F. Goulet (514) 759-3401

Suppliers of Coroplast, Qualex, Monsanto, CIL and Celloflex greenhouse glazings.

A. DOW STEAM SPECIALITIES
7469 Trans Canada Highway
North Service Road
St-Laurent, Quebec H4T 1T3
Angus Dow (514) 332-3660

Distributors of Nortec collectors and components.

HYDRO-MECHANIQUE
2 Boul. l'Ormlere, Box 188
Neufchatel, Quebec G2C 1B9
Camille Cauchon (418) 842-3662

Distributors of Nortec collectors and components.

FLAMIDOR CORP.
625 Boul. Pierre Bertrand
Vanier, Quebec G1M 2E4
Raymond Beaulieu
(418) 681-7211

Suppliers and installers of Lennox Solarmate domestic hot water systems and Lennox solar collectors in the Quebec City area.

AAF LIMITED
400 Stinson Boulevard
Montreal, Quebec
H4N 2G1
T.W. Rogers (514) 748-6931

U.S.-built EnerCon water-source heat pumps for solar-assisted systems.

ZIMMCOR CO.
2100 Remembrance Road
Lachine, Quebec H8S 1X3
Order Desk (514) 637-5851

Glazing extrusions and aluminum sheets for air system absorber panels.

B.D. WALT CO. LTD.
590 Hodge Street
Montreal, Quebec H4N 2A4
(514) 748-8714

Distributors of Arkla Solaire domestic hot water, space heating and air conditioning systems.

VEPTEC LIMITED
670 Stuart Street
Montreal, Quebec H2V 3H3
Jean Guay (514) 271-8186

Nortec collectors and components.

Designers

LORRAIN GERIN-LAJOIE AND SIMARD
4070 Jean Talon West
Montreal, Quebec H4P 1V5
P. Gerin-Lajoie (514) 731-3556

Involved in solar heating system design and a three-year study of solar-heated apartment buildings.

NORMAN SLATER, ARCHITECT
4845 Sherbrooke St. W.
Montreal, Quebec H4R 1G6
(514) 932-4164

Design of passive and active solar systems.

SNC GROUP
1 Complex Desjardins, Box 10
Desjardins Postal Station
Montreal, Quebec H5B 1C8
M. Schwisberg (514) 282-9551

Design engineering, project management and construction services for solar heating and cooling systems.

SYNERCO SYSTEMS FOR ENERGY CONSERVATION INC.
639 St. Jacques
Granby, Quebec J2G 3P6
Peter Kupin (514) 372-7943

Specializing in the design and installation of complete solar-heated residential and commercial buildings.

SOLARGETICS LIMITED
5767 Plantagenet Street
Montreal, Quebec H3S 2K4
C. Marsolais (514) 738-5520

Design and installation of hybrid solar heating systems.

TANSEY ASSOCIATES
533 Davaar Avenue
Outremont, Quebec H2V 3A7
Peter Tansey (514) 273-3795

Consultants offering solar design and "package deal" services.

PAUL THIBAULT & ASSOCIATES LIMITED
Suite 2, 2675 Marcel Street
St. Laurent, Quebec H4R 1A6
Paul Thibault (514) 337-1838

Design of large scale active and passive solar systems, cost analysis and consultation on systems and components.

S. ALBERT & CO. LTD.
5763 St. Laurent Blvd.
Montreal, Quebec H2T 1T2
A. Stilber (514) 273-6361

Consulting engineers involved in design and installation of solar systems and collectors.

CENTRE DE DEVELOPPEMENT TECHNOLOGIQUE
University of Montreal
Box 6079, Station A
Montreal, Quebec H3C 3A7
E. Bilgen (514) 344-4892

Scientists and engineers offering services in consulting and design.

MICHEL DALLAIRE
Suite 5, 859 Mgr. Grandin
Ste-Foy, Quebec G1V 3X8
(418) 651-7994

Active and passive solar-heated building design.

ECONERGIE LTEE.
Suite 109, 85 St. Charles W.
Longueuil, Quebec J4H 1C5
(514) 670-5400

Consultants specializing in the integration of solar energy storage with existing mechanical systems of a building.

KARLAS IRBITIS
12007 Lachapelle Street
Montreal, Quebec H4J 2M5
(514) 334-5571

Designer of parabolic, sun-tracking solar collector.

Contact

BRACE RESEARCH INSTITUTE
McDonald College
McGill University
Ste. Anne de Bellevue, Quebec
H0A 1C0
Thomas Lauand (514) 457-6580
Ext. 341

Research into low-cost solar systems as well as solar greenhouses. Plans for owner-builder projects.

CLAUDE PARLSEL
9 Avenue Querbes
Outremont, Quebec H2V 3V7
(514) 270-5472

University of Montreal architecture professor providing information on solar heating systems.

AYER'S CLIFF CENTRE FOR SOLAR RESEARCH
Box 344
Ayer's Cliff, Quebec J0B 1C0
(819) 838-4871

This is Nick Nicholson's terrain, with several solar designs in various stages of completion and receiving varying reviews from informed solar energy observers. Nicholson offers publications, workshops and solar energy lectures, at which he excels.

GROUP DE RECHERCHE SUR LES ENERGIES NOUVELLES
Faculte de l'Amenagement
Universite de Montreal
Box 6128
Montreal, Quebec
Roger Camous (514) 363-7556

Information distribution; applied research; design consultation.

SESCI Section Quebecois
Ecole Polytechnique
Box 6079, Station A
Montreal, Quebec H3C 3A7

Roger Drouin (514) 652-8549

MINIMUM COST HOUSING GROUP
School of Architecture
McGill University
Box 6070, Station A
Montreal, Quebec H3C 1G0
W. Rybczynski (514) 392-8021

Research into low cost solar systems.

CENTRE FOR BUILDING STUDIES
Concordia University
1455 de Maisonneuve Blvd. West
Montreal, Quebec H3G 1M8
Dr. M.M. Shapiro (514) 879-5857

Research and development of monitoring and control equipment, solar systems and components; courses at graduate and continuing education levels.

DEPARTMENT OF PHYSICS
Universite de Sherbrooke
Sherbrooke, Quebec
J1K 2R1
Max Krell (819) 565-3586

Studying solar collectors for use in space heating in northern climates.

LES INSTALLATIONS ZONAIR INC.
1234 Rue Cachine'
St-Vincent-de-Paul, Quebec
H7C 2N7
Jean-Yves Phaneuf
(514) 661-5540

Research and development of solar energy systems.

P. FAZIO & ASSOCIATES LTD.
118 Ashington Road
Pointe Claire, Quebec H9R 2Z2
(514) 697-8990

Instrumenting, monitoring and data assessment of solar installations, as well as research into new storage systems.

MPB TECHNOLOGIES INC.
Box 160, 21051 N. Service Road
Ste Anne de Bellevue, Quebec
H9X 3L5
Dr. M.P. Bachynski (514) 457-2035

Research/development on solar systems business and management consulting.

ALBERTA
Manufacturers
SUNDROME SOLAR
32 Klamath Place S.W.
Calgary, Alberta T2V 2J1
Jim Hawkins (403) 278-4424 or
(403) 255-1236

Manufactuers of the Sunscrubber air panel, with Lascolite fibreglass glazing and a light aluminum absorber backing. Prices on request. Available in kit form. The company also offers a demonstration flat plate water

heating collector for classroom use, as well as educational slide packages on various renewable energy subjects.

SUNERGY SYSTEMS LTD.
Seebe, Alberta T0L 1X0
Michael Kerfoot (403) 278-4424

Manufacture and install the Phoenix Solar Greenhouse and do-it-yourself kits.

Suppliers

BARTLE & GIBSON COMPANY LTD.
9840 - 62 Avenue
Edmonton, Alberta T6E 0E3
John Kendall (403) 435-4176

Grumman collectors and domestic hot water systems and components. Design services for pool, space and commercial heating.

SOLARTECH
3902 1A St. S.W.
Calgary, Alberta T2S 1R6
(403) 243-0564

Good source of components for do-it-yourselfers and amateur inventors. Also offers photovoltaic cells, Raypack solar collectors and complete domestic water heating systems in the $2,000 price range. Information package $1.00 Raypak Hot Water Supply Collectors 37½ inches by 82½ inches, Single Glazed $420.00

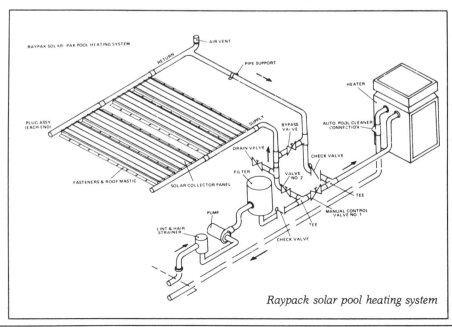

Raypack solar pool heating system

SUN ENERGY ENTERPRISES
379 Norseman Road N.W.
Calgary, Alberta T2K 5N8
Sales Dept. (403) 275-0060
Distributor for Solarsystems Industries products.

BARTLE & GIBSON COMPANY LTD.
1439 - 10th Avenue S.E.
Calgary, Alberta T2G 0X1
Sales Dept. (403) 264-2460
Grumman collectors and domestic hot water systems and components.

THE WOODEN EWE LTD.
Box 1387
Fairview, Alberta T0M 1L0
Mark A. Craft (403) 835-4216
Supplier of solar hardware, glazings, pre-fab collectors.

FARRELL ENGINEERING
5342 Copithorne Rd. N.W.
Calgary, Alberta T2L 0L3
Bill Allen (403) 282-6723
Nortec collectors and components.

FARRELL ENGINEERING
1061 - 109th Street
Edmonton, Alberta
Nortec collectors and components.

SOLAR KING SOLAR CONTROL PRODUCTS (1977) LIMITED
Box 181
St. Albert, Alberta T8N 1N3
Lawrence Ninowsky
(403) 458-2163
Supply and install "Reflecto-Shield" window insulation.

R. M. HARDY AND ASSOCIATES LIMITED
219 - 18th Street
Calgary, Alberta T2E 6J5
D. Empey (403) 272-8761
Installation, retrofitting and monitoring of solar equipment.

Designers

APPROPRIATE DESIGN
Box 181
Midnapore, Alberta T0L 1J0
Graduate architects offering design services for passive solar

systems, do-it-yourself collectors, energy conservation.

REID CROWTHER & PARTNERS LIMITED
Box 5600, Station A
Calgary, Alberta T2H 1X9
A.M. Smith (403) 253-3301
Design services, including integrated solar heating system design.

DIRK AND PRICE ENGINEERING LTD.
207 Wildwood Drive
Calgary, Alberta T3C 3E2
Frank Meriwether
(403) 242-4476
Design and install space heating/cooling systems and hot water heating for commercial, industrial and residential use, including pools.

JAMES F. MACLAREN LIMITED
10240 - 124th Street
Edmonton, Alberta T5N 3W6
D. Bromley (403) 482-7341
Analysis and design of solar heating and energy systems. Offices across Canada.

UNDERWOOD MCLELLAN (1977) LIMITED
11831 - 123 Street
Edmonton, Alberta T5L 0G7
Stanley Hayden (403) 452-6650
Solar heating/cooling systems design.

WIEBE FOREST GROUP LTD.
604 - 24A Street N.W.
Calgary, Alberta T2N 2S4
John Wiebe (403) 283-6658
Design, specifications and working drawings for solar projects; inspectors available for installations.

Contact

TANG LEE
Faculty of Environmental Design
University of Calgary
Calgary, Alberta T2N 1N4
(403) 284-6608
Active solar advocate offering information on energy conservation, solar architectural design, sizing of active solar heating systems.

SESCI
North Alberta Chapter
11047 - 81st Avenue
Edmonton, Alberta T6G 0S3
Katie Benschop (403) 434-6326

SESCI
South Alberta Chapter
Box 204
Grande Prairie, Alberta T8B 3A4
Mark Craft (403) 825-4216

HELIOS HABITAT
Seebe, Alberta T0L 1X0
Michael Kerfoot (403) 264-7062
Information and education about technologies for conserver society, including "Hands on" workshops at a demonstration village; stackwall cabin construction with integrated greenhouse, solar hot water collectors and conservatory.

ALBERTA RESEARCH COUNCIL
11315 - 87 Avenue
Edmonton, Alberta T6G 2C2
Despite all that oil Alberta has this department to supply information and to research renewable energy. They have a comprehensive library on renewable energy, a network of wind and solar monitoring systems and samples of domestic hot water systems.

SASKATCHEWAN Suppliers

SOLAR HEATING LTD.
Box 166
Regina, Sask. S4P 2Z6
J.R. Borden (306) 527-9822
Solar-aire collectors and eutectic salts heat storage systems. Design services in Saskatchewan, B.C. and Alberta.

WESTERN SOLAR SYSTEMS LIMITED
3812 Hill Avenue

Regina, Sask. S4S 0X5
Boris P. Korpan (306) 586-4100

Supply and distribute international Solarthermics and Sun-Trac solar furnaces and collectors.

CONLEY & CO. CONTRACTORS LTD.
205 McDonald St., Box 1008
Regina, Sask. S4P 3B2
(306) 545-7447

Grumman collectors and domestic hot water systems and components.

MECON SALES
Box 1603
Regina, Sask. S4P 3C4
Ron Smith (306) 545-7997

Nortec collectors and components.

SUNWISE ENTERPRISES LTD.
2 Kingsmere Avenue
White City, Sask. S0G 5B0
Terry MacDonald (306) 568-2060

Supply and install Fafco solar heating systems; solar pool blankets.

MECON SALES
437 - 34th St. E., Box 1312
Saskatoon, Sask S7K 0S9
Greg Eyolfson (306) 652-5905

Nortec collectors and components.

Designers

CONCEPT CONSTRUCTION LIMITED
Suite 2, 271 - 2nd Ave. S.
Saskatoon, Sask. S7K 1K8
Keith Funk (306) 242-7035

Keith Funk specializes in the design and construction of rather conventional-looking passive solar homes which have a built-in Trombe heat storage wall. The company will supply working drawings, specification sheets for building projects, and is itself building new solar homes in Saskatchewan and Alberta at an accelerating rate.

SAL R. SOTTILE
Box 192
Lebret, Sask. S0G 2Y0
(306) 332-4836

Architect venturing into energy-conserving building design using solar, wind and biomass systems.

SUNHOUSE
Suite 200
1818 Scarth Street Mall
Regina, Sask. S4P 2G3
Henry Lorenzen (306) 523-4433

Designers and builders of solar pre-fab and custom homes; solar retrofitting. Suppliers of Solar-aire collectors and eutectic salts heat storage system.

Contact

SESCI
Regina Chapter
Box 3959
Regina, Sask. S4P 3R9
Henry Lorenzen (306) 523-4433

SESCI
Saskatoon Chapter
Dept. of Mechanical Engineering
University of Saskatoon
Saskatoon, Sask. S7N 0W0
Greg Schoenau (306) 343-2211

SESCI
Swift Current Chapter
416 Hayes Drive
Swift Current, Sask. S9H 4H9
Dr. H. Davidson (306) 773-4621

DR. ROBERT S. DUMONT
Dept. of Mechanical Engineering
University of Saskatchewan
Saskatoon, Sask. S7N 0W0
(306) 343-5987

Consultation and courses entitled "Energy Conservation and the Use of Solar Energy."

MECHANICAL ENGINEERING DEPARTMENT
University of Saskatchewan
Saskatoon, Sask S7N 0W0
Greg Schoenau (306) 343-2211

Research and development of agricultural solar systems, including grain drying systems, solar collectors for agriculture waste heat greenhouses, air-to-air heat exchangers, active solar system design, passive solar system design.

SED SYSTEMS LIMITED
Box 1464
Saskatoon, Sask. S7K 3P7
J.D. O'Shea (306) 244-0976

Mechanical engineers specializing in the research and development of solar systems utilizing phase-change energy storage systems. Now investigating an ice-making heat pump system for domestic heating.

Trombe wall in action. Consisting of a thick vertical slab of concrete or masonry, it faces south with a covering of glass to trap sunlight. Heat is absorbed in the thermal mass and is vented into the house either by fan or a natural thermosiphon effect.

MANITOBA
Manufacturers

DELTAIR LIMITED
355 Johnson Ave. W.
Winnipeg, Man. R2L 0J2
Bob Krueger (204) 669-6272

This firm makes and sells the
Deltair self-contained air collector
which was first developed in
Alabama. This unit attaches to the
outer wall of the house and hot air
is ducted directly into the home at
the top, while inside air enters the
bottom of the collector. Price on
request.

SOLAR RESEARCH SYSTEMS
345 Higgins Avenue
Winnipeg, Man. R3A 0V4
E.A. Speers (204) 947-1733

Manufacture Sol-Heater swimming
pool heating system. Custom
design.

Suppliers

SOLAR-TECH
951 Thomas Avenue
Winnipeg, Man. R2M 3L5
Wilf Scheuer (204) 669-4208

Raypak collectors, Rho Sigma
controls, Grundfos pumps, Tedlar
glazing, absorber plates, etc;
catalogue available, as well as
design, advice and installation
services.

SUN VALLEY POOL
1421 Erin Street
Winnipeg, Man. R3E 2S9

Distributors of Grumman
collectors, domestic hot water
systems and components.

MECANITEC LIMITED
399 Selkirk Avenue
Winnipeg, Man. R2W 2M3
Jim Phimister (204) 586-8428

Design and install residential hot
water, heating and swimming pool
systems; supply Fafco, Thermo
Solar products, heat pumps and
Barber-Colman controls.

HYDRON-AIRE
1180 Sanford Street
Winnipeg, Man. R3E 2Z9

Nortec collectors and components.

MINT SYSTEMS LTD.
1162 Richard Avenue
Winnipeg, Man. R3E 3J3
Jim Gair (204) 775-8714

Arkla Solaire domestic hot water,
space heating and air conditioning
systems.

Designers

J.D. WELCH
66 Thatcher Drive
Winnipeg, Man. R3T 2L3
(204) 269-1648

Architect designing energy-
conserving buildings, solar energy
systems. Lecturer on solar systems
and buildings. Has retrofitting
experience.

W.L. WARDROP & ASSOCIATES LIMITED
77 Main Street
Winnipeg, Man. R3C 3H1
G. J. Maguet (204) 956-0980

Consulting engineers offering solar
system design.

UNIES LIMITED
1666 Dublin Avenue
Winnipeg, Man. R3H 0H1
Dr. G.K. Yuill (204) 633-6363

Design, research and development
on solar energy.

ROSEISLE BUILDING & DESIGN WORKSHOP
Roseisle, Man. R0G 1V0
John Hockman (204) 452-8964

Design and drawings for active
and passive solar-heated homes,
including owner/contractor-built
air type systems.

NEW PROGRESS CONSTRUCTION LTD.
Suite 2D, 1975 Corydon Ave.
Winnipeg, Man. R3P 0R1
Anand Thawani (204) 489-8869

Expertise on solar heating for
industrial, commercial and
residential applications.

Contact

SOLAR ENERGY SOCIETY OF CANADA INC.
Suite 608, 870 Cambridge St.
Winnipeg, Man. R3M 3H5
(204) 284-3076

Manitoba is hardly a hotbed of solar
industry, but it is the location for
Canada's national solar organization,
SESCI. This loose organization
attempts to promote and develop solar
technology in Canada, as well as
educate the public about renewable
energy. Local chapters exist across the
country and a bimonthly newsletter
entitled *Sol* is sent to all SESCI ·
members. Membership and
subscription, $15.00 per year.

NEW BRUNSWICK
Suppliers

ALLIED INSULATION LTD.
113 Highfield Street
Moncton, N.B. E1C 5NH
(506) 384-1853

Distributes the Solector line of air
and liquid collectors; drain-down
and closed-loop systems from
Thermo-Solar Inc.

J.F. TAYLOR ENTERPRISES
Box 3369, Station B
380 Ridge Row
St. John, N. B. E2M 3Z9
(506) 672-3216

Nortec liquid collectors.

ACADIA SOLAR CENTRE
22 Baig Boulevard
Moncton, N.B. E1E 1C8
(506) 386-2616

Champion solar furnaces, panels
and pool heaters, as well as
installation services.

CITY SOLAR CENTRE
169 Main Street
Fredericton, N.B. E3A 1C6
(506) 472-0458

Fafco pool heating systems and
Champion Solar Furnaces.
Installation service available.

Designers

DESIGN WORKSHOP N.B. LTD.
48 Bonaccord Street
Moncton, N.B. E1C 5K7
(506) 855-1990

Design of both active and passive
solar buildings.

W.H. CRANDELL AND ASSOCIATES (MANAGEMENT) LTD.

1133 St. George Blvd., Box 36
Moncton, N. B. E1C 5K7
Douglas Grass (506) 855-1990

Architects and planners designing active and passive solar buildings.

ADI LIMITED

Box 44
Fredericton, N.B. E3B 4Y2
J.H. Collyer (506) 454-4491

Architectural and engineering firm with expertise in solar applications.

SOLAR BUILDING AND DESIGN LIMITED

Box 219
Shediac, N.B. E0A 3G0
(506) 532-3424

Design and construction of solar systems.

Contact

SESCI
New Brunswick Chapter
569 Canterbury Drive
Fredericton, N.B. E3B 4M6
Nancy McInnis (506) 453-2669

UNIVERSITY OF NEW BRUNSWICK

Dept. of Mechanical Engineering
Frederiction, New Brunswick
Verne Creton (506) 453-4513

Professional engineer and solar energy consultant providing lectures and non-credit course: "Solar Energy for the Layman."

NOVA SCOTIA

Manufacturers

VALLEY ENERGY SYSTEMS

Box 1237, R.R.1
Wolfville, Nova Scotia
B0P 1X0
(902) 542-3344

In addition to selling airtight stoves and composting toilets, this small firm offers its own solar water heating device that takes advantage of direct heat transfer (no heat exchanger or glycol solution). Price: $120. Also offers advice on solar greenhouse construction and heat design analysis.

KERR CONTROLS LTD.

Box 1500
Truro, Nova Scotia B2N 5V2
(902) 895-9281

Now manufacturing a flat plate water heating collector, with a tempered glass cover and copper absorber plate, insulated with high density rigid urethane. Kerr does not sell directly to the public, but rather through a network of distributors.
Kerr Solar Panel 16.25 by 42.75 inches: approx $700/each.
Control Module (Heat Exchanger, diaphragm expansion tank, pressure gauge, automatic differential controller, dual pumps. Made by TACO.) Approx. $1,150.

Suppliers

ENERGY ALTERNATIVES

2 Croft Street, Box 671
Amherst, Nova Scotia
B4H 1B1

One of the few broad-spectrum alternative energy hardware sources in the Maritimes. Thermo-Solar hot water systems, Fafco pool heaters, and two lines of solar and greenhouse glazings. Canadian distributor for a large array of solar components for active and passive systems.

THE KALWALL SOLAR FURNACE (Patent Applied For) Cat. No. 1387 Operation of the Solar furnace is simple . . . efficient!

This drawing shows a typical solar furnace. It consists of a very small space, a "hot box" actually, that is highly insulated on three walls, the floor and the ceiling. The outside "weatherwall" has a solar window (it is strongly recommended that the Kalwall Corporation's Sunwall be used because it transmits solar energy, yet it is highly insulating, shatter-proof and highly impact resistant).

A row of collector storage tubes is positioned close to, and along the entire length of the solar window wall. The more tubes used, the more heat stored—and ultimately transferred to the interior of the building. These tubes are commonly filled with water, but may have other storage media.

For a more efficient solar furnace, solar and heat control curtains are employed. The solar curtain is located between the tubes and the solar wall. At night and on days when there is no sunshine, this curtain is lowered to the floor to increase the insulation at the solar wall. As an alternative, special high solar transmitting heat trap solar windows may be employed. More information on these windows is available from Solar Components.

The Kalwall solar furnace is completed by an interior insulated partition which can be built on the job conventionally, or built with the Kalwall Doublewall Removable Panel System. The partition seals heat stored in the tubes for use when required.

Natural convection currents move the air around the tubes and out of the solar furnace through air vents installed in the partition. A fractional horsepower blower can be installed—and controlled by a thermostat—to increase the rate of air flow. The output of this blower can be connected directly to the existing hot air system with ducting. This too can be thermostatically controlled.

Write or phone for brochure and price list.

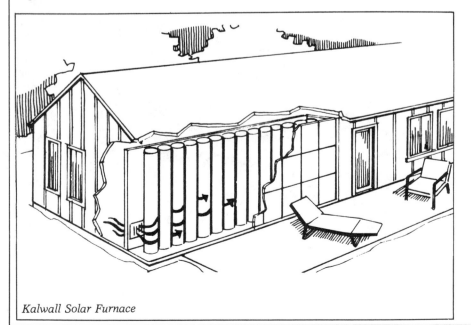

Kalwall Solar Furnace

SUN-LITE STORAGE TUBES & CONTAINERS: For use in passive solar energy systems, Sun-Lite storage tubes are designed to be placed in a vertical fashion, behind "solar windows" (i.e. Sun-Lite Glazing Panels) for direct collection and storage of solar heat. Utilizing the efficiency of a cylindrical cross section, the tubes are available in four standard sizes with sealed bottoms. The tube diameters listed are nominal to facilitate canister type packaging.

Although not designed as pressure containers, the tubes are more than capable of holding water or rock. The storage tubes are corrosion-free, light-weight, durable and inexpensive.
22 gallon approx. $55.00
128 gallon approx $75.00

Window Quilt $5.95/sq. ft. (Increase insulation value from R1.8 of glass to R5.5 with quilt.) Kalwall Glazing .025-inch-thick: 85 cents per suare foot; .040-inch-thick: $1.00/sq. ft.

QUEST ENGINEERING LTD.
2635 Clifton St.
Halifax, N.S. B3K 4V4
(902) 455-6693

Grumman solar systems sold and installed. Also offer design consultation and engineering advice.

ENVIROCONTROL PRODUCTS LIMITED
Suite 306, 6080 Young St.
Halifax, N.S. B3K 5L2
(902) 453-1117

Distributor of Nortec solar collectors and related hardware.

Designers

SPERRY, MACLENNAN, SOOSAAR & ALLISON
The Building Block
15 Victoria Road
Dartmouth, N.S. B2Y 2V5
(902) 469-9000

Active and passive solar-heated buildings designed and planned.

PARKER/TRUITT ASSOCIATES
Box 58
Armdale, N.S. B3L 4J7
G. Robert Parker (902) 422-7381

Comprehensive design service including site planning and system design.

RAYAR SCIENTIFIC LTD.
11E Pettipas Drive
Dartmouth, N.S. B3B 1K1
(902) 469-1876

Design consulting on solar heating systems.

SOL-ABODE
Energy Efficient Homes
Peter Ripple, Designer
R.R.1
Elderbank, N.S. B0N 1K0
(902) 384-2867

CBCL LTD.
6100 Young St. Box 1269N
Halifax, N.S. B3K 5H4
(902) 455-7241

Consulting engineering firm involved in designing and monitoring projects with DSS/NRC. Produce a solar booklet.

HOME ENERGY CONSERVATION LTD.
Box 753
Wolfville, N.S. B0P 1X0
(902) 542-9433

Physicist/energy consultant doing solar space heating design and sizing as well as solar siting surveys, drafting.

Contact

ECOLOGY ACTION CENTRE
Forrest Building
Dalhousie University
Halifax, N.S. B3H 3J5
Susan Holtz (902) 422-4311

Resource and information centre stimulating public involvement in energy and environmental issues.

PRINCE EDWARD ISLAND

Suppliers

ELECTRICAL SOLAR CENTRE
R.R.2
Winsloe, P.E.I. C0A 2H0
(902) 964-2367

This is an electrical contracting firm offering supply and installation of Champion solar furnaces and Fafco swimming pool heaters.

SOLAR ENERGY SYSTEMS INC.

Seawood Mark I, Stanley Bridge, P.E.I.

Stanley Bridge, P.E.I.
C0A 1E0
(902) 886-2655

Solar furnaces, VertaFin collectors, solar monitors and other items from Champion Home Builders.

ALTERNATECH ASSOCIATES LTD.
Emyvale, P.E.I. C0A 1Y0
(902) 658-2537

John Ramsay is now acting primarily as a consultant but has previously offered solar systems and components, including Solarsystems, Revere and Grumman.

Designers

SEAWOOD ESTATE INC.
Stanley Bridge, P.E.I.
C0A 1E0

This firm offers plans for a 2,133 sq. ft. solar home known as the Seawood-Mark I. Free information. Plans $150.00.

ALLISON & SPERRY LTD.
West River Workshop
St. Catherines, P.E.I.
C0A 1H0
(902) 675-2391

Architects and planners designing active and passive solar heated houses. Consultation on retrofitting existing buildings.

MILLER-SOLSEARCH ARCHITECTS
49 Pownal Street
Charlottetown, P.E.I.
C1A 3W2
(902) 892-9898

Design, construction and planning of solar systems.

Contact

THE INSTITUTE OF MAN AND RESOURCES
50 Water Street
Charlottetown, P.E.I. C1A 1A4
(902) 892-0361

Testing, demonstration projects and research into renewable energy sources.

SESCI P.E.I. Chapter
Box 1041
Charlottetown, P.E.I. C1A 7M4
Dave Murray (902) 658-2233

Midwestern Solar Furnace, Paducah, Kentucky

NFLD. Supplier

HEATING PRODUCTS LTD.
Box 751
St. John's, Nfld. A1C 5L4
(709) 753-7344

Offer Nortec collectors and components.

GOVERNMENT PROGRAMMES

Individuals and firms seeking information and/or assistance from federal coffers should contact:

RON BIGGS,
Co-ordinator, Solar Energy Programmes
Public Works Canada
Ottawa, Ontario K1A 0M2

SOLAR ENERGY PROJECT
National Research Council of Canada
Montreal Road
Ottawa, Ont. K1A 0R6

CANADIAN GOVERNMENT PUBLISHING CENTRE
Supply and Services Canada
Hull, Quebec K1A 0S9

(Offers a series of professional-level solar design publications and reports, for $3.00 each.)

U.S.A.

MID WESTERN SOLAR SYSTEMS
2235 Irvin Cobb Drive
Box 2384
Paducah, Kentucky 42001

Solar furnaces (detached from home, usually placed on ground level). Installed for $5,000 to $10,000, depending on size of home and the heat pump used. Also portable solar grain dryer. (U.S. prices.)

GRUMMAN ENERGY SYSTEMS INC.
4175 Veterans Memorial Hwy.
Ronkonkoma, N.Y. 11779
(516) 737-3737

Famous for its aircraft and well-built aluminum canoes, Grumman has entered the solar field with high quality products and a marketing approach that stresses reliability. Components and heating packages available throughout North America.

ZOMEWORKS INC.
Box 712
Albuquerque, New Mexico 87103
(505) 242-5354

Innovative passive solar products — beadwall design, skylids, etc.

BERRY SOLAR PRODUCTS
Box 327
Edison, New Jersey 08817
(201) 549-3800

Solarstrip (continuously electroplated black chrome on copper plate for collector plates). Black chrome outperforms black-painted surfaces by 23—117 percent, according to Berry.

NATURAL POWER INC.
Francestown Turnpike
New Boston, New Hampshire 03031
(603) 487-5512

Solar and wind power accessories.

SOLTEC
2160 Clay Street
Denver, Colorado 80211
(303) 455-3309

Solar life support systems—utilizing the sun to produce energy in a controlled environment.

Fafco Collector Cutaway View

FAFCO SOLAR
235 Constitution Drive
Menlo Park, CA 94025
(415) 321-3650

Fafco is perhaps the biggest name in swimming pool heating, with more than 100,000 panels sold in the past decade. Suppliers throughout U.S. and Canada.

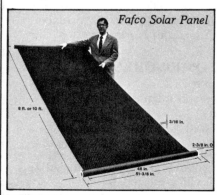

Fafco Solar Panel

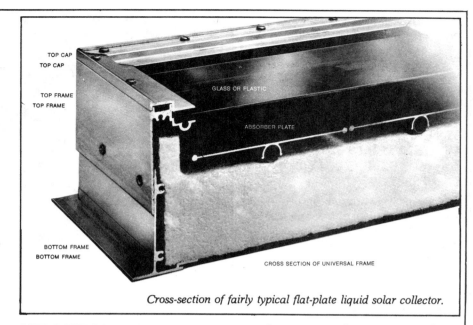

Cross-section of fairly typical flat-plate liquid solar collector.

NEW JERSEY ALUMINUM
Box 73
North Brunswick, New Jersey 08902
(201) 249-6867

Universal aluminum frames for the components of flat plate solar collectors.

WES (Weather Energy Systems) INC.
39 Barlows Landing Road
Pocasset, Mass. 02559
(617) 563-9337

Creative approaches to passive solar energy. Offers plans for solarium/greenhouse which attaches to house and serves as a large volume solar collector. Heat is blown into house when needed by an automatic fan system (Vent-Axia fan with Plexus 2 controller), or, at night, back into the greenhouse to prevent damage to plants. Also offers Plexus I, a sophisticated, solid-state temperature control system

Vent-Axia Fan from WES Inc.

to integrate various sources of heat.
Solarium Plans $85 (U.S. prices)
Plexus 2 $295
Vent-Axia Fans $120—$277
Plexus I (on request)

Random Comment

Although a solar swimming pool heater may not at first glance fall within the purview of the conserver society vision, the manufacturers of the Aquasol system in Smiths Falls, Ontario, see it as a logical foot in the door of consumer acceptance and a hard-nosed business venture. In the first place, with the rising cost of driving to the beach, more people are building pools than ever before. The people at Solartronics reason that those who own their own swimming pools—perhaps as many as 400,000 in Canada—are both financially astute and are trendsetters in their communities who can set a valuable example for their neighbours.

The President of Solartronics Limited, Rick Shorkey, presents the economic argument like this. "It costs a lot of money to build a pool in the first place, say $6,000 for an average 16 x 32 foot pool and you want to get as much use from it as possible. Without heating the water it may only be comfortable in July and August in eastern Ontario. Heating it extends the outdoor swimming period from May to September."

The conventional method of pool heating has been a $900 gas heater using $500 worth of fuel per year (1978 prices). The Aquasol system made by Solartronics (since January 1978) will cost about $2,200 installed on the average 16 x 32 foot pool. Then the only fuel cost is running the tiny water pump. So by eliminating the heating fuel cost, the system is paid for in less than five years and after that, pure gravy.

The federal government has bought the argument by making Solartronics the recipient of the first PASEM (Program of Assistance to Solar Energy Manufacturers) grant which pays 75 per cent of all labour, materials and overhead expenses plus 50 per cent of capital equipment costs, a total of $198,000 towards the $282,000 needed to set the company rolling. All these figures make it obvious that the company's president is a Chartered Accountant.

The pool heating system itself, but for the control unit, is simple. Small (2 x 4 feet), lightweight (6 lbs. empty, 11 lbs. when full of water) single-glazed plastic panels are mounted in relays on a south-sloping roof, hillside or other support, joined together by one-and-one-half-inch ABS header pipes and hooked in via the control unit to the pool's filter and pump system.

In the morning, when the sun heats the panels eight degrees above pool temperature, the control unit automatically floods them with water and the pool begins to heat up. Once it reaches a preselected temperature, the control unit shuts off the panels, which drain automatically except for periodic flooding to prevent them from overheating.

If the pool should overheat in August, the panels will continue operating at night as giant radiators, till the water is cooled down to the selected temperature.

Because they wanted to be sure the first systems installed would actually work, the Solartronics people insisted they be bought completely installed and guaranteed. But now they will also sell a manual system (you have to open the valve when you want heat and shut it to prevent cooling at night), which is simple enough to install oneself and save another $600.

For their next phase of development, Solartronics will be using a grant from the National Research Council to adopt their pool heating panels to cottage hot water systems by next spring. Because there will be no need for storage or antifreeze or additional heat exchangers, the systems will be economic to buy and will begin to produce a cash saving as soon as they are installed.

A big priority of all Solartronics projects is that they not only save non-renewable fuels, but that they also make economic sense and appear attractive to the average Canadian consumer. Systems from $849—$2,649.

AQUASOL is produced by:
Solartronics Limited
9 Hershey Avenue
Smiths Falls, Ont. K7A 4W7
(613) 283-6666

—David Creighton
Maberly, Ont.

LIVING WITH A PASSIVE SOLAR SYSTEM

For over a year, my husband and I waded through heaps of technical writings on solar energy systems, and concluded that a passive system would be best for us. One major difference between active and passive systems is automation. Passive systems don't have any—they just sit there and let the homeowner do the regulating.

I had visions of myself spending six hours a day, at great caloric cost, running from room to room, up and down stairs, opening and closing windows, doors, drapes, dampers and draught conrols.

However, now that we're here and the system is operating, I find that none of that has happened. Any adjustments needed are made as I go about my routine household tasks, and in spite of its lack of knobs and switches, passive works.

You can read about the technology of passive solar elsewhere, but I will outline the major factors we included in our design. Our two-storey home is built into a south-facing hill, so that it appears to be one storey from the north side. The south side has many windows, the north, none. Smaller windows on the east and west ends give cross-ventilation. The lower level, containing the living-dining-kitchen areas has an insulated concrete floor. Registers in the ceiling above the centrally placed wood stove circulate hot air by convection to the upper level bedrooms. A three-foot overhang on the roof admits all the winter sun and none of the summer sun to the bedrooms. As backup to the sun and wood stove, we have electric baseboard heating.

After four seasons of use, here are our findings on its livability:

1. Everybody thinks we're crazy.
2. The concrete floor made my legs ache for the first week. Getting used to it and putting "cushion floor" in the kitchen ended that problem. No one else has ever been bothered by the hardness of the floor.
3. When you drop a dish or glass or lamp, it breaks.
4. The concrete floor is not cold. The children ran around in sock feet all winter and never complained or caught a cold.
5. The floor holds its heat without backup assistance for two days. If we are away for a weekend, we needn't worry about frost on the African violets. It is cool when we return, and takes nearly two days to reheat to its capacity.
6. Even on the coldest winter morning, with the fire out, you can't see your breath in the house.
7. Throughout the winter, two logs in the stove and the sun will keep us well above 70 degrees F on a 4 degree F day. If the outside temperature is 14 degrees F, I close off the stove and look for a piece of shade in which to sit. At that temperature the sun alone is capable of keeping the whole house at 75 degrees.
8. We have not yet found it necessary to put in the three-foot overhang above the living room windows to block out the summer sun. The curtains can keep out the little bit that sneaks in.
9. It does not look like a solar home. The nice man from the mortgage department thinks it's a standard residence.

10. The floor doesn't look like a concrete floor. It's as smooth as glass, and with a coat of dark brown concrete paint, it generally passes unnoticed.

11. Passive heating converts to passive air conditioning at the flick of a season. With the help of a dehumidifier to keep down the sogginess of heat waves, the house has been consistently cooler than outside, and the upper floor has never been uncomfortable for sleeping.

12. We used our electric heat for the bathroom, the children's play areas on very cold days, and when we ran out of wood. Our heating bills for the winter averaged $10 a month. We hope to do better next year.

13. The floors don't squeak.

— *Victoria Cameron*
Oxford Station, Ontario

Books

CONSUMER HANDBOOK OF SOLAR ENERGY
(For United States & Canada)
By John H. Keyes
Morgan & Morgan
145 Palisade Street
Dobbs Ferry, New York 10522
$14.25, 273 pages (Paperback)

"Buying a pig in a poke has been the subject of untold numbers of jokes since the Middle Ages," writes author and holder of several solar equipment patents John H. Keyes. "Yet today the manufacturers of much of the solar equipment on the market are requiring their customers to do just that."

In this clear, simply-worded and much-needed book, Keyes does his best to help the sunstruck neophyte open the poke and examine the contents before buying. If, after reading this book, the energy conscious shopper still goes awry, he will have no one but himself to blame.

Keyes is remarkably frank in his exposure of the sins of the still booming solar industry, going so far as to admit that some of the manufacturers of products he designed himself are "guilty of deceptive marketing practices." He is too discreet, or perhaps conscious of libel dangers, to name them, but the practices

themselves come in for sharp scrutiny. He sums them up in rules of thumb, such as:

"Rule Number 11: Never buy anything — not even a cup of coffee — from anyone who tells you that 'it takes a collector one-half (or one-fourth or 15 to 30 per cent) the square footage of your home to heat it.' Run — don't walk — away from that show-room. Worse yet, if that kind of statement appears in the manufacturer's literature you're in bad company. Don't buy.

"That salesperson, that company, and that manufacturer have to be confidence artists and rip-off specialists. There's no polite way to put it. Obviously it takes a different sized solar-radiation collector and storage unit for a given house in Yuma, Arizona, and that *same* house in Green Bay, Wisconsin. Only a fool or a crook would tell you otherwise."

Equally blunt is Keyes' advice on buying stock in solar companies. "There are enough sleazy practices going on right now in the solar energy area to curl the hair on any Securities and Exchange Commission investigator's head," he says. "Rule Number 25: Unless you got rich trading in penny uranium stocks, don't dabble in solar energy stocks, at least until 1980."

The author's statements are backed up with facts and figures, tables and diagrams and with liberal helpings of common sense. Perhaps equally valuable, he has gone through the tedium of working out calculations and drawing up his own tables to show solar shoppers how to compare the efficiencies of gas, electric, oil and solar furnaces as they would actually operate in various climates and in each reader's very individual home.

The tables — Keyes calls them "Nomograms" — are easy to understand, even if your level of mathematical sophistication was arrested somewhere in Grade Three. Claimed by the author to be accurate "within 10 per cent," these Nomograms will enable the buyer to estimate exactly how good an insulator his own house is and what size solar collector it needs, given the climate in his

region. The tables include Canadian locations.

In some cases, Keyes frankly admits, simply putting in sufficient insulation would be cheaper than buying a solar furnace. Such honest advice is more than worth the book's price.

THE SOLAR HOME BOOK
By Bruce Anderson with
Michael Riordan
Cheshire Books
300 pages, Softcover: $10.95

One of the few solar building books that seems destined to withstand the test of time. Widely respected by scientists and laymen alike.

ISLAND UNIVERSE BOOKS
415 Parkside Drive
Toronto, Ontario
M6R 2Z7
Sylvia Argue
(416) 766-5391

Literature and plans on renewable energy, design, etc. Appropriate to Canadian conditions, by mail; catalogue free.

SOLAR HEATING CATALOGUE NO. 2
Edited by Michael Glover
Energy, Mines & Resources

Canadian Government Publishing Centre
Supply and Services Canada
Hull, Quebec K1A 0S9
120 pages, Softcover $2.00
($2.40 outside Canada)
Postpaid

The free lunch reincarnate (almost). Invaluable directory to solar manufacturers, designers, distributors, installers, researchers and sources of information. Unbeatable for $2.00, we can only hope that the government, or someone else, keeps it up to date.

THE 1979 SUN CATALOG
Solar Usage Now, Inc.
Box 306
Bascom, Ohio 44806
$2.00, 300 pages
(Paperback)

This helter-skelter, newsprinty, 300-page catalogue of solar hardware and alternative energy gadgets makes fascinating reading and is full of delights both for solar dreamers and the serious do-it-yourself enthusiast. *The Sun Catalog* is the place to find selective black chrome absorber plates, glass foam insulation, a variety of differential controllers and an inexpensive, $31.00 damper actuator kit. I was very excited to discover a variable-speed propeller fan which delivers up to 250 cubic feet per minute wired directly to a small array of photovoltaic cells which form the only power source. The hotter the sun, the faster the fan goes. Although most of the items are related to solar heating, other renewables are represented, such as a hydraulic ram pump and a wind-powered water pump, along with a comprehensive section of educational materials and miniature solar systems.

If you were pondering where to buy a solar-powered car for your great aunt, the answer is on page 273 where ''the world's first commercially built solar-powered vehicle'' is offered for $4,250., (it includes a pedal assist). Less extravagant and somewhat extraneous listings include a solar-powered music box, solar watches and a meat-roasting heat pipe designed to speed roasting time and reduce meat shrinkage.

Sandwiched between most acceptable offerings (unlike the *Harrowsmith Sourcebook* or the *Whole Earth Catalog,* this is a true catalogue, designed to *sell* the items described) are various items which might well be classified as solar junk. Other hardware mentioned may be available at the local building suppliers but this should not deter anyone from buying the catalogue; it is a wonderful source of ideas.

That *The Sun Catalog* has expanded from its original 1976, 32-page issue to its present 300-page version is indicative of the rapid growth of interest in solar energy in the U.S. in the last three years. In keeping with the Canadian tradition, the catalogue put out by Solerco, the Canadian counterpart of Solar Usage Now, is still at the 32-page stage, although, qualitatively speaking, the Solerco catalogue rates a bit higher.

— Elizabeth White
Toronto, Ontario

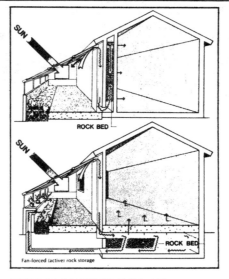

Fan-forced (active) rock storage

THE PASSIVE SOLAR ENERGY BOOK

A Complete Guide to Passive Solar Home, Greenhouse and Building Design
By Edward Mazria
Rodale Press
435 pages, Softcover $12.95

Intelligent, thorough, clearly written—in short, the very best book yet on the subject of passive solar design.

DRAWING ROOM GRAPHIC SERVICES LIMITED

Box 86627
North Vancouver, B.C.
V7L 4L2
40 pages, booklet $2.25, Postpaid

Good, basic, condensed introduction to solar potentials in Canada, especially strong on helping a homeowner or prospective homeowner calculate his heat requirements and the solar alternatives open to him. SOLPLAN 2, available from the same address for $3.25, deals with retrofitting situations.

Before you spend any money on your house to incorporate passive solar heating, or to buy solar equipment for an active system, you must make a hard assessment of your access to sunshine.

From a solar point of view, there are five kinds of sites:

CLASS 1: FANTASTIC SOLAR SITE: a flat or south slope to the southern horizon, no trees in the way, and no prospect of someone building a skyscraper between you

and the sun. If you are sure you have a super solar site, you can proceed with analyzing the performance of your design.

CLASS 2: NEARLY FANTASTIC SOLAR SITE: where, by judicious pruning of vegetation, ripping down the occasional billboard, and perhaps removing the tip of an intervening mountain or two, your house can have unlimited access to sunshine all year during the prime collecting hours of 9 AM to 3 PM.

CLASS 3: IFFY SOLAR SITES: where the sun is obscured during some portion of the day by some unremovable obstacle. In this case, to discover if solar heating is worth a significant investment, you will have to determine how much sun will be incident on your collecting area, especially during the important collecting hours in the late fall and through early spring.

CLASS 4: DEFINITELY NOT A SOLAR SITE: something big and permanent is between you and the sun, like a cliff, mountain, or an apartment building. Forget about tapping the sun, and buy more insulation.

CLASS 5: A POTENTIALLY DISASTROUS SOLAR SITE: this is a tough one. You might have what apears to be a prime class 1 site, build a nifty solar renovation, and suddenly discover a drive-in movie screen between you and the sunshine. Before investing in a solar home, you must check the potential for some neighbour erecting an edifice. This is best done in your planning department. Zoning regulations generally describe a building envelope: an imaginary shape into which a building must fit. You should plot the building envelopes for surrounding lots and see how these would affect your solar potential if they were filled with concrete and wood. Note that zonings change from time to time. This is usually done in a public hearing process.

There is no legislation in Canada to protect a solar system from shade. You may be able to enter into a restrictive covenant with your southerly neighbour to protect your access to sunshine. Any such encumbrance should be on the title of the property, duly registered, and not just a simple obscuration. We would be interested in hearing of any precedents created.

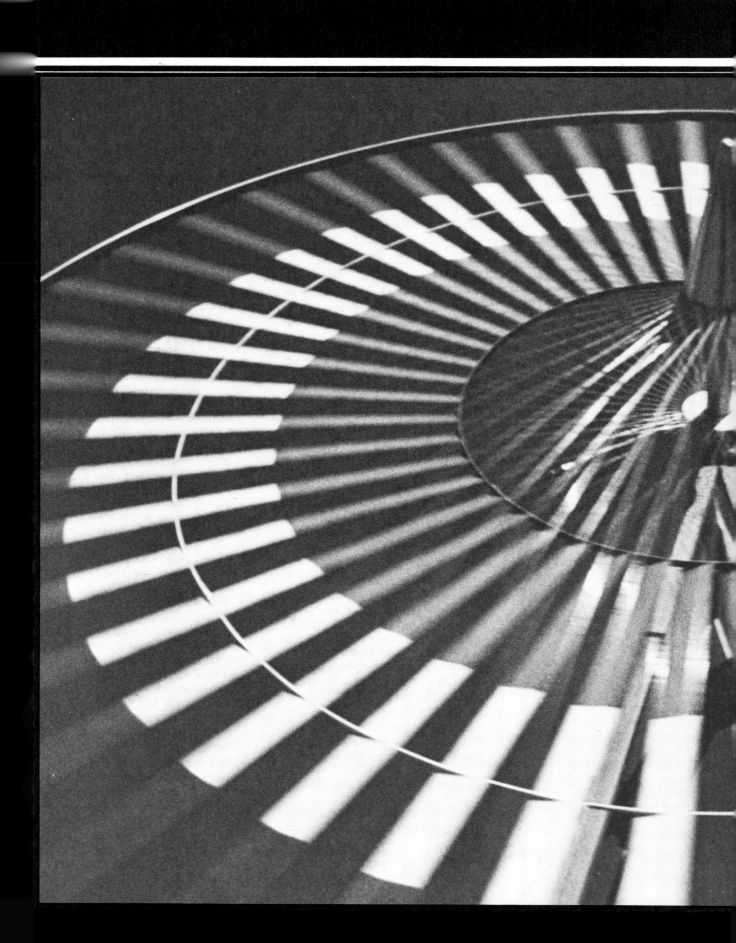

BIANCHI '79

The Board On A Stick Paradox

Toward an energy independence, fiercely

Several years ago an enterprising energy writer sought out the grand old man of North American wind power, M.L. Jacobs, whose Wind Electric aerogenerators remain the standard of excellence nearly 50 years after they were built. When asked about the chances of a great technological breakthrough, the invention that would extract vast amounts of energy from a modest-sized wind unit, Jacobs responded with this pithy prediction: A board nailed to a broomstick will do as well as anything else in a 20 mph wind.

Relatively few original Jacobs units remain undiscovered today, and those that become available

tend to carry a price tag that commands respect. Although the occasional vintage wind plant does become available, the near future of wind energy will hinge on small companies manufacturing new units—either reproductions of the classics or completely new designs.

There are currently about 50 different wind generator models available from 20-odd manufacturers in North America. To date, no one has produced the sort of side-by-side, controlled condition testing that would make the choice among these easier for a would-be purchaser. Donald Marier, editor of *Alternative*

Sources of Energy magazine recently gathered specification and performance sheets from a great many manufacturers, but, with varying ground rules and test criteria, the information proved less useful than might have been hoped for.

Marier says that the most interesting thing which emerged was the similarity in efficiency among the units, perhaps a reinforcement of Jacobs' prediction. ''The main thing to consider when buying a new wind plant,'' advises Marier, ''is will it stay together?'' He predicts that many of the wind firms existing today will be gone in five years, and the prospective buyer should meet the people he or she intends to deal with to get an idea of their economic stability and the level of service they can provide.

Of special interest to many observers are two firms which are setting out to follow in the Jacobs tradition of quality. Their units are the Dakota Wind & Sun 4 kw, 140-volt model and the Aeropower SL 1500, 24-volt unit. Both utilize a superior, time-tested governor and blade control design initiated by Jacobs. Unlike the Jacobs, both incorporate solid state electronic controls.

From this point, the approach differs. Dakota opts for the heavy, direct-drive Jacobs-type generator. Aeropower uses a smaller, geared-up alternator. Both companies make reliability and quality top priorities. Mario Agnello of Aeropower says that their machine will produce a peak of 2100 watts, although it is rated conservatively at 1500 watts.

According to tests, the unit will produce more power per month than the more expensive and highly respected Dunlite plant from Australia.

This can be accounted for by Aeropower's attention to the importance of low cut-in speed (it generates power in lower winds than the Dunlite) and a solid mid-range output. The art of wind machine design is maximizing the more prevalent wind speeds at a particular site and, for many North American situations, Aeropower has produced a seemingly superior unit.

Dakota's approach can best be described as improving the already proved Jacobs. They've extracted more power by lengthening the armature, but they've kept the reliability, the slow speed efficiency and they've added a three-year guarantee. The Dakota needs annual greasing (service requirements should play an important role in any wind plant purchase decision), and brushes must be replaced every three years or so. The Aeropower has a cog belt drive which is reputed to last

three years as well. Both units can be owner-maintained, but the Aeropower, being lighter, would be easier to install.

There are, of course, many more choices, and the following list of current wind power sources indicates the diversity of the field today. Who will emerge as the paragon of quality and reliability remains to be seen, but one certainty exists: no one is likely to make enormous gains in efficiency. Greater output will cost considerably more; the energy available from the wind is proportional to the area swept by the blades. To cover a greater area requires a bigger, heavier rotor and entails greater sophistication, cost and risk.

While long-time observers of the solar energy movement have all but stopped counting the number of successful projects now under way (thousands in North America, and growing exponentially), even the most rabid of wind power enthusiasts will admit that this technology, if not in the doldrums, just hasn't progressed as quickly.

Of all the owner-user alternative technologies, wind remains the most remote, the most demanding, the most alternative. And yet, there are those who have been willing—or forced by the high cost of new electrical service installation—to make the best of existing, off-the-shelf technology, determined to make it work. The most successful have been those with an instinctive flair for things mechanical, those who bought well-established, time-proved equipment or those who located a wind generator firm willing and able to see that their system worked—and kept working.

Within the next decade, small-scale wind energy systems are certain to become both more reliable (with a greater availability of equipment and appropriate appliances) and more economically viable. In the meantime, wind power will likely remain an alternative for the adventurous and the fiercely independent.

—David Simms
Ayer's Cliff, Quebec

WIND SYSTEMS

CAREFUL ECO SYSTEMS
Box 1212
Whaletown, B.C. V0P 1Z0
(604) 886-7336
An important Canadian source of both wind and water-generating equipment as well as Clivus Multrum composting systems. These people live with the devices they sell, and stand behind their merchandise.

We sell the Australian made Dunlite wind generator which is unquestionably the best in the world. Because of its reliability this wind generator is the choice of coast guards and telecommunications companies around the world. There is even one in Antarctica which has given eight trouble-free years of service to date. Unfortunately wind generators are expensive, especially when you add up the cost of batteries and towers. To help keep prices reasonable we manufacture our own Dunlite approved towers and offer plans to those wishing to build their own towers. To help soften the initial cost we suggest good used batteries might be employed for the first few years. The Dunlite comes in a 2 kw and a 5 kw size. We have a 110 volt D.C. 2 kw Dunlite that operates our house on Cortez Island, which includes lights, stereo, small fridge, washing machine and power tools. We don't use all our power and plan to hook up our neighbour's house as well! The system has been so reliable that we now take it for granted. Interestingly it has not failed us once in the year we have had it but Hydro on Cortez has been interrupted a few times in the year!! The 500 watt Soma wind generator can be pole mounted (telephone pole is ideal).

Few people put their wind generators high enough (probably because of tower expense). As you go higher, the speed of the wind increases so that it will gain 15 per cent from a 30-foot to a 60-foot height. Since the power in the wind

increases as the cube of the velocity, this 15 per cent increase in wind speed will give an increase in power of approximately 50 per cent. Tower height is often the cheapest way to get more power.

The turbulence at 60 feet will be much less than at 30 feet so the wind generator will not be subjected to the battering effect of turbulence and the bearings and other wearing parts will last much longer.

Dunlite 2000 Watt Wind Generator from Australia $5,185.
Dunlite 5000 Watt Wind Generator $6,985.
Towers for Dunlite Generators:
40 feet — $1,240
70 feet — $2,990

Soma 500 Watt, 24 Volt Self-Feathering Windgenerator $2,100

Batteries: Lead-acid (antimony) flat plate type. Expected life is 10 years, although up to 15 years is possible with proper capacity, location and maintenance. Bolt type terminals, extra large sediment and electrolyte capacities. Five-year pro-rated guarantee.

8 volt 100 amp hr — $ 55
8 volt 200 amp hr — $103
8 volt 220 amp hr — $115
8 volt 240 amp hr — $125
8 volt 260 amp hr — $135
8 volt 300 amp hr — $155
4 volt 600 amp hr — $175
Ultimate heavy duty battery, expected life 20-25 years.
Fourteen batteries needed for 110 volt system. Four batteries needed for 32 volt system unless the 4 volt batteries are used in which case 28 and 8 batteries needed.

DAKOTA WIND AND SUN
Box 1781
Aberdeen South Dakota
(605) 229-0815

MODEL: BC4
Maximum output: 4000 watts
(140 volts DC)
Horizontal axis, upwind,
three blades
Rotor diameter: 14 feet

Cut-in wind speed: 8 mph
Rated output: 4000 watts at
27 mph
Price: $5,470 (U.S.)

Other models: 10,000-watt model to be available this fall.
Dealerships: 23 U.S. dealers; write for list.
Canadian distributor:
Massawippi Wind Electric
R.R.3
Ayer's Cliff, Quebec J0B 1C0
(Dakota BC4: $6,400 Canadian)

WHAT DO CUT-IN AND CUT-OUT MEAN? Usually these terms are used to describe the minimum wind for which the generator attains useful voltage and the maximum wind the generator can use before shutting itself down. The cut-in wind speed should be matched to the area where the machine will be used. For instance, if your average wind speed is 12 mph, the cut-in should be about ⅔ of 12, or about 8 mph. This is a general rule to obtain a useful system. When the cut-in is far below the average wind, the chances are higher that the blades will be damaged in high winds. The cut-out wind speed has to be determined from the blade and governor design. Not all machines have automatic cut-out because the blades and governors are designed for high power and have sufficient pitch control to accommodate high winds.

WILL DC POWER WORK IN PLACE OF AC (COMMERCIAL) POWER? It will for many uses, but the most notable exceptions are refrigerators, freezers and furnace fans (they are usually induction motors). Resistive loads, such as baseboard heaters, incandescent lights, and brush type motors work equally well on AC or DC. Devices called inverters are available to change the DC energy to AC, especially for small loads such as freezers. Another type of inverter, called a synchronous inverter, may be used to mix the DC energy with the commercial AC energy in your home. When the wind is blowing strong, most of the wind energy is used in your home, slowing down the watt-hour meter. In fact, if your use of electricity is low, the meter will run backwards and you are effectively selling energy to the power company at the same price you paid for it. There is a safety consideration that must be mentioned, and that is that if the commercial power fails, there must be a way to stop your energy from hurting a lineman. The Gemini Synchronous Inverter stops working without the commercial power to time it, which leaves you in the cold, too. Yet this machine has to be given consideration because it can greatly cut down on the everyday consumption from the power company.

For those people isolated from commercial power, we want to make the point

that industrial freezers and refrigerators are made with separate motors and compressors, which leaves the option of changing the motor to a DC type, and then the unit will operate from DC power and batteries.

WINCO — DIV. OF DYNA TECHNOLOGY
7850 Metro Parkway
Minneapolis, Minnesota 55420
(612) 853-8400

The Wincharger is, as they say, old as the hills and just as steady. The advertising material appears the same as it did two generations ago, with suggestions that the units can power "lights, iron, radio, washer, (cream) separator, water pump and electric refrigerator." But not all at once. Low price, matched by low power output.

MODEL: Winco-Wincharger
1222H
Maximum output: 200 watts,
15 volts
Horizontal axis, upwind,
two blades
Rotor diameter: 6 feet
Cut-in wind speed: 7 mph
Rated output: 200 watts at 23 mph
Price: $450 (U.S.)
Other models: 24, 28, 32 and 36-volt models
Canadian distributor:
Maier Still Agencies Ltd.
5985 Atlantic Drive, Unit 6
Mississauga, Ontario L4W 1F4
(416) 677-0664
Eastern U.S. distributor:
Energy Systems
4874 Cherry Tree Lane
Sykesville, Maryland 21784
(301) 795-3828

COULSON WIND ELECTRIC
RFD 1, Box 225
Polk City, Iowa 50226
(515) 984-6038

Rebuilt Jacobs, Winchargers and Winpowers.
Accessories: towers, batteries, appliances.

R.A. SIMERL INSTRUMENT
238 West Street
Annapolis, Maryland 21401
(301) 849-8667

Hand-held anemometers (approx. $85); Remote indicating anemometers ($110—$395); Transducers ($70).
All prices U.S. funds.
Has 5 Canadian distributors and hundreds of U.S. outlets.
Write for addresses.

Devices for on-the-spot wind speed measurement.

ANEMOMETER RSC. is favoured for shipboard use. The transducer (wind sensor) is mounted on the top of a boat mast or cabin and connected to meter. Meter is waterproof and may be illuminated with 12-volt lamp, supplied. Power furnished from ship's battery. A weatherproof switch is supplied for changing meter readings. Outside diameter of meter bezel is 5". A hole 3-3/8" in diameter is required for enclosed meter movement housing back of meter dial. Meter may be installed in bulkheads up to 1¾" thick by means of standard mounting device, supplied. Meter dial and bezel finished in dull black for glare free reading. Complete system includes: transducer, 50' of cable, stanchion, switch, meter. $135.00.

MODEL BTC: Ranges: 0-35 and 0-70 mph. 0-30 and 0-60 knots. Cup type folding rotor. No batteries required. Compact, rugged, accurate. Just hold in the wind. Read wind velocity on scale. Non-directional, sustained, smooth readings. Cups fold for storage. The Sims Model BTC hand-held anemometer is a professional wind instrument. Cups open or close for storage instantly. Available with other dial calibrations. Supplied with protective vinyl case. An excellent instrument for on-the-spot wind observations. Cup and vane type rotors are not interchangeable, but are equally accurate. $85.00.

FUTURE RESOURCES AND ENERGY LIMITED
Box 1358, Station B
Downsview, Ont. M3H 5W3
(416) 630-8343

Swiss-made Elektro Wind Generators $1,500 to $30,000
Gemini Synchronous Inverters (Prices on request).

THERMAX CORPORATION
Box 275
Hawkesbury, Ontario
(613) 632-8111

Low output Helius rotor design for the curious or one-light-bulb families. The company also offers a "Windmaster" Helius device for measuring wind speed near ground level (must be connected to a recording device).

HELIUS rotor kit:
Rated output: 35 watts at 15 mph
Designed for attachment to TV tower.
Price: $295 (Canadian) includes rotor and generator
Windmaster: $750
Windbook: $2.00

The Helius solution to the problem of inefficiency is to replace the solid vane material with a "one-way windscreen" material called "Windiode."

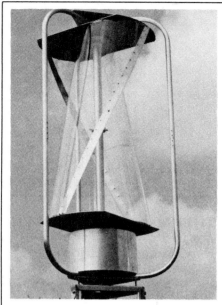

Windiode material acts as a silent one-way wind valve. With this new wind science material, the wind passes through the returning convex vane with low resistance, but is blocked on entering the driving concave vane, thus producing the maximum driving force.

There are several forms of Windiode material, selected according to application and scale.

The basic mechanical form of Windiode (Type A) consists of many small triangular or square pyramids molded into a sheet of plastic material. The edges of these pyramids are all cut so that the leaves formed by the sides of the pyramids—hinged at the base by the plastic material itself—can open outward under wind pressure from within the pyramid (i.e. from behind the Windiode sheet).

Wind from the front of the sheet, however, only closes the leaves more firmly against each other and makes the sheet impervious to the wind. The one-piece, molded-hinge configuration ensures silent operation and long life.

NORTH WIND POWER CO. INC.
Box 315
Warren, Vermont 05674

One of the better organized sources of wind generator equipment, North Wind built its reputation on rebuilt Jacobs and is now going into production of its own Eagle generators. Attractive, useful catalogue.

MODEL: 3kw, 32V (Eagle III)
Maximum output: 4500 watts, 32 volts DC
Horizontal axis, upwind, three blades
Rotor diameter: 13.6 feet
Cut-in wind speed: 8 mph
Rated output: 3000 watts at 27 mph
Price: $4,000 (U.S.)
Other models: 2 kw 32 volt; 2 kw 110 volt; 3 kw 110 volt
Accessories: Wind measuring equipment, inverters, batteries, back-up generators, wind-powered water pumpers.

ENERTECH CORP.
Box 420
Norwich, Vermont 05055
(802) 649-1145

Offers its own Enertech 1500-watt generator, as well as selection of other designs and wind accessories.

MODEL: 1500
Maximum output: 1650 watts, 115 volts AC
Horizontal axis, downwind, three blades
Rotor diameter: 13 feet
Cut-in wind speed: 9 mph
Rated output: 1500 watts at 22 mph
Price: $2,900 (U.S.)
Other models: Sparco wind-powered water pump ($300 to $350 U.S.)
Wincharger 200 ($625 U.S.)
Sencenbaugh 500 ($2,560 U.S.)

Sencenbaugh 1000 ($2,950 U.S.)
Dunlite 2000 ($4,020 U.S.)
Accessories: Measuring equipment and controls
Canadian distributor:
Energy Alternatives
2 Croft Street, Box 671
Amherst, Nova Scotia B4H 1B1
(902) 667-2790

WELLINGTON WIND POWER
Box 15
Wellington, Ont. K0K 3L0

MODEL: Teal
Maximum output: 5000 watts at 110 volt DC
Horizontal axis, upwind, three blades
Rotor diameter: 18 feet
Cut-in wind speed: 12 mph
Rated output: 5000 watts at 22 mph
Price on request.
Other models:
Whistler (600 watts) $950
Mallard (1000 watts) $1,250
Canada Goose (8000 watts)—price on request.
Also rebuilds Jacobs wind generators.
All prices in Canadian funds.

WHIRLWIND POWER CO.
2458 W. 29th Avenue
Denver, Colorado 80211
(303) 477-6436

MODEL: A
Maximum output: 2000 watts at 24, 32, 48, 120 and 240 volts
Horizontal Axis, downwind, two blades
Rotor diameter: 10 feet
Cut-in wind speed: 8 mph

Rated output: 2000 watts
at 25 mph
Price: $2,000—$2,700 (U.S.)
Accessories: Towers, immersion
water heating elements, inverters,
regulators, back-up generators,
lighting systems.

WIND TURBINE CO. OF CANADA LIMITED

21 Howard Avenue
Elmira, Ont. N3B 2C9
(519) 669-5421

This company designs, builds
and, when requested, erects self-
supporting and guyed Trylon
towers at $25 to $35/foot
(Canadian).

KEDCO

9016 Aviation Blvd.
Inglewood, Ca 90301
(213) 776-6636

Newish design from a California
aerospace firm.
MODEL: 1200
Maximum output: 1200 watts,
14 volts DC
Horizontal axis, downwind,
three blades
Rotor diameter: 12 feet
Cut-in wind speed: 7 mph
Rated output: 1200 watts
at 22 mph
Price: $2,300 (U.S.)
Other models: 2000-watt
generators, 3000-watt generators

INDEPENDENT ENERGY SYSTEMS, INC.

6043 Sterrettania Rd., Dept. H
Fairview, Pennsylvania 16415
(814) 833-3567

Manufacturers of an improved
Jacobs-type unit known as the
Sky Hawk.

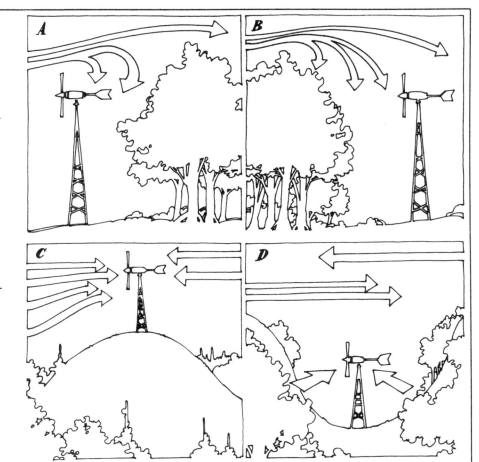

A barren hilltop is perhaps the ideal location for a wind generator, as large trees or buildings, either in front of or behind a wind machine, create turbulence which lowers efficiency. The rule of thumb is that a wind generator should be at least 25 feet above the tree tops, and 300 - 500 feet from major obstructions. Some valley situations can present problems of low wind speed and turbulence.

MODEL: Sky Hawk IV
Maximum output: 4500 watts,
110 volts DC
Horizontal axis, upwind,
three blades
Rotor diameter: 15 feet
Cut-in wind speed: 7 mph
Rated output: 4000 watts
at 23 mph
Price: $3,895 (U.S.)
Accessories: Tapered, self-
supporting and guyed towers;
inverters; batteries; DC
appliances; wind measuring
instruments.

WIND SYSTEM

Initial Cost: Complete Sky Hawk Wind Electric System $3,800 to $6,200. Average installation cost includes federal solar tax credits.

Other Costs: Have to replace battery set every 10 to 12 years if independent wind system is chosen. Longer replacement cost if longer-

life batteries are purchased initially. Little maintenance.

Intangibles: Natural disasters.

Assets: You own your own utility company and can sell it. Federal tax credits available on all renewable energy sources. Have no electric bills upon retirement. More reliable than electric company (with back-up generator). Daily reduction in your electric bill if a synchronous inverter is used.

Savings: If your electric bill is $46.00 per month ($552/year), with a 25 per cent annual fuel inflation rate, then in 20 years your annual fuel bill would be $43,000. The cumulative cost—the total spent on electricity over the 20 year period—would be around $190,000.

CONVENTIONAL

Initial Costs:
A. Diesel or gasoline generator. $2,000 to $10,000 for continuous duty units.

B. *Utility Hook-up. $7,000 to $10,000 per mile above ground. $10,000 to $50,000 per mile below ground.*
C. *Electricity in building. Pay your electric bill every month year after year $5.00 to $500.00 per month.*

Other Costs: Price increases (10 to 25 per cent per year) for electricity. Directly or indirectly pay state, federal, local taxes, fuel price increases and other hidden costs. Noise and air pollution from a diesel or gas generator. Power failures. Pollution from the generation of electricity by large power plants (nuclear, coal or oil).

Intangibles: Political instability in oil producing countries. Demand outstripping supply. Inflation factor. Possible rationing of either electricity or fuel to produce electricity. Strikes, closing of mines, civil unrest disrupting supply. Power failures.

Assets: Can sell depreciated gas or diesel generator. Structure easier to sell to general public (for now).

Savings: None (an electric bill is exactly like paying rent).

—*Independent Energy Systems*

DYNERGY CORPORATION
Box 428, 1269 Union Ave.
Laconia, New Hampshire
03246
(603) 542-8318
MODEL: 5M
Maximum output: not available
Vertical axis, three blades
Rotor diameter: 15 feet

Cut-in wind speed: 10 mph
Rated output: 3300 watts
at 24 mph
Price: $11,000 (U.S.) Includes alternator and base.

BEST ENERGY SYSTEMS FOR TOMORROW INC.
Route 1, Box 106
Necedah, Wisconsin 54646
(608) 565-7200

MODEL: B 24-2500 Inverter
Maximum load: 2500 watts
Input: 24 volts DC
Output: 120 volts AC
Efficiency: 90 per cent
Solid state
Weight: 63 lbs.
Price: $1,400 (U.S.)
Other inverters: 1000 watt, 12 volt to 5000 watt, 48 volt ($1,000 to $2,400 U.S.)

WADLER MFG. CO.
Rt. 2, Box 76
Galena, Kansas 66739
(316) 783-1355

Two models of Savonius-rotor wind machines designed to keep an area of open water in ponds during winter. The units do not generate electricity, but rather

are attached to a propellor which is submerged in the pond. Useful for waterfowl owners and with potential use for decreasing winterkill of fish in small bodies of water.

MODEL: Pondmaster 672
Four bladed, vertical axis,
Savonius rotor
No generation component.
Cut-in wind speed: 1 mph
Thaws frozen ponds.
Prices on request.
Other models: Pondmaster 370,
two bladed rotor
Canadian distributor:
Ketchum Mfg. Co. Ltd.
396 Berkeley Avenue
Ottawa, Ontario K2A 2G6
(613) 722-3451

CANADIAN ENERGY CONVERSION INDUSTRIES
2779 Lake City Way
Burnaby, B.C. V5A 2Z8
(604) 420-3030

DC to AC inverters, prices on request. Now developing wind generators of 2 types:
Can-Am (wheel propeller),
Darrieus (vertical axis).

NATURAL POWER, INC.
Francestown Turnpike
New Boston, New Hampshire
03031
(603) 487-5512

A complete line of wind accessories including:
Wind recording instruments
($325—$1,000)
Wind speed compilators
($800—$2,000)
Meters ($200—$375)
Anemometers ($50)
Batteries (12 volt DC
lead-acid $100)
WECS Performance analyzer
($1,000)
WECS Control panel
(110 volt DC $450)
Alternators ($400—$425)

Regulators ($50—$75)
Gemini inverters
($1,000—$4,000)
Octahedron module towers
All Prices U.S. funds.
Canadian Distributor:
Crowfield Associates
R.R.1, Krapaud, P.E.I.
C0A 1J0
(902) 658-2233

The Series A35 DC Ampere-Hour Meter is a device which measures the amount of current (amperes) in a circuit during a unit of time (hours) by summing or integrating the instantaneous current value over time. The AC35 DC Ampere-Hour Meter is useful in battery systems to determine remaining battery capacity, or to measure the energy generated or consumed by a particular device. $270.00.

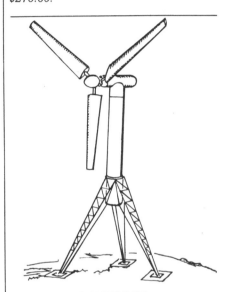

MILLVILLE WIND AND SOLAR
Box 32, 10335 Old Drive
Millville, California 96062
(916) 547-4302

MODEL: 10-3-Ind.
Maximum output: 10,000 watts,
240 volt AC
Horizontal axis, upwind,
three blades
Rotor diameter: 25 feet
Cut-in wind speed: 9 mph
Rated output: 10,000 watts
at 25 mph
Price: $6,250 (U.S.)
Other models: Wincharger, 200 watt; Dempster wind-powered water pumps; towers; batteries; inverters; gauges.

AERO POWER SYSTEMS INC.
2398 Fourth Street

Berkeley, California 94710
(415) 848-2710

MODEL: SL1500
Maximum output: 1500 watts
12 and 24 volt units
Horizontal axis, upwind,
three blades
Rotor diameter: 12 feet
Cut-in wind speed: 6 mph
Rated output: 1430 watts
at 25 mph
Price: $3,195 (U.S.)
for 24 volt unit
Other models: SL1000 (12 volt)
$2,895 (U.S.)

Also available are inverters ($995 to $1,630), heavy-duty deep cycle batteries (6-volt, 350 amp hour) at $165 each.

Unarco-Rohn Towers, from Peoria, Illinois, are available as follows:

Tower Height	Price
30′	$430.00
40′	630.00
50′	700.00
60′	765.00
70′	1,025.00
80′	1,085.00

CANUSA ENERGY CO.
R.R.2
Wainfleet, Ontario L0S 1V0
(416) 899-1888

Rebuilt Jacobs wind generators:
$5,100 to $5,200 (Canadian)
Towers: $20 per foot approx.

Proprietor Ron Rose, who lives in a solar and wind-powered home, offers the following first-hand

advice about one brand of inverter now on the market:

We have been operating a Gemini Synchronous Inverter since June, 1977. We find this inverter a very poor device:
1. Takes too much power to operate.
2. Too expensive to purchase.
3. Cabinet becomes electrically charged.
4. Too easily damaged by voltage surges.
5. The Gemini Company will not send proper schematics to repair the inverter. Repairs are done at the owner's expense, and, in our experience, repairs are either poorly done or not inspected properly before the unit is returned to the owner.

DUNLITE
28 Orsmond Street,
Hindmarsh, S.A.
Australia 5007
Telephone 463832

For those who prefer to deal directly with the manufacturer, Dunlite is in Hindmarsh waiting. Be prepared for the expected (and unexpected) problems of long distance shopping, as well as customs rituals. Prices in Australian dollars: F.O.B. Down Under.

MODEL: 2 kw
Maximum output: 3000 watts at
24, 32, 48 and 110 volts
Horizontal axis, upwind,
three blades
Rotor diameter: 13½ feet
Cut-in wind speed: 8 mph

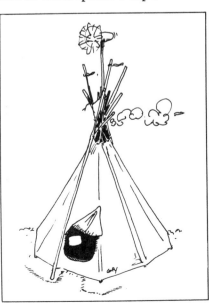

Rated output: 2000 watts
at 25 mph
Price: $3,800 (Australian)
Other models: 5 kw (110 volt)
$4,800 (Australian)
Major U.S. distributor:
Enertech Corporation
Box 420
Norwich, Vermont 05055
Canadian distributors:
Careful Eco Systems Ltd.
Box 1212
Whaletown, B.C. V0P 1Z0
(Dunlite 2 kw: $5,185 Can.)
Amherst Renewable
Energies Limited
Box 387
Perth, Ontario K7H 3G1
(Dunlite 2 kw and 5 kw:
prices on request)

GRUMMAN ENERGY SYSTEMS, INC.
4175 Veterans Memorial Hwy.
Ronkonkoma, N.Y. 11779
(516) 737-3709

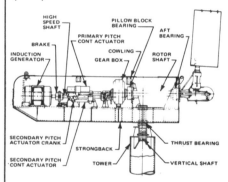

Windstream 33 wind generator
(horizontal axis, downwind, three
blades) being developed for late
1979. Expected to produce 10 kw
to 20 kw.

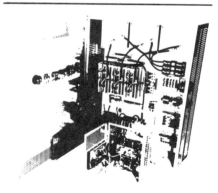

WINDWORKS
Box 329, Rt. 3
Mukwanago, Wisconsin 53149
Gemini solid state synchronous
inverters converting variable DC

power to AC at standard line
voltages and frequencies. 8-kw
capacity $1,465; 4-kw capacity
$788.

ZEPHYR WIND DYNAMO
Box 241
Brunswick, Maine 04011
(207) 725-6534

Very low speed — Permanent
Magnet alternators designed to
match the input speeds of most
wind turbines.
Output range: 1500 watts to
15,000 watts in voltages specified
by the buyer.
Other products: OBT Student
Windmill for school
demonstration $675 (U.S.)

MASSAWIPPI WIND ELECTRIC COMPANY
R.R.3
Ayer's Cliff, Quebec J0B 1C0

David Simms, who has lived for
four years in a wind-powered log
home, will act as a consultant for
others planning wind systems. He
occasionally offers rebuilt Jacobs
units, and is the Canadian
distributor for Dakota Wind and
Sun.

SENCENBAUGH WIND ELECTRIC
Box 11174
Palo Alto, California 94306
(415) 964-1593

Model: 1000
Maximum output: 1200 watts,
14 or 28 volt
Horizontal axis, upwind,
three blades
Rotor diameter: 12 feet
Cut-in wind speed: 6 mph
Rated output: 1000 watts
at 23 mph
Price: $2,650 (U.S.)

WIND POWER SYSTEMS
Box 17323
San Olego, California 92117
(714) 452-7040
MODEL: Storm Master 10
Maximum output: 6000 watts
Horizontal axis, downwind,
three blades
Rotor diameter: 32.8 feet
Cut-in wind speed: 8 mph
Rated output: 6000 watts
at 18 mph

Prices on request.
Accessories: Wind plant energy
simulator $700 (U.S.)

THE ALTERNATE CURRENT
Box 905
Boulder, Colorado
(303) 442-7193

MODEL: ALTOS BWP-8B
Maximum output: 2000 watts
at 24 volts DC
Horizontal axis, upwind,
multi-bladed wheel propeller
Rotor diameter: 7.6 feet
Cut-in wind speed: 10 mph
Rated output: 1500 watts
at 28 mph
Prices on request.
Other models: BWP-12A
2200 watt, 115 volt

OAKRIDGE WINDPOWER
Route 1
Underwood, Maine 56586
(218) 826-6446

Has 850 (1500 watt 32 volt)
rebuilt Winchargers for $1/watt.

Also sells batteries, towers, inverters. Will install within 500 miles.

DAF INDAL

3570 Hawkestone Road
Mississauga, Ont. L5C 2V8
(416) 275-5300

Developing vertical axis Darrieus wind generators in the 50-kw range.

ALTERNATECH ASSOCIATES LTD.

Emyvale, P.E.I. C0A 1V0
(902) 658-2537

John Ramsay has moved from direct sales of Enertech hardware to alternative energy consulting.

PINSON ENERGY CORP.

Box 7
Marston Mills, Mass. 02648
(617) 428-8535

MODEL: C2E Cycloturbine
Maximum output: 4000 watts
Vertical axis, three blades
Rotor diameter: 12 feet
Cut-in wind speed: 7 mph
Rated output: 2000 watts
at 24 mph
Price: $5,000 (U.S.)
includes 30-foot tower.

AMERICAN WIND TURBINE

1016 East Airport Road
Stillwater, Oklahoma 74074
(405) 377-5333

MODEL: 12 foot
Maximum output: Not available
Horizontal axis, upwind,
multi-bladed wheel propeller

Rotor diameter: 11½ feet
Cut-in wind speed: 10 mph
Rated output: 1000 watts
at 20 mph
Price: Approx. $2,000 (U.S.)
Other models: 16 foot
(2000 watts)

FRIESEN INDUSTRIES

32032 South Fraser Way
Clearbrook, B.C.
(604) 859-7101

Control switches and inverters as well as back-up generators, (diesel, LP gas, natural gas, gasoline) Pelton hydroelectrical wheels and wind equipment.

ENERGY SYSTEMS

4874 Cherry Tree Lane
Sykesville, Maryland 21784
(301) 795-3828

Line of electrical generators which operate with the power from the PTO shaft of a tractor, as well as an extensive line of gasoline and diesel portable power units. Dunlite and Wincharger generators, as well. Ships to U. S. and Canada.

WATER PUMPING UNITS

Old Baker "Run-in-Oil" windmills are often the only standing monument to many abandoned homesteads, and after 90 years the company is still producing them for Amish farmers and land owners in remote areas. A Baker serves only to pump water, does not generate electricity, and thus is a true "windmill."

U.S. source
HELLER-ALLER CO.

(Est. 1886)
Napoleon, Ohio

Offers Baker windmills, towers, pumping equipment. Write for price list.

Canadian distributor:
THE PIONEER PLACE

Route 4,
Aylmer, Ontario N5H 2R3
Baker windmills and towers, as well as British-made diesel power units.

One of the first things a person notices when driving through an Amish community is that nearly every farmhouse has an old-fashioned windmill quietly pumping water. For years of trouble-free service, and cheap water pumping, a windmill is mighty hard to beat.

The construction of the Baker windmill is perhaps the simplest of any on the market. All the parts run in oil, and there is no mechanism above the oil bath where trouble often develops in other models. All bearings are cored and die cast to insure perfect castings. Also drilled and reamed to make them positively smooth.

The Baker wheel is oversize throughout and has 25 per cent more wind surface than the average wheel. The numerous wheel blades make an even and steady-running mill. Collects the maximum power from the lighter breezes. Wheel is scientifically designed—practically storm-proof.

Windmill heads are manufactured in four different sizes. Most Amish farms use the 8-foot wheel, and some get by with a 6-foot. Very few use the 10-foot, or the 12-foot sizes.

Some people want a windmill in front of their house, barn or shop, simply for the old-fashioned look it gives to the place. If that is what you want, you may wish to select a 6-foot wheel, and go to a relatively short tower of 15 or 20 feet.

However, if you are serious about using the windmill, you will get the most service from a tower that puts the head eight or 10 feet above all surrounding houses, barns, trees within a 300 foot radius. Baker heads will fit any make tower: many Baker heads are running on other make towers.

Windmill head, 6 foot — $595.00
Windmill head, 8 foot — $840.00
Windmill tower:
15-foot $625
20-foot $695
25-foot $750
35-foot $860

LISTER DIESELS: For a dependable source of power, these diesels are hard to beat. They run for hours for very small amounts of fuel, and low cost. This is the motor that most Amish farm families go to, especially for cooling milk, where dependable day-after-day service is a must.

They are expensive, but the quality is fantastic. The model 8/1 is a single cylinder model, has eight horsepower, and runs at 850 rpm's. Weight of bare engine is 777 pounds. This model is priced in the $2,400 range. If interested, write us for company brochure and exact pricing.

ENERGY SYSTEMS
4874 Cherry Tree Lane
Sykesville, Maryland 21784
(301) 795-3828

Old-line Dempster "Annu-Oiled" waterpumping windmills and towers. Also replacement parts and pump cylinders.

6-ft. windmill — $455 (U.S.)
8-ft. windmill — $675 (U.S.)

SOLACE ENERGY CENTRES
2425 Main Street
Vancouver, B.C. V5T 3E1
(604) 879-5258

Another source for Pelton hydroelectric units and Billabong hydraulic rams.

Pelton Wheel

ENERGY ALTERNATIVES
2 Croft
Amherst, Nova Scotia
(902) 667-2790

Offers two models of Sparco windmills to pump water. The Diaphragm Type (Model D) will draw water from a lake, spring, creek or dug well. It will lift water 13 feet over a horizontal distance of 30 feet. ($360.00) The Piston Type (Model P) is priced at $410.00 and will draw water up from a well or from under a bridge or pier. Maximum lift 333 feet.

HYDROELECTRIC POWER

CAREFUL ECO SYSTEMS LTD.
Box 1212
Whaletown, B.C. V0P 1Z0

Source of Pelton wheel hydroelectric power units from small turbines to 10,000-watt units. This firm also distributes Billabong hydraulic water-pumping rams.

With a DC hydroelectric power plant batteries are used so that your system can supply many times the output of the power plant. This is a marked advantage if you have periods of heavy

power consumption. During periods of low power consumption the batteries are automatically charged. Batteries give a small system the necessary surge power needed to start electric motors. For this reason a small DC power plant can be much more useful and versatile than a larger AC plant. Since batteries in a water power system are usually recharged within a few hours you can get by with used batteries. This helps to keep the initial cost low. We need the following measurements to determine cost and power potential of a hydroelectric system for your stream: head or fall of your stream, distance over which the head is developed, the amount of water flowing in your stream and the distance from power plant to load. We will then calculate the size of hydroelectric unit your stream could operate, the diameter and cost of pipe, and the size and cost of wire needed. We charge $10.00 for this service which is refunded on the purchase of one of our hydroelectric units. If you want to take your own measurements we suggest the method below or the methods in "Low Cost Development of Small Water Power Sites" by Hans W. Hamm. The cost is $4.00 from VITA, 3700 Rhode Island Ave., Mt. Rainier, Maryland U.S.A.

Water Flow: Find or make a place in the stream where the water all flows through a narrow slot. Place a 5 or 10 gallon bucket under the flow and see how many seconds it takes to fill it.

$$\frac{\text{Size of bucket in gallons}}{\text{number of seconds to fill}} = \frac{\text{flow in}}{\text{gallons/second}}$$

HEAD: (vertical fall of your stream): Start at the point where water will enter your system. With a solidly supported carpenter's level sight along the level to a 10-foot pole held vertically by a friend. Have your friend move the pole downhill until you are sighting just to the top of the pole. This gives you a head of 10 feet to the bottom of the pole. Move your level to the bottom of the pole and repeat this process until you come to the proposed location of the power plant. Add up the number of 10-foot drops plus any remaining drop at the end to get your head in feet. We also rent an altimeter for finding head.

Power available from our smallest Pelton Wheel Power Plants using one nozzle:

Up to three nozzles can be used. If you have enough water to operate two or three nozzles then you can get two or three times the power shown in the following table. This table is for nozzles with a standard bore jet. If you do not have enough water flow to satisfy the values given in this table, we can give you a small bore jet at no extra cost. You must have at least one-quarter the water flow shown in which case you will get one-quarter the power shown.

Fall of water in feet	Water flow gallons/second	Power watts
50	.7	280
75	.88	500
100	1.0	800
125	1.1	1000
150	1.2	1500
200	1.4	2200
250	1.6	3100
300	1.75	4200
400	2.0	6500

Even if your stream can only produce 200 watts of power this is enough to operate a small house. This would allow you to draw 500 watts for 9 hours per day, which is the equivalent of having a refrigerator (constantly plugged in but assuming it runs one one-third of the time) plus three 60-watt lights and a stereo on for 9 hours per day.

Water Power Plants: DC plants are best used when you cannot produce your peak power demands from the stream. Batteries are used so your system can supply more power than your stream can produce. This is important for starting electric motors. The batteries are automatically recharged during periods of low power consumption. 110-or 220-volt AC units are approximately $1,500 more than the same size DC unit. One year guarantee.

2000 watt 32 volt DC water power plant with small turbine — $1,650.
3000 watt 32 or 110 volt DC water power plant with medium turbine — $2,770.

5000 watt 110 volt DC water power plant with medium turbine — $3,870.
10000 watt 110 volt water plant $6,200.
Small turbine with one nozzle, no generator, regulator or sheaves — $888.
Medium turbine with one nozzle, no generator, regulator or sheaves — $1,360.

Billabong Hydraulic Ram: This machine is a simple automatic device that makes water pump itself uphill. Water can be forced about as far horizontally as you desire, but long distances require a larger pipe. Generally speaking, a ram should not be used to lift water over 200 ft. vertically. There is no external power needed and the ram has only two working parts. The only maintenance needed is to keep leaves and debris cleaned away from the intake and to replace valve rubbers if they get worn. The original cost is almost the only cost.

Two things are needed to make the ram work; (a) enough water to run the ram (almost 10 times the amount of water you want pumped) and (b) enough height for water to fall through the drive pipe to work the ram (approx. 1/10th the height you want the water pumped up to). Water may come from a spring, pond, or creek.

How it works; the water starts to run down through the drive pipe, going faster and faster until it forces the impetus valve to close suddenly. The weight of the moving water, suddenly stopped, creates very high pressure and forces some of the water past the non-return or delivery valve and into the air chamber, compressing the air more and more until the energy of the moving water is spent. This compressed air acts as a spring and forces the water up the delivery pipe to the storage tank in a steady stream. The snifting plug wastes a bit of water but takes in a bubble of air with each stroke. This is necessary to keep air in the air dome and it must not get plugged or the air dome will become filled with water and the ram will stop.

A gate valve is recommended on both the drive and the discharge pipe to avoid the necessity of emptying the pipes during cleaning or maintenance. If the intake fall is not over 20 feet and if the intake is kept clean of leaves and debris there will be almost no maintenance.

The ram is most efficient when the volume of the air chamber is equal to the volume of the discharge pipe. Therefore the larger size rams are best suited for long discharge pipes providing there is enough water to operate them. The length and diameter of the intake pipe can be altered from that suggested in the following table. Essentially the volume of water in the intake pipe must be equal to the suggested volume. In order to insure your ram works for a very long time and with minimum maintenance, check with us before you make any changes in the intake pipe. Allowance must be made for spent drive water to be drained away. The snifting plug must at no time be immersed in the spent water from the impetus valve.

Prices $377—$1,550.

HYDRAULIC RAM TABLE

No. of Ram	PIPES		Galls. per Min. required to operate Ram	Discharge Capacity Galls. per Hour	Weight in lbs.
	Drive	Discharge			
3	1"	½"	1¼ – 4	10 – 20	29
4	1½"	½"	3 – 7	15 – 35	35
5	2"	¾"	6 – 14	30 – 60	55
6	2½"	1"	12 – 25	55 – 100	125
7	3"	1½"	20 – 40	100 – 200	200
10	4"	2"	25 – 100	125 – 500	700

Minimum Fall in Feet from Supply to Ram	Height in Feet Water may be Elevated	Length of Drive Pipe in Feet
2	4	12
2	6	12
2	8	12
3	15	15
4	25	20
5	35	30
6	48	40
7	63	50
8	80	60
10	100	75
12	120	95
14	140	110
16	160	125
18	180	146
20	200	160

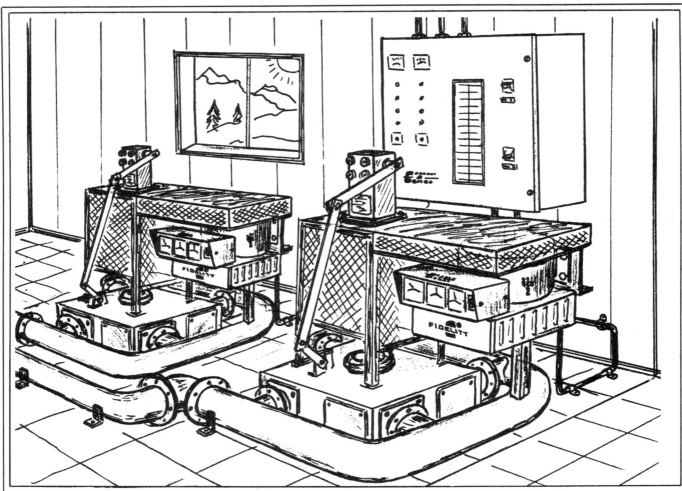

Twin vertical shaft hydroelectric units from Small Hydroelectric Systems & Equipment.

SMALL HYDROELECTRIC SYSTEMS & EQUIPMENT
15220 S.R. 530
Arlington, Washington 98223
(206) 435-3148

Knowledgeable people selling components for independent, small-to medium-scale hydro-electric plants. Their catalogue is almost indecipherable to anyone not versed in the subject, but they appear willing to offer advice. Ready-to-run turbines, $2,500 and up.

EQUIPCO, LTD.
Box 2112
Tacoma, Washington 98402
(206) 572-2360

Fidelity alternators and electrical controls for hydroelectric systems.

HYDROELECTRICS CANADA LIMITED
Box 54
Silverton, B.C. V0G 2B0

Parts and kits for constructing Pelton turbine generating plants.

MOUNTAIN WATER POWER
Telegraph Creek, B.C.
V0J 2W0

Small hydroelectric systems for northern homesteads. D.C. and A.C. systems. Send $2.00 for pamphlet describing the systems.

ALLIS-CHALMERS
Milwaukee, Wisconsin 53201
(414) 475-3328

Allis-Chalmers is best known to most of us as a tractor manufacturer, but the firm is also the developer of the tube-turbine concept. This design for generating hydroelectric power at low-head sites had previously been put aside as uneconomical, but with the rise in energy prices some observers feel that many dams in North America could now be outfitted with units such as this

to contribute substantial amounts of electricity.

The Allis-Chalmer units now available range in output from 50 to 5,000 kilowatts. They make use of the "propeller in a pipe" concept that minimizes construction requirements and maximizes flexibility in arrangement and operating characteristics. The company says that standard components are used, and installation does not require deep foundations or a large powerhouse.

This new approach to what is really a traditional market is making it feasible to develop sites which a few years ago were considered uneconomical. Few of the dams in North America today have operating turbines. Many had their turbines removed when oil was cheap and abundant, while the majority have never been used for electric generation. Most of the standard tube turbines could be installed in existing dams. They are particularly well adapted to run-of-the-river situations where they have minimal effect on the upstream pond and on the flow downstream. As a result they are being promoted as one of the most environmentally acceptable forms of energy production.

—Michael Asti-Rose

Random Comment

I live with a Wincharger. A 1500 watt, 32 volt, four blade generator which towers 56 feet above the ground. We paid half as much for it, installed and working, as we would have had to pay to get the Calgary Power transformer mounted on a pole in our yard. The decision to buy a wind generator was as much political as it was practical.

We live in Alberta, land of infinite, non-renewable (is that a contradiction in terms?) resources. Our provincial energy minister Merv Leach, said only a few weeks ago that wind and solar energy were not viable for Alberta and that we would look ridiculous if we started developing renewable energy resources when we had so much oil and gas and coal still to use here.

Yet here in the rural areas of this province, groups are battling constantly with power companies regarding expropriation of agricultural land. Farmers at Dodds-Round Hill won at least a temporary postponement against a power development there. So did the citizens group at Genesee Keep-Hills. Those were both to be coal-fired operations which would have resulted in massive strip-mining of viable farm land. A struggle that still continues west of Red Deer involves a hydro-electric project that will flood instead of strip agricultural land there. It seems that increased consumption of electricity can only end in environmental disaster of one kind or another— flooding, strip-mining, or nuclear alternatives which aren't really alternatives at all.

Tying into a power grid just didn't seem feasible when we wanted to live in harmony with our earth. Tying into the wind did. We painted the word ''Peace'' on our yellow tail-fin to celebrate.

We had lived on our farm for two years without electricity. We managed quite well, using naphtha and coal oil and candles. We went to bed earlier in the winter, and came to appreciate the coming of dusk in a way we hadn't when growing up with lights that came on at the first hint of darkness setting in. Living without power would have been an option for me indefinitely—it was not a priority to have electricity here. But then Opportunity came along. The Wincharger was installed, it worked, and it was great to put our petroleum bar (naphtha, kerosene, and assorted funnels, spouts and lanterns) away.

We have not, however, been trouble-free with this unit. We have had plenty of wind, so didn't feel a need for a back-up gas generator until something went wrong with a relay which prevented power coming to the batteries from the tower. An operator's manual helped us considerably, as did the expertise of people who lived with generators before the lines came in. We do not expect to run much more than lights off the plant— our refrigerator is propane-run, a warm insulated garage substitutes for a block heater in winter, and overall our electrical needs are small. We look forward, though, to running 110-volt tools off an inverter, and attaching a 32-volt motor to a water pump and a washing machine.

It's a good system to live with. I get a good view from atop the tower, and enjoy listening to the music of the rotors as they generate. Does all this sound soapy and romantic? I guess the novelty hasn't worn off yet.

I still don't quite believe that it works. Is it really possible to turn a light on because the wind blows? Nothing short of amazing as far as I'm concerned.

—Barbara Palm White
Winfield, Alberta

Books

THE WIND BOOK
By Ian Hornby
Pollution Probe
53 Queen Street
Ottawa,Ontario
$2.00

WIND MACHINES
By Frank R. Eldridge
Mitre Corp.
Westgate Research Park
McLean, Virginia 22101
$2.00

THE HELIUS WIND BOOK
By Colin Kerr
Thermax Corporation
Box 275
Hawkesbury, Ontario
$2.00

CATCH THE WIND
By Landt and Lisl Dennis
Four Winds Press
50 West 44th Street
New York, New York 10036
$7.95

ELECTRIC POWER FROM THE WIND
By Henry Clews
Enertech
Box 420
Norwich, Vermont 05055
$2.00

HARNESSING THE WIND FOR HOME ENERGY
By Dermot McGuigan
Garden Way Publishing
Charlotte, Vermont 05445
134 pages, $4.95

PLANNING A WIND POWERED GENERATING SYSTEM
Enertech Corporation
Box 420
Norwich, Vermont 05055
46 pages, $2.00

WIND POWER FOR FARMS, HOMES AND SMALL INDUSTRY
By Jack Park & Dick Schwind
RFP-2841/1270/78/4
N.T.I.S.
Springfield, Virginia 22161
$9.50

Rebuilt Jacobs wind generator, Sawyerville, Quebec.

A GUIDE TO COMMERCIALLY AVAILABLE WIND MACHINES
RFP-2836/3533/78/3
Rocky Flats Wind
Systems Program
Rockwell International
Box 464
Golden, Colorado 80401
121 pages, $7.25

SIMPLIFIED WIND POWER SYSTEMS FOR EXPERIMENTERS
By Jack Park
Helion, Inc.
Box 445
Brownsville, Ca. 95919
80 pages, $6.00

THE HOMEBUILT, WIND-GENERATED ELECTRICITY HANDBOOK
By Michael Hackleman
Earthmind
4844 Hirsch Road
Mariposa, California 95338
194 pages, $8.00

WIND & WINDSPINNERS
By Michael Hackleman
Earthmind
4844 Hirsch Road
Mariposa, California 95338
115 pages, $8.00

THE WILDERNESS HOME POWER SYSTEM AND HOW TO DO IT
By Jim Cullen
Wilderness Home Power Co.
Box 732
Laytonville, Ca 95454
$10.95

WIND ENERGY BIBLIOGRAPHY
Windworks
Box 44A, Rt. 3
Mukwanago, Wisconsin 53149
$3.00

ENERGY FROM THE WIND
(bibliography)
Burke & Meroney Publications
Engineering Research Center
Foothills Campus
Colorado State University
Fort Collins, Colorado 80523
$7.50

Publications

ALTERNATIVE SOURCES OF ENERGY MAGAZINE
Route 3, Box 90A
Milaca, Minnesota 56353
$17/year in Canada (6 issues)

RAIN—JOURNAL OF APPROPRIATE TECHNOLOGY
2270 N. W. Irving
Portland, Oregon 97210
$12.50/year in Canada
(12 issues)

WIND POWER DIGEST
Jester Press
54468 County Road 31
Bristol, Indiana 46507
$9/year in Canada (4 issues)

BRACE RESEARCH INSTITUTE
MacDonald College
of McGill University
Ste. Anne de Bellevue
Quebec H9X 3M1

Do-It-Yourself leaflet number 5:
"How to Construct a Cheap Wind
Machine for Pumping Water"
(Savonius rotor plans)

Construction Plans

WINDWORKS
Box 44A, Route 3
Mukwonago, Wisconsin 53149

Construction plans for 25-foot
diameter sail windmill ($25) and
12-foot propeller windmill ($15)

VITA
(Volunteers for International
Technical Assistance)
3706 Rhode Island Avenue
Mt. Rainier, Maryland 20822

Pub. No. 11132-1: Savonius rotor
Pub. No. 11133-1: Essex fan blade
windmill
Pub. No. 11133-3: US-AID Fan
blade windmill
Pub. No. 11131-1: Helical sail
windmill

EARTHWIND
26510 Josel Drive
Saugus, California 91350

Vertical axis windmill plans ($7)

SENCENBAUGH WIND ELECTRIC
678 Chimalus Drive
Palo Alto, California 94306

Plans for horizontal axis propeller
windmill ($12)

FLANAGAN'S PLANS
Box 891, Cathedral Station
New York, N.Y. 10025

Plans for "The Quixote" sailwing
rotor ($25 U.S.; $29 outside U.S.)

NORTH WIND POWER CO. INC.
Box 315
Warren, Vermont 05674

Plans for 12-foot and 16-foot
diameter windmills ($10)

BIANCHI '79

A Tranquil Place In The Country

Recollections of an owner/builder

What we needed, the reasoning went, was a tranquil place in the country, in a beautiful setting, which would be largely self-sufficient. A few chores a day, chop some wood, pick some vegetables, and all the rest of the time to ourselves.

Over a period of three years, before we actually left the city, we made preparations. We drew plans for a monstrous stone and log house, studied building techniques, gardening, animal husbandry, mechanics, aerodynamics, ancient philosophy and the life and times of Leonard Seppella. We wanted to be ready for anything.

We didn't have a lot of money so we decided to lease government land. The first area we applied for

was on a very large lake in central B.C. with no access except by water or air. We were told by the local land officials that, considering our inexperience and the difficulties involved, we would be much wiser to get a place on a road near a power line. Sage advice.

We didn't take it. We wanted to be on our own, so we stayed in that area. Our first application-to-lease was rejected because it was in a forest reserve. The next because it was on an island. Another because Victoria just couldn't see why we would need such a piece of land. We were getting pretty far out by this time. Finally, after three years, we had an application accepted.

It was a beautiful setting. A

natural harbour protected on all sides (except that of the prevailing winds), a 40-foot-wide valley for a garden (solid clay), and a 300-foot-steep hill with an excellent view and a nice spot on the top (which *looked* level) to build on. As for tranquility, well except for the incessant bashing of waves against our boat, it couldn't have been better. It was eight miles, over water, to our nearest neighbour.

We quickly built a small frame cabin to live in until the end of the summer (by which time we expected to be able to move into the house) and another cabin to serve as a workshop and storage space.

Then we started to gather logs. There were hundreds of them spread around the lake from log booms that had broken up over the years. Our plan was to get them all out of the lake right away so that they could season while we built the foundation. It soon became obvious that our electric winch (the only piece of equipment we had bought new) was not going to make it. We sent it to Vancouver for repairs. It took eight months to come back.

In the meantime our battle with the internal-combustion motor began. We had one used outboard motor. The first time it broke down we paddled our very heavy boat through some very heavy weather. Then we had to bounce up and down like fools and wave at passing tourists to get a lift over to the landing. We bought two more (used) outboard motors. We also had two chain saws, a motor on our generator and another on the rototiller. We had to become intimate with every one and they resisted intimacy with the implacability of a court magistrate.

It was the beginning of our apprenticeship.

That first summer was the beginning, also, of our relationship with the lake. Everything we did involved the lake. Much of our food came out of it or from its shores; our building supplies (logs, stone, sand), our water, water for the garden, all came from the lake. The garden itself (we had to build it from the subsoil up) and, indeed, *everything*, had to be transported over the lake.

For a time when we first arrived, in the spring when the winds were gentle, we took the lake for granted, received what we needed from it, and thought no more about it.

The first real encounter was when we brought over a circulating fireplace core. It was large and heavy (far too big, we learned later, to be efficient). We had an old river boat, a long canoe-shaped thing with a flat bottom, and the only way the fireplace would go in was upright. It made us very top-heavy but the lake looked calm so we set off.

About halfway across, it began to get rough. It had, in fact, been rough when we left but since we had a following wind with the waves breaking away from us, and no experience, we hadn't been able to tell how rough it was. We slowed to a crawl. The fireplace was tied down, but we still had to steady it. It was too late to turn around. Anyway, we couldn't go against the waves because they would have broken our old craft in two. Going with them, the water came in the low-cut stern. So it was in and out of the troughs, staying on exactly the right angle so that we wouldn't be turned over or swamped from the side, doing our best to stop the fireplace from smashing its way through the side of the boat, bailing when we absolutely had to, taking quick glances at the nearest islands that seemed to move away as we approached them. We were terrified and cursed the lake for terrifying us.

We made it to the islands. Euphoria. We bailed the boat, set the fireplace straight, and waited. After about 15 minutes, with the glow of success still in us, we decided to try for the next island. It was only a quarter of a mile and it was getting dark; we wanted to get home.

It was rough but we made it. On to the next, another quarter of a mile away. After that it would be only a mile to home.

We didn't make it to the next. The water in that particular area was rougher than any other part of the lake, and we had to face into it to get to the island. Again we were

terrified, humbled, angry at the lake and our short memories. We forgot home and concentrated on staying afloat.

Eventually we were deposited on the beach of the mainland. Waves immediately began pouring in the stern. We turned the boat broadside to the waves. They began breaking it up. We tied two long ropes to the bow, pulled the boat around, and held it facing the waves. It pounded a bit but it was the best way. We waited. The lake kept us there for three hours, playing with the boat and fireplace, then suddenly let up and allowed us to go quietly home.

By the end of the first summer we had gathered 25 logs (we needed over a hundred), cleared the building site and dug out about half the foundation. We gave up working on the house when it became too cold for our temporary cabin. Instead, we winterized the building that had originally been a workshop. We lived in that building for six years.

It was three more summers before we had the foundation finished.

Transporting materials turned out to be the major part of the job. We moved 100 tons of stone and sand from beaches near and far to the harbour by water, from there to the bottom of the hill by wheelbarrow and from there to the top with the winch and a series of cables and pulleys and boxes that would have astounded Zorba himself.

Nomadic Architecture

It was a magnificent foundation: double stone wall with fibreglass insulation between the walls, nine feet high at one end (*not* a level site) and three and a half feet thick, all on solid bedrock.

Magnificent but not necessary. Even two feet thick would have been more than enough and it needn't have had meticulously placed stones on the inside where they wouldn't be seen and would only gather dust.

Well, it took Bess of Hardwick seven years to build Hardwick Hall, too. We had the satisfaction of knowing that it would be there a long time—unless the mountain collapsed under it.

Our boat had carried, pushed and pulled the entire foundation over the lake. It was a good boat, shaped for the lake, but it was decrepit when we got it and too rotten to be worth repairing. When the lake was rough we simply had to stay where we were—usually on the wrong side. We paced back and forth, railed, and decided, many times, to get a new boat that would be covered and powerful and able to take us across in any weather.

Finally we got it. We felt invincible.

Then, one beautiful sunny day in moderately rough weather, a wave smashed through the windshield and half-filled the boat. It was a wave like any other, not especially big or curled at the edges, or vicious looking. But it happened. A ton of water rose out of the lake and threw itself at the windshield.

Sitting in the seat, soaked and covered with broken glass, in that moment of shock before fear, we were sure the boat was going down. We panicked and started bailing as fast as we could.

The boat wasn't going down. We bailed it out and went home with no more problems. It was merely an admonition. The boat *could* go down.

The log work turned out to be almost as slow as the stone work. With the logs, perhaps because wood is so much more malleable than stone, we came to realize that unless you set a standard of workmanship (not too high) from the beginning, it's possible to become trapped in an infinite regression wherein you work for a closer and closer fit until you find that you are spending your entire life on one log. It is, no doubt, as good a way as any to spend your life. "If a poet can make one good image in a lifetime . . . . " But some compromise finally has to be lived with in order to get the job done.

We were pretty far into the regression before we set our standard. As a result it took us two more years to get into our house.

In the meantime the lake continued its instruction. One winter we lost all our food in a fire. It was during freeze-up, the lake not yet solidly frozen, so we couldn't go anywhere. We waited a few days, then became impatient, and hungry, and decided to try it.

For about a mile out in front of our place the ice was bad—slushy and unpredictable. From there on it looked blue and permanent. I decided to go alone on the snowmobile over the first part, at full speed, to expose the slush so that it would freeze overnight and we would have a solid trail for the next day. About a mile out, almost to the good ice, the snowmobile went down.

It was a heavy machine but it was lighter in pounds per square inch than I was.

I had watched, through the glasses, a wolverine drown in that same spot during the previous winter.

I broke a lot of ice, became thoroughly waterlogged, took in too much oxygen but finally managed to slither out. Once on the ice I went another 10 yards on my stomach, like a snake, distributing my weight absolutely evenly. Then I stood and walked. When the ice cracked and showed signs of not supporting me, I prayed. To the lake.

It's done. We have a large stone and log house in a beautiful setting and the place is largely self-sufficient. It gives us the comfort of continuity. As for the tranquility . . . .

—A. Southgate
Topley Landing, B.C.

OWNER/BUILDER ARCHITECTURE

YOUR ENGINEERED HOUSE
By Rex Roberts
McClelland & Stewart Ltd.
25 Hollinger Road
Toronto, Ont. M4B 3G2
or
J.B. Lippincott Co.
East Washington Square
Philadelphia, Pa 19105
$4.95, 237 pages
(Large format paperback)

"The sun comes up in the east and goes down in the west. Your engineering must begin with this obvious but all-governing fact. If bacon is to be fried by daylight, the kitchen will look southeast. If shaving is to be by daylight, the bathroom will be close by.

"Two vital work areas have been located on your previously blank piece of paper. You spend crucial morning minutes at lavatory and stove, and you have given the southeast sun a chance to make those desperate minutes as warm and cheerful as your nature may permit. The house, at least, will begin its day pleasantly.

"A cry, 'The eggs are boiling,' can be heard through the bathroom wall. Your house, while pleasant, is also efficient."

Another cry, "Oh good, another Alternate Architecture book!" rings out. Fortunately not so. This book is, rather, a basic primer for shelter-provision. It starts one, maybe two steps before building, and if you, like me, have never really thought about what a home is for, much less built one, then this book is indispensable. Why it is not more widely publicized is quite beyond me, so I'm doing my bit to help.

"The subject of this book is how to get a good house for little money, but no pound of ink and

Prefab

paper can do more than suggest paths for your own thinking to follow.

"Let's pretend that you are four years old, therefore not as yet possessed by a set of store-bought answers. At this age and in this frame of mind every one of your questions begins with 'Why?' Why brings a 'because' response. Somewhere between Why and Because you can learn How to build a house.

"I believe this process is called thinking. Thinking is more readily observed when it is absent than when it is present. You can recall hundreds of examples of not-thinking, most of them committed by yourself, some by others. We are talking about houses, and when we talk about houses, not-thinking gets expensive."

This book moves from thinking to practical guidelines. "It fits the thinking of an engineer, who hopes to be at once disciplined and creative. It approximates the way in which the first architect-builder-craftsman-head-of-the-family reached his decisions." The chapters are:

What Is Your House?
Where Shall It Be?
When Shall It Be Built?
How Will It Be Built?
Why Will You Build It?
Who Are You?

This is a practical book in the basic sense of the word. It will tell you how to build walls, doors, windows, ceilings, a roof, floors and foundations. And why they're built the way they are. It even tells you why certain things shouldn't be built, even though everyone builds them. For instance basements: "The historical and technical reasons for basements have long since disappeared. There is not one single thing on my list of day-round and year-round activities that I would put in a basement unless the basement were already there."

Many things explored are details I've rarely seen in any other book or considered in house building. Window heights, selecting wood and other basic materials, window placement, plumbing and electrical routing, wall placement, site planning, interior design to reduce dust-catching surfaces, ventilation, placement of artificial illumination, and even sound reduction in a house—not by sound-proofing but by design. "Most of the building methods which make for an irritatingly noisy house are expensive, while most of the methods which make for good acoustics are cheap. This represents the something for nothing bonanza of all time."

If this book were priced to reflect its worth, it would be the major cost in house construction. In a world of inflated prices and exaggerated claims of usefulness, this book has to be the best "something for (almost) nothing bonanza of all time."

You will end up with a house that is truly *yours*, and will not only know how to build it but, immeasurably more important, why you built it that way.

—*Roger Nixon*
Dwight, Ontario

THE OWNER BUILT HOME
By Ken Kern
Scribner's
374 pages, paperback $8.95

The cover subtitle calls this "A How-to-do-it Book," but it remains one of the best in its field because it is, in Kern's own words, "a how-to-think-it" book.

INTRODUCTION

The author has long had the compulsion to express feelings and thoughts in regard to the home-building industry and the wish to do something constructive for the people who suffer under it—both the construction worker and the home buyer alike. No critic as yet comprehends entirely why our houses are so poorly constructed, why they look so abominable, why they cost so much for construction and for maintenance, and why they are so uncomfortable. Some critics blame the building contractors personally; others feel that the fault lies with urban codes and building restrictions. Some believe that expensive housing is due to the high interest rates charged by the banks; others blame the trade unions for hampering efficient construction. Every writer on the subject seems to fondle some pet corrective measure. And every year some noted architect develops a sure-fire technical solution to the housing problem. Even more often the building-material manufacturers come up with a new wonder, an improved wallboard or window or what-not, which can be installed with a 10-minute saving in labour.

Everyone in the building industry appears to be busily engaged in making "improvements" in his personal area of concern, but quality makes a steady decline. The end product is as inadequate, unsatisfying, and costly a house as ever. The architect spends more and more time at his drafting board, exhausting possibilities of new construction techniques and more economical arrangements; the contractor conscripts ever more specialized equipment for building efficiency; the banker resorts to undreamt-of schemes to make it possible for everyone to buy his new home—even if he lacks money to make the down payment; building-material manufacturers work overtime in their laboratories making "more and better things"— presumably for better living. With all this bustle one might well expect some major improvements in new-home construction. Whatever improvements have occurred are insignificant in comparison with the improvements that should be made. The causes of the world's housing problem still remain.

Tracing these causes to their sources has helped me to view the problem in perspective—comprehensively. The process has also suggested some workable alternatives as solutions to personal housing needs. Here they are in the form of seven axioms, listed in order of importance for the prospective owner-builder.

1. When building your home, pay as you go. A building loan is a type of legalized robbery. More than any other agency, banks have been successful in reducing would-be democratic man to a state of perpetual serfdom. The banks have supported and helped to determine social and political conventions and have amassed phenomenal fortunes through unearned increment. As "friends" of the homeowner they have made it possible for him to take immediate possession of his new home—and to pay for it monthly for 20 to 30 years. Most people who fall

into this trap fail to realize that the accumulating interest on their 30-year mortgage comes to more than double the market value of their house! If one expects any success at all with keeping costs of his new home down to a reasonable price one must be entirely free from interest rates.

2. Supply your own labour. *Building trades' unions have received—and not unjustly so—a notorious reputation as wasters of speed and efficiency in building work. We all know that painters are restricted to a certain-size brush and that carpenters are limited to a certain-size hammer (upon threat of penalty from union officials). Apparently more width and more weight might conceivably speed up a project to the point where some union man would prove to be expendable.*

The disinterest that the average journeyman has in his work, despite his high union-pay rate, is appalling. The lack of joy-in-work or of acceptance of responsibility among average workmen can be accounted for partly by the dehumanizing effect of the whole wage system. So long as the master-and-slave type of employer-employee relationship continues to exist in our society one can expect only the worst performance from his "hired help." Until the dawn of the new era approaches one would do well, from an economic as well as from a self-satisfying standpoint, to supply his own labour for his own home insofar as he can.

3. Build according to your own best judgement. *At the apex of the poor-building hierarchy—and perhaps the greatest single*

impediment to good housing—is convention. Building convention takes two forms: first, there is convention that is socially instilled, commonly called "style," which can be altered through education. The second type of convention is more vicious and politically enforced.

Building codes, zoning restrictions, and ordinances all fall into this class of impediments. In urban jurisdictions politically controlled convention calls the shots for practically every segment of the building industry. Ordinance approval or disapproval makes the difference between having a house or having none at all. Or it may make a difference of $1,000 (on the average) wasted because of stupid, antiquated building laws.

If we are to be at liberty to build our own home at less cost, we must necessarily be free from building-code jurisdiction. This means we must locate outside urban control—in the country or in small-township districts.

4. Use native materials whenever possible. *Much of an architect's time is spent keeping abreast of the new, improved building materials, which manufacturers make each month. Many of the products are really worthwhile, but, more often than not, in cost they are entirely beyond the reach of the average home builder. Basic materials, like common cement, have not appreciably advanced in price over the past dozen years, but some of the newer surfacing materials and interior fixtures have skyrocketed in price during this same period.*

By not using these high-cost materials, one, of course, avoids this

problem. Emphasis should, instead, be placed on the use of readily available natural resources—materials that come directly from the site or from a convenient hauling distance. Rock, earth, concrete, timber, and all such materials have excellent structural and heat-regulating qualities when properly used.

5. Design and plan your own home. *One ten-percenter with whom we can well afford to do without when building a low-cost home is the architect-designer-craftsman-supervisor. Experience in this aspect of home building has led me to conclude that* anyone *can and* everyone *should* design his own home. *There is only one possible drawback to this: the owner-builder must know what he wants in a home, and he must be familiar with the building site and the regional climatic conditions. Without close acquaintance with the site and the regional climate and without a clear understanding of the family's living needs the project is doomed to failure no matter who designs the house. An architect—even a good architect—cannot interpret a client's building needs better than the client himself. Anyway, most contemporary architects design houses for themselves, not for their clients. They work at satisfying some aesthetic whim and fail to really understand the character of the site or the personal requirements of their client . . . .*

MINIMUM COST HOUSING GROUP

School of Architecture
McGill University
3480 University Street
Montreal, Quebec H3A 2A7

Offers graduate studies in minimum cost housing, as well as a selection of publications for do-it-yourself builders. Write for publication list and prices.

It has been estimated that the average North American uses 100 litres of water when he showers and 300 litres every time he bathes. In areas of the world where water is not plentiful or in parts of our own country, such as the North, where it is not accessible, using this amount of water simply to wash is not possible. Members of the group set to work to develop a system which used little water, was inexpensive and yet effective.

During the preliminary stages of the project, their work was based on a concept developed by Buckminster Fuller in the late '40s. While in the Navy, Fuller discovered that the grease which covered his hands and face as a result of working in the engine rooms of ships, would disappear after a few minutes on deck. Realizing that this was due to the mist in the air, he later developed a mechanized "fog gun" which made use of an electric compressor to break up water and spray it. As he became heavily involved in numerous other projects, Fuller discontinued work on the fog gun.

At first the McGill group worked with hand-operated atomizers which were basically adaptations of garden pesticide sprayers. Last year they experimented with an electric compressor which produces a fine vapour by spraying water through a nozzle. Both worked well for hand-washing. Their most recent project completed only recently, largely through the efforts of graduate student Alex Morse, has involved the development of a shower—more specifically a 10-minute shower—which uses one litre of water! And it works. Based on the same principle as the hand-washers, it contains no electrical or expensive parts and its components are available just about anywhere in the world.

The water reservoir consists of the container for windshield wiper fluid in Volkswagens and pressure is provided by a bicycle pump. A person wanting to take a shower would use the pump to generate sufficient pressure, step into the stall and shower for 10 minutes, at which point the pressure would begin to decrease.

No norms exist to test the real effectiveness of this kind of shower from the point of view of hygiene. But the subjective impressions of those who have used it have been positive. The soap is rinsed off without any problem.

The shower unit sounds almost too simple to be true. What must be remembered, says Professor Rybczynski, is that it went through a number of different stages involving the use of expensive components such as electric compressors. The goal was a simple, inexpensive and effective system whose parts could be obtained just about anywhere in the world.

SHELTER INSTITUTE
38 Centre Street
Bath, Maine 04530
(207) 442-7938

Such a basic idea—teach people to build low-cost (under $10,000) energy-efficient homes by using their own designs, their own labour and locally available materials (primarily wood). The simplicity of the idea, however, has created quick success for the Shelter Institute and international media coverage. One can only hope that similar centres spring up in other regions. Write for information and booklist.

Three Week Course $300 per person, $450 per couple.

NORTHERN OWNER BUILDER
Rd. 1
Plainfield, Vermont 05667
Mail-order source of owner-builder books and home plans.

THE TIMBER FRAMING BOOK
THE TIMBER FRAME RAISING BOOK
All by Stewart Elliott

Dovetail Press Ltd.
Box 1496
Boulder, Colorado
(303) 449-2681

A series of attractive books for those to whom the cash-n-carry two-by-four is anathema.

30 ENERGY-EFFICIENT HOUSES . . .You Can Build
By Alex Wade and
Neal Ewenstein
Rodale Press
Emmaus, Pennsylvania
$9.95, 316 pages
(Large format paperback)

"Except for my father, every generation of my family has built its own house. This goes all the way back to my great-great-grandfather, Jacques, who built his 18-by-20-foot log house on land granted him by King George of England back in the 1780s. The house still stands and is in use as a barn. My aunt recently chased away NBC when they wanted to buy it for a Bicentennial Special."

Alex Wade begins this new book with a statement of his reactionary belief that a new home is still a reasonable expectation for North Americans and that an energy-efficient house can still be built for $5,000.

Timber-framing is intimidating to the novice, but Stewart Elliott and a group of volunteers raised a 1,200 square foot home in a day.

Rather than hammering away at this philosophy, Wade launches into 30 case histories of people who have built such houses and the reader comes away convinced that an architecturally stimulating and energy-efficient home is well within the reach of most of us. Although several homes of rambling design are included, the author clearly is biased toward smaller plans which make the most efficient use of space and materials. These homes — most in the 1,000 to 1,400-square-foot range — do not *seem* small, because of intelligent use of open areas, built-in storage space and pleasing placement of windows and skylights.

This is a useful book that also happens to be personal, readable and well-illustrated by both drawings and Neal Ewenstein's fine photographs.

HOW TO DESIGN & BUILD YOUR OWN HOUSE
By Lupe DiDonno &
Phyllis Sperling
Alfred A. Knopf, 1978
368 pages, softcover $12.50

Four years of architecture school compressed and explained for the would-be house designer. Proof, as the authors state, that "the talents required for house-building are not sex-linked."

SHELTER II
Edited by Lloyd Kahn, Jr.
Home Book Service,
Box 650
Bolinas, California 94924
224 pages, softcover, $10.00
(Postpaid to U.S. and Canada)

An eclectic, simple-shelter, idea-generating picture book.

SOFT-TECH
Edited by J. Baldwin
and Stewart Brand
Whole Earth Catalog/Penguin
Box 428
Sausalito, California 94965
$5.00, 176 pages (Softcover)

The Whole Earth Catalog founders are now over 40 and, if it isn't readily apparent that they are growing older, it is clear that they've grown more skeptical. In a time when every other engineering school dropout seems to be publishing an alternative energy book, Stewart Brand, J. Baldwin & Company manage to ferret out, review and report on the best. Most of the material first appeared in CoEvolution Quarterly, but it deserves much wider reading.

"One of the more distressing aspects of the anti-tech movement is that it has tended to discourage doing homework. Ignorance IS bliss, but there is no future in it. Equally distressing is the number of projects undertaken by people of good heart who are willing to try new things, but who also have not done their research. The thousands of leaky domes are a sad example. Right-eousness doesn't guarantee good results."

—*J. Baldwin*

"Soft-Tech is a term we've used and defended since the late sixties. It first emerged in Great Britain, but then dropped out of fashion to be replaced by Alternative Technology (AT) *and* Appropriate Technology (AT). *'Soft' signifies something that is alive, resilient, adaptive, maybe even loveable. The other terms are administrative.*

"Governor Jerry Brown's aide Jacques Barzaghi recently quoted a Gregory Bateson remark — 'There are just two kinds of people in the world. The cuckoos. And the administrators.' Jacques said, 'Gregory, I hope I will always be a cuckoo.'

Same here. And to help that here's a book of cuckoo technology."

—*Stewart Brand*

LOG CONSTRUCTION Instruction

B. ALLAN MACKIE SCHOOL OF LOG BUILDING
Box 1205
Prince George, B.C. V2L 4V3
(604) 964-6935

Hands-on courses in log construction, at $100 per week. Regular course lasts eight weeks, although short courses in *piece-en-piece* construction are occasionally available. The school suggests that students plan on additional living costs of approximately $150 per week while taking the course at Prince George.

Each client should have his/her own basic set of log builder tools: a good chain saw, a good 3½ lb. oxhead axe, a pair of scribers. No serious builder can work without these. Becoming at ease in using one's own set of tools, as well as proficient in their upkeep, is essential to your future abilities as a competent log builder.

A set of basic tools is: peeling spud, axe, axe files & stone, 28" carpenter's level, lumber crayons, 25' Lufkin tape, indelible pencils, chalk line, chain saw files & tools, hammer, chisels, gas can, utility knife, peavey, jack knife.

Recommended saws are Jonsered, Husqvarna and Stihl. There are cheaper saws but the penalty of owning one is hearing loss. Their extreme noisiness brings all class discussion to a standstill. Each saw must be equipped with a chain brake which stops the chain instantly in case of kickback. 20″ bar and standard chipper chain are recommended.

Those who do not already own a set of tools are advised to wait until arriving at the school for advice on makes, models, and for a possible discount on group purchase.

FANSHAWE COLLEGE
Community Services
Box 4005, Terminal C
London, Ont. N5W 5H1
(519) 452-4436

Summer courses in log house construction taught by Pat Wolfe.

RUMAC SCHOOL OF LOG BUILDING
Box 5146, Armdale
Halifax, N.S. B3L 4M7
(902) 477-8472 or 852-4081

New log building school run by Michael MacKenzie and Allan Ruttan. Nine-week course is offered for $900.

CHANTERELLE SCHOOL OF LOG BUILDING
Box 532
Ignace, Ont. P0T 1T0
(807) 934-2977

One and two-week courses in spring and early summer. Ten week course on *piece-en-piece* and timber framing. $75/week.

PAT WOLFE LOG HOMES
Ailsa Craig, Ont. N0M 1A0
(519) 293-3221

Low-key and conscientious, Pat Wolfe offers log building courses through the spring and fall months. Eight-week course near Cobourg, Ontario, $500. One-week courses at King City, near Toronto, $160. Wolfe also offers his own log scribers and will build log homes on request.

The provincial government has been doing more testing on wood for R

factor information. The results are that the R factor of wood increases as the temperature goes down. This information proves that log homes are a very good energy efficient form of building.

To improve the courses, I'm bringing in professionals from other building trades to hold one day discussions on such topics as plumbing, electrical, drafting and blacksmithing. I feel that log building also involves some knowledge of the related trades.

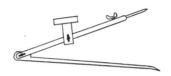

THE PAT WOLFE LOG SCRIBERS
A scriber is essential for tight close-fitting log work. This scriber has been designed with a double bubble adjustable leveling device. With this the accuracy of the scriber can be faultless. Made of steel, the scriber's over-all length is a compact 11″. An indelible ink pencil is included. Price: $24.00 (Postage included)

Builders

LINDAL CEDAR HOMES
Box 2080
New Westminster, B.C.
V3L 5A3

International builder of cedar home kits.

SERVIVAL ONE
R.R.3
Tweed, Ont. K0K 3J0
(613) 478-6830

Handcrafted log houses, squared or chinkless construction.

HYLAND LUMBER LTD.
Haliburton, Ontario
(705) 457-1011

Logs for builders. Delivery available.

COLONIST HOMES LTD.
Box 111
Warkworth, Ont. K0K 3K0
(705) 924-2745

Builders of custom log homes, constructed of hand-hewn British Columbia red cedar, with cedar shingle roofing, thermopane windows, individually priced.

KOOMAN LOG HOMES LIMITED
R.R.1
Bentley, Alberta T0L 0J0
(403) 748-2270

Specializing in custom-built, chinkless round-log homes. Erected in their building yard, numbered, dismantled and shipped to new owner. Will erect or completely finish, if desired. Average home of 1,800 square feet will cost approximately $16-$18 per square foot for the log work, or roughly $30,000.

TIMBER STRUCTURES
Box 233
Sharbot Lake, Ont. K0H 2P0

Energy-efficient homes—both post-and-beam and scribe-fitted logs. Design and consulting service also.

Colonist Homes Ltd.

TREE HOUSE LOG HOMES

R.R.1, Site 112
Parksville, B.C. V0R 2S0
(604) 753-3019

Handcrafted, chinkless log homes, built on or off site.

BUILDING WITH LOGS LIMITED

Box 158
Barrie, Ont. L4N 1Y5
(705) 726-1966 days
(705) 728-5800 evenings

Construction of log buildings of various types—*pièce-en-pièce*, dovetail keying, Scandinavian full-scribe.

PIONEER LOGS

R.R.2
Singhampton, Ont. N0C 1M0
(519) 922-2836

Ian McKay and Brian Christie will rebuild a restored log home on your site, or create a custom design using new or old squared logs. They dove-tail the corners, erect the building on their site first, then move it to you. Fully finished buildings or plans whereby the owner completes the flooring, chinking, roof, etc.

PETER C. PURKIS

R.R.1
L'Orignal, Ontario K0B 1K0
(613) 675-2298

Log cabin/house construction, either as kit or complete job. Built to customer's plans.

Wilderness Log Homes

Kits $4,000 and up
Summer homes $10,000 and up
Homes $15,000 and up
Instruction $500/wk.

LOGCRAFT INC.

R.R.3
Perth, Ont. K7L 3C5
(613) 267-4605
278-2738 evenings

Logcraft constructs energy-efficient log buildings from logs both old and new, in a wide variety of styles from Scandinavian to timber frame to *pièce-on-pièce*. They will do log shells or entirely finished houses, depending on what the customer wants. They build throughout eastern Ontario and western Quebec.

*—David Creighton
Maberly, Ontario*

WILDERNESS LOG HOMES

5680 N. Green Bay Ave.
Milwaukee, Wisconsin 53209
(414) 228-1230
or
Route 2
Plymouth, Wisconsin 53073
(414) 893-8416

Economical log home kits, either eight-inch round-sided logs with flattened upper and lower surfaces, or half-logs, designed to be built against interior framing (and giving an exceptional wall insulation value of R-26.25.) Ships across North America. Prices for logs-only pre-cut kits, $3,900 to $25,250 (freight "approximately $1 per mile" not included).

R.L. HULTON LOG HOMES AND BARNS

600 Oakwood Avenue
Toronto, Ont. M6E 2X8
(416) 652-0234

Supplies dismantled hand-hewn antique square log buildings with plans for reconstruction and each log tagged for identification. Sizes from 750 to 2,500 square feet, at prices from $3,800 to $50,000. (Delivers everywhere.)

NORTHWEST LOG HOMES LIMITED

Box 4714
Quesnel, B.C. V2J 3J9
(604) 992-2442

A small firm providing log building services in its own region (catalogue $2.00), but primarily of interest for a range of 45 log building designs—from saunas to 4,000-square-foot masterpieces. Stock plan prices include five copies, for lender, builder, subcontractors and building inspector. Catalogue of plans $4.95. (Plans $75 to $165.)

CONSCIOUS CONSTRUCTION ALTERNATIVES

Box 26
Maberly, Ont. K0H 2B0

Handcrafted timber frame and log houses, utilizing appropriate technology.

MISTIC LOG HOMES

Box 30, Site 23, R.R.5
Prince Albert, Saskatchewan
(306) 763-3330

Machined, interlocking poplar, pine or spruce logs in home kit form. Designed for economy and under the supervision of the Department of Northern Saskatchewan. Prices under $10,000. Write for details.

ARCADIA SHEDS
82 Arcadia Road
Westwood, Mass. 02090
(617) 762-8778

Plans for making attractive, traditional wooden sheds and outbuildings. (Plans $.50 to $4.75.)

Tools

THE BLAIRHAMPTON ALTERNATIVE
Box 748
Haliburton, Ont. K0M 1S0
(705) 754-2290

Tabloid-style catalogue of alternative tools, especially good source for log builders. Send $1.00 for current copy. Prices shown are for Ontario and Quebec; postage extra to other provinces or the U.S.

Alaska Chain Saw Mini-Mill $60—$130
Froe $23
Adze Head (Scoop) $25
Jonsered Chain Saws $425—$505
Hand-Powered Winch (2,200 lb. vertical lift) $295

RINGING ANVIL TOOLS
c/o Colin Campbell
R.R.1

Black Creek, B.C. V0R 1C0
(604) 337-5387

Good source of hand forged tools for log builders and wood carvers. Campbell is prepared to custom design tools. Among the offerings are scribers, gouges, chisels, adzes, curved knives.

WELBECK SAW MILL
R.R.3
Durham, Ont. N0G 1R0

Source of logs, floor planking, log building tools.

HYLAND LUMBER LTD.
Haliburton, Ontario
(705) 457-1011

Logs for builders. Delivery available.

Random Comment

THE PERSONAL SAWMILL
A well-designed, well-built log house is a thing of beauty, and doubtless a joy to live in. However, not everyone who builds his own house has the desire to build and live with logs. We admire log houses, but did not wish to live in one, so when we made our decision to move to an isolated wilderness location, we were faced with the problem of procuring lumber for building. With lumber costs high and going higher, a lumber yard of our own became highly desirable. So we bought a sawmill. To be sure, there are drawbacks and frustrations in making your own lumber, but we think they are far outweighed by the satisfaction of having a constant, ready supply of whatever lumber we want, when and as we want it.

We have owned two small sawmills, and have personal knowledge of a third, each a different type, and each satisfactory for the needs of a family or group wishing to build a home, outbuildings, and supply the routine lumber needs of country living. Such a mill can also, possibly, produce a small income.

Our first sawmill was a *Corinth portable "pipe mill,"* so called from its construction. And the

"portable" means only that it had an axle and wheels, and could be moved with a tow truck. The wheels were removed when the mill was set up, and the frame supported on built-in jacks that kept things level. With a 48-inch blade hammered to the correct r.p.m., powered by a big diesel engine, this was a conventional mill, in that a carriage moved the log into the blade, which remained stationary. It required two people to operate, one sawyer and one coolie-labourer to off-load boards and slab. After many adventures learning to operate the mill, my husband and I turned out all the lumber to build our home, a large rambling place, as well as sheds, barns, assorted outbuildings and fences, to the tune of many thousands of board feet of lumber at a really minimal cost. Granted, we got a bargain on that mill, but there are still bargains about, searched out with time and effort.

When our building was done, or so we thought, and we had what we considered an adequate supply of lumber on hand, we sold the mill. Four years later, when we were about to have neighbours for the first time, we and they decided to buy a new sawmill together. They needed to build their home, and our lumber pile was down to scraps. (It is, by the way, truly amazing how many boards are required in the day-to-day processes of country living!) We did a lot of research and inquiring into small sawmills, and settled on the Mobile Dimension Saw manufactured in Oregon, and commonly called an *Oregon Mill.*

This is a one-man saw, and is a pleasure to work with. It turns out absolutely precise lumber, with not a hair of deviation from end to end. We can cut any log up to 36 inches in diameter with the mill in a permanent set-up in its building, and in very few places would the problem of larger logs arise. The mill cuts perhaps a bit more slowly than a conventional mill, but that is compensated for by the ease of using the lumber "as is," without the necessity of planing any but interior finished boards. It will have paid for itself before the first house is built. Unlike the conventional mill, with the Mobile Dimension Saw the log

Living on an isolated island off the coast of British Columbia, the Gifford family has become proficient in milling their own lumber, in this case with a Mobile Dimension saw.

is held stationary, and an assembly of three blades is moved into the wood by rack and pinion gears powered by a Volkswagen engine mounted on the saw assembly. It all rides down the track together, and looks a bit strange when you are used to a conventional mill. But it works to perfection, and that is the main consideration.

This mill, like our first sawmill, is mobile and comes with a set of wheels that mount in the middle of the frame for moving from site to site. We have built a permanent building for our mill, allowing us to cut in any of the Northwest nasty weather, and we bring our logs to the mill rather than the other way round. The mobility can, however, be a great advantage if you have really fine logs that cannot be moved easily due to size, or a log supply in scattered locations. Even with the permanent building, given sufficient motivation, we *can* take our mill to the logs.

A third small-scale sawmill is made by *Belsaw*, in Kansas City, Missouri. A friend has one, powered by an old tractor, and he has been nothing but satisfied with it, building his own home, barns, two other houses, and selling enough lumber to pay for machinery, maintenance and more. This mill won't cut logs as large as will the Mobile Dimension Saw, but can be

operated efficiently by one man, and in most places would handle any logs available.

All this is not to put down the ubiquitous *Alaska Sawmill,* available in Canada from The Blairhampton Alternative, which has been the indispensable helper to so many homesteaders, new pioneers, small farmers, and wilderness types. It is one possibility for setting up a personal lumberyard, and certainly should be considered if only from the cost standpoint.

The other invaluable part of our lumber production is a planer-moulder, also made by Belsaw. This turns our boards into beautiful smooth panelling, ship-lap, tongue-and-groove flooring or cove moulding. With special bits, it will produce fancy beading, picture moulding, quarter, half, and full round dowelling—even closet poles.

Wherever there is a reasonable supply of timber and the need or desire for a lumberyard of your very own, these small, personal sawmills come into their own, and can be truly invaluable. Just one note of caution: The sawmills are all from the United States with nothing comparable made, to our knowledge, in Canada. All must be paid for in U.S. funds, and are subject to Canadian excise taxes and possibly provincial taxes as well. Check with Customs and

Excise when considering the overall cost.

— *Katherine Gifford*
Port Clements, B.C.

MOBILE MFG. CO.
Box 258
Troutdale, Oregon
(503) 666-5593

Sell the Mobile Dimension Saw (Oregon Mill), Model 127 for $6,995 (U.S.). Provide duty-remission number, so Canadian customers do not pay duty.

BELSAW MACHINERY CO.
3679 Field Building
Kansas City, Mo.
(816) 561-9255

Sell a one-man sawmill for $2,300 to $2,400 (U.S.), and a planer-moulder saw for $748 (U.S.). Canadians must pay duty.

Information

LOG HOUSE PUBLISHING COMPANY LIMITED
Box 1205
Prince George, B.C. V2L 4V3

Building With Logs
77 pages, softcover
ring-bound $10.00

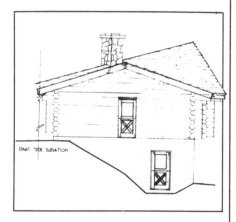

Notches of All Kinds
Hardcover, $15.00

The Canadian Log House
Annual magazine of log building news and advice. $5.00/year. (Back issues available from 1974. Write for prices.)

Log House Plans
169 pages, paperback $10.00

B. Allan Mackie's books are the definitive soures of information on log building and design. Some of his socio-historical comment, however, remains open to debate.

The Lawg Caybun Concept in Building

But time has taught me that those who refer to all log buildings as "cabins" are severely handicapped in their ability to study timber construction methods. At first, I was merely curious as to this derogatory figure of speech and began to ask people to describe for me the mental image they visualized: the kind of log house they wanted. Invariably they replied that this disparaging term embodies their highest admiration. However, now, several years of teaching later, I am convinced that the term "log cabin" has done greater injury to the proper development of good log buildings than have all the bark beetles, termites, dry rot, mildew, lightning strikes, and bad workmanship in history.

"Log cabin" is a U.S. term linked with that country's deep-rooted ambitions to expand. Originally their "log cabins" referred to southern slaves' quarters (of which Uncle Tom's was one). When the British bond was cut and the individual U.S. citizen began to act out his private dreams of empire, the westward (and attempted northward) expansion moved new homesteaders even farther afield. Their gun-toting frontiersman became a folk hero in the new republic and his Lawg Caybun became the symbol of his territorial conquests. Thus I do indeed see that the noun combines original roughness with an aura of admiration. But it must take a special kind of person to do it.

As a purely political symbol, the Lawg Caybun is repugnant enough to my Canadian view of things. But as architecture it is entirely contemptible. Even in its heyday, it was more symbolic of self-interest than of admirable building practices, and its legacy is not only the degradation of log building craftsmanship but also the continued encouragement of woodbutchering of today's endangered timber resources. The terminology is an alien presence in the Canadian vocabulary. The French from earliest Champlain (Port Royal, 1605) used logs magnificently and in over-strength. The British, too, held to the pièce-

en-pièce timber framing techniques they had always used, resisting what they considered to be the inferior (though quicker and easier) horizontal log building style. Even where such groups as the United Empire Loyalists arrived in Canada as refugees and in great haste contrived quick shelter, their word was "shanty" or sometimes "hut" but never "cabin." And later when they built the family home, almost always of logs, it was a house. Naturally. A log house is a house just as plainly as a log church is a church. Only better.

MUIR PUBLISHING COMPANY LTD.
Gardenvale, Quebec H9X 1B0
(514) 457-2045

LOG HOME GUIDE FOR BUILDERS AND BUYERS
An annual publication offering comprehensive coverage of the log home industry in U.S. and Canada. 188 pages, colour. Fully illustrated directories of pre-cut and hand-hewn log home companies, schools, teachers and associations, tools and equipment, home heating section, book reviews, mail order book shelf. $7.50 postpaid.
Publish a monthly newsletter "The Log Home Industry Newsletter" for industry members $36/yr.

LOG BUILDING TOOLS & HOW TO MAKE THEM
By R.D. Arcand
Box 132

Sorrento, B.C. V0E 2W0
62 pages, softcover

Sketchy but otherwise unavailable information on creating one's own log building tools.

Contact

CANADIAN LOG BUILDERS ASSOCIATION
Box 1521
Prince George, B.C. V2L 4V5

Organization of professional log builders, setting standards, codes of ethics and publishing a bi-monthly newsletter.

THE ONTARIO LOG BUILDERS ASSOCIATION
Box 129
King City, Ont. L0G 1K0

Contact between professional and amateur log builders. Membership $7.00 per year, including three newsletters.

First thing that most people react to when they are shown an example of Scandinavian 'full scribe' logwork is the lack of "chinking" between the logs. In Ontario, many people are unable to associate 'true log architecture' with something that does not have chinking. Apart from the fact that there is no such thing as 'true log architecture,' chinking, it should be pointed out, is a procedure applied to buildings in order to eliminate the time required to Custom fit each log to an airtight fit. It has gained so much notoriety over the generations that it now has become the stereotype by which

other forms of log/timber architecture are measured. As valid as that form may be, the 'full scribe' or 'chinkless' fitting of logs together is every bit as important to our Association. It lacks no heritage of its own, as examples of 'full scribe' buildings may be found in Norway and Finland that date back to the twelfth and thirteenth centuries. These are buildings still intact today! So, if you are enthused with the possibilities of log/timber architecture, be prepared to accept the fact that over the centuries and throughout the world, many forms have progressed to the point of recognition as valid types of log/timber construction. Certainly not the least of these forms is French Canadian pièce-en-pièce construction which uses the framing of timbers to contain horizontal filler logs which may be "full scribed" to a tight fit or left loose for subsequent chinking. There is much literature available on these different forms and the OLBA will be pleased to direct you to them.

If as a buyer you have, temporarily at least, gotten past the hurdle of recognizing other building types besides the 'chinked' variety, you have traded that obstacle for the more awesome adventure of finding a competent craftsman/contractor to build or assist you with the building of your house. As with all other purchases of such value, go slow, ask questions, get references, ask more questions, get names of previous dealings, and ask still more questions. On the one hand, established craftsmen/contractors have enough pride in their log/timber projects to inundate you for hours with pictures, names, and even actual examples of their building prowess that you can amble through. Notwithstanding that our craft/industry is very new in its rebirth, and many builders are in their first or second year of business, even these craftsmen will show you examples of their apprenticeship work with an established builder, at an extended training school devoted to log/timber joinery, or of projects of their own development. No builder worthy of this association's support will balk at the need to substantiate his expertise with names and dates and locations. Inevitably then, it boils down to the Latin phrase of old—'caveat emptor.'

UNDERGROUND DESIGN

UNDERGROUND DESIGNS
By Malcolm Wells
Self-Published
Box 1149
Brewster, Maine 02631
88 pages Paperback
$6.00 (U.S. funds)

"Damp dark slimy suffocating mouldy crawly slithery spidery Dracula coffin death in eternal utter darkness."

That, according to author Malcolm Wells, is the immediate image evoked in many minds when the term underground architecture is mentioned. Others think of basement apartments or subterranean parking garages, but only the enlightened minority share Wells' view of underground living space: dry, bright, solar heated and blissfully silent.

"When *Popular Mechanics* published a feature on underground architecture in March 1977," Wells relates, "the mail response was the largest in the company's history." When Wells, a practising architect with an underground office near Philadelphia, published his own article on the subject and took part in an Underground Architecture Day, he found himself faced with more than 5,000 letters of inquiry about the subject. This book is his answer.

Rather than being a design and construction manual for would-be underground owner-builders, this book serves mainly to introduce some three dozen designs created by Wells over a period of 13 years. In addition to a variety of homes, the designs include underground offices, libraries, museums, schools, a liquor store and even something he calls the "Organic Mortuary" (in which the deceased would have lain in state with a panoramic glass wall as a backdrop providing a view of a living garden of native plants, trees and shrubs).

Unfortunately, "would have" plays an important role in describing many of the book's designs, for the large majority of them have never been built. This tends to detract from the author's credentials, but it must be remembered that, in the fledgling field of modern underground design, this is one of the very few

ENTRANCE

available sources of information.

"If some of these designs had been built," Wells admits, "the results could have been a real problem, but now, thanks largely to our experiences in (our own) experimental office, we have begun to understand some of the natural phenomena involved in this new/old way of building."

Perhaps the most important— and painful—lesson learned from the underground office project was the fact that the earth is *not* a particularly good insulating material. Although the uninsulated underground building proved more energy-efficient than any comparable above-ground structure, Wells discovered that the earth surrounding it worked constantly to wick away heat, in effect trying to bring the building down to its own 55 degree F temperature. "A few feet from where I sit," Wells writes in his introduction, "hundreds of tons of wet New Jersey soil are quietly draining the warmth from this room. They're doing it slowly, I'll admit, but it seems now as if they'll go on doing it forever. I get up and put another small log on the slow-burning wood stove, and the chill goes away."

Properly insulated, with south-facing windows, other solar/

underground designs have proved extremely easy to heat and cool, using the surrounding earth not as an insulator but as a mammoth thermal flywheel.

Wells now advocates that all underground buildings be insulated with an exterior cladding of rigid blue Styrofoam boards, which have a closed cell construction to resist moisture ("they use it for buoys") combined with superior insulating qualities. Immediately inside the layer of insulation, Wells recommends a vapour barrier of 1/32-inch butyl sheeting with carefully sealed seams to stop the obvious threat of dampness.

Such specific recommendations are relatively scarce in this 88-page book, and the author comes down heavily on the side of not building an underground home without professional architectural advice. Undeniably, Wells' book has helped ignite interest in the subject, and some individuals — infused with the owner-builder spirit— may be tempted to go it alone, building with this book as their only guide. A better course, before attempting to build under the wildflowers, instead of over them, would be to read the following book.

EARTH SHELTERED HOUSING DESIGN: guidelines, examples, and references
By The Underground Space Center
University of Minnesota
Van Nostrand Reinhold Company
318 pages, paperback, $9.95 (U.S.) plus postage
Hundreds of underground or earth-sheltered structures are in use or nearing completion in the U.S. and Canada, with Minnesota emerging as the headquarters of design expertise. In 1977, the Minnesota legislature established The Underground Space Center at the University of Minnesota to promote the use of underground space, primarily for commercial and industrial uses. However, the phenomenal interest of individuals in underground housing prompted the engineers to undertake a one year design study.

Earth Sheltered Housing Design is the result of that study, and an impressively thorough book it is, indeed. Every detail relevant to underground construction is analyzed, with the primary stress resting on energy conservation. Site orientation, soil types, vegetation, thermal mass, ventilation, humidity control, waterproofing, insulation, drainage techniques, structural materials — these are just a few of the specifics discussed. For each detail, problem areas are identified and recommendations made for the most cost-effective solutions.

One caution: Although this is a technical book, aimed at architects and builders, it still doesn't give you everything you need to know to build an earth-sheltered house. The forces exerted by the earth, hydrostatic pressure, large loads — all these factors need to be taken into consideration — by a qualified engineer. Until enough data have been collected to allow the formulation of reliable rules of thumb, such as are used by the conventional building trades, the owner-builder will need to consult a professional for soil analysis and structural design.

The second section of the book consists of floor plans, sectional drawings, photographs, specifications, and one page descriptions for each of 16 *existing* earth-sheltered homes. No architect's mere whimsy, these are the real thing. There is a wide variety of imaginitive design represented here . . . from the rock-lined Davis cave built for $15,000 to the 7,000-square-foot Alexander house in California.

Rounding out the book is a series of appendices on energy calculations and comparisons with above ground structures, building codes and financing. And finally, there are some 20 pages of references, catalogues and a bibliography. And an index. With the choice in underground housing books so limited, it's nice that one of the few available is so complete.

—*Phillip Monner*
Cobourg, Ontario

BUILDING WITH STONE

BUILD YOUR OWN STONE HOUSE USING THE EASY SLIPFORM METHOD

By Karl and Sue Schwenke
156 pages, Paperback $6.50

The Schwenkes have taken the slipform stone construction method described in general terms by Helen and Scott Nearing and produced a book that provides detailed instructions, photographs and useful charts and tables.

Little did we know in those early planning stages that we would end up moving each and every stone at least twice, and more often three or four times. The cumulative poundage of stone we hefted on that first house amounted to nearly a thousand short tons, and that back-breaking figure does not include the weight of materials for footings, foundations, nor concrete for backing the walls. This weighty figure will daunt the dilettante, as well is should. Stone house building is not for the dabbler . . .

SLIPFORMING

The "slip" of slipforming derives from the practice of "slipping" forms up the wall as you erect it. The slipform has several good talking points—especially for erecting stone walls. Reusing the form several times as it makes its way up the wall conserves expensive form-wood, and its 19-inch height makes for a comfortable working depth in which to lay stones. Further economy derives from the fact that in building your own forms, you build in provisions for bracing and wiring.

Theoretically, you could build a slipformed stone house with as few as eight standard forms (four to each side of a corner), but the process would be an interminably long one, and would result in radically different drying times within the walls. This is particularly true if the house you envision is a large one. The number of forms you will need is directly proportional to the size of structure that you will wish to build. While eight forms might well be enough for small structures like tool, potting or wood sheds, the odds are that you will need far more forms for your house.

The actual process of setting up forms, preparing them for a pour and then stoning them is, in practice, a set of routines that makes the work flow along at a good steady pace. Once underway, our exterior walls rose at the daily rate of 19 inches in height by 24 to 35 feet in length (depending upon weather, breakdowns and other unforeseen happenings). Our daily routine was to get three or four standard length forms ready for pouring in the morning. This practice left us the entire afternoon to cope with the actual placement of stone and concrete.

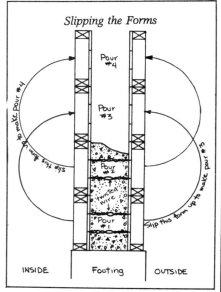

Each morning began with what we came to call the "unveiling." This was when we removed the forms from concrete and stone that had dried for a minimum of three days. The stone which we had so laboriously laid in place three days before emerged to view for the first time, and the patterns of colour, the shapes and the textures thus revealed were a constant source of matutinal satisfaction—a fine way to start a day.

Removing the forms from a previous pour is not always as easily done as it is said. This is particularly true when it comes to the forms that are first laid on the footing. Here you contend with an aggravating lack of elbow room in that you are working at the bottom of a narrow excavation where "prying" room is at a premium. Further aggravation is added as the friction of the form on top of the one you want to remove defies heavenly imprecations, brawny muscles and an unhealthily large "cussin' vocabulary."

The first time I encountered this problem I had exhausted my imprecations and muscles, and was well launched into my last refuge when I became aware of an onlooker. It was my neighbour, Ken Alger, who stood in slack-jawed, admiring awe of my tantrum. "That's the first time," he grinned, "I ever heard a feller carry on like that for so long, and never use the same word twice!"

HOW TO BUILD A LOW COST HOUSE OF STONE

By Lewis and Sharon Watson
Stonehouse Publications
Box 4002
Sweet, Idaho 83670
96 pages, Paperback $5.95
(Canadian Funds)

In 1972, this couple built an 1,100-square-foot house of stone, using the slipform method, for $2,090. Their book claims it can still be done. Less detailed, but a good companion to the Schwenke book.

THE OWNER BUILDERS GUIDE TO STONE MASONRY

By Ken Kern, Steve Magers and Lou Penfield
192 pages, Paperback $7.95

steps under construction

Three experienced stonemasons combine to produce a fine, well-illustrated book on building with stone, including, but not limited to, various slipform methods.

Farmers view fieldstone in a different light from that seen by builders. Most farmers will encourage you to haul stone from their fields and pastures—an excellent source of this material. To them, stones are merely objects which have been breaking their ploughs and straining their backs for generations. Often the landowners and their ancestors have already done most of the work by piling stones along the borders of ploughed fields or around trees in pastures. One has only to carry it from these piles to a truck.

As stone is removed from these piles remember that people are not the only inhabitants of stone shelters. Stone piles often house creatures ranging from mice to rats to blackwidow spiders and poisonous snakes. Whenever you are collecting stone it is wise to wear gloves and watch where you step.

Another source of fieldstone is found along roadsides. The shoulders of old dirt roads are often lined with stones graded to the side during years of maintenance. Two people, one walking alongside and one driving, can quickly load a truck. But do not overload the truck, for stone is heavy. What may seem like a small quantity can easily weigh over a ton. When loading, constantly check the truck's springs. It is tempting to throw on just one more piece—which

could break the axle.

Abandoned mining operations are another good source for locating building stone. Such stone has already been reduced to useful size and tends to be piled, making it handy for loading. You will probably have to pick through these piles, referred to as tailings, for they will contain quantities of unuseable debris.

STACKWALL

STACKWALL: HOW TO BUILD IT

By The Northern Housing Committee
University of Manitoba
417 Engineering Building
Winnipeg, Manitoba
$12.50, 94 pages (Paperback)

This is a no-frippery guide to cordwood construction, written in humourless, engineering-school English. It has none of the personality of the book reviewed above but is much better organized in its presentation and appreciably more thorough.

The authors recommend using 24-inch-long log butts, which give an insulation (R) value of 18 to 20 — equivalent to a fibreglass-packed six-inch stud wall and far better

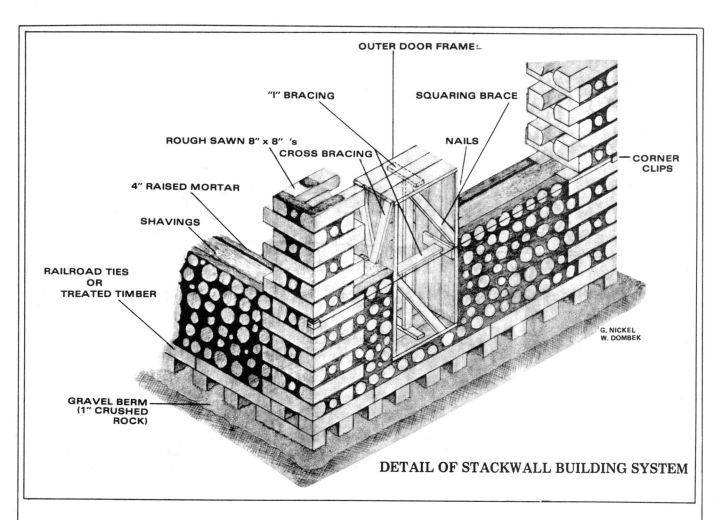

OUTER DOOR FRAME

"I" BRACING

ROUGH SAWN 8" x 8" 's

CROSS BRACING

SQUARING BRACE

NAILS

CORNER CLIPS

4" RAISED MORTAR

SHAVINGS

RAILROAD TIES
OR
TREATED TIMBER

G. NICKEL
W. DOMBEK

GRAVEL BERM
(1" CRUSHED
ROCK)

DETAIL OF STACKWALL BUILDING SYSTEM

than conventional housing.

The price of this book is inexplicably steep, but the information is solid and the directions for laying foundation, building proper corners and installing doors and windows superior to those in the Henstridge book (this is the guide to buy, if you are only buying one).

BUILDING THE CORDWOOD HOUSE

By Jack Henstridge
Plain Deal Pauper Publicatons
824 Charlotte Street
Fredericton, New Brunswick
$6.00, 96 pages (Paperback)

In this and the following book, Canada seems to be taking the lead in reviving the technique of building with cordwood, also known as stackwall construction.

Anyone able to build a log pile should be able to take advantage of what must be the simplest and cheapest-of-all owner/builder construction methods. Built up

with one-to-two-foot lengths of log, a cordwood house is strong, well-insulated and can be as architecturally complex as you wish.

Jack Henstridge takes you through the thought processes that led him to build his own large cordwood dwelling, and provides a running account of its construction.

The how-to material tends to run a bit thin in spots, and Mr. Henstridge's exuberance in publishing his own book occasionally leads him astray (the odd snapshot of a boat or vintage aircaft he admires have somehow managed to sneak into print). Still, anyone giving serious thought to building with cordwood should find useful guidance here.

LA MAISON DE "BOIS CORDE"

By Jack Henstridge &
Francois Tanguay
L'Aurore
R.R. 1

Inverness, Quebec G0S 1K0
$6.95, 121 pages (Paperback)

A French-language guide to cordwood construction.

Francois Tanguay has translated New Brunswicker Jack Henstridge's manual on the topic and added a final section, describing the construction of his own round "bois corde" home in Quebec. Tanguay says he completed the house for $6,000 and feels the method is easy enough to "wake people up from their indifference" toward home construction.

NOMADICS

HERITAGE TIPI

Box 910, Station Main
Calgary, Alberta
(403) 265-8474

Authentic, Sioux-design, all-weather tipis. Heritage says that one-third of all its customers live year-round in tipis—"even in the most severe northern conditions." Summer workshops on tipi technology free to groups of 20 or more individuals.

16-foot Sioux: $439 (Canada)

20-foot Sioux: $549 (Canada)

Add $20 shipping and handling.

GREENPEACE EXPERIMENTAL FARM
R.R.1

Denman Island, B.C. V0R 1T0

Too poor to own a house, too proud to live in a tent? The Eco-Cabin may be the solution. Actually, this 120-square-foot mini-cottage is both aesthetically pleasing and a possible answer for the escapist, the neo-builder or anyone wanting an inexpensive seasonal shelter. The floor plan is a pentangle, and walls consist of 15 equilateral triangles. (For Buckminster Fuller fans, this is derived from the geometric solid known as an icosahedron.) Entire cabin can be built, according to Greenpeace, for less than $1,000.

Eco-Cabin Plans (18-pg. Booklet): $3.50

The Greenpeace Eco-Cabin, with pentangular floor plan, can be built for less than $1,000—much less if salvaged materials are used.

MATERIEL

BURCHELL SUPPLY CO.
198 Andrews Avenue

Smiths Falls, Ont.

(613) 283-0609

Lightning rods and related paraphernalia.

LOTHLORIEN WOODWORKING
R.R.1

Ompah, Ontario

(613) 479-2425

THERMAL WINDOWS & DOORS

In building a new house, one of the larger expenses is the windows, running around $3,000 and up for a full set. And they're only available in a few standard sizes and styles, unless you're willing or able to pay an extra 30 to 40 per cent more to get something special. When building his own house four years ago, these constraints prompted John Inglis of Lothlorien Farm, Ompah, to build his own windows. He enjoyed it so much, and saved so much money, that he's been

making windows for other people ever since.

Lothlorien Woodworking—Custom Windows is now a business unique in Eastern Ontario. Building quality thermal windows "of virtually *any* style and shape," John says, "Our prices are very competitive with *standard-sized* commercial units, and for the larger sizes of window, we are significantly cheaper."

"I think we have more design flexibility here than anywhere else I've seen or heard about. Some customers have really interesting ideas too, which is rapidly increasing our repertoire."

Another feature of Lothlorien windows is the emphasis on quality. They use pinned and glued mortise and tenon joints at every corner of the frame, the sash and the screen. "Other manufacturers in Canada simply nail the frames together, and they have no stiffness or strength on their own. Also we use a half-inch air-spacing in the thermal glazing. Most other windows have three-eighth inch or less, and the difference in insulation value is significant."

—David Creighton
Maberly, Ontario

AMERICAN MARKETING SYSTEMS INC.
26 Broadway

New York, N.Y. 10004

(212) 482-8404

Suppliers of a new, double-walled polycarbonate clear plastic glazing material. The sheets come in widths of up to 80 inches and thicknesses of 2 to 6 mm. Known as Thermo-Insul Wall. Has potential for use in solar windows, greenhouses and in storm window applications (the material is rigid and quite break-resistant).

INSULPAC SPECIALTIES COMPANY
Box 187

Thornbury, Ont.

(416) 291-4999

Suppliers of AIRCAP, a double-layered plastic sheet completely covered with trapped bubbles of air. Can be used as temporary insulation for greenhouses and windows. Very flexible. It comes in rolls.

INSULSEARCH LIMITED
Box 99
Norval, Ont. L0P 1X0
(416) 456-3598
OR
INSTA-FOAM INTL. INC.
Box 21
Etobicoke, Ont. M9C 4V2
(416) 622-6844 or 6845

A new twist on log-building chinking: inject urethane foam between the logs, after the exterior strip of hard chinking has been put in place. The foam expands by 60 times its liquid volume and sets within a minute to provide both insulation and an air-sealant effect. Surplus foam is trimmed with a knife before interior chinking is applied. Insta-Foam Kits are available from $18 to $575, but certain insulation contractors can also perform the service.

GRANT'S LUMBER & BUILDING MATERIALS
Box 1058
Meaford, Ont. N0H 1Y0
(519) 538-2584
Custom wood sash and trim, as well as windows and door frames particularly for restoring older homes to original condition.

VELUX-CANADA LTD.
Suite 2,
252a J.B. Deschamps
Lachine, Quebec H8T 1C5
(514) 636-8570

Source of quality roof windows, flashings and shades. An improvement over most skylights in that they can be opened in hot weather, and that optional built-in shades can be used at night to cut heat loss. Brochure on request.

Double-Paned Roof Windows
$183—$396
Triple Insulated Windows
$198—$473

Random Comment

MacLACHLAN WOODWORKING MUSEUM
1316 Princess Street
Kingston, Ont.
(613) 549-2260

The MacLachlan Woodworking Museum ("A Tribute to Wood in the Service of Man") is located in a two-storey log house built originally in 1853 in Lanark County near Smiths Falls, Ontario. In 1967 the house was carefully dismantled and moved to its current site in Kingston. The exhibits on both floors are a gold mine for anyone working in the area of log house restoration. The exhibits, all excellently labelled and explained, show the history of log house building as it was done in the 19th century. There are numerous tools of that era and a great deal of information detailing the use of each tool—everything from log harvesting and squaring to maple sugaring and flax spinning. Many of the tools I have not seen in any other pioneer museum nor in any other book on the subject.

But fascinating as it is, the museum is not just a place to store charming and archaic tools. Many of the exhibits, photographs and information hand-outs detail the renovation of this particular type of log house and we were able to receive new information about modern, practical methods and materials used in restoring our old place. For example, a standard problem—proper, long-lasting chinking—was solved when we were given a three-page instruction sheet explaining the details of correct chinking, the same information tested on the renovation of the museum house itself. This information outlined the ingredients, proper ratio mix, method, equipment, etcetera. The instructions were very complete and meticulous. In addition, we were given a fourth sheet of information on the same subject— an addendum that followed up on the earlier recommendations. (Later, we learned that officials from Upper Canada Village in Morrisburg believed that the "MacLachlan Chinking Method" was superior to that used on the log houses at the village).

But the museum itself was only a secondary source. Visitors to the museum who wish more information are invited to call on Mr. Sandy MacLachlan, the owner and chief renovator. He is available nearby at the showroom of the MacLachlan Lumber Co., adjacent to the log museum. For our rather complex problems relating to foundation and floor joists, Mr. MacLachlan took time from his business schedule and gave us information about these areas, along with diagrams. We found him most approachable and encouraging. Sandy MacLachlan could be considered the Allan Mackie for the "lawg caybun" school.

The Woodworking Museum is located on the site of the MacLachlan Lumber Company,

1316 Princess Street, Kingston, Ontario, Phone (613) 549-2260. The admission to the museum is cheap: Adults 50 cents, children and students 25 cents. All the advice, information pages, diagrams and, of course, the encouragement were free and no one tried to sell us anything.

—W.J. Smart
Islington, Ontario

PRE-FABRICATED BUILDINGS

A caveat to those considering the purchase of a pre-fab farm shed, and who live in heavy snow country. The curved sectional aluminum-arch (quonset-hut type) buildings put out by Aztec Manufacturing of Toronto, and its predecessor, Wondersteel, may *not* take the heavy snowloads commonly experienced west of the Rockies. *Thirteen* of these buildings have collapsed in B.C. in the past couple of winters —a small airplane hangar in Nakusp, an equipment shed in Burton, and others in such widely-spread but snowy areas as Pemberton, Creston, Salmo and Golden. These space-age structures may seem like a quick and easy solution for sheltering stock and equipment, but not if your area experiences more than a foot or two of snow.

—Frank Appleton
Edgewood, B.C.

BURY THAT HOUSE!

You don't have to be a groundhog, recluse or Neanderthal man to enjoy living in an underground house. It does help to have a keen appreciation of what cutting several less cords of wood for each winter's warmth can mean.

When deciding what kind of home we would build on our newly acquired farm property, we finally opted for a partially buried design. It was a decision we've been glad of many times since.

Having no major southern slope to work with, we chose a location with good southern exposure and a very slight incline to the north.

We excavated four feet at the south and got eight feet at the north. A little more digging and earth-moving provided for a substantial footing and a four-foot

insulated crawl space under our main structure.

After backfilling and earth berming, the 12-foot-high (four feet for the crawl space) and 12-inch-thick block walls were completely buried. We sloped the blocks slightly on the west side and left the south part of the east wall to be post and beam framed with the south wall. This allowed us some east and west windows.

The southern wall is on grade and is filled with windows of various sizes from floor to ceiling.

A balcony-like second floor is completely above ground but the roof slopes up from the ground at the north so that we have no north facing walls or windows.

Almost everyone who visits our house has the same comment— "It's so bright and sunny in here!" It really is hard to believe we are halfway into the ground.

In the winter the sun makes its daily sweep across the sky very low and manages to shine through every window. It casts its golden rays almost to the north wall of our 28-foot-deep house.

On those days we turn our wood stove very low and let the sun do its thing.

The house is designed to be an efficient passive solar collector. The blocks are insulated with six inches of styrofoam on the south side and absorb and hold the heat well. And being underground we are only trying to raise the temperature from about 47

degrees F instead of from a frosty 20 degrees below.

In the summer the sun rises almost behind the house to the east and continues overhead never shining in until it sets in the west. The blocks stay cool and our living room is a pleasant place to be on a hot and sweltering July day. Still bright and airy, it's like a basement without the dinginess.

The coolness in summer is a bonus, since we were primarily interested in dealing with our sometimes severe northern Ontario winters.

We put the design to the test when we had to leave the house for five days during the worst cold snap in February. Temperatures of 30 degrees below were recorded here and yet we returned to find no signs of internal freezing. Our house plants were a little on the dry side but very much alive and even a dish of water left on the floor resisted freezing.

We have no backup heating system to our airtight wood stove so we were surprised and encouraged to know we can leave the house in winter without worry of pipes freezing or plants dying.

We are so pleased with this semi-underground living that we'd like to share our experiences with anyone who would care to write for more details.

—Mikell Billoki
—Lloyd Greenspoon
R.R.1
Gore Bay, Ontario
P0P 1H0

Toward A Composting Society

What hath Victoria wrought?

When Queen Victoria pulled the chain on the world's first automatic flush toilet, installed by her loyal subject Thomas Crapper, she signalled a tidal wave of waste. Since this ignoble beginning, more tons of fresh water, literally oceans of it, have been fouled by the flush toilet system. In the process, millions of tons of nitrogen, potassium and other nutrients, potentially salvable from human waste, have been lost from the food chain—either washed away or contaminated with heavy industrial metals.

This pristine, "flush and forget" mentality is being increasingly recognized for what it is—environmentally crude and uncivilized—and increasing numbers of people are seeking alternatives to waterborne sewage systems. While the general motivations of saving water, saving energy, and preventing pollution run strong, many of those considering waterless toilet systems are settling in areas beyond the sewage lines, where the choice may be between a septic system and an outdoor privy.

Old alternatives are being rediscovered and new inventions being developed in an attempt to provide an acceptable system of waste disposal which retains the value of human excreta. New waterless systems are finding increased public acceptability, but long social and technological traditions of waterborne sewage disposal still must be overcome.

While water has been used to dispose of bodily wastes since the time of the Roman empire, the waterborne sewage system with its flush toilets, miles of sewers, and centralized treatment plants has largely expanded with the industrial and urban expansion of the mid-twentieth century. At great expense to the taxpayer, governments and the sewering industry continue to extend this system to smaller and smaller communities as well as in developing nations. In 1977, $588,000,000 was committed for the expansion and maintenance of waterborne sewage systems in Ontario alone.

Achieving even basic waterborne sanitation for the world would require an immediate investment of nearly $200 billion. The public cost of installing a centralized sewage system in North America averages $12,000 per home and is steadily rising. As well as the increasingly, and in many cases prohibitively, expensive costs of this system, waterborne sanitation entails a massive misuse of natural resources. Each person uses an average of 11,000 gallons of clean water per year to wash away 225 pounds of waste. In the flush toilet, water is contaminated and human waste removed from the food cycle. Having mixed these two valuable resources the centralized sewerage system then proceeds at great cost to separate the water and the human waste. The most advanced water treatment plants do not completely purify the water, and reduce, or even remove, the value of human waste as a soil conditioner and fertilizer.

A variety of techniques have been developed to reduce the wasteful aspects of the waterborne sewage system. Reduced-volume flush toilets and a myriad of water saving devices ranging in sophistication from a brick placed in the tank, to improved flush mechanisms are now available. Cities can remove the sludge from the water treatment plants and apply it to the soil where some of the nutrients may be recovered. This method is limited because of health risks, because of problems with heavy metals and because, in this raw state, sludge is high in nitrogen and will "burn" vegetation.

Some cities market their sewage commercially in a slightly more treated stage as fertilizer under such zippy names as Milorganite (Milwaukee) and Philorganite (guess). While these enterprises are admirable in their attempt to return nutrients from human waste to the soil, central sewage systems contain increasing amounts of heavy metals and toxic substances which reduce the acceptability of these products.

The waste water from central sewage systems can be applied to the soil through a variety of techniques. Through irrigation of crops, or merely by percolating water through soil into the ground, water can be purified to an acceptable level, and many nutrients in the waste water are recovered in the soil. Waste water is also applied in several sites to add nutrients to fish farms.

While all these methods contribute to an improvement of the waterborne sanitation system's shortcomings, they do not realize the full potential value of human waste, or reduce the costly use of water sufficiently. This latter factor is of particular concern for such arid areas as California. Nor do these improvements alleviate the great economic burden of centralized systems on the community.

A variety of alternatives to the waterborne sewage system have been developed. Homeowners with sufficient land can employ the traditional septic tank-leach field disposal method. This method takes advantage of the natural purifying qualities of soil, but still uses water as the medium of disposal. While digestion of sludge in the septic tank allows the recovery of nutrients, some nutrient value is still lost. This method can only be applied to a limited number of areas where there is sufficient soil, and is not applicable to most urban areas, or to arid regions.

The alternative, therefore, must be a waterless system. Waterless toilets include chemical, incinerating, oil flush, biological digestors, and composting toilets. While the problem of contaminating water is eliminated by all these methods, only the composting toilet recovers the nutrients in human waste for reuse.

Composting units range in sophistication from a simple pit dug out of the ground to the electrically-assisted commercial toilets designed for in-house installation. A wide variety of techniques is represented by the 20 to 30 commercial units now available in North America. Nearly infinite variations are to be found in the range of homemade privies and toilets.

All these systems gather human excreta into a composting site. This environment must contain certain materials and conditions for composting to occur, and it is the capacity of the various techniques to achieve this balance and contain human waste which determines each unit's success or failure.

Composting human waste requires the addition of cellulose (plant material), temperatures between 32 degrees C and 70 degrees C, moisture and a balanced ratio of carbon to nitrogen between 25:1 and 35:1 parts carbon to nitrogen.

Composting occurs either with or without oxygen. Without oxygen (anaerobic) composting creates foul-smelling gases as a by-product. Aerobic (with oxygen) composting is essentially odourless and pathogens and parasites are not encouraged in this environment. Composting toilets therefore are divided into those which create anaerobic conditions and those which achieve aerobic conditions.

Pit latrines and privies are examples of anaerobic composting toilets. These primitive devices are still used extensively in non-industrialized regions. Unless the site for these toilets is chosen with care, the excreta can leach into supplies of drinking water or into food crop areas. The familiar ammonia smell of outhouses is the result of the carbon/nitrogen ratio dropping below 25:1. The pits are not often constructed for easy recovery of the composted material, and so the value of the compost is usually lost.

Variations of the outhouse have been developed which allow for the recovery of the compost and for the aeration of the compost pile. Two basic aerobic privies are the drum privy, and variations on the Farallones Institute Two-Chamber composting privy.

The drum privy works by placing a 55 gallon steel drum beneath the toilet hole. This can be a simple design, or can include a wheeled base to allow for easy transportation, and a jack used to press the drum's lid against the toilet assembly to form a seal. Once the drum is full it can either be emptied or buried to allow composting to continue. This system cannot generally allow for easy aeration and still maintain the transporting advantages of the drum.

The Farallones Two-Chamber System is an outhouse with the addition of concrete block pits. One side of the pit is screened to allow for aeration of the pile, and can be removed to recover the humus. These systems are easily built by the do-it-yourselfer, and the design can be varied to suit the specific location and load requirements of each application. However, these aerated outhouses are not generally suitable for in-house installation and require more handling of waste than do the commercial units.

The major step in composting toilet development took place in Sweden in 1939, when Rikard Linstrom invented the first self-contained, in-house composting unit, now known as the Clivus Multrum. The Clivus employs a large (4'x7'6''x7'4'') fibreglass tank which receives both human excreta and kitchen waste. The base of the tank is sloped at a 30 degree angle to allow wastes to migrate towards the removal tray.

The key features of the Clivus Multrum and all other commercial units, are that they contain the wastes in an impervious tank, pass the air over or through the pile, and vent the air away from sensitive noses. These features allow for the recovery of humus, and the installation of composting toilets in the house.

The Clivus Multrum's size attempts to parallel the natural conditions of a compost pile, but this has led to many installation problems. The toilet seat must be located upstairs directly above the tank itself. The fibreglass structure is also too large to fit through most door frames, which often results in either building a separate addition to accommodate the Clivus or widening a door to allow the entry of the Clivus. With the exception of the Toa-throne (Humus II in Canada), all other commercial units are designed to fit into a regular size bathroom. The Toa-throne, while only slightly smaller than the Clivus, is made of plastic and is constructed in two halves which allows for greater ease of installation.

Compact composting toilets overcome the problems of

handling a normal volume of waste with the aid of heaters and an electric fan. These additions accelerate the evaporation of moisture and maintain temperatures that are high enough to maintain composting and discourage pathogens. These

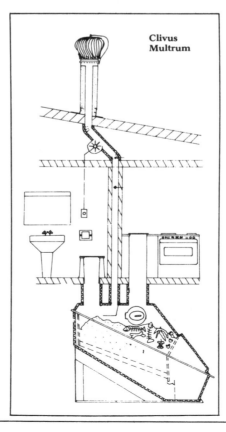

Clivus
Multrum

smaller units would be better described as accelerated composting toilets or dehydrating composting toilets.

While there have been some difficulties with insect infestation and odour releases into the home, the better models on the market, if properly installed, will avoid these problems. The primary obstacle to greater use of composting toilets is North America's love affair with throw away technology. This "out of sight, out of mind" attitude is compounded by an antipathy towards having one's own excrement stored in the house. Only public education and a growing awareness of the economic and environmental costs of the waterborne sewage system will overcome this problem.

— *Doug Stewart*
Toronto, Ont.

COMPOSTING TOILETS

CROWDIS CONSERVERS
R.R.3
Baddeck, N. S. B0E 1B0
(902) 295-2275

**CLIVUS MULTRUM
U.S.A. INC.**

14A Eliot Street
Cambridge, Mass. 02138

MODEL: Clivus Multrum

The Clivus Multrum is the original commercial composting toilet. It is also the largest with separate chutes for kitchen and toilet wastes, and usually requires two floors or a separate addition to the house for installation. Its large size allows increased loading and a composting process which closely parallels natural compost heaps. At a basic package price of just over $2,000 it is the most expensive compost toilet.

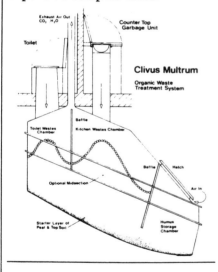

FUTURE ECO-SYSTEMS LIMITED

680 Denison Street
Markham, Ont. L3R 1C1
(416) 495-6450

MODEL: Humus II (Toa Throne)

Sometimes referred to as the son of Clivus Multrum, the Humus II is somewhat smaller and has only one chute for both kitchen and toilet waste. It also employs an

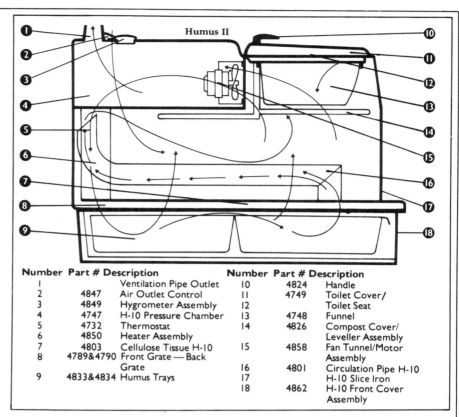

Humus II

Number	Part #	Description	Number	Part #	Description
1		Ventilation Pipe Outlet	10	4824	Handle
2	4847	Air Outlet Control	11	4749	Toilet Cover/
3	4849	Hygrometer Assembly	12		Toilet Seat
4	4747	H-10 Pressure Chamber	13	4748	Funnel
5	4732	Thermostat	14	4826	Compost Cover/
6	4850	Heater Assembly			Leveller Assembly
7	4803	Cellulose Tissue H-10	15	4858	Fan Tunnel/Motor
8	4789&4790	Front Grate — Back			Assembly
		Grate	16	4801	Circulation Pipe H-10
9	4833&4834	Humus Trays	17		H-10 Slice Iron
			18	4862	H-10 Front Cover
					Assembly

"air staircase" in the tank to facilitate the movement of air through the pile. Its size provides less capacity than the Clivus Multrum, but this size and the unit's construction allow for easier installation than the Clivus. Lists at $1,299.

ENVIROSCOPE, INC.

2400 W. Coast Highway
Suite D,
Newport Beach, Ca 92663

MODEL: Carousel

The round chamber of the Carousel is divided into four

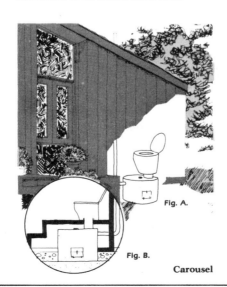

Fig. A.

Fig. B.

Carousel

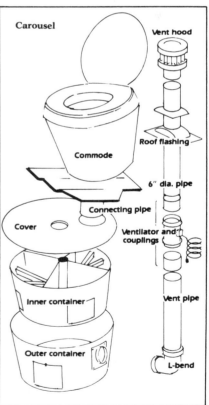

Carousel

tanks, which revolve to allow each section to be used in turn. Air ventilation system is not as effective as the other two large composting toilets. It may be easier to install in some locations. List price is $1,260.

CLIVUS MULTRUM U.S.A. INC.

14A Eliot Street
Cambridge, Mass. 02138

MODEL: Bio-loo

At 25'' wide, 31½'' long, and 26'' high the Bio-loo's size is average for compact units. Has two chambers, one of which can be heated to 158 degrees F to pasteurize the humus. It is equipped with a manually operated rotor to mix the pile, and requires electricity for the heater and ventilation fan. The Bio-loo must be emptied more frequently than other models. Lists at $845.

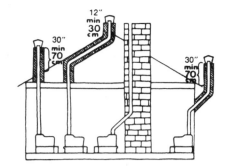

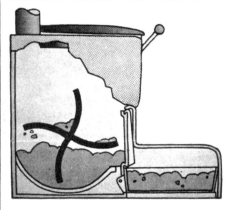

1. What can be put into the Multrum?

Besides urine and excrement; toilet paper, kleenex, tampons, sanitary napkins, disposable diapers (not the plastic part) and similar bathroom wastes can go in the toilet. Practically all organic kitchen and household wastes—especially those which could be a potential odour problem—can go in the garbage chute. These include cooking liquids, paper towels, grease and fat, dust pan and even vacuum cleaner refuse, vegetable and meat scraps, peelings, and even bones and eggshells. Some large bones will emerge incompletely deteriorated but will help rather than harm the process because of their calcium contribution. Newspaper used for pet litter may, if torn up a bit, also be included.

2. What should not be put in the Multrum?

Cans, glass, plastic, chemicals (including such things as sani-flush and other "sanitary" agents) or large amounts of liquid of any kind. Nor should large quantities of unshredded newspaper which can easily be disposed of by other means be included. Corrugated cardboard when present in larger than minute quantities should be omitted because it contains boron, a plant toxicant. Also, any materials which could get hung up on the air ducts and impede the settling of the mass such as straw or hay should be either shredded before being put in or not put in at all. Absolutely no paints or other toxic substances which might damage plants on which the humus is to be used should be put in.

3. Is the addition of kitchen garbage necessary?

Yes, the addition of kitchen garbage, or some other material high in cellulose such as leaves, sawdust, shredded hay or straw, is necessary. This cellulose material is needed to absorb the liquids, thereby preventing "waterlogging" and the resultant anaerobic conditions. This material further enhances aeration by giving the pile a loose structure. The decomposition of the cellulose material also provides the heat energy needed to evaporate the water. Another important function is to form a compost pile large enough to promote stability during external temperature and humidity variations. Finally, the cellulose material provides carbon and growing surface for those organisms which will take in and convert nitrogen and other nutrients to stable forms.

4. How often does the Multrum have to be emptied?

The chamber where decomposition takes place is never emptied. Only the material which has passed under the lower partition and into the storage chamber is to be removed. Frequency of removal and quantity of material are dependent on the use characteristics of the household. The storage chamber is large enough to store several years' worth of compost from an average family (4 to 6) before removal of any material is necessary.

5. How much compost is produced?

If the Multrum were used as the only toilet and kitchen waste depository, about 80 pounds of compost (about 20 pounds on a dry weight basis) would be produced per person per year. This would amount to about one and one half cubic feet per person per year. But, because use is bound to be somewhat irregular (people work during the day and go on vacations), the actual amount will probably be somewhat less.

6. What are the fertilizing qualities of the end product?

Multrum compost is an excellent soil amendment because it is high in organic matter (58 per cent on a dry weight basis) as well as plant nutrients. The percentages of major plant nutrients—nitrogen, phosphorus and potassium (the "N-P-K" in terms of N, P_2O_5, K_2O) are 2.4 per cent, 3.6 per cent and 3.9 per cent. Thus, about 3 lbs. of dry weight (about 10 lbs. "wet" weight) is roughly equivalent to 1 lb. of "10-10-10" fertilizer. The minor plant nutrients, calcium, magnesium and sulphur, as well as several trace

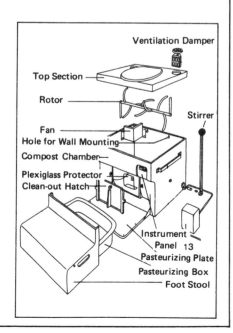

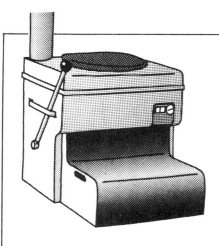

nutrients, are also present in significant amounts. For additional information ask for our literature titled "Chemical Analysis of Clivus Multrum Compost."

7. Is the end product safe to use in gardens?

Chemical analysis of compost samples from seven Multrum units has shown that detected amounts of potentially toxic metals are well below those levels considered acceptable for composted sewage sludge to be applied to agricultural soils. Analysis for soluble salts which might be harmful to soil and plant life shows that Multrum compost can safely be applied at the rate of 1.6 dry tons per acre, which is equivalent to 104 pounds "wet" weight of compost on a 20 x 20 garden plot. This rate of application will give a nitrogen application rate of 90 pounds per acre, which is considered moderately high. It is important to note that about 72 per cent of the nitrogen in Multrum compost is bound organically, so that it will be released slowly. Since no industrial waste products (toxic chemicals, etc.) which are usually present in sewage treatment plants are introduced to the Multrum, the end product will be free of these materials. (For additional information ask for our literature titled "Chemical Analysis of Multrum Compost end Product.")

8. Is the end product (compost) free of disease-producing organisms?

Bacteriological analysis of samples from 9 Multrum units showed that Multrum compost has a bacterial composition similar to that of soil. In particular, the numbers of pathogenic bacteria found in the Multrum compost were very low, and the kinds (species) of pathogenic

bacteria were those which also occur widely in soil. It is also noteworthy that neither this study nor a separate study of 8 additional Swedish units found any fecal coliform bacteria (which are indicators of fecal contamination). Pathogenic organisms are not likely to survive 2-4 years in the Multrum chamber because conditions there are unfavourable to them:—The temperature is too low much of the time (optimal conditions for these organisms are those of the human body), there is no "host" organism, and they are likely to be consumed by the organisms that bring about the composting process. For additional information ask for our literature titled "Analysis of Bacterial Populations in the Final Product of Clivus Multrum."

9. What about viruses—are they destroyed by the process?

Such viruses as hepatitis, which find water to be a better medium for their existence than soil, will probably die sooner in the Multrum than in a sewage treatment plant. Any viruses which can survive extended periods of time in ordinary soil conditions could be present in the humus from the Multrum. Compared to waterborne sewage systems, the Multrum is certainly less likely to either support viruses or to spread them.

10. Why doesn't it smell?

A natural draft, like that in a chimney, causes a suction effect toward the vent opening above the roof, which in turn causes air to be drawn in through the air inlet under the compost storage chamber door. However, whenever the garbage chute or toilet is opened, air will also be drawn down these openings into the container and up the vent. Actually, a minute amount of air is being constantly drawn down the toilet and garbage chutes even when they are closed, so that the toilet room and kitchen are ventilated by the Multrum and kept free of odours. The small exhaust fan, recommended for most installations, will insure against the infrequent possibility of odour caused by downdrafts in the vent.

11. Would any odour coming from the vent above the roof be

offensive or constitute air pollution?

Aerobic decomposition does not produce noxious gases (carbon dioxide and water vapour are the main waste products of micro-organisms in this process). There is consequently, less odour from the Multrum vent than from the plumbing vents on most houses.

12. Don't the chutes and toilet stool get soiled and produce odours?

Soiling is infrequent due to the large diameter of the stool and chute. Odour is not a problem even when there is soiling because the draft is maintained carrying odours down toilet and kitchen waste chutes when the lids are open.

—Clivus Multrum, Inc.

BIO-SYSTEMS TOILET CORP. LIMITED
255 Gladstone Street
Hawkesbury, Ont. K6A 2G8
(613) 632-9502
MODEL: Bio-toilet M-B, M-C

The Canadian-made Bio-toilet previously employed a rotating drum, but has discontinued this line. The new design is a simple tank divided horizontally by a screen. Raw sewage is contained by the screen, while the composted material drops through the screen into a holding tray

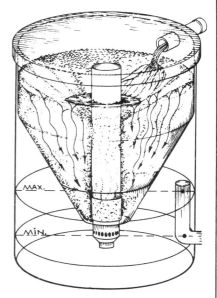

which can be removed for retrieval of the compost. The M-B model uses a heater and a fan, while the M-C model claims to need neither of these. Lists at $675 for the M-B and $495 for the M-C. Also available are "grey water" filtration systems at $295 -$395.

ENVIROSCOPE, INC.
2400 W. Coast Highway
Suite D,
Newport Beach, Ca 92663

MODEL: Carousel
Simply the bottom half of the large Carousel. Lists at $915.

SANTERRA INDUSTRIES LIMITED
1081 Alness Street
Downsview, Ont. M3J 2J1
(416) 661-2560

MODEL: Envirolet
The Envirolet, Bio-toilet, Humus models, Mullbank, and Tropic all have the same basic design, namely a compact tank with a horizontal screen dividing raw sewage and humus. The primary differences are in the ventilation and heating systems. The Envirolet has an "aeration basket" which facilitates aeration from the four sides as well as the top and bottom of the pile. The heater is connected to an air grid system which not only radiates heat to the pile but also squirts air into it. Lists at $695.

FUTURE ECO-SYSTEMS LIMITED
680 Denison Street
Markham, Ont. L3R 1C1
(416) 495-6450

MODEL: Humus H-5, H-5B, H-10
The Humus is the most widely used compact composting toilet in Canada. Called the Mull-Toa in Sweden, it uses a pressure chamber to recirculate air before

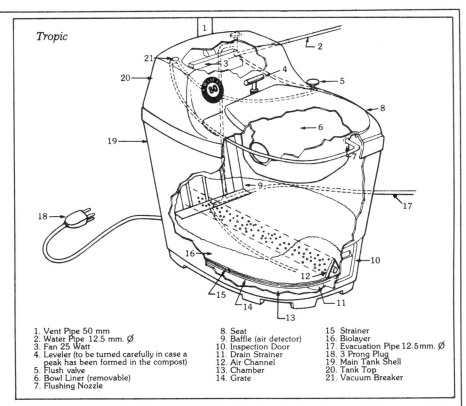

Tropic

1. Vent Pipe 50 mm
2. Water Pipe 12.5 mm. Ø
3. Fan 25 Watt
4. Leveler (to be turned carefully in case a peak has been formed in the compost)
5. Flush valve
6. Bowl Liner (removable)
7. Flushing Nozzle
8. Seat
9. Baffle (air detector)
10. Inspection Door
11. Drain Strainer
12. Air Channel
13. Chamber
14. Grate
15. Strainer
16. Biolayer
17. Evacuation Pipe 12.5 mm. Ø
18. 3 Prong Plug
19. Main Tank Shell
20. Tank Top
21. Vacuum Breaker

it goes up the vent, and to prevent odours from escaping into the house. The heater warms the air rather than the pile as in some models. The H-5 is intended for cottage use, while the H-5B is an industrial model. The H-10 is designed to handle a family year-round. Listed at $759 for the H-5, and $909 for the H-10 (vent kit included).

CANADIAN INVENTOR LIMITED
Box 541
Don Mills, Ont. M3C 2T6
(416) 447-6941

ENERGY ALTERNATIVES
2 Croft Street
Amherst, Nova Scotia
(902) 667-2790

RECREATION ECOLOGY CONSERVATION OF U.S. INC.
9800 W. Bluemound Road
Milwaukee, Wisc. 53226

MODEL: Mullbank Ecolet
Long established in Sweden, the Mullbank has recently opened an operation in Canada. The pile is warmed by a heating coil in the horizontal screen. Air is circulated by a fan simply by drawing it in

through a vent in the front of the unit, up through the pile and then through the vent. The "Mullbadd" over the heating coil contains micro-organisms capable of starting the composting. The manufacturer claims that it never has to be replaced and can survive freezing temperatures. Lists at $715.

ENTALPI WASTE RESEARCH LIMITED
Millgrove Side Road
R.R.2,
Dundas, Ontario L9H 5E2
(416) 689-7308

MODEL: Tropic
Air is circulated in a fashion similar to the Mullbank. The base of the tank is equipped with a heating pad to maintain appropriate temperatures in the pile, and a "process starter" is included to provide fast start-ups after periods of disuse. Entalpi also sells the Bowli toilet which uses a drum set horizontally in the unit. The drum is turned manually to mix the pile, and facilitate aeration. The Bowli is designed for cottage use for six or seven people. The Bowli-N.E. is the same model without the electrical elements. The Bowli is listed at $749 and the Tropic is listed at $699.

THE FARALLONES INSTITUTE
15290 Coleman Valley Road
Occidental, Ca 95465

MODEL: Farallones Two-Chamber

One of many models for the do-it-yourselfer, the Farallones Two-Chamber is the best documented design. Like most homemade models, the Farallones adds to the traditional privy design a means to aerate the heap. The Farallones' version has two chambers, one side of which is screened to allow aeration. The screen can be removed for turning and removal of the compost. Once the first chamber is full it is turned into the second chamber for continued composting. Approximately $100.

Random Comment

McGILL'S "MINIMUS" MOULDERS ON

If you've always figured that the only way to say goodbye to the flush toilet was to say hello to the thousand dollar composter, you may be surprised to learn that Canadian ingenuity has solved the problem.

While the now famous Clivus Multrum mouldering toilet continues to loom large on the pages of contemporary alternative magazines and books, the aptly dubbed "Clivus Minimus" is quietly shattering the myth that imported and expensive is better.

The Minimus, based on the principles and design of the Multrum, is the work of McGill University's Minimum Cost Housing Group (MCHG). It is fabricated of concrete blocks and is designed to be built on-site for less than $200 in most cases. You can build it yourself with the help of the plans in MCHG's four dollar publication—*Stop The Five Gallon Flush!*

The plans are quite simple and adaptable to various housing situations. If the basic idea is followed, all should go well.

We built ours at the same time as our house was being built, so it became part of the main structure, buried with our other block walls.

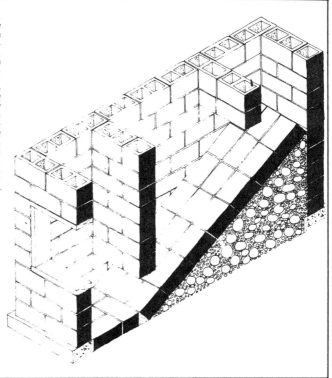

*Right, design for a low-cost, homemade composting toilet built using the same principles employed in the Swedish-designed commercial model. Dubbed **Clivus Minimus**, it is the work of the McGill University Low-Cost Housing Group, which is seeking alternate, low technology designs for third world countries. Fabricated with cement blocks, and given a substantial coat of sealant (bitumen), this unit would receive both toilet and kitchen wastes. In addition, the unit would need a chimney-like exhaust pipe and non-corrosive ventilation ducts to assure that oxygen is supplied to the mouldering heap.*

This necessitated the use of 12-inch blocks instead of the suggested four- and eight-inch blocks. (MCHG suggests that it may even be built of plywood if properly waterproofed and sealed.)

Our clean-out hole is outside and the toilet is located on the second floor. We decided against a separate kitchen waste hole, feeling that it would only mean one more hatch to worry about keeping airtight. Instead, we carry our kitchen scraps up to the toilet daily.

The throne itself is a simple wooden box around a metal shute in the floor. It must be well sealed and have an airtight cover. We think of it as the simplicity of an outhouse without the midnight trips into the bush during a winter snowstorm.

Our Minimus has only been in operation for six months—late winter through summer and we have run into some of the difficulties we were forewarned might occur.

The liquid build-up during the first year is a problem and we've dumped bales of peat moss into the clean-out chamber to absorb the excess. (This black soaked moss has proved to be an

excellent fertilizer for our flower garden.)

We've also had some problem with flies, which can be minimized by preventing them (as best you can) from entering or leaving the chamber at all vents and accesses. The addition of sawdust should help until the internal balance of the pile is established.

The last problem is the one everyone asks—"Doesn't it stink?" Well, we have to be honest. On a few particularly hot and humid nights this summer we could detect an unfamiliar odour wafting up from the hole when we had occasion to use it.

Normally, however, there is a noticeable downdraft when you open the lid of the toilet which carries foul odours up the vent and outdoors. But the same way a wood stove may suddenly experience a downdraft in its chimney, changes in wind direction or barometric pressure can affect the efficiency of this vent.

The odour is always temporary and to anyone used to country living, no more offensive than being downwind of a neighbour giving his manure spreader a workout on his hay field in the fall.

After the pile is well established (about two years of use) these problems should disappear. We have much faith and can't wait to scoop out that first pile of safely pasteurized garden compost. The natural cycle will be complete as we return to the land all that has been taken from it.

And the few initial problems are well worth their slight inconvenience as we notice the drastic saving of water from our modest well and think of the time we will never spend with plunger in hand.

—*Mikell Billoki*
Gore Bay, Ontario

HITTING THE FAN: PART I

This is just a quick summary of the trials and tribulations we have had with our "Humus" brand toilet. It was installed late last summer and the instructions were followed to the letter. From the start it was unusually noisy, but not knowing how it was supposed to sound, we put up with it. After several weeks the smell became very noticeable and proceeded to get worse. The solution was to extend the vent pipe another six feet above the peak of the roof. Shortly after this the fan assembly came adrift from its mounting, severing the power cords in a shower of sparks. (It was in use at the time), and this was a very disconcerting event, to say the very least. After an hour or so of struggle I managed to repair the damage wreaked by the amok fan assembly. It was returned to operation.

Now the slice iron seems to be seized in place. This model has the built-in slice iron, and yes, I have loosened the lock nut. To say the least, I am not looking forward to digging the accumulated waste matter out to correct the problem.

However, all complaining aside, it seems to be an excellent alternative to the standard methods of waste disposal.

—*Stephen Lambert*
Creemore, Ontario

PART II

Our "Humus" toilet has been in operation for almost six months,

and as an interim compromise we find it good. We expect to build a house in the near future, with a Clivus Multrum-type system, but it was neither practical nor economically sound to install one in our present dwelling, a mobile home. The Humus is an incredible improvement over both the outhouse and the pail toilet, but it is not perfect. There are several things we have found which will, if done consistently, keep odour to a minimal, tolerable level:
1. Keep the room at or near 68 degrees (F).
2. Don't put much, if any, toilet paper in it.
3. Make the exhaust stack as high as possible to create good draft.
4. Keep the lid shut!

Although the instructions with the toilet don't mention this, citrus and banana peels, etc., need to be cut up into one-inch or two-inch squares or the stirring mechanism gets stuck.

Our only major complaint with the Humus is the fan noise. In an otherwise silent house, with only nature's sounds, it is an intrusion. However, we are finding it a useful interim system, and would like others to know that the Humus is an acceptable system given the methods of care I have mentioned.

—*Miriam R. Scott*
Campbellford, Ontario

Books

ON SITE SEWAGE DISPOSAL
By Jack L. Abney
Air Pollution Control Dept.
Room 207, Civic Center Complex
Evansville, In. 47708

ALTERNATIVE WASTE SYSTEMS
By Robin Billou-Adams and John O'Brien
National Center for Appropriate Technology
1522 K. St. N.W., Suite 1036
Washington, D.C. 20015
Publication No. B006

COMPOST SCIENCE: JOURNAL OF WASTE RECYCLING
Rodale Press
Emmaus, Pa.
1 year, six issues, $6.00

COMPOSTING: A STUDY OF THE PROCESS AND ITS

PRINCIPLES
Rodale Press
Emmaus, Pa.

COMPOSTING
By Harold Gotaas
WHO Monograph, Series No. 31
Geneva, Switzerland

**STOP THE FIVE GALLON
FLUSH: A SURVEY OF
ALTERNATIVE WASTE
DISPOSAL SYSTEMS**
Minimum Cost Housing Group
McGill University
Montreal, Quebec

**ALTERNATIVE WASTEWATER
FACILITIES FOR SMALL
UNSEWERED COMMUNITIES
IN RURAL AMERICA**

By R.J. Otis and
D.E. Stewart
Small Scale Waste
Management Project
University of Wisconsin
Madison, Wisconsin

**LOW COST TECHNOLOGY
OPTIONS FOR SANITATION**
By Witold Rybcynski et al
UNIPUB
Box 433, Murray Hill Station
New York, N.Y. 10016

**RURAL WASTEWATER
DISPOSAL ALTERNATIVES**
State Waste Resources
Control Board
Box 100
Sacramento, Ca 95801

CLEAN WATER
By Leonard Stevens
E.P. Dutton & Co.
New York, N.Y.

**GOODBYE TO THE
FLUSH TOILET**
Edited by Carol Hupping Stoner
Rodale Press
Emmaus, Pa.

THE TOILET PAPERS
By Sim Van der Rym
Capra Press
Santa Barbara, Ca 93101

SEPTIC TANK PRACTICES
By Peter Warshall
Anchor Press
Garden City, N.J.

**COMPOSTING TOILETS AND
GREYWATER DISPOSAL:
BUILDING YOUR OWN**
By Clark Zandy and
Steve Tibbets
Alternative Waste
Treatment Association
Route 3
Bath, Me 04530

Bob Isaac-Renton, kneeling at the ecological throne, and Vic Enns are partners in Vancouver's well-stocked Solace Energy Centre.

Mail Order Fertility

A guide to the postal seedsmen

Canada's first seedsman — one David Landreth — stayed in Quebec City just long enough to feel the nip of a bona fide Canadian winter before seeking greener pastures in Philadelphia, where he went on to become America's first mail order seed-marketer.

Although Landreth did much in the line of cross-pollination and importing of formerly unavailable varieties, it was left to Luther Burbank, a later American seed grower (1849 - 1926), to perfect the other half of the seedsman's art: hyperbole.

"I have tested the best grains from all over the world, and mine yield nearly double," said Burbank in his catalogue, the same catalogue in which he is described as, "unquestionably the greatest student of life and living things in America, if not the world."

Following the trail opened by Burbank, many contemporary seed catalogues are withering exercises in exaggeration. How, for example, does one pick from among these three descriptions of three different pea varieties in a just-arrived catalogue:

Little Marvel: "Sweetest flavoured of all early peas . . . ."
Blue Bantam: "Most gardeners consider this to be the sweetest and most delicious of all peas . . . ."
Hundredfold: "Considered by many as the very finest of all dwarf peas . . . ."

And how, without occult powers, does the winter-bound gardener choose beet seed from the following descriptions:

1) "The texture and eating quality is supremely fine and the colour is unusually rich and appetizing . . . ."

2) "A real taste thrill, extremely sweet, very tender, with melt-in-your-mouth flavour . . . ."

3) "Wonderfully uniform in growth and size, and with luxurious red interior colour, free of zone rings. The promise of its appetizing appearance is fully met in its outstanding quality and flavour . . . ."

Although buying through seed catalogues is fraught with pitfalls, it does have clear advantages over the mass market racks of seed that seem to spring from every drug-store, discount mart and service station waiting area.

Not only do the mail order companies usually offer better prices, much more choice in varieties and, often, more uniform and better quality seed, they are the first to bring out new vegetable strains.

One novice Canadian organic gardener sold more than $400 worth of surplus sweet corn simply by picking an extra-early hybrid — Stokes' *Earlivee* — a variety that ripened when the local tongues were hanging out for corn and people were eager to pay premium prices.

There is an art to reading even the most conservative catalogue, not dissimilar to reading letters of recommendation: pay close attention to all positive attributes but watch carefully for obvious omissions.

For example, "Gold Pak 28: The most outstanding strain of Gold Pak on northern muck soils. Roots mature slightly later than the regular strains and retain unusual hybrid-like uniformity over a longer period than other strains. Unsurpassed for interior colour and exterior smoothness and shape." But wait. Before rushing down to the post office to order a quarter-pound of this carrot seed, reflect for a moment. There is no mention of flavour in this description, and while it is possible that these carrots are delicious, I would be willing to bet that they have the same amount of flavour as the crispy commercial sticks found in supermarkets.

On the other hand, if the catalogue does admit to a weakness, treat it as gospel. Think twice if you see something like "nearly all of the stringiness has now been bred out of this superb bean." As it is the job of the description to sell seeds, most of them have good things to say. But some say more than others.

Among the minimum information we would like to see is the variety's growing season. There are obvious differences between a tomato that ripens in 40 days and one that takes 80 to reach maturity. Amazingly, some seed catalogues gloss right past this in their rush to the superlatives.

When a seedsman recommends a particular variety as his *best*, then it is sure to be worth trying. On the other hand, he is very likely to overpraise his latest introduction in hopes of getting it off to a good start.

If the catalogue does not rave, then the variety in question may be inferior. Most seed companies carry varieties about which they feel no particular enthusiasm, but list them because of continuing demand. Some will be inferior to more recent entries, but a few will be non-sexy, old-fashioned varieties just as good as the most highly recommended newcomers.

If a friend, neighbour, or the farmer down the road suggests a particular variety, don't be put off if the seedsman doesn't wax enthusiastic. He may prefer another because he introduced it, or he may feel that the seed has a reputation that will stand without a sales pitch.

One seed catalogue term that is always reliable is "All-American Winner," the seedsman's equivalent of an Oscar. An independent research unit established by major seed companies tests new varieties in 30 different areas in Canada and the United States and only those found superior receive All-American Winner status.

A single seed catalogue is all that anyone really needs and the nearest will usually be satisfactory. But it is fun to compare, and almost every catalogue has some varieties not listed by any of the others. Last year I ordered seeds from six companies. Each had one or more varieties that I wanted to try, varieties not available from the others. There is no catalogue that gives the lowest prices on every variety, so money is saved by shopping around.

Careful garden planning, of course, is a must before diving into your selection of seed catalogues. Many winter-bound gardeners have become carried away by all those beautiful photographs and ordered enough seed to start a canning factory.

The following seedsmen will send a copy of their current catalogue, free of charge, unless otherwise noted. The season peaks for most seed houses in the period from December through February, and early ordering helps assure that substitutions won't be made to fill your order. The bigger companies will supply catalogues year-round and cater to the needs of greenhouse growers and windowsill gardeners.

Should you decide to place an order from a particular catalogue, that company will normally arrange to send a free catalogue the following year, but will drop your name from the mailing list if you fail to order.

Many mail order seedsmen have a minimum order, or place a handling surcharge on small orders. To avoid this problem, it helps to find a kindred soul or two and place your seed orders jointly. For the past few years, a small number of couples of our acquaintance have had an annual "seed party," in which we pore through a good selection of catalogues and pool our orders.

Deciding which seed varieties to order is easily one of the most pleasantly vexatious problems of the gardener's year.

—Kenneth Allan
Kingston, Ontario

SEEDS

(Editor's Note: The seed variety listings given after each review are intended to convey the flavour of a particular catalogue. Prices and availabilities change from year to year, and readers are advised to order only from the company's current catalogue.)

STOKES SEEDS LIMITED
Box 10
St. Catharines, Ontario L2R 6R6
or
Box 548
Buffalo, New York 14240

Stokes continues to produce the single most useful seed catalogue in North America, aiming it primarily at market gardeners. The rest of us benefit from variety descriptions that are thorough, useful and commendably non-sensational. This is one company that goes out of its way to describe the relative merits of each vegetable and flower listed, including size, colour, disease resistance and the use for which it was bred (large commercial, market growers and/or home gardeners).

This, combined with a selection of more than 600 varieties, has made Stokes the largest mail order seed house in Canada. Most corn, bean and pea seed is treated with Captan, a pink fungicide that helps prevent rotting of early plantings in cool, wet soil. Organic gardeners should therefore watch for varieties available with Stokes' designation of UT — Untreated.

ONION: Stokes Exporter: 100 days. Our most popular and versatile hybrid onion. Exporter has been widely accepted and used in all major northern onion growing areas, for the past six years. Bulbs are larger than Trapps No. 2, or Canada Maple, and are globe shaped, with fairly small necks. Exporter has lots of skin, which is well retained in storage. This variety always seems to get away to a vigorous start in the spring, and keeps growing during the hot weather, just before harvest. A valuable choice, for many areas where growers are forced to seed a second time. Exporter is reported to show a fairly good tolerance to fusarium, and is almost

as hard as Canada Maple. A Stokes Seeds Introduction. (Precision Sized Seed.) Pkt. 55 cents.

SPINACH: Melody: *43 days. Our best "plain-leaved" hybrid, Melody provides amazing yields, 40 per cent greater than Viking which is the standard used by canners and freezers. Leaves are semi-savoyed and sprout on the top half of the plant, which provides a high percentage of dirt free leaves at harvest. Thick juicy leaves are dark green in colour and oval shaped. Tolerant to both strains of Peronspora, mosaic virus, and blue mould. Use for fresh market, processing, freezing or late spring and early autumn crops. All-America Winner. (Sized Seed.) Pkt. 55 cents.*

TOMATO: Sub-Arctic Maxi: *48 days. Our earliest tomato for fresh market in northern areas. Reselected by Canadian research scientists in both Ontario and Alberta, from extra-early "bird's nest" plant types. Concentrated clusters of 2 oz. fruit at the centre of each plant are protected by fairly sparse, open, extra-dwarf foliage. Plants are very susceptible to early blight. An excellent choice for far northern regions or for home gardeners who like to enjoy the first tomato. The largest fruited of the Sub-Arctic class. Pkt. 50 cents.*

JOHNNY'S SELECTED SEEDS
Albion, Maine 04910

Northern organic gardeners will find a kindred soul here — all seeds are untreated, many bred with an eye to chilly Maine summer weather and thus easily adaptable to Canadian conditions.

This is a catalogue that tends to inspire trust — many listings include the first-hand impressions gained by Johnny's small crew on their farm in Maine. Rob Johnston Jr. ("Johnny") and Company have a strong organic orientation and no seeds are treated with fungicides. In addition, many

varieties have been grown without artificial fertilizers or pesticides, although some seed does come from "conventional" sources.

A few extra-early varieties not found in the Canadian catalogues are *Ashworth* sweet corn (69 days to maturity with excellent flavour), *Whippersnapper* cherry tomatoes (which ripen even before the amazing *Sub-Arctic* types) and *Beagle* peas, of which Johnny's says, "If you count the days to your first fresh peas in the spring, as we do, plant *Beagle.*"

Once staunchly opposed to hybrid seeds, this company is now offering a number of F1 hybrids, apparently in recognition of the advantages that crossbred vigour can offer in the way of increased production and disease resistance. Good people to deal with. (Please send 50 cents, refundable with first order, to cover cost of catalogue.)

HOT PEPPER: Early Jalapeno: *75 days. One of the hottest of the hot peppers. 3½" x 1¼" conical, blunt fruits come in early, dark green changing to red. This is the best pepper to grow for dried hot-pepper seasoning. This is a special early strain. Minipack 45 cents; Pkt. 60 cents.*

CORN: Mandan Bride: *98 days. A lovely, untampered-with corn which we believe to be from the Mandan tribe of what is now North Dakota. This is a "flour" corn, distinct from flint corn in that nearly the whole kernel is soft, white starch, — easy to grind. The 8-to 12-rowed ears, which are slightly shorter than Garland, come in a striking array of colours including purple, white, variegated, red, yellow — some with a beautiful, translucent "rosy" effect. Ears mature very early on 5-to 6-foot plants. Limit one packet per order. Pkt. 70 cents.*

WAX BEAN: Beurre De Rocquencourt: *46 days. A wax variety grown by us, and bred by Vilmorin, France. Very early bearer of thin, 6 to 7" yellow pods. Plants are dwarf and upright. Recommended where nighttime temperatures are cool. Very prolific. Black seed. Pkt. 70 cents.*

THOMPSON & MORGAN INC.
132 James Avenue East
Winnipeg, Manitoba R3B 0N8
or
Box 24
Somerdale, New Jersey 08083

Thompson & Morgan has twice been listed by the Guinness Book of World Records — once for the most countries served by a seed company (130) and the second time for publishing the largest seed catalogue in the world, by the number of entries.

North Americans receive a truncated version of the full-blown British catalogue, but it is, nevertheless, unlike any other. Even experienced gardeners will fail to recognize many of the vegetable strains, with many exotic and novelty listings in evidence. *Alphatoco* beans for sprouting — T&M says they are sweeter and crisper than ordinary mung beans — *Ha-Ogen* melons from Israel, *Apple Squash,* and various tropical oddities for the greenhouse owner.

Judging by the number of exclamation points and the general descriptive frenzy, we suspect that a refugee from the Fleet Street tabloid press world had a hand in writing this catalogue.

NEW! ASPARAGUS BEAN: Orient Express (T&M Exclusive) 100 per cent stringless. Earlier maturing — vast crop. Slim gourmet shape and irresistible flavour. *We have long admired the asparagus bean for the enormous crops it can produce but have always fought shy of offering it because of its tendency to stringiness and long season to harvest. Then a few years ago, we had the great pleasure of being introduced to a wise and venerable Japanese gentleman who had been working on 3 major areas of improvement to the bean — Orient Express is the result. It crops earlier, is now completely stringless and has a glorious flavour.*

Technical Information. *Although early maturing, it does require a warm August to give of its best. The shorter your season the* earlier it should be started off. Sow indoors in peat pots in March and April ¼-inch deep in a temperature of 70 to 75 degrees F and plant outside when all frost danger has passed. Provide poles, trellis or fencing, etc. for them to climb and remember you won't need many plants. Four well-grown *Orient Express* will provide a family of 6 with regular pickings plus some for the deep freeze. Harvesting will begin in late July to mid-August, and go on until frosts. Steamed, lightly boiled, stir-fried, or eaten fresh its flavour is magnificent. And chopped into 4-to-6-inch lengths it looks like the slim gourmet beans served in France. (50 days planting out to harvest). Pkt. $2.50, 2 pkts. $4.75.

SPINACH: Low oxalic acid content. Monnopa (T&M Exclusive) 45 days. A unique spinach with almost no oxalic acid (an agent that causes loss of calcium from the blood). Ideal and now being widely grown commercially for baby food. The amount of oxalic acid is also related to the bitterness of spinach and so this variety is particularly fine flavoured. It is extremely bolt resistant under reasonable conditions and very winter hardy. Pkt. $1.00, 2 pkts. $1.90.

CYCADS . . . once food for Dinosaurs Cycas Revoluta 1 to 3 feet. Surface sow. Very long lived. Withstands frost to 25 degrees F. Germination 1 to 3 months, 70 to 75 degrees. Very, Very Old! 110 million years ago it had evolved to the stage where it was so abundant as to be one of the most successful adaptations this planet had ever known. Sometime all those years ago a new strain was evolving which was even more successful and is now widely spread throughout the world — today we call that plant 'The Conifer.' The Cycad, however, still retains all its prehistoric characteristics. It is a fascinating plant to grow, easy, long lived. With each order we'll send you full instructions. Pkt. of 3 seeds $3.20, 2 pkts. $6.10.

DOMINION SEED HOUSE
Georgetown, Ontario L7G 4A2

There is a sign in a Toronto record store that says, "Sam has everything . . . if you can find it. If you can't, ask Sam's clerks . . . if you can find Sam's clerks."

Dominion, which has Canada's second largest mail order seed selection, makes Sam's system appear fastidious by comparison. Still, Dominion has a large, satisfied clientele across Canada, and their catalogue rivals Stokes, Burpee's and the other big houses for the sheer number of listings.

Unfortunately, the Dominion catalogue is put together somewhat like a Chinese puzzle, with multiple listings of the same vegetable scattered throughout the book. Those who care not a whit for organization may find this great fun on long winter nights, but Dominion's overuse of superlatives in variety descriptions quickly strains one's credibility. Dominion doesn't even bother to list the days to maturity of most varieties.

Still, all the old favourites and new All-Americans are here, along with such tempting oddities as *Ringmaster* onions (a Spanish type bred to produce distinct "onion rings" upon slicing), *Tom Thumb Butterhead* lettuce (bred for single-serving salads and window sill culture) and *Three Kings* peas, a British variety that throws pods in groups of three and is said to be one of the easiest of all peas to pick.

Dominion should do its customers a favour and produce a catalogue worthy of the seeds it sells. (Will not ship to the United States.)

HYBRID TOMATO: Early Cascade. This new introduction must surely be close to the perfect garden tomato. Where else do you find these features all in one variety? It is early, very early, producing tasty, bright red, quality fruit a week to 10 days before such as Springset, and it is a heavy and continuous bearer averaging as many as 70 fruits per plant. It is tall, taking little garden space. Should be grown on poles or other support at least 3 metres high, pruned to single or double stem. Give regular light fertilizer applications to support and encourage the heavy crop. Ripe fruit holds on the vine unusually well. Adaptable, and strongly tolerant to verticillium, fusarium and other diseases. The medium size fruit (4 to 6 oz.) is smooth, highly coloured, tasty and appreciably crack-resistant. There is none other like Early Cascade on the market today. Pkt. 75 cents.

TOMATO: Giant Beefmaster Hybrid. Replaces Giant Beefsteak as a superior and more desirable variety; earlier, and with tolerance to verticillium, fusarium and nematodes. Extremely large, solid, meaty, tasty, thick-walled fruits, and unusually mild. A magnificent big beauty of appetizing rich colour for slicing, canning, cooking and juice. For the many,

many housewives who like the beefsteak type this is a prize sort far exceeding older types. Pkt. of 30 seeds 60 cents.

TOMATO: Early Giant Hybrid. A week earlier than Wonder Boy, combining earliness, quality, great size and heavy yield in high degree. May be staked or cage-grown. Make companion planting with Wonder Boy. Pkt. of 30 seeds 60 cents.*

WILLIAM DAM SEEDS
West Flamboro, Ont. L0R 2K0

A small, low-key seed house which Rene Dam continues to operate with a certain Old World flavour — listings are dominated by traditional, time-tested, favourites, conservatively described.

True to its Dutch roots, William Dam offers many varieties familiar only to the North American gardeners of European origin who make up an important part of the company's business. Others of an adventurous nature may wish to try *French Summer* leeks (grown for use in salads), *Blue Pod Capucijners* peas for drying or *Holstein Blood Red* rhubarb (ready for picking one year after sowing seed). Hard-to-find seed such as lentils and mangel beets are also available.

Dam is a fine source for garlic bulbs, asparagus roots, Jerusalem artichoke tubers and horseradish (Maliner Kren) roots. (Perishable plant and rootstock shipped within Canada only.)

BRUSSELS SPROUTS: Rubine Red. This is really something in your garden to talk about. Plants with red foliage and red sprouts. A specialty with distinct flavour. A beauty in your garden. Pkt. 60 cents.

JERUSALEM ARTICHOKES: Helianthis Tuberosous, free-growing, winter hardy perennial, 5 to 8 feet. Member of the sunflower family. Valued as a vegetable are its starch-free tubers. Native of North America and very easy to grow. Tubers can remain in the soil in winter. Good summer windbreak with yellow flowers in September — October. Per 10 tubers: $2.75.

MARIGOLD: Tall, mixed. Marigolds control nematode (Aaltjes) damage. Common marigold in a rotation planting of the home garden will control eelworms for 3 years in those areas planted. The home gardener is commonly unaware of the stunting damage caused by nematodes feeding on plant roots. Planting time: May. 125 g. covers about 5,000 square feet. 25 g. $1.50; 125 g. $3.75.

DELPHINIUM, PACIFIC GIANTS

ISLAND SEED
CO. LIMITED
Box 4278, Station A
Victoria, B.C. V8X 3X8

British Columbia's most extensive mail order seed catalogue with some cloud-loving West Coast specials, such as their exclusive *Vancouver Island* tomato. Variety descriptions succinct but with a minimum of information.

WATERMELON: Klondike. 85 days. Dark green skin with stripes. Oblong shape, weighing up to 20 pounds. Suitable variety for the Pacific Coast area. Flesh deep red, crisp and sweet. Pkt. 49 cents.

CORN SALAD: 45 days. Broad green leaves. Use as lettuce for salads. Used in summer and winter salads to a great extent in France. Pkt. 49 cents.

KALE: Thousand Headed. For chicken feed and stock feed. Height to 4 feet. Long stem. Dark green smooth leaves. Suitable for ensilage. 30 gms. 75 cents.

VESEY'S SEEDS LIMITED
York, Prince Edward Island
C0A 1P0

Thousands of Maritime and northern New England gardeners rely on the Vesey family to

provide them with seeds that grow — and grow well — in adverse climatic conditions.

The Vesey catalogue changes little from year to year, and gardeners can count on the Veseys to have tested all varieties offered in their own market garden plots. Unfortunately, they no longer offer corn, bean or pea seed without fungicide coating.

Stonehead Hybrid Cabbage: Stonehead was named for its extremely solid interior as this cabbage is actually almost the same in weight as a stone of similar size would be! This is a second early variety, maturing in about 50 days from early set transplants and weighing, at maturity, from 3 to 4 pounds each. For an early sort, it is very resistant to splitting and when ready will stand quite a long time in the garden or field. For customers without greenhouse facilities, this sort, like the other varieties we catalogue, can be grown very easily by sowing the seed very thinly anytime during late April, May or June in their permanent garden location and after plants are up well, thinned out to about 20 inches apart. This F-1 Hybrid Cabbage has been outstanding in our own trials here at York and we highly recommend its tidy size and uniform maturity to commercial growers and home gardeners alike. Pkt. 60 cents.

Beacon Hybrid Sweet Corn: For a great number of years, we have been searching for a main crop corn variety, that would combine earliness, large size, with good tip fill, and of course, most important of all, excellent flavour. In the Beacon variety, we believe we have found it! This new sort matures about the same time as North Star, but is superior in every respect. Stalks are about 6 feet tall, and the 8-to 8½-inch ears are mostly 14 to 16 rowed. We do not think the flavour can be beaten, and this fine new variety is especially recommended for freezing. 125 g. $1.00.

Citron: This is the early red-seeded sort used for preserves. 100 days. Pkt. 25 cents.

BURPEE SEED COMPANY
Warminster, Pennsylvania 18991
Clinton, Iowa 52732
Riverside, California 92502

Burpee is big. It is now owned by ITT and its catalogue lists such horticultural gimcracks as instamatic (Soil) Moisture meters and wash-'n wear vinyl "Farmer Fred" scarecrows.

Nevertheless, Burpee retains its reputation for fast, conscientious service to both sides of the border.

This all-colour catalogue contains a respectable number of vegetables available nowhere else, including *Big Girl* hybrid tomatoes (one-pound fruits of exceptional flavour on disease resistant plants), *Royal Oak Leaf* heat resistant lettuce and *Snowbird*, an extra-early snow pea for the north or for compact urban gardens. (Write to address nearest you.)

BURPEE EXCLUSIVE LETTUCE: Royal Oak Leaf. *50 days. You can pick this delicious loosehead lettuce well into hot summer weather. The heat-resistant, long-standing plants produce large rosettes of oak-like, dark green leaves. They're tender, tasty and vitamin-rich, with thick succulent midribs. Royal Oak Leaf makes a beautiful, tasty salad from spring to summer and again in fall from a later sowing. (Seed Tape available.) Pkt. 75 cents.*

GARDEN CRESS: Burpee's Curlycress Brand. *10 days. Useful, easy-to-grow greens with dark green, finely cut, curled leaves. Enjoy its pungent flavour in salads, blended with cream cheese or mayonnaise in sandwiches, in party spreads, and as a refreshing garnish. Can be sown the year 'round and eaten in just 10 days from seeding — outdoors from early spring to fall (and winter in the South and Pacific Southwest), with sowings every two weeks; indoors on the kitchen window sill in winter. Slow to bolt. Also excellent for delicious sprouts; see Bio-Snacky Seed Sprouter. Pkt. 50 cents; 1 oz. $1.25.*

BURPEE EXCLUSIVE TOMATO: Big Girl Hybrid VF. *78 days. After over 10 years of breeding and field testing, Big Boy's sister was introduced in 1976 and has proved a big hit in thousands of home gardens. Burpee's Big Girl Hybrid VF ripens large, solid fruits with many weighing a pound and more. They're real beauties, bright scarlet-red right to the top (no green shoulders) and remarkably crack-free . . . perfect to slice or cut in wedges. And the mouth-watering flavour! Just wait until you taste Big Girl Tomatoes vine-ripened from your own plants. They stay extra-healthy, too, and bear a bumper crop right up to frost, with their "built-in" resistance to fusarium and verticillium wilts. Seed'n Start Kit available. Pkt. 75 cents.*

HARRIS SEEDS
Moreton Farm
Rochester, New York 14624

One hundred years ago, Joseph Harris, the second son of a tenant farmer from Moreton Corbett, Shropshire, England produced his first seed catalogue. Having emigrated to western New York State, Harris was a successful farmer and agricultural writer — apparently one with a sense of humour. Commenting on his widely respected swine raising manual, Harris wrote, "The publishers, somewhat to my annoyance, called it 'Harris on the Pig.' "

In presenting his first seed catalogue, Joseph Harris said, "It is 16 years since I commenced to grow seed, but this is the first year that I have issued a catalogue. I fear it will be a poor one, but I shall try and comfort myself with the reflection that no one will be asked to pay anything for it."

Three generations later, the Harris Seeds catalogue remains one of the most readable, instructive and intelligent available. Harris has an impressive number of exclusive varieties, but has yet to recognize the organic gardening movement. *All* corn, bean, beet, cucumber and pea seed is treated with Captan.

ITALIAN BUSH BEANS: Green Ruler. *Improved Bush Romano Type. 51 days. With Green Ruler, famous plant breeder Dr. Shigemi Honma of Michigan State has developed a distinct improvement on the Bush Romano type. It has the same rich "beauty" flavour but is considerably earlier, and its pods are somewhat longer. They are flattened, firm and meaty, very low in fibre and delightful to eat. The spreading bush vines yield heavily. Thousands of our customers enjoy the distinctive flavour of Italian beans, and the modern bush vines are a welcome development. Green Ruler is the best example of this type we've seen yet. Pkt. 60 cents.*

SILVER QUEEN: Tenderest, Most Delicious White Corn. *94 days. Most of us here think that this is the best corn we have to eat, and we still look forward to it. Its quality is really extraordinary, always tender and extra-sweet with a flavour all its own. It matures late, but it's a special treat in late summer and fall.*

The ears are large and handsome, well filled with 14 to 16 rows of glossy white kernels and they will hold on the stalk for a week or 10 days with no sacrifice of quality. They're great for freezing too.

The plants are large and husky, 7 feet tall or more, and yield heavily. Wait until the soil has warmed up before planting, since it does not have the vigour of Quicksilver in early plantings, but to cap the season with sweet corn at its very finest, be sure to include Silver Queen in your corn patch. Pkt. 75 cents.

BUTTERCRUNCH: The Ideal Home Garden Lettuce. (M.T.O.) *64 days. This distinctive variety is by far the most popular garden lettuce. Developed by Dr. George Raleigh of Cornell, it is vigorous, dependable and easy to grow, but it is of far better quality than ordinary kinds. The broad dark green leaves are delicious to eat, but the best part is the heart of loosely folded leaves and thick, crisp, tender ribs, sweet and "crunchy." It is our favourite lettuce.*

Considerably larger than Summer Bibb, it stands even longer without bolting, retaining its superb quality for a long time without becoming bitter. Enjoy it all season, from early spring transplants, outdoor sowings even in warm weather and from late plantings until freezing weather in the fall. Its delicate flavour and crispness will delight you. Pkt. 50 cents.

Harris' Frosty peas, recommended for their earliness and good freezing qualities.

W.H. PERRON & CO. LTD.
515 Labelle Blvd.
City of Laval, Québec H7V 2T3

Perron is the country's third largest seed house and their $1.00 catalogue, one of the more lavish available, comes in either French or English. Variety descriptions are terse and not particularly useful, but the selections are extensive, with All-America winners and a number of surprises.

Perron is one of the few companies to offer *Tampala*, a dark green potherb that they claim is superior to Swiss chard and spinach. Among the other European specialties are Rapi, shallots and *Flageolet* green beans, which you shell.

CABBAGE: Hybrid Minicole. Exceptional mid-season variety. The heads are ready to cut small, very hard and round. But contrarily to King Cole or Superette, if you let them in the garden, they still continue to grow very slowly for the 2 or 3 months following without splitting, remaining at a good frigidaire size. Dark green. 66 days. Pkt. $1.25.

Garden Huckleberry (Solanum nigrum). Plants 60 to 90 cm. high, producing an enormous quantity of small round violaceous black fruits about 2 or 3 times larger but quite similar to black currants. Tasteless nature but good in pies or jelly. Same culture as for the tomato. Pkt. 50 cents.

CELTUCE: or "Celery Lettuce." A vegetable different from any you have ever tasted. Young leaves are eaten as lettuce or boiled as greens. Stalks can be sliced in strips and eaten like celery, raw or cooked, served with butter or "à la vinaigrette" or baked "au gratin." Loaded with vitamins A, B, C and G. Pkt. 40 cents.

DANDELION: Giant Improved. A superior selection with very large leaves. The plants are compact and measure 45 to 60 cm. in diameter. The leaves are thick, tender and tasty. 95 days. Pkt. 50 cents.

LOWDEN'S BETTER PLANTS & SEEDS
Box 10
Ancaster, Ontario L9G 3L3

Edward Lowden is now in his 90s, but with his wife, Betty, continues to operate one of North America's unique cottage seed industries.

The originator of several famous varieties of blackberries and raspberries, Lowden is continuing

his plant breeding experiments, perhaps in hopes of finding just one more new strain that might rival his 1926 discovery, the Lowden Blackberry.

"That was a gift from God," says Lowden. "I was working in my gardens one afternoon and I came across one plant that was superior to all the others. I cultivated it separately."

In addition to offering berry rootstocks, the Lowdens take pride in their selection of ultra-early tomatoes, bred for northern climates. They recently introduced *Imur Prior Beta (IPB)*, a Norwegian tomato, and the business shows no signs of slowing down.

Lowden, who was profiled in an early issue of *Harrowsmith* magazine, says that he doesn't really want "any more publicity now. We received more mail than we could properly take care of last spring and had to return a pile of

orders and have a lot more carried over for the fall."

The catalogue itself is short — about 10 pages, mimeographed and hand-stapled. To spare this small company unnecessary expense and effort, only those seriously intent on ordering should request a catalogue.

RED RASPBERRIES: Williamette. One of the largest and firmest of our raspberries. Because of this, many prefer it above all others for freezing. We grow more of it than any other. In the 35 or so years we have grown it, we have never yet detected a virus infected plant. 5 for $3.00.

Large Italian Tomato: This tomato was also sent to us by a customer. It is shaped like the small Roma, long and pointed at the blossom end. It has green shoulders and is quite large, 10 oz. to nearly 1 pound. Pkt. 50 cents.

Russian or Quaker Comfrey: This is a wonder plant of exceptional nutritional

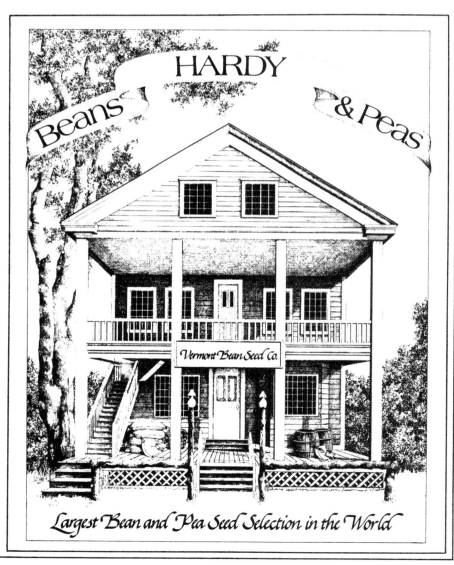

Largest Bean and Pea Seed Selection in the World

and medicinal value for man and beast. The fresh green leaves may be cooked like spinach. It is thought to contain more Allantoin (a curative substance) than any other plant, making it valuable for internal or external sores. Asthma sufferers especially have claimed help from it. It is hardy, perennial and of great vigour, usually set 3 feet apart each way. On strong rather moist land it gives very heavy yields of green fodder for stock. I am surprised that dairy farmers have not caught on to its value for summer feed as have those with goats. Strong started plants: 85 cents, 3 for $2.25, 10 for $5.00, postpaid.

VERMONT BEAN SEED CO.
Garden Lane
Bomoseen, Vermont 05732

Claiming the "largest bean and pea seed selection in the world," this company offers a useful, handsome catalogue with many varieties unavailable elsewhere. Postage rates to Canada are high, but many northern gardeners buy Guy Thomas' beans and peas in large quantities to offset shipping charges. None of the seed is treated with fungicides. Send 25 cents postage and handling for the 32-page catalogue.

Jacobs Cattle Bean: 85 days. Sometimes known as the Coach Dog Bean or Dalmation Bean. An old Vermont, Saturday-night-at-home special favourite. One of the most beautiful beans in the world. Pure white seed with deep maroon splashes. The plant grows 24 inches high and makes a tasty shelling bean at around 65 days, or let it dry for winter use. One of our very favourite for drying and baking. Another heirloom family bean. ¼ lb. 95 cents; ½ lb. $1.75.

Wren's Egg Bean: 65 days. Sometimes known as the Speckled Cranberry or King Mammoth Podded Horticultural Bean. Larger than the French Horticultural Bean in size, many prefer the Wren's Egg for its very productive growth and unusually fine shelling qualities. This is a very popular home garden bean which yields well in a very small area. Pods are medium dark, 5 inches long, wide and thick. Largest of all the horticultural beans. Everbearing from the 65th day until end of the garden season. Our seed is a new highly-improved disease-resistant strain. We strongly urge all gardeners to include this variety in the garden. Excellent frozen or fresh shelled. ¼ lb. 95 cents.

Scarlet Runner Bean: 70 days. The king of the ornamental beans. Grows to over 10 feet tall with large clusters of bright scarlet flowers blossoming all summer. The most

prolific ornamental bean we offer. The more you pick it — the more it bears. The plant develops 12 to 16-inch pods with large black and scarlet-coloured beans which are absolutely delicious when cooked fresh. Ideal for growing up the side of a porch, garage or house as a vine for shade. The Scarlet Runner has unusually large leaves which maintain a lush garden green colour all summer. An heirloom ornamental bean. It should also be noted that the flower attracts hummingbirds. ¼ lb. 95 cents; ½ lb. $1.75.

Scarlet Runner Bean "Tee-Pee": Here is an interesting way to introduce children of all ages to the pleasures of gardening. Simply set six 10-foot poles in a circle and bind them together at the top. Then tie mesh, Gro-Net, or string between the poles (for vine support) all the way up to the top, leaving room for a "doorway." Plant the Scarlet Runner bean around the outside every 4 inches except where the doorway is to be located and it won't take long for the vines to cover the Tee-Pee. Children love playing in the Tee-Pee, picking the beans and eating them. For children interested in their own garden project this is ideal! ¼ lb. 95 cents; ½ lb. $1.75.

LINDENBERG SEEDS LTD.
803 Princess Avenue
Brandon, Manitoba R7A 0P5

Specializing in "prairie-type, northern varieties," Lindenberg is a conservative seed house with many loyal followers in Canada

(does not accept orders from the United States).

Two early corn varieties, *Yukon* and *Early Dawn*, have made recent appearances, along with the fast ripening *Alaska* muskmelon.

Caragana Seed: Siberian Pea Tree. The quick growing and attractive Western shrub that is exceptionally hardy. Makes an attractive hedge in summer and a "snow fence" in winter. Can be planted in the open 1 inch deep and 2 inches apart. Some prefer to start them in a bed and transplant them when they are 12 inches high after cutting them back to 6 inches. 25 g. 50 cents.

Starfire Tomato: This Prairie-developed variety is non-staking and compact (approximately 12 inches high and 22 inches in spread). Fruit clusters are located on strong branches near the centre of the plant, thereby limiting fruit spoilage caused by contact with wet soil. With an average size of 150 g. and a favourable acid content, this variety is superior for fresh tomatoes and canning. It is earlier and a better yielder than Beefsteak. 0.8 g. pkt. 35 cents.

Pop Corn: Plant in banks of short rows so that the plants pollinate each other. Keep away from other varieties, since cross-pollination will reduce the "popping" effectiveness of this variety. Pkt. 25 cents.

C.A. CRUICKSHANK LTD.
1015 Mount Pleasant Road
Toronto, Ontario M4P 2M1

Cruickshank is known primarily for Canada's finest selection of flower seeds, bulbs and plants, but they also offer some specialty vegetable items, such as *Golden Midget* sweet corn which bears 4-inch ears on 30-inch stalks.

Spring Charms Collection No. 75: An "All-Star" collection of miniature bulbs for rockery or border. For several years this has been one of the most popular collections we have ever offered. Anemone Blanda, Crocus E.P. Bowles, Chionodoxa sardensis, Iris reticulata, Crocus Largest Yellow, Crocus Sieberi, Eranthis cilicica, Narcissus lobularis, Crocus Joan of Arc, Chionodoxa Luciliae, Iris Danfordiae, Scilla Sibirica. 12 each, 144 bulbs — $30.95 value for $27.25.

Forcing Collection No. 15: A small collection of bulbs easy to force for the winter window garden. You can make up a number of pots of lovely bloom at an extremely modest cost. A splendid gift collection for beginners — order several for your friends who do not realize how simple it is to grow bulbs in pots. 3 Narcissus Golden Harvest (large golden yellow Daffodils), 3 Narcissus Geranium, 3 Hyacinths (3 varieties, top size), 6 Tulips General de Wet (orange, fragrant, best tulip for forcing). 15 bulbs — $7.65.

GEORGE W. PARK SEED CO.
Box 31
Greenwood, South Carolina 29647

Mainstream varieties and some southern specialties — okra, crowder peas and *Dixie* butterpeas — that may interest northerners looking for a challenge. Park also supplies sweet potato plants, but only within the United States.

MUSTARD GREENS: Sow seed outdoors early spring. For fall crop sow 6 to 8 weeks before first fall frost. Sow 1 to 2 inches apart, in rows 15 inches apart. ¼ ounce sows 25 feet.

Southern Giant Curled: 50 days. An exceptionally long-standing curled type. Spicy, pungent flavour, high vitamin content make it a treat. ¼ oz. 40 cents; 1 oz. 95 cents; ¼ lb. $2.50.

COWPEAS: Black Eyed. Popular cream with dark eye. The dwarf plants bear an abundant crop. 1 oz. 35 cents.

PEANUTS: Red Tennessee. Splendid large nutty, sweet kernels. Two to five to the pod. (Cannot be shipped to California.) 2 oz. 35 cents.

McFAYDEN SEED CO. LTD.
Box 1600,
Brandon, Mantoba R7A 6A6

This is the mail-order arm of McKenzie Seeds, whose cardboard seed display racks serve the mass market across Canada.

After a highly successful year in 1978, McFayden is going into mail order in a big way, with a large all-colour catalogue.

Their listings are distinguished mainly by a selection of seeds for kitchen sprouting (mung beans, Chinese cabbage, Fenugreek) and certified seed potato eyes (Red Pontiac, Netted Gems and Norland, priced at 100 for $7.49).

One newcomer is *Midget Leaf* lettuce, which is ready in just 42 days for early spring salads.

PEAS: Sugar Snap (edible pod). An outstanding All-America Award Winning new pea type. Sugar Snap can be used as an edible podded type or shelled and used like regular peas. The pods are round, firm and really juicy and may be cut up for use in salads. They are also ideal for cooking or freezing, or just to be eaten raw. Vines will require support. Large econ. pkg. 50 g. 59 cents.

GARLIC CHIVES: A fantastic new vegetable variety which combines all the growing characteristics of both garlic and chives. Tops look like chives and have a mild garlic flavoured taste, while the roots look and taste like garlic. Plants are winter hardy. An excellent new vegetable which you can use in salads, soups or stews. Pkt. 69 cents.

GRACE'S GARDENS
Autumn Lane
Hackettstown, New Jersey 07840

The Ripley's Believe-It-Or-Not of seed companies. Never mind taste, Grace offers the *biggest* of everything — six-and-a-half-pound tomatoes and quarter-ton squash that would easily crush the unfortunate gardener who fell beneath one. Grace has expanded her line to include a page of normal-sized French and Oriental vegetables.

World's Most Expensive Melon Seed: Win $250 by beating the 197 lb. record with seeds from this world record watermelon. Ed harvested 1,717 seeds from his giant and you can now purchase up to 3 seeds for your garden. World Record Melon Seed, $1.00 each, 3 for $3.00.

BRAGGER TOMATO: Earliest Maturing Giant! You can be the first to brag about your giant tomatoes with the Bragger — because it matures earlier than most other giant varieties! You'll often get tomatoes weighing 2 lbs. and with your extra care . . . who knows, maybe a state

or national record! Truly excellent flavour too! Solid meaty flesh is a beautiful deep red that's just great in salads or sandwiches (you'll only be able to fit one slice per sandwich!) Resistant to cracks and seams. A tomato you're sure to brag about. Pkt. $1.00.

Bob's 451 lb. Giant Grows 7½ lbs. A Day!! Bob, a Coatesville, Pa. greenhouseman started with seeds taken from a huge orange squash called Hungarian Mammoth, Cornell strain (named after Ray Cornell, founder of the Churchville, Pa. Pumpkin Show — Oct. 1978). With just 5 seeds planted in early June the vines were growing 9 feet a week by July 15 when the flower "set."
Record Vine Produces 1,016 lbs. of Fruit. The 15x20 garden plot was well fertilized with 10-10-10 weekly feeding of liquid fertilizer, a fungicide every 10 to 14 days and lots of water! Between mid-July and September 15 it all happened — 475 lbs. — over 7½ lbs. per day! (At the official Guinness weigh-in it shrunk to 451 lbs.) Even as amazing, 2 other fruits on the same vine weighed 300 and 255 lbs. — 1,016 lbs. in all!
Grace's Gardens Offers Seed From World Record. I'm proud to offer my customers seed taken from the actual 451 record for only $5 per seed (2 seed limit as only 100 seeds available). Ask for Bob Ford's World Record Squash. I also offer 452 seeds taken from the 300 and 255 lb. sisters harvested from same vine for $1 per seed, ask for Bob Ford's Same Vine Giant Squash.

T&T SEEDS LIMITED
Box 1710
Winnipeg, Manitoba R3C 3P6

"I have used seeds from T&T for years," writes Dr. John A. Gow, "and swear that every one of them grows. They don't offer endless varieties, but the seeds they do carry are very good. I know because I live on them."

HYBRID MUSKMELON: Alaska. New. One of the earliest maturing muskmelons in existence; when ripe turns light reddish-orange on the exterior. Football-shaped fruits have beautiful, moist salmon coloured flesh. Delicious eating. For early fruit, suggest starting indoors. Oversize pkt. 15 seeds.

SWEET PEPPER: King of the North. Good early pepper for home gardens. Vigorous, hardy and prolific. Dark green fruit, thick mild-flavoured flesh. Specially developed for northern conditions. Oversize pkt. 1/16 oz. 39 cents.

EARLY TOMATO HYBRID: Mustang. It is early in producing fruit and the plants, due to their hybrid vigour, will resist many adverse growing conditions. This is one of the best varieties for ripening indoors late in fall. It is very productive and a sure fruiter. Try it. Pkt. 25 hand-crossed seeds 39 cents.

ONTARIO SEED COMPANY
Box 144
Waterloo, Ontario N2J 3Z9

Previously bound in the centre of an ORTHO promotional booklet, the Ontario Seed Company catalogue now appears on its own. Nuts-and-bolts listings, but *Early Cascade* is a new tomato this year. Requiring an 8-to-10-foot stake, this cultivar has produced an average of 72 fruits weighing four to six ounces each per plant.

True Watercress: Must be grown along stream banks or in moist areas for best results. Once established it will produce broad leaves which should be harvested in spring or fall for many years. Matures in 52 days. Price: pkt. 39 cents.

Hybrid Scallopini Squash: You are likely to fall in love with an entirely new, different kind of summer squash, Hybrid Scallopini. Growers start harvesting the rich, green, flavourful, scallop fruits from the bush plant early, and continue over a long season. Harvest fruits in young, immature stage (3 inches in diameter or less) for best quality. An All-America award winner from Petroseed Research, there's nothing like it on the market. Can be fried or boiled and offers a bonus. Scallopini is excellent raw in salads, due to its sweet flavour. Pkt. 50 cents.

ALBERTA NURSERIES AND SEEDS LIMITED
Bowden, Alberta T0M 0K0

The company's specialty is seed and planting stock for short-season, high-altitude growing areas, and they have a deserved following in the West. Has gooseberry, raspberry and currant plants, as well as asparagus and rhubarb roots.

POTATO EYES: Netted Gem. All cut from the finest certified seed. Potato eyes are the easiest way to plant potatoes. Do not take any chance of sowing run down or diseased seed. Netted Gem is known as the finest table potato particularly for baking. Pure white flesh of superb quality and the best winter-keeper. 50 Eyes $5.50.

ONION: Red Wethersfield (M). Better known as the Hamburger onion. Nothing finer for hamburgers, salads, sandwiches or for any other purpose. Flesh is white, juicy, crisp and of superior flavour. Very good keeper in storage. Pkt. 5 g. 50 cents.

CUCUMBER: Morden Early (E). The earliest cucumber listed and very productive. Most popular variety producing large quantities of medium sized cukes. Splendid for early dills, pickling or slicing. A must in short season districts. Pkt. 5 g. 50 cents.

J. LABONTE & FILS
560 Chemin Chambly
Longueuil, Quebec J4H 3L8

The only seed catalogue we know of with girls in bikinis and miniskirts. Partially bilingual, but all seed listings are *en francais seulement.*

Labonté is especially proud of its *Québec 13* tomato, which is claimed to be the most popular among market growers in the

Montreal area, "because of its exceptional yield and disease resistance."

Six varieties of tobacco seed are offered, including several for grow-your-own pipe smokers (*Petit Havane, Grand Rouge, Parfum d'Italie* and *Rose Quesnel*).

Send $1.00 to cover cost of the catalogue.

FEVES—HARICOTS: Brittle Wax (St-Sacrement). (55 jours). Toujours la variété la plus en demande pour le jardin de familie et le marché. Grande gousse jaune doré de 15 à 18 cm ronde et entierement sans fil. Produit presque tout l'été quand la température est favorable. Semence blanche avec point noir. Paquet 40c, 100 g. 65c, 250 g. 95c, 500 g. $1.60, 2 kg $6.00, 5 kg $14.00, 10 kg $24.00, 20 kg $46.50, 50 kg $100.00.

TABAC: Petit Havane. (Petit Canadien Rouge) La semence est comme de la poussière et vous devez semer en couche ou à l'intérieur en la couvrant très légèrement avec un peu de terreau ou de sable. Quand les plants ont quelques feuilles, repiquer a 5 ou 7 cm de distance. Transplanter en pleine terre en laissant 90 cm de distance entre les plants. Les semis se font a la fin de février ou au début de mars. 1 paquet suffit pour 1,000 plants. 50c.

PIKE & CO. LIMITED
10552 - 114 Street
Edmonton, Alberta T5H 3J7

"We're very conservative in Alberta, you know," said a Pike's spokesman when asked about their most recent catalogue. "We don't like to try new things."

Indeed. Pike's slim seed listing booklet appears not to have changed much in a generation, but Prairie gardeners can count on not getting seeds suited only to balmier climates.

SWEET CORN: Altagold — Raised by the University of Alberta and introduced by us to the gardening public several years ago and is now being grown by most critical gardeners. Altagold is the earliest large-ear (open pollinated) sweet corn ever raised, and a variety which will produce ears anywhere in Alberta and many parts of the N.W.T. Grows only 3½ to 4 feet high and the ears are carried low. It produces 3 or 4 large ears 7 to 8 inches long, varying from 8 to 14 rows of excellent flavour and good colour. It is exceptionally good for quick freezing. Large pkt. 35 cents.

PEA: Improved Stratagem, Re-selected Stock — (Height 2½ feet). The largest cropping second early pea in existence, and the very best pea for this North-West climate. The haulm is very robust, bearing a profusion of immense pods, 6 inches in length and frequently containing 10 large flavoured marrow peas. Pkt. 35 cents.

STRAWBERRY SEED: Hardy Ever-bearing — Introduced by R. Simonet of Edmonton, produces great quantities of fruit throughout the season. Flavour of the Wild Strawberry but produces larger fruit. May be started inside. Pkt. 35 cents.

HORTICULTURAL ENTERPRISES
Box 34082
Dallas, Texas 75234

For *semillas auténticas Mexicanas,* this is the best source, with more than 30 varieties of pepper, from mild to fiery, and other unusual selections like *Chu Yu* and *Shia Kuan,* Chinese tomatoes.

GUËRO — *mild, medium pepper.* Used fresh in salads, also sauces. This pepper thought to be a favourite of Montezuma II, Aztec Emperor.

SANTA FE GRANDE — *hot, small pepper.* Medium thick fleshed; heavy cropper . . . used fresh in salads, sauces or pickled. Yellow/orange-red. U.S.

TABASCO — *hot, small pepper.* Originally from Mexico . . . used fresh in sauces or pickled. Fine flavour. Light green/red. U.S.

CAYENNE — *hot, long pepper.* Used fresh or dried (crushed or powdered). Dark green/red. U.S. (Write for price list.)

EARLY SEED & FEED LTD.
198 Idylwyld Drive South
Saskatoon, Sask. S7K 3S9

Sells seed grain and forage seeds by mail as well as vegetable seeds. Specializes in varieties that are best for the prairies, for example *Far North* cantalope — "extremely early in Saskatchewan and excellent quality."

BUCKWHEAT SEED: A short season cash or honey crop. Seed in early June. Canada No. 1 Seed, 100 lbs. $12.00.

SPRING WHEAT: Neepawa. Certified, $10.25 per 100 lbs.

FLAX: (Per 100 lbs.) Certified — Dufferin $24.00; Noralta $24.00.

SHELL BEANS: Great Northern. An excellent white shell bean for baking. Makes delicious pork and beans. 125 g. 50 cents.

KITAZAWA SEED CO.
356 W. Taylor Street
San José, California 95110

Some unusual Orientals here with exotic names — *Miyashige* radishes, *Pak Choi* mustard, *Aka Shiso* greens.

GAZE'S FARM AND GARDEN SUPPLIES
Box 640
St. John's, Newfoundland
A1C 5K8

Small, low-key company that handles varieties which do well on The Rock. Gaze recommends *Outdoor Girl,* a British variety, for gardeners who are unable to ripen other tomatoes because of unfavourable climate.

SANCTUARY SEEDS
1913 Yew Street
Vancouver, B.C. V6K 3G3

Non-hybrid vegetables, grown organically as much as possible. This young company also grows its own herb seeds too, and is especially interested in medicinal herbs — horehound, catnip. They sell dried herbs.

PARSLEY: Hamburg Rooted. This parsley is grown mainly for its roots both in cooking and in medicine. 90 days. 30 gms. 50 cents.

CAROB: Jacaranda Procera. This is a tropical tree, best grown indoors or in greenhouses. Soak the seeds 3 days first. Used as a chocolate substitute. Ornamental. Pkt. 50 cents.

JOJOBA: A native of the Sonoran desert, this plant furnishes an oil soon to replace the sperm whale oil of commerce. Excellent results have been obtained with external applications of the oil to skin problems. Grow indoors in pots. Pkt. 50 cents.

HERBST BROTHERS SEEDSMEN, INC.
1000 N. Main Street
Brewster, New York 10509

A relatively new entry among the stable listing of companies serving home gardeners, Herbst has been in the commercial seed business since 1876.

Their new catalogue caters both to commercial growers and serious home gardeners, with an outstanding number of choices for many species (10 varieties of zucchini, 14 types of Chinese cabbage).

Herbst also includes a fascinating section devoted to tree and shrub seeds, including Azalea, Catalpa, Nannyberry, English Holly and, for those with patience, Giant Sequoia.

CELERY: Summer Pascal (Tall Fordhook) 120 days. Plant: 23 inches tall, upright, full-hearted with dark green foliage. Stalks: 9 inches to first joint, thick rounded, smooth, dark green, easy blanching. Originated by Univ. of Mass. Improved strain of Summer Pascal for the East, adapted to both upland and muck soils. 5 gr. 50 cents; ½ oz. $1.50; 1 oz. $2.25.

STRAWBERRY CORN: 110 days. Deep red coloured kernels, purple husk and shape similar to strawberries. Can be used to decorate table along with gourds. Plants are small producing 2 to 4 ears per stalk. 10 gr. 50 cents; 1 oz. $1.00.

BISHOP FARM SEEDS
Box 338
Belleville, Ontario K8N 5A5

One of the last homes of the 39-cent seed packet. Bishop's is what it says it is: a farm seed company, whose stock in trade is forage and corn seed, sold in bulk. Nine varieties of alfalfa, 12 clovers, various timothys, grasses and pasture planting mixes.

The vegetable section hews mainly to the time-tested farm garden favourites, reasonably priced. Onion sets by mail and a selection of seed grains — oats, barley, buckwheat, rye and wheat — in quantities of one pound and up for small holders.

SEMENCES LAVAL, INC.
3505 Boul. St.-Martin
Laval, Québec H7T 1A2

Their catalogue is free, colourful, and lists more than 400 varieties, but it is *en français seulement.* They do not accept U.S. orders.

J.A. DEMONCHAUX CO.
827 N. Kansas Avenue
Topeka, Kansas 66608

Since 1945, Demonchaux has offered *specialités françaises.* Their 25-cent catalogue includes three varieties of endive, two types of salsify and two of sorrel. Planting guide for all items is sent free with every order of seeds.

PEAS: Petit Pois (Petit Provençal) 2 oz. 65 cents.

WELSH ONION: Pkt. 60 cents.

ASPARAGUS: Argenteuil Early. Pkt. 60 cents.

GREEN BEANS: Triomphe De Farcy. 2 oz. $1.35

Briefly Noted

DE GIORGI BROTHERS INC.
P.O. Box 413
Council Bluffs, Iowa 51501

CHAS. C. HART SEED CO.
Wethersfield, Connecticut
06109

JENKINS HDWE. & SEEDS
Box 2424
London, Ontario N6A 4G3

McLAUGHLIN'S SEEDS
P.O. Box 550
Mead, Washington 99021
(Catalogue: $2.50)

SEED CENTRE LIMITED
Box 3867, Station D
Edmonton, Alberta T5L 4K1

TREGUNNO SEEDS LTD.
126 St. Catherine Street North
Hamilton, Ontario L8R 1J4

D.V. BURRELL SEED GROWERS COMPANY
Rocky Ford, Colorado 81067

EARLY WALCHEREN BROCCOLI.

SHADES OF GREEN
Box 57
Ipswitch, Mass. 01938

SHEPPARD'S BULB FARM
6707 Bradner Road, R.R.1
Mount Lehnan, B.C. V0X 1V0

TSANG AND MA INTERNATIONAL
1556 Laurel Street
San Carlos, California 94070
Chinese vegetable seeds and plants.

GLECKLER'S SEEDMEN
Metamora, Ohio 43540
Unusual vegetable seeds.

HALIFAX SEED COMPANY LTD.
5860 Kane Street, Box 338
Halifax, Nova Scotia B3J 2N7

J.L. HUDSON, SEEDSMAN
Box 1058
Redwood City, California
94064
Vegetable, flower and cactus seeds.

Random Comment

Not many small gardeners know about B.C. Pea Growers in Brooks, Alberta, but it is a really astounding source for seeds.

They deal mostly in large market garden orders, but do have a small quantities listing. They offer any variety of peas at 40 cents per pound, versus $1.60 or so from other places. Other examples: Garlic, $1.50 per pound; Cucumber seed (11 varieties), 45 to 60 cents per 10 gram packet; Onion seed (11 varieties), 60 cents to $1.20 per 10 gram packet.

A real saving might be made by a group who's willing to order, say, 100 pounds of peas and split the seed and cost (only $18 to $30, depending on which of the 30 varieties you pick).

—Sandra Cumming,
Calgary, Alberta

T&T Seeds' catalogue may be brief, but their prices are absolutely unbeatable. In some cases they are 50 per cent lower than those of their competitors. Where else in Canada can you get a packet of any kind of seeds for 34 cents?

The quality of the seeds is excellent. If only they would list the maturation dates of their vegetables . . . .

—E.J. Woytiuk
North Battleford, Saskatchewan

Burpee publishes absolutely the best catalogue available, although prices range from reasonable to exhorbitant. Service is excellent, and we have never had to pay duty on seeds ordered from them or other U.S. companies.

—Lynn Anstett
Hazelridge, Manitoba

I wholeheartedly recommend Stokes Seeds for measuring up to their claim of "finest seeds and finest service." The dedicated people there will even answer questions pertaining to cultural problems that you may personally encounter — a very rare service indeed in this hurried age.

—Kathleen Haslam
Victoria, British Columbia

THE SOWER
Box 159
Bear River, Nova Scotia

In its chatty, 30-page catalogue, The Sower offers untreated seeds "wherever possible" and even a few organically grown seeds. A Seed Lovers Co-op is another service of the three-year-old Nova Scotia organization, which aims to promote small scale seed saving. Co-op members, for a $10 fee, will enjoy a 10 per cent discount on seeds sold through the catalogue, a newsletter and a forthcoming publication, Save Your Own Seed. A catalogue chart shows income levels from a ¼-acre garden used to grow seed in comparison to the same space used to grow vegetables for market; seed sales are more than double in all cases and more than four times as high in the case of beets. Vegetable, flower, herb and even a few shrub and tree seeds are offered for gardeners.

—Sharon Airhart

I buy my garden seeds from Stokes Seeds Ltd., St. Catharines, Ontario and Vesey's Seeds Ltd., York, P.E.I. Stokes has the best catalogue I have ever read. It is organized alphabetically with no repetitions and has complete culture information from preferred soil types, depth of planting, and expected ripening times to pest control, organic and so on. But, although the number of varieties is limited, I buy as much as I can from Vesey's. It is our most local seed company and does some of its field testing in Kentville, N.S., only about 50 miles from us. While I don't discount our Maritime mini-climates (our first fall frost averages a month earlier than gardens 10 miles away on the tempering Bay of Fundy), when Vesey's says a tomato will ripen in 65 days I have hope that it will. I have strong doubts, though, about Stokes' predictions from hot and steamy St. Catharines. Vesey's also has the lowest prices I know of: 20 cent and 35 cent packets still abound. The other Canadian seed company I have dealt with is Dominion Seed House. Its seeds are good and there are many interesting novelties that are fun to try, but I don't like their unattractive, disorganized and repetitive catalogue.

I am on a pleasant mailing list and receive many seed catalogues from the U.S. These are fun to browse through and occasionally contain a complimentary seed packet, usually lettuce or tomatoes. (I had eight varieties of lettuce and six of tomatoes last year, my own little research station.) I have never bought anything from these catalogues, keeping my dollars at home, but have sent for free or 10 cent trial offers advertised in various gardening magazines. This was several years ago and I am still blessed with offerings of giant egg-plants, casava melons and banana squash, none of which grows here.

—Molly Miron
Upper Kennetcook, N.S.

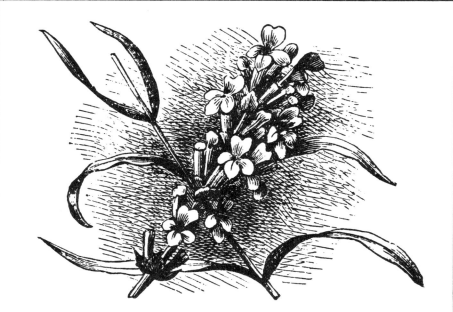

HERBS

ROSS PARLETTE
R.R.4
Cobourg, Ontario K9A 4J7
(416) 342-2188

Eight-page catalogue of herb plants.

TARRAGON: (Artemesia Dracunculus) Hardy French Tarragon with flavour of Aniseed. Can be used fresh to prepare stimulating salads, fish and meat dishes. May also be used to make tarragon vinegar. One plant $3.00, available spring and fall.

SWEET CICELY: (Myrrhis Odorata) Aromatic leaves with sweet scent of myrrh. An invigorating tea may be made from green seeds, and a wine from roots with flavour of aniseed. One plant $3.00. Available in spring only.

RUGOSA ROSE: (Fragrant Red) A hardy strain of Rugosa developed especially for the large ruby red seed hips. These hips, known to be one of nature's richest sources of vitamin C can be used to make nutritious jellies and nectars. In addition to vitamin C, they also contain vitamins A, E, B1, B2, Niacin, Calcium and phosphorus. One plant $4.00, available spring and fall.

OTTO RICHTER & SONS
Box 26
Goodwood, Ontario L0C 1A0

An extensive, 300-strong listing of seed, including sacred plants used by Tibetan lamas to stimulate psychic powers, herbs used by other cultures for ritual suicides and an herbalist's black bag full of other rare offerings. Their stock in trade, however, is a fine selection of culinary herb seed. Send 75 cents for catalogue.

GINSENG: Panax quinquefolius. American ginseng is a slow growing perennial herb found growing wild in cool and shady hardwood forests throughout eastern and central North America.

The American ginseng root has the same properties as the Asiatic ginseng (Panax schin-seng) which has been used in the Far East for thousands of years.

The virtues of ginseng were claimed to be so fantastic that Western doctors dismissed the plant as a panacea. While these fantastic claims haven't been verified, after some 25 years of study, Russian researchers have confirmed ginseng's powerful yet harmless tonic properties. Used as a general tonic when you feel "rundown," ginseng is excellent, stimulating both physical and mental functions. The Russians have also shown that ginseng has a stimulating effect on the gonads of sex glands, male or female, while having no harmful side-effects as some hormones do. As a result, ginseng is often prescribed by Russian doctors for those who complain of sexual failure. Also, Russian researchers found that ginseng helps build up body resistance to disease and strain, either physical or nervous.

Wild ginseng has been in such demand that it has become exterminated in many areas where it was once abundant. Ginseng is now cultivated to a large extent, although cultivated roots are considered somewhat inferior to those found wild.

We are pleased to offer high quality stratified seed. The seed can be planted *anytime from September until the ground freezes in forests or in specially prepared beds. In the following spring, the seedlings will appear and in 5 to 7 years will mature.*

As ginseng seed must not be allowed to dry out it requires special handling to prepare it for shipping. For this reason the seed is somewhat expensive.

Detailed cultural instructions are included with each order. Fall shipment only. Pkt./$5.

HENBANE: Hyoscyamus niger. *Powerful cerebral and spinal sedative used since remote ages to induce sleep and allay pains. Often an ingredient in witches' brews for its power of throwing victims into convulsions. Pkt. /75 cents.*

BAYBERRY: Myrica pensylvanica. *Aromatic shrub, native to the Maritimes. Astringent action of root bark abates diarrhea and hemorrhages; and as a gargle, soothes sore throat. Wax-covered berries are used to make aromatic candles and soap. Berries are boiled in water, liberating the wax which floats on top. Pkt./75 cents.*

Wormwood

ASHBY'S
R.R.2
Cameron, Ontario K0M 1G0
(705) 359-1115

Simple, mimeographed catalogue specializing in herbs and wild plants. There is a small catalogue for 20 cents with most listings and "for the herb nut," a 30-page catalogue for 50 cents. Ships plants to Canada and the U.S.

DOGBANE, Black Indian Hemp: *Apocynum cannabinum. Plant $1.50*

COMMON WORMWOOD: *Artemisia absinthium. Seeds $.75; Plant $1.50*

HORSERADISH (cuttings): *Armoricia rusticana. Shipped September 15 through May 15. 12 for $4.50*

Chicory

CENTENNIAL GARDENS
Box 4516, M.P.O.
Vancouver, B.C. V6B 3Z8

Twelve-page catalogue with limited selection of vegetable seed, but some interesting herbal entries.

PIONEER DYE PLANTS — Bloodroot: *Likes moist woody soil, perennial. A very ornamental white blooming plant, the root of which supplied the Indians with rich red and orange dyes to colour moose hair and porcupine quills. 60 cents/Pkt.*

MEADOWSWEET: *One of most important of nature's remedies. This herb is said to be the natural form of acetylsalicylic acid (Aspirin). Should be used as a dried leaf. 60 cents/Pkt.*

WHITE TOMATO: *A rare pure white tomato that is non-acid. Strongly recommended for those who cannot take acid fruits. Very attractive served with red. 50 cents/Pkt.*

ROSMARINUS SEEDS
R.R.1
Souris, P.E.I. C0A 2B0
(902) 687-3460

Ships herb plants within Canada and offers a small selection of herb seeds. Horseradish, comfrey, Jerusalem artichokes and garlic roots and sets. Will not accept U.S. orders.

CURRY PLANT (helichrysum ssp.) *Narrow, downy grey leaves really smell like curry powder. $1.75/plant.*

PYRETHRUM (Chrysanthemum Cin.) *An insecticide powder is derived from lovely painted daisy flowers. $1.75/plant.*

SHALLOTS: *The delicately flavoured, gourmet-acclaimed member of the onion family. (Commercial stock) ½ lb. for $1.60 postpaid.*

GOLDEN BOUGH RETAIL STORE/SANCTUARY SEEDS

1913 Yew Street
Vancouver, B.C. V6K 3G3
(604) 733-4724 or
(604) 733-5061

HAWTHORN HILL
R.R.1
Waubaushene, Ontario
L0K 2C0
(705) 538-2049 or
(705) 534-3628

Source for organically grown dried herbs, roots, bulbs and tubers for such perennials as comfrey, nettles, mints, chives, tansy, yarrow. Send $2.00 for catalogue and 5-herb introductory offer.

ABUNDANT LIFE SEED FOUNDATION
Box 374
Gardiner, Washington 98334

Slim, handsome catalogue with hand-lettered listings that border on the useless. Anyone serious about ordering from this group

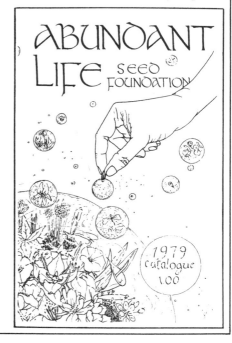

should be prepared to check with other catalogues and references to understand what you are buying.

This said, Abundant Life deserves praise for its efforts to ''acquire, propagate and preserve the plants and seeds of the North Pacific Rim.'' Their selection of tree and wildflower seed is growing, and Abundant Life is organizing seed collection and plant identification tours of coastal British Columbia and Washington State.

LARKSPUR: Self-sows; bee plant; purple. Annual. Pkt. 40 cents.

LUNARIA, or Money-plant. Dries into paper silver dollars. Choice of purple or white. Biennial. Pkt. 40 cents.

Tobacco

THE REDWOOD CITY SEED COMPANY
Box 361
Redwood City, Ca 94064

Craig Dremann runs this mellow little company almost single-handedly, and the slim catalogue is most notable for its herbs and other rarities: *Siberian* Ginseng, Buffalo Berry, Cardoon (an artichoke-like vegetable) and Orach (a cultivated green from France). Two catalogues are available: *Catalogue of Useful Plants* — 25 cents; *Supplement*—75 cents. Wholesale bulk price list free with S.A.S.E.

HOPS (Humulus Lupulus) Common Hops. Perennial herbaceous twiner whose cone-like 'fruit' is used for flavouring beer and formerly in medicine. The plant is used for fibre, being made into yarn and linen. Shoots grow up to 25 to 30 feet. Best sown in autumn to sprout in spring. Cultural directions with seed. Pkt. 50 cents.

DYE PLANT: Genesta Tinctoria. Dyer's greenweed. Woodwaxen. Evergreen

often nearly leafless shrub to 3 ft. with yellow flowers. Needs to be planted in a sheltered position if grown in the North. Sow seed in spring in small pots, shifting to larger pots until 2 yrs. old; at which time they should be transplanted out into their permanent position. Packet 35 cents.

CLYDE ROBIN SEED CO. INC.
4233 Meyer Avenue, Box 2855
Castro Valley, Ca 94546
(415) 581-3467

A lovely little catalogue of wild flower and tree seeds — natives of both U.S. and Canada. Send $1.00 for catalogue.

EXOTICA SEEDS
820 S. Lorraine Blvd.
Los Angeles, California 90005
(213) 935-8181

Steven Spangler offers a selection of tropical delights that will often be most suitable as house plants and in greenhouses for northerners — from Papaya and Guava to Jimson Weed. $2.00 buys a catalogue and a sample of seeds.

ACHRAS SAPOTA: Sapodilla, Chicle, Chewing Gum Tree. A beautiful tree with glossy leaves, Chicle is tropical in requirements, lending itself easily to indoors or greenhouse cultivation. The taste is comparable to a crunchy brown sugar texture and the gummy-white sap is the main ingredient for Chicklets Gum. 75 cents/Pkt.

PHOENIX CANARIENSIS: Canary Island Palm. All over California, this stately palm towers along the roadsides. The seeds germinate readily and growth begins quickly and as it matures becomes hardy to 15 degrees F. Although it does resemble the date palm, the trunk is thicker and it seems to thrive in cooler conditions. 75 cents/Pkt.

Pear Guava

PELLETT GARDENS
Atlantic, Iowa 50022

Honey plants — trees, shrubs and flowers selected especially for nectar production. (Ships seed throughout North America. Plants within U.S. only.)

RUSSIAN OLIVE (Elaeagnus angustifolia) The abundance of white, silvery gray foliage makes this a most striking shrub or small tree. It is desirable for grouping and extensively used in windbreaks. It blooms in late spring or early summer and is one of the best of honey plants. Bees visit the flowers in large numbers from early morning until late evening. The grayish white berries are much sought by birds. Very hardy and drought resistant. Plants, 18 inch up seedling, 5 for $7.00; 15 for $16.00; postpaid.

ANISE HYSSOP (Agastache anethiodora) Wonder honey plant attracts bees by the thousands. Long Period of Bloom — The flowers of Anise Hyssop are visited by the bees so eagerly over a long period in many localities, it has been termed ''Wonder Honey Plant.'' Where it does well it furnishes an abundance of bloom beginning early in June, blooming freely usually for two or three months and with some bloom lasting until frost. As soon as it is daylight in the morning until twilight in the evening, we find bees working Anise Hyssop. The small seed requires moist conditions for germination; plants bloom first year from seed. Perennial to three feet tall, flower heads lavender blue. Seed packet 80 cents; ¼ ounce (5000 seeds) $3.50; Per ounce, $12.00 postpaid. One year plants, 50 for $4.00; 20 for $14.00 postpaid.

PURPLE LOOSESTRIFE (Lythrum salicaria) An ideal honey plant for your flower border. A honey plant of major potential for wet land. Purple flowers on long spikes in late summer and fall. A nice ornamental growing to three feet or taller. Very good for flower gardens, hardy perennial, adapted to most soils, grows well in most gardens. Purple loosestrife blooms over a long period and flowers are very heavily worked by bees.

Especially adapted to moist or boggy land. Under these conditions it spreads extensively by self-seeding in many situations. From New England states west to Iowa it has naturalized in many situations on wet land such as boggy or marshy areas and along streams. The acres of bloom are a pretty sight in late summer and fall and many times reported as a major source of nectar. In our experience Purple Loosestrife grows easily in our cultivated gardens. Though the fine seed requires very moist conditions to get started, the planting requires little maintenance once established. Only on wet land do we see Loosestrife spreading by itself.

Though very moist conditions required for germination, we do have some reports of success in naturalizing when the seed was only scattered in wet places in winter and early spring. Small young plants transplant readily when dormant.

The seed is tiny, with a very large number of seeds per ounce. Seed: 60 cents per packet; ½ ounce, $3.00; one ounce, $5.00; 2 ounces, $9.00 postpaid. Write for price of larger quantity. Plants, 6 for $4.00; 25 for $12.00; 50 for $20.00; postpaid.

Atropa Belladonna

J.L. HUDSON, SEEDSMAN
Box 1058
Redwood City, California
94064

This 110-page catalogue may intimidate the novice — all herb and flower listings are alphabetical, under their Latin names. A selection of vegetables is included, along with many items not to be found elsewhere.

RAUWOLFIA: Apocynaceae. About 45 species of shrubs or trees, usually glabrous, native to S. Africa and the tropics. Lvs opposite, flowers & fruit small. Grow in a compost of loam, peat & sand. 75 cents.
Caffra. A fast growing tree to 25 ft. Leaves large, shining, semi-deciduous. Flowers small, white. $1.00.
Serpentina. Shrub to 3 ft; lvs 3-10" long. Flowers pink, tubular; fruit a small black berry. India. Yields a medicine used in treating of schizophrenia.

VIBURNUM: (vy-BURN-um) Snowball. Caprifoliacae. One of the most popular ornamental shrubs. They also make excellent refuge for birds as well as food during the winter, all kinds of wild life relish their berries. Seed can be planted in the fall in border lands or edges of woods or stratify them for spring planting; they germinate readily.

Unlike most trees Viburnum require a warm spell of about 60 days and then a cold period of a month or two; thus if the seed is planted in Sept. outside it will do. 25 cents.

ATROPA: (A-thro-pa) Solanaceae. BELLADONNA. Mainly grown for its drug properties.—Belladonna. Shining black berries; 3 ft; poisonous; a drug herb. 50 cents.

HERBS 'N HONEY NURSERY
Route 2, Box 205
Monmouth, Oregon 97361

DAVID CROCKETT POPCORN CO.
Box 237
Metamora, Ohio 43540
(419) 644-4061

Offers four varieties of popcorn seed for $2.00.

EPICURE SEEDS
Box 69
Avon, New York 14414

European herb and vegetable seeds.

LEEK: Royal Favourite Suttons. One of the oldest, most distinctive tasting vegetables. No longer relegated only to flavouring the stock pot, leeks are the star attraction in vichyssoise and bouillabaise. To the people of the British Isles, leeks are indispensable for winter dishes.

When nights are long and cold, the Scotsman comes home to cockaleekie, a delicious contrivance of chicken and leeks. The Welsh welcome leek in puddings and pies. It's even their national emblem. The English regard it as a hearty winter treat, boiled till tender and served with butter and paprika. Royal Favourite is everything a British leek should be: Large. Pure white stems. Rich, dark green leaves. Very hardy. Very hearty. 55 cents per pkt.

NAVET-TURNIP: Des Vertus Marteau. You have just found a brand new vegetable. Smooth, rich and buttery. When you first taste it, you just won't believe it's a turnip. No bitterness, no turnipy taste. Not even a hint. Try it parboiled briefly, then sliced for the casserole and covered with a few spoonfuls of sour cream and a sprinkling of chopped basil. When you're ready to serve, give it a dash of salt and a squeeze of lemon. When they ask what it is, just say it's Des Vertus Marteau. 5 gms. 55 cents pkt.

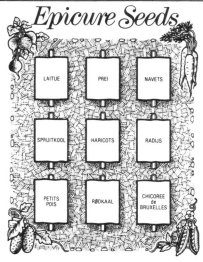

Epicure Seeds

CELERY: Wensleydale Solid Giant White — Hurst. Solid, crunchy, meaty, pure white stalks of superb flavour. The heart is large, full and tightly folded. Absolutely delicious. The tall, long heads are crisp and stringless, with a clean, clear celery taste. Wensleydale requires earthing up, but it's well worth it. Very rewarding. Just try some. 50 cents pkt.

EMERSON COLLEGE OF HERBOLOGY LTD.
5810 Cote de Liesse
Montreal, Québec H4T 1B1
(514) 342-5444

Home study course in advanced herbology $160.00.

DOMINION HERBAL COLLEGE
7527 Kingsway
Burnaby 3, B.C. V3N 3C1

A correspondence course, as well as seminars in herbology.
—Catherine Reed
Kelowna, B.C.

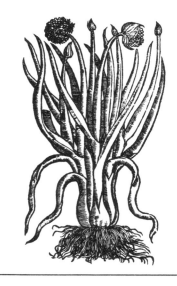

Mushroom Spawn

As the price of mushrooms threatens to exceed the tariff on the steak that goes under them, many off-season gardeners are taking to the cellar to put in a crop of cultivated mushrooms.

The process can be as simple or complex as you wish to make it, but one essential is starter spawn — dry flakes or powder consisting of dormant mushroom mycelia, comparable to the roots of green plants.

Quite a number of seed companies now offer mushroom spawn, but that from professional supply houses tends to be cheaper and more reliable.

The following companies will supply starter spawn, compost activators and free literature upon request:

—Jo Frohbieter-Mueller

MUSHROOM SUPPLY CO.
Toughkenamon, Pa 19374

STROLLER RESEARCH CO.
Box 1701
Santa Cruz, Ca 95060

J.B. SWAYNE SPAWN CO.
Kenneth Square, Pa 19348

UTICA SPAWN CO.
2201 E. Hamlin Road
Utica, Mi 48087

STOKES SEEDS
Box 10
St. Catharines, Ont. L2R 6R6
VITA FLAKE SPAWN: Pure culture process spawn in large shredded flake form. Easy to handle, vigorous in growth —success more certain. Maintain a growing temperature of 60 to 70 degrees F/ 16 to 21 degrees C. Fresh strawy horse manure mixed with the soil improves quality. ¼ lb/113 gr. sows 16 sq. feet/1.5 sq. m.: 4 oz. $3.40.

W.H. PERRON & CO.
515 LaBelle Boulevard
City of Laval, Quebec
H7V 2T3
MUSHROOMS (Fr. Champignons). Culture—Mushrooms can be grown in cellars, under greenhouse benches or in any room where the temperature can be maintained around 18 degrees C in winter, and which does not receive any direct lighting. Home gardeners can grow mushrooms outdoors in shady areas by rolling a piece of sod 10 cm deep, moisten soil thoroughly, sprinkle the fine spawn on the surface, then cover the spawn with the sod again. Harvest mushrooms which grow through the grass in 7 weeks. 1 bottle sows 3.5 sq. metre. Complete cultural directions in English sent free with each order or demand. Pure culture in bottles: Each $6.75.

MUSHROOM PEOPLE
12783 Sir Francis Drake Blvd.
Box 607
Inverness, California 94937
(415) 669-1197

There is a tendency to suspect the motives of anyone who sells compost for more than a dollar a pound, but Mushroom People's catalogue is intriguing, nonetheless. Supplies for growing Agaricus, Wood Blewits (Clitocybe nuda) and Shiitake. More sensational is the offering of materials for the culture of two psilocybe or psychedelic mushrooms.

WOOD BLEWITS (Clitocybe nuda) A tissue culture isolated from a large specimen of these purple mushrooms. Tests have shown it to fruit readily on commercially available leaf mulch. Excellent flavour. (Culture comes on agar medium in a test tube.) $20.00 ppd.

SHIITAKE (Lentinus edodes) This is a live sterile culture of the oriental black forest mushroom. Use it to prepare spawn, synthetic logs or your own oak or alder logs. One fellow grew it on sawdust and on getting no fruiting threw the sawdust in the yard whereupon it fruited nicely. Nothing like fresh shiitake omelet for breakfast. (Culture comes on agar medium in a test tube.) $20.00 ppd.

SPORES: Our spores are in the form of spore prints. Used frugally they can provide thousands of isolations in time to come. This is advantageous because different clones isolated from spores have different genetics and fruiting abilities and you may wish to isolate several and test them separately. Surefire sterile systems offer contamination-free starts, but not flexibility in isolating clones of different vitality. Our systems have been designed to allow for contamination and still permit isolation, as is done in mushroom research. We now offer two spore varieties.

Psilocybe cubensis: The classic mushroom — easy to grow, fruits rapidly indoors, and produces the largest mushrooms. From Palenque, Mexico. More than one person has gotten mushrooms over one pound each and twelve inches in diameter from this strain on straw compost! $10.00 ppd.

Mushroompeople

NURSERIES

BOUGHEN NURSERIES VALLEY RIVER LIMITED
Box 12
Valley River, Manitoba
R0L 2B0
(204) 638-7618

In moving from Chatham, Ontario to the tip of Lake Nipissing, we rejoiced in the wooded hills and long silent snowbound winters. What we missed most, however, was the succulent fruit that the sunny south had grown. Our small homestead included no abandoned orchard — in fact, orchards of any description are few and far between at this latitude.

For two years we resisted the temptation to buy those promising green-tipped saplings shipped from southern nurseries, certain they would never survive our ritual two weeks of -40 degrees F. Then we discovered Boughen Nurseries. Located north of the 51st parallel, this is a family business which grows all the nursery stock it sells, with the exception of some roses. If these young trees can survive infancy in the tough Prairie winter, surely they could be weaned to our relatively southern clime.

The Boughen catalogue offers more variety than we could cope with. Still, we managed to choose good eating, cooking and storing apple trees, with several varieties

of pears and plums. The descriptions are adequate and accurate, even mouth-watering. The pages are dotted with planting and growing tips, encouraging the organic approach: ''You need not spray your own trees. We grow lots of fruit without using chemicals.''

Besides fruit trees, Boughen Nurseries lists pages of bush fruits, including some native small fruits such as nannyberry, high bush cranberry, and Saskatoon berries. We resisted the urge to try the native grape, but will probably succumb next spring. Roses, ornamental shrubs, evergreens, shade trees and hardy perennial flowers complete the offerings.

The Boughen family stands behind their 67-year-old reputation. The slender saplings arrived at just the right time for planting, carefully wrapped, and in good condition. If the trees fail to leaf out by mid-summer, the stock is replaced at half-price. For now, all we have is leaves, but healthy ones. They hold the promise of sweet juicy treats that will be worth the wait. (Try to order before May 1 to assure that the varieties you request are still in stock.)

—Merilyn Mohr
Astorville, Ontario

PLUM: Pembina. *A favourite with everyone. Red plum, large in size. Excellent for eating out of hand. Also good to grow commercially. Fruit is in great demand. Has the California ''Red June'' flavour. Each $8.95.*

APPLE: Rosthern 18. *Could very well be the hardiest apple we grow. Very beautiful when in fruit. Good size red fall apple. Reliable excellent yielder. Extra fine cooking apple and a favourite eating apple. Size 3 to 4 ft. $7.95 each.*

SASKATOONS: Everyone likes Saskatoons with fresh cream or preserved. Also makes excellent pies. Plant a row along your garden and enjoy this wonderful fruit. Each $4.00.

SIBERIAN PEARS: The Siberian Pear is one of the very hardiest and most beautiful of trees for this part of Canada, that is, all across the Prairie Provinces, and is becoming increasingly popular as proved by the amount of big trees and seedlings we have sold during the past years. Good for streets or parks. Siberian Pear, 3'-4' or 90-120 cm. $5.50 each; 10 for $45.00; 1 year seedling — 25 for $25.00.

For those wishing to plant a large windbreak, Siberian Pear are ideal. Some farmers have planted them in their fields to prevent roads from difting in during the winter. We have sold windbreaks composed largely of pear trees after the customer has seen the windbreak we have on our nursery grounds.

A few hundred trees would fence in any place and in 8 or 10 years would be a line of beauty with their shiny leaves and strong stems. (These trees grow large enough to be used in the manufacture of furniture in Siberia.) Plant a few hundred and they will increase the value of your farm greatly in 10 years.

E. GRIMO NUT TREE NURSERY
Lakeshore Road, R.R.3
Niagara-on-the-Lake, Ontario
L0S 1J0
(416) 935-9773

These people have all sorts of nut trees at reasonable prices. Their service is wonderful and if you have any complaints or problems, you get *personal* answers and every kind of assistance. (Ships across Canada and, except for grafted stock, to the U.S.)

—J. Adams
Palgrave, Ontario

ALPRICOTS (sweet-kernelled apricots) These dual-purpose trees produce not only a fine crop of apricots but also a nut that is the equal of any almond in flavour. They are suitable for growing wherever the apricot can be grown.

We prefer to graft onto apricot rootstocks. However, apricots do best on well-drained light soils only. For other soils and conditions, we suggest using Myroabolan plum rootstocks. Please indicate apricot or plum rootstocks when ordering. 1. Vineland 60031 — large attractive fruit, good flavour & colour, kernels are sweet and good cracking. 2. Vineland 510915 — fruit is medium size, good flavour, kernels are sweet and plump, very good cracking.

SWEET CHESTNUT: (Castanea mollissima and C. mollissima X C. dendata) *The Chinese chestnuts and their hybrids are hardy from about -30 degrees to -35 degrees C or more. In the hybrids, the Chinese parent provides blight resistance and larger nut size, while the American parent gives superior hardiness and upright (timber type) growth habit. The cultivars listed below are the most outstanding available. It is very important to have two or more selections for cross pollinations.*
1. Layeroka — our best Chinese selection, large nut size, sweet flavour, vigorous and healthy, very productive, suitable in Lower Great Lakes fruit growing districts. 2. Douglass No. 1 — large nut size, good flavour, F1 American hybrid, very hardy, vigorous grower, productive. 3. Douglass No. 1A — similar to Douglass No. 1, an F2 selection.

SHAGBARK HICKORY: (Carya ovata) *The shagbark hickory is a slow grower, producing a long tap root first. After it is established, it grows quickly. The nut is selected for size and cracking ease primarily. Glover sdlg. 6″-8″ $4.00.*

GAYBIRD NURSERIES
Box 42
Wawanesa, Manitoba

It is imperative for us Westerners, with our short growing seasons, to have seeds that grow out here. One of the major suppliers is *Alberta Nurseries and Seeds Ltd.* of Bowden, Alberta, which offers an excellent selection.

Nursery stock is an even touchier subject. I have spent literally hundreds of dollars trying to get eastern stock to grow here. Alberta Nurseries, again, is most successful, and you *must* list *Gaybird Nurseries.*

To order from Gaybird is a real treat. The catalogue is small, but includes many unusual selections. It is, as far as I know, the only source of western-hardy apricot trees. Ed Robinson runs Gaybird, and his stock comes lovingly

wrapped in recycled puffed wheat bags and bread sacks. His free seed bonus came to me in a 1952 United Church collection envelope.

The only fault I can find with him is that he doesn't often label his plants, so you may be left guessing what is what when your order arrives. Altogether, it is a most enjoyable experience to order from Gaybird and I endorse him unconditionally.

—*Kathryn A. Sinclair*
Winterburn, Alberta

BOUNTIFUL RIDGE NURSERIES
Princess Anne, Maryland
21853
(301) 651-0400

Perhaps, with luck, Canada will some day have a national, full-service mail order nursery such as Bountiful Ridge. After four generations of family operation, the Kemps continue to provide quality service with an excellent selection of fruit, nut, vine and vegetable species. Especially tempting is the collection of colonial apple trees, offered as semi-dwarf specimens and grafted onto a special rootstock for early bearing. These include Yates, Roxbury Russett, Baldwin (formerly known as the Steele's Red Winter or Woodpecker Apple), Hubbardston and Lady, popularly known as the Christmas Apple because of its high quality and exceptional aroma.

The catalogue goes out of its way to point out disease-resistant varieties for organic gardeners, but Northern growers will have to avoid the many warmer zone listings. Ships throughout North America.

APPLE: Granny Smith. *A very high quality green apple grown primarily in the United Kingdom and South America. It is now being tried in many areas of the U.S. where the season is long enough for maturity. It requires 180 to 200 days from bloom to maturity; ripens about late October in zone 7. Will do best in zones 7-9. Used for dessert and cooking. Keeps up to 180 days in cold storage. Try some. Semi-Dwarf trees are available.*

RUSSIAN MULBERRY: (Morus Tatarica) *Fast growing, wide spreading*

tree that bears giant, jet-black, long, slender, sweet fruit that is ideal for pies, jams or wines. Fruit is about 2½" long. Bears in three years. Practically disease-free. Ripens late June in zone 7. Hardy to zone 4. Grows to 40 feet. Plant 30 feet or more apart for best results. Heavy 2'-3' plants. Each $2.95; 3 to 9 plants, each $2.70; 10 or more plants, each $2.25.

PEAR: Anjou (Beurre d'Anjou) A large, fine pear that is buttery and melting, with a sprightly flavour. The tree is a fine grower, very productive, and an early bearer; one of our best varieties for the home and orchard trade. Anjou is partially resistant to fire blight. Ripens mid-September in zone 7. Does best in zones 5-7.

HEICO NURSERIES AND TREE FARM
Box 638
Brantford, Ontario N3T 5R4
(519) 449-2684

Small list of trees and shrubs, with a growing emphasis on nut-bearing species.

Filberts: (pre-pruned) 3-5 yr. $13.95 + $2.85 for postage. 100 cm. Black Walnut $7.95 plus postage.

J.E. MILLER NURSERIES INC.
Canandaigua, New York 14424

Commendable selection of fruit trees, berry bushes and grape vines, with a strong orientation toward growers in the northern United States and the more temperate zones in Canada.

MILLER'S 20-25 BELOW ZERO APRICOTS: Two new hardy varieties make it possible to grow apricots where no other varieties can survive. Breeders worked for 20 years crossing cold, northern Manchurian apricots with high quality American varieties. Results are trees that take 25 below zero weather. These are our best varieties for home gardens . . . compact, disease-free, highly ornamental and productive.

Moongold — Earliest of the two varieties. Fruit ripens about July 10-15. The soft golden coloured fruits are of medium size. The flesh is a most attractive orange-yellow. Fruits are firm and sweet with delightful apricot flavour. The freestone fruits make delicious preserves. Unsurpassed for eating out of hand. Tree is free from disease, sturdy and vigorous.

Sungold — The medium sized fruits are brightly coloured clear gold with attractive orange blush. Fruit is nearly round with thin tender skin. The flesh is clear orange, tender, juicy, mild and sweet. Freestone, a real taste treat for eating out of hand or for making tasty preserves. The tree grows more upright than Moongold and fruit ripens about a week later.

Pollination: These varieties are NOT self-pollinating. You must plant one Moongold and one Sungold for pollination. 3 ft. dwarf trees, $7.95 each, 2 for $14.95.

ANTIQUE APPLE: Sops of Wine. One of the oldest apples known. It originated in medieval England, so its actual origin is a guess. Highly regarded for cooking, cider, apple wine. Good dessert apple, too. Dark, crimson skin. White flesh is flecked with red, giving it a hint of wine. Makes the juices flow when you take a crunchy bite. Bears early and reliably.

NATURAL WOODLAND NURSERY LTD.
544 Conestogo Road West
Waterloo, Ontario N2L 4E2
(519) 889-1071

The specialty here is growing "natural fauna," and the company offers expertise in rehabilitating slopes, gravel pits and energy corridors. Both retail and wholesale services are provided, as well as landscape designing and work on historical gardens. Write for catalogue.

NEW YORK STATE FRUIT TESTING COOPERATIVE ASSOCIATION
Geneva, New York 14456

As stated in the introduction to their yearly *Catalog of New and Noteworthy Fruits*, the Association was organized in 1918 for the purpose of introducing for testing new fruits recommended as worthy of trial by the New York State Agricultural Experiment Station. Over the years the membership has spread to the point where the Association has become an international organization.

In return for an annual membership fee of $5.00, members receive a catalogue and an invitation to a meeting held each year at Geneva, N.Y. featuring an exhibit of new fruits, conducted tours of the Station, and a programme of talks by fruit specialists.

We find the services of the Association valuable not only for their wide selection of moderately-priced orchard trees and small fruits available by mail order, but for the truly helpful information provided on each variety as well. A brief description of the performance of each fruit, plus its strong and weak points are presented; they aren't trying to *sell* you anything.

The catalogue also offers 18 old-time apple varieties on semi-dwarf rootstocks (other rootstocks on special order). Also, six different clonal rootstocks are offered to commercial and backyard growers. Scions are also available for grafting.

The Association asks for a contribution to help defray the costs of its catalogue.

—Louise Langsner
Marshall, North Carolina

SEARS -McCONNELL NURSERY
Port Burwell, Ontario N0J 1T0

This is Canada's largest nursery, recently affiliated with the Sears' empire. Selections are interesting, but somewhat limited in scope by the mass marketing approach of the company.

shrubs that attract birds (Black Cherry, Fire Thorn, Bittersweet, Hawthorn and others).

Ships anywhere in Canada, but cannot accept orders from the United States.

Exceptional value for $1.00 each:

Golden Chain Tree	8-12"
Gingo Tree	8-12"
White Cedar	6 yrs.
Norway Maple	3'
Red Cedar	5 yrs.
Spice Bush	5 yrs.
Tree of Heaven	3 yrs.
Pin Oak	3 yrs.
Burr Oak	4 yrs.
Red Oak	5 yrs.
Black Locust	18-24"
Washington Hawthorne	8-12"
Wild Pear	8-12"
Douglas Fir	6 yrs.
Upright Euonymus	3'
White Birch	3'
Northern Balsam	5 yrs.
Hemlock	5 yrs.
Linden Tree	2-3'
Amur Maple Shrub	2'
Copper Beech	12"
Balm of Gilead	3-4'
White Fir	6 yrs.
Grey Alder	3'
Moose Maple	2-3'
Austrian Pine	6 yrs.
Basswood	3'
Col. Blue Spruce	7 yrs.
White Pine	5 yrs.
White Spruce	6 yrs.
Sycamore	3'
Wild Black Cherry	3'
Nannyberry	2'-3'
Red Osier Dogwood	3'
Manitoba Maple	3-4'
Pin Cherry	3'
Choke Cherry	3'
Grey Dogwood (clump)	3'
Serbian Spruce	8-12"
Serviceberry	12"
Silky Dogwood	3'
Silver Maple	3'
Lombardy Poplar	3'
Little Leaf Linden	2-3'
White Beech	2-3'
Red Elderberry	2-3'

SHERIDAN NURSERIES LTD.

700 Evans Avenue
Etobicoke, Ontario M9C 1A1
(416) 621-9111

This is a posh, 136-page, all-colour catalogue, primarily designed to serve Sheridan's seven retail garden centres in the Toronto and Montreal areas. Mail orders are accepted, but must total $40 or more, shipping costs extra. The catalogue sells for $1.00, and, if nothing else, is well worth the price as a reference guide to landscaping shrubs and trees. Sheridan is considering stopping its mail order service.

KEITH SOMERS TREES

10 Tillson Avenue
Tillsonburg, Ontario N4G 2Z6
(519) 842-5148

This long-established, organically oriented nursery could be classified as a national treasure. The catalogue is mimeographed and only eight pages long, but is overwhelming in its selection and in the fair prices charged ($10 per hundred for Colorado Blue Spruce seedlings, five-foot Black Walnuts for $3.00 each).

Somers also offers berry plants, shrubs, unusual woodland plants and a list of 17 different trees and

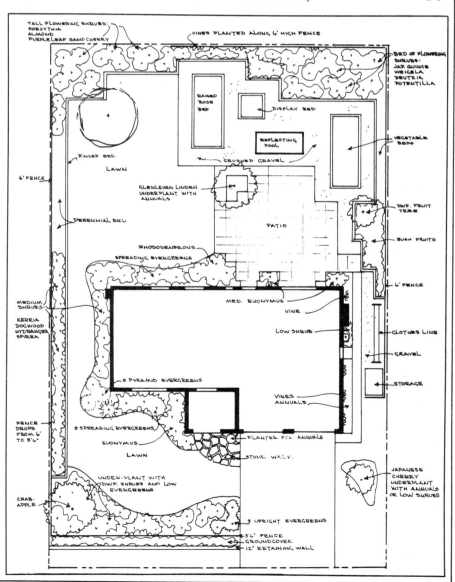

Black Elderberry	2-3'
Fraser Fir	12''
Green Beech	18''
Sassafrass	18-20''
Red Bud (Judas Tree)	8-12''
Pagoda Dogwood	3'
Manchu Cherry	12''
Canadian Red Maple	3'
Horn Bean	3'
Black Ash	2'
Hackberry	12''
Yellow Birch	3'
Hard Maple	3'
Kentucky Coffee Tree	8-12''
Flowering Crab Seedlings	8-12''
Scotch Pine	6 yrs.
Sugar Maple	3-4'
Tulip Tree	12-20''
Norway Spruce	6 yrs.
Mountain Ash	18-24''
White Ash	3-4'

Woodland Plants (Shipped in season — *Fall Shipment only)

Rattlesnake Fern	(EACH)	.50
Interrupted Fern		.50
Cinnamon Fern		.50
Maiden Hair Fern		.50
Christmas Fern		.50
Ostrich Fern (large)		.50
Sensitive Fern		.50
Bloodroot (large/white flowering)		.50
Marsh Marigold		.50
Jack-in-the-Pulpit		.50
Hepatica		.50
Trillium (White, Red)		.50
May Apple		.50
Skunk Cabbage		.50
Golden Rod		.50
Canadian Columbine		.50
Wintergreen Vine		.50
Day Lilies		.50
Violets (Purple, Blue, Yellow)		.50
Wild Ginger		.50
*Solomon Seal		.50
*Cinquefoil (Pale Yellow)		.50
*Black-Eyed Susan		.50
*Turks Cap Lilies		.50
*Jewel Weed		.50
*Meadowrue		.50
*Blue Bottled Gentian		1.00
*Fringed Gentian		1.00
*Blue Lobelia		1.00
*Cardinal Flower (Red Lobelia)		2.00
*Joe Pye-weed		.50
*Queen Anne's Lace		.50
Poke-Weed		.50

Water Plants

Water Iris	(EACH)	.50
Water Cress		.50
Burr Reed		.50
Arrowhead		.50
Water Lilies/white		2.50
Water Lilies/red		2.50
Yellow Water Lily		2.50
Small Northern White Water Lily		2.50
Cattail (Bulrush)		.50 ea. 2/1.00

MUSSER FORESTS, INC.
Box 86
Indiana, Pennsylvania 15701
(412) 465-5686

This is the largest tree nursery of its kind in the United States, with many Canadian customers. Good selection of evergreens, hardwoods, shrubs and ground covers. Quantity prices should be attractive for someone planting a windbreak or woodlot.

PONDEROSA PINE — Pinus ponderosa. Sometimes called Yellow Pine or Bull Pine. Grows from 150 feet to 200 feet. Will reach 6 feet in 6 to 7 years, starting with a 3 year seedling. Hardy from zone 7 to zone 4. Its needles are 2 or 3 in a bundle and 5 to 11 inches long. Thrives in full sun and poor soil. It is one of the tallest and most important pines of the Western states. It is used as an ornamental tree because of its fast rapid growth and dark green foliage. Because of its fast upright and open growing habit, it is not recommended for small places. Older trees develop a characteristic plate-like bark. Good for naturalizing specimen, windbreaks and timber. 2-yr. seedlings 3-5'' $20.00 per C; $100.00 per M. 4-yr. seedlings 10-16'' $24.00 per C; $120.00 per M.

SHINGLE OAK — Quercus imbricaria. Also known as northern Laurel Oak. Grows to 75 feet. Its lustrous laurel-like leaves turn yellow to russet in fall and remain on the tree far into winter. Grows best on moist soils along streams or on hillsides. Name was derived from early pioneers making split shingles out of its timber. Also can be used as a windbreak if planted 4 feet apart and trimmed properly. Good from zone 8 to 4. 3-5'' $30.00 per C; $200.00 per M.

PACHYSANDRA TERMINALIS — Spurge. Excellent in masses under heavy shade of trees. A dense, lustrous evergreen, trailing vine type of ground cover, white flowers, Spring. It thrives under evergreens or anywhere. If planted 6 inches apart, it will give a pleasing effect immediately and in 2 years' time form a solid ground cover. Any soil, water liberally. It is very hardy. Grows in sun or shade, 6 to 8 inches tall. Fine for terraces or any place where grass is not successful. Full sun or full shade. Sold in lots of 50 at one-half the 100 rate. Mass of roots. Heavy cuttings, well leaved. 1-yr plants—heavy cuttings, 3-4'' $17.00 per C; $130.00 per M.

KELLY BROS. NURSERIES, INC.
Dansville, New York 14437

Wide variety of strawberries, blueberry bushes, nut trees, grape vines. Ships to Canada.

CONRAD LOAN
R.R.5
Kemptville, Ontario R0G 1J0
(613) 258-2826

Jerusalem artichoke rootstocks.

THE NORTHERN NUT GROWERS ASSOCIATION
c/o R.D. Campbell, Secretary
R.R.1
Niagara-on-the-Lake, Ont.
L0S 1J0

This is an international association of amateur and professional growers dedicated to nut culture in colder climates. The $8.00 per year membership fee brings a newsletter and access to meetings, nut gathering expeditions and other projects.

Also available from the same address are $3.00 memberships in the Society of Ontario Nut Growers, better known as SONG, a group active in encouraging the planting of nut trees in the province. Offers twice-a-year newsletter and special events.

CAMPBERRY FARMS
R.R.1
Niagara-on-the-Lake, Ont.
L0S 1J0
(416) 262-4927

R.D. Campbell, who is active in promoting public interest in northern-hardy nut trees, also operates a small nursery. He offers a number of raspberry and strawberry plants especially suited to high quality, home garden production, as well as English walnut, chestnut, hazelnut, hickory, pecan and other trees, which he says are "hardy in southern Ontario and to a latitude as far north as Montreal." Quantities limited, and he is able to ship only within Canada.

DEAN FOSTER NURSERIES
Route 2
Hartford, Michigan 49057
(616) 621-2419

Founded in 1837, this nursery is strong on northern hardy stock, especially strawberries and raspberries. Offers both wholesale and retail catalogues and will ship to Canada.

We propagate, grade, pack and sell Certified Virus-Free planting stock that is hardier and superior to most any nursery stock available today. Due to the severe sub-zero weather during 1977, many nursery stock buyers suffered huge losses from spring dug plants and trees. Our nursery stock is fall dug and held at 28 degrees F in our modern cold storage rooms until the customer requests shipment or pick-up of his order. Fall digging of dormant plants, trees and root stock is the only method that can be practised to insure against winter injury in nursery planting stock. We also back up our stock with the liberal guarantee that is listed in this book. All nursery stock leaving our facility has been twice inspected, once in the growing fields and once in our packing rooms, prior to shipment.

STRAWBERRY: Red Rich —The Gourmet Berry. Giant size berries: Bright red to the core and nature sweet. Unsurpassed for freezing. They hold colour and flavour all during the season. Red Rich ripens early in season and continues until frost. Plants are large and vigorous with attractive green foliage. 25/$9.55; 50/$14.30; 75/$17.90; 100/$21.50; 1000/$95.50.

GILBERT'S PEONY GARDENS
Elora, Ontario N0B 1S0

One of the country's leading peony producers.

PHIPPS' AFRICAN VIOLETS & SUPPLIES
R.R.1
Paris, Ontario N3L 3E1

For those seriously interested in African violets and gesneriads. Send 75 cents for availability list. Canada only.

CRAMER'S NURSERY
White Fox, Saskatchewan

Hardy trees and plants, including asparagus, raspberries and "sub-zero carnations."

McMILLEN'S IRIS GARDENS
R.R. 1
Norwich, Ontario N0J 1P0

Canada's most extensive selection of iris, including dwarf and other unusual varieties. Free catalogue.

BEAVERLODGE NURSERY LIMITED
Box 127
Beaverlodge, Alberta T0H 0C0
(403) 354-2195

Hardy plants for northern gardens, including small fruits, tree fruits, shrubs, asparagus, mint, chives, climbers, hedges, flowering trees, deciduous trees, evergreens, perennials.

—*Barbara Palm White*
Winfield, Alberta

SEED SAVERS' EXCHANGE
c/o Kent Whealy
R.R.2
Princeton, Missouri 64673

Kent Whealy's idea for establishing a clearing house for the exchange of unusual seeds appears to be catching on. The third annual newsletter has grown to 32 pages, mostly filled with the names and addresses of gardeners willing to trade their hard-to-find seed for your hard-to-find seed. (One member of the exchange has 448 varieties of beans.)
Annual Newsletter: $2/copy.

IMPORT PROCEDURE
Agriculture Canada has just changed its procedures for allowing the importation of small quantities of nursery plants. Canadians wishing to purchase plant or plant products from the United States must first write to the following address to receive an information packet and an identification number which the customer then sends to the U.S. nursery along with his order. (The nurseries themselves do not have import numbers.)
The Food Production & Marketing Branch
Plant Quarantine Division
Agriculture Canada
K.W. Neatby Building
Ottawa, Ontario K0A 0C6

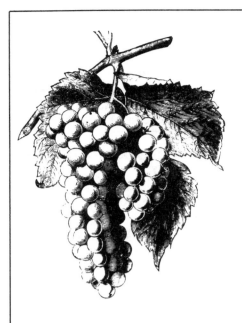

Grape Vines

Most mail order nurseries and local garden centres offer table and juice grapes, generally of the native *labrusca* type, known for the sweetness and "foxy" taste it imparts to the juice and wine it produces. Oenophiles generally avoid *labrusca* wines, classifying them as "pop" wine, or worse. Concord is perhaps the best known of the *labruscas*, and it continues to be widely grown for juice, jelly and kosher wines, but many vintners are ripping out their old vines and replacing them with French hybrid or *vinifera* type grapes.

Many home gardeners are content to grow the *labrusca* types, especially because these vines are better suited to northern conditions, being more disease-resistant and cold hardy. Some *labruscas* are exceptionally tolerant to frost (Beta being the most widely recommended for cold areas), but most are far from impervious to severe winter conditions. Concord, for example, can be damaged at temperatures of minus 20 degrees F, and thus must receive protection in many areas. The most commonly available *labruscas* in Canada are Niagara (white fruited), Agawam (red), Fredonia (black), and Concord, which is blue. (Contrary to popular opinion, white wine can be made from coloured grapes, provided the skins are removed before fermentation.)

Those willing to gamble and protect their vines during the winter are increasingly trying their hand at growing the more subtly flavoured European or California wine grapes.

The French hybrids, crosses between North American and European varieties, with taste and aroma approaching the subdued character of the pure *viniferas*, have been successfully grown on a small scale in many parts of this continent. Those recommended for their general hardiness and adaptability are:

Aurora (Excellent for eating, juice and white wine.)

Marechal Foch (Good disease resistance and the base for a fine dry, red wine.)

Seyval (Healthy, adaptable to cold areas, makes a noteworthy white wine.)

De Chaunac (Must be cluster-thinned, but robust and the precursor to a good red wine — from blue berries.)

Baco Noir (The choice for poorly drained, heavy soils but vulnerable to spring frosts. Makes a red wine.)

BOUGHEN NURSERIES VALLEY RIVER LTD.

Box 12
Valley River, Manitoba
R0L 2B0

Offers Beta vines at $3.75 each, as well as native wild grapes at $3.25.

J.E. MILLER NURSERIES, INC.

Canandaigua, New York 14424
(800) 828-9630

Located just south of Lake Ontario in the heart of the New York state wine country, Miller offers an excellent selection of short-season grapes, including Seneca, which is said to be "as hardy as native grapes" and Ontario, which is exceptionally disease-free and "requires no spraying." Among the list of French hybrids are Aurora-Seibel, Foch, Baco Noir, all at $2.25 per vine or 10 for $19.95. Ships to Canada.

Those willing to attempt what has long been said to be impossible will find the following pure *vinifera* varieties to provide better odds than most:

Gamay Beaujolais (Native of France's famed Beaujolais region, this is a vigorous grape that can produce a superb red wine.)

Pinot Noir (This is the grape that makes the great burgundy wines of France. Not as productive as *Gamay Beaujolais*.)

Pinot Chardonnay (Classic white grape from which the white burgundies are made. Lush foliage, moderate production.)

Gewürztraminer (Adapted to cooler growing regions, this is an aromatic German white.)

White Riesling (The venerable white grape of the Rhine and Moselle Valleys, with a distinctive varietal taste and bouquet.)

SMALL-GROWER SUPPLIERS:

ZIRALDO FARMS & NURSERIES

R.R.1
Niagara-on-the-Lake, Ontario

Twenty-nine varieties (three *vinifera*, 17 French hybrids, nine *labrusca*). Minimum order of 25

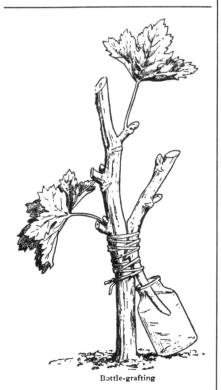

Bottle-grafting

vines. Prices range from 85 cents each for *labrusca* to 90 cents for French hybrids and for grafted French hybrids (including Marechal Foch, Delaware, Seyval 2576, Dutchess) and *vinifera* (Pinot Chardonnay, Gamay Beaujolais, Riesling) $1.80. Seedless *labrusca* (Himrod, Festivee, Suffolk Red) are $2.00. Discounts for orders of over 100 and 1,000. Prices are F.O.B. — shipping and packaging extra.

McCONNELL NURSERIES
Port Burwell, Ontario N0J 1T0

Seven varieties available. French hybrids (Foch, Aurora, Cascade) at $2.99 each or one of each type for $7.99. *Labrusca* (Concord, Fredonia, Niagara, Caco) for $2.49 each or one of each for $7.99. Shipping extra.

BOUNTIFUL RIDGE NURSERIES INC.
Princess Anne, Maryland 21853

Serving Canada and the U.S., Bountiful Ridge carries about 45 grape varieties. Their *labrusca* table grapes sell at $1.90 a vine, wine grapes (22 types of French hybrids) at $2.15, and their seedless *labrusca* for $3.35. Shipping extra.

TURKOVICS VINEYARD AND GRAPE NURSERY
Glencoe Road
West Bank, British Columbia

JOHN PETRETTA GRAPE NURSERY
1340 Dilworth Cres.
Kelowna, British Columbia

BYLAND NURSERY
Box 222
West Bank, British Columbia

Located just outside Kelowna, Byland offers table grapes (seedless Himrod, Campbell) and three French hybrids (Foch, Riesling, Patricia) at $1.70 each, $12.00 for 10. Shipping extra.

NELUMBIUM LUTEUM.

Aquatics

MOORE WATER GARDENS
Port Stanley, Ont. N0L 2A0
(519) 782-4052

Canada's most extensive offering of bog plants and water lilies, mostly winter hardy varieties, but also a selection of exotics, including lotus and tropical night blooming lilies. Also available are fiberglass garden pools, water pumps, and, for those able to pick them up at the greenhouse, goldfish breeding stock.

WATER LILY: Attraction — An immense flower opening a bright garnet red and deepening each day until it becomes a rich crimson. Its sepals are almost white with faint rose streaks. This is a very vigorous and prolific lily. It does well in most any location. Price $12.00.
Papyrus: The stalks are triangular, surmounted with a tuft of threadlike leaves.

Good as a background plant for pools. Plant similar to Umbrella Palm. Height 4' to 6'. Price $1.25 each, 3 for $3.00.
Red Coral Snails: A beautiful coral-red snail. Active and prolific. The best snail for aquarium use. 2 for $.50; $2.50 per dozen.

How To Plant Your Lily Pool

Water Lilies are easily grown. The three requirements for their successful culture are: Plenty of sunlight, rich soil and quiet, shallow water.

We recommend planting the lilies in boxes or wood pails allowing at least one cubic foot of soil for each root, more if possible. A box 24 inches square and 12 inches deep makes an ideal container.

The best soil is a mixture of three parts rich garden loam with one part well-rotted cow manure, although any good garden loam will give satisfactory results.

The plants should be set so that the crown, from which the leaves grow, is even, or slightly above the surface of the soil. It is advisable to sprinkle sand or fine gravel on the top of the soil to prevent the fish from disturbing the soil and discolouring the water.

The lilies should have from six to 12 inches of water over the soil or crown of plant — the best depth is eight inches. In deep pools use supports to hold the boxes up within approximately eight inches of the surface of the water. Boxes in which the lilies are planted can easily be set without draining the water from the pool, in fact it is better to use this method, as water that has been standing is usually much warmer than a freshly filled pool.

Hardy lilies, after once being planted, need no further care other than to remove the sand the following spring and fork in a top dressing of cow manure or fertilizer. With reasonable care the plants will be a source of beauty for many years.

Many people will harbour the idea that running water in a lily pool is to be preferred. This is not the case. Water lilies and aquatic plants do best in still water.

Your pool should NOT be drained to plant tropical lilies. Plant in the water that has

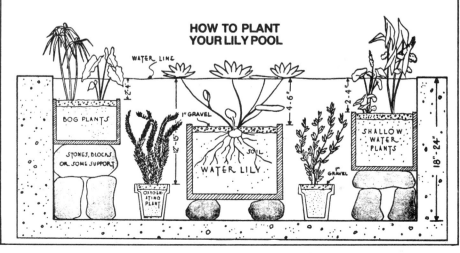

HOW TO PLANT YOUR LILY POOL

stood in the pool — fresh cold water will chill the plants.

CARE OF PLANTS ON ARRIVAL

Have all boxes filled with soil and everything ready before you commence to plant. Unpack the package carefully to avoid

Sacred Pink Lotus

breaking stems, and immediately float the plants in a pail or tub of water until you are ready to plant. Lilies and other aquatics wilt easily if exposed to sun or wind, but they will keep fresh for several days if floated in a tub of water.

WHEN TO PLANT

Hardy lilies may be planted from May till September — May and June are the best months. Tropical lilies should not be set out until after the first week in June. Earlier planting is not safe.

WINTER CARE OF THE POOL

The best protection for hardy water lilies is to leave the water in the pool and cover with boards, on top of which is placed a heavy covering of leaves or straw. By this method very little freezing takes place, and plants and fish overwinter under natural conditions.

If the pool is too large to cover with boards, drain the water, place the lily boxes in a

corner of the pool and protect with leaves, straw or manure. Or, the boxes may be taken into a cool basement and kept covered with moist burlap. Do not allow the plants to become dry — more roots of hardy lilies are lost in winter by being kept too dry than by being frozen.

Tropical lilies may be overwintered in a greenhouse, but are best treated as annuals.

LOTUS: *Lotus tubers look very much like bananas. When unpacking them, care must be taken not to break them, as the growing tip is brittle and breaks easily. Planting in cold water may cause the Lotus tuber to become dormant.*

The weather should be warm before Lotus are planted. Plant them horizontally (never upright), covering them with an inch or two of soil. Rich soil is best, but avoid fresh manure. A water depth of 4 to 6 inches is sufficient at first. As the plant develops the depth of water may be increased.

WILDLIFE NURSERIES
Box 2724
Oshkosh, Washington 54903

Perhaps the only peaceful confluence of wildlife preservationists and the hunting public. Wildlife Nurseries offers a fascinating number of plants, seeds and rootstocks to be used to attract and support wild fowl and animal populations. Offers seed mixtures for upland game birds, deer, ducks, geese and songbirds. This is perhaps the only retail mail order source for wild rice seed and seedlings. Ships to all of North America.

Also offers crayfish, fresh water clams, Daphnia (water fleas), fresh water shrimp, bullfrogs, pheasants and mallard ducklings for stocking purposes.

GIANT WILD RICE SEED: *Most famous of natural duck foods, we furnish only fully-ripened seed. Plant 2 bushels per acre, but can be scattered thinner. Limited supply. $125.00 - bu.; $33.00 - pk.; $13.00 - 2 qts.*

Young Wild Rice Plants: *(Mid-June delivery) Plant 1,000 per acre. $95.00 - 1,000; $35.00 - 300; $15.00 - 100.*

Deep Water Duck Potato Tubers: *One of the best for bluebills and other diving ducks. Plant 1,000 per acre, preweighted. $95.00 - 1,000; $33.00 - 300; $13.00 - 100.*

American Lotus Seed: *Ornamental, mallard - wood duck food, fish cover. $30.00 - 250; $8.00 - 50.*

White Waterlily Tubers: *Ornamental, bluebills, teal and other waterfowl feed on tubers and portions of this plant. Excellent for fish. Plant 750 per acre, preweighted. $90.00 - 750; $15.00 - 100. Parent Rootstock ends — $2.00 each.*

Yellow Waterlily: *Also known as "Spatterdock," grows same as above — white waterlily. Large sprouted rootstock ends only. $2.50 each.*

Hardstem Bulrush Roots: *Stand wave action, protects eroding shores. Blinds, furnishes seed for ducks. Plant 1,000 per acre. $95.00 - 1,000; $36.00 - 300; $15.00 - 100.*

PERENNIAL GRAIN: *(Agrotricum W-21) A cross of Wheat with Tall Wheat Grass. Sturdy, stiff stalks provide good winter cover. Grain (about the size of rye) does not shatter easily and is available to wildlife for long winter periods. Spring planting may not produce grain the first year. Fall plantings produce grain the following year. Plant 40 to 70 lb. per acre. Postpaid at $2.75 per lb. or $25.00 - 10 lb.*

Sericea Lespedeza Seed: *Sericea should be planted where there is a shortage of Quail cover, as this is more of a cover plant than food. It furnishes nesting sites, warm at ground level in winter and overhead protection — ideal loafing or resting habitat. Plant same as BiColour seed, adjacent to cultivated crops and Quail food plots, broadcasting 20 lbs. seed per acre. Seed $6.50 per lb. or $5.95 per lb. in 10 lb. lots. Postpaid.*

FRESH WATER CLAMS: *This natural food for fish lives in almost any pond, stream or lake. They filter large quantities of water, leaving it clean by consuming enormous amounts of algae. They spawn microscopic young, which until reaching the size of a pea or larger, are eaten readily by fish and ducks alike. $15.00 for 25.*

FRESH WATER SHRIMP: *Excellent waterfowl food, especially Bluebill and Ringbill, plus other diving ducks. $30.00 for 200.*

Collecting Tree And Shrub Seeds

FRIENDS OF THE TREES SOCIETY
Box 567
Moyie Springs, Idaho 83845

This is a fledgling, non-profit organization of tree lovers in the Pacific Northwest of the United States and the interior of British Columbia. They hope the idea will spread widely, and are now involved in collecting, selling and trading tree seed, as well as in publishing a newsletter and leaflets which provide information on tree seed collection and propagation and which serve as a forum for the exchange of information among tree and shrub lovers. Membership $3.00. Informational leaflet, "Collecting Tree Seeds," $1.00. Seed offerings include mulberry, rose hips, honeysuckle beechnuts and others at 60 cents per packet, and oak, walnuts, butternuts, filberts, etcetera at $1.00 per packet.

The following is an excerpt from "Collecting Tree Seeds"

What are some of the steps to becoming a proficient seed collector? If you don't already have one, acquire one of the better identification manuals for trees and shrubs. The next step is to locate the trees/shrubs which you wish to collect seed from. Special field trips can be made to locate superior seed trees.

A good habit to get into is to notice the trees that you pass by in your everyday life. Everyone travels to some extent or another. Some kinds of tree seeds can be collected year-round.

As you travel about, take careful note of the varying stages of seed ripeness of trees you come across. Keep a journal of tree ripening dates from year to year. Though some years are "early" and others "late," still the various kinds of trees and shrubs will ripen their seed in a certain sequence.

Make a mental or written note about special trees which have not ripened their seed crop yet. Try to come back when the crop is ripe. Some seeds must be collected within several days or several weeks of ripening. Other seeds can be left on the trees and collected at any time for months afterwards or even during the winter.

Over the years you will build up a route of favourite seed trees and you could get very precise at showing up at just the proper time for seed collection.

When looking for seed trees there are a number of things to look for. Some concern the individual tree and others the whole stand of trees.

In a forest situation, collect seed from trees which are in the prime habitat for that species. Find the best stands for the particular species you are looking for. Avoid collecting in stands containing numerous poorly-formed, excessively limby, off-colour, abnormal or diseased trees or shrubs.

Although trees of extreme youth and old age may yield excellent seed, vigorous trees in middle age are best for seed collection. It is best to collect seed from healthy, vigorous trees or shrubs of reasonably good form, that are making average or better growth.

Consider prospects of adequate cross-pollination before collecting seeds from individuals isolated from others of their kind. This is particularly important for collecting in cities and towns.

Seeds collected from suppressed or subdominant trees yield poor quality seed. The trees grown from them are less resistant to disease, insects, and other natural stresses, and also show a greater variation from the normal form of the species. Trees grown from the seed of crooked-stemmed, spreading or crippled mother trees are, for the most part, of poor form. If the defect is due to

weather or damage by man or beast, then the bad form may not be carried over in the seed. However, it is best to avoid seed from malformed trees.

"Wide crowned, short-boled, thrifty trees growing in the open are usually very prolific seed-bearers. As they owe their unsatisfactory form wholly to the light conditions under which they grow and not to inherent characteristics due to climate and soil, seed collected from them is equally as good as that collected from trees of superior quality in commercial stands." (Toumey)

Owing to seasonal conditions, in some years trees will produce an abundant seed crop and in other years a light crop. This varies from tree to tree but, in general, light or heavy crops will be found widespread throughout a given area for a given species. It is better to obtain seed from trees which are bearing an abundant crop rather than from trees with a light crop.

Pollination in an area will also determine the seed fill. A warm, moderately dry spring increases pollination and will increase the development of food reserve in the seed.

Avoid trees that are diseased, weak-looking, or which are suffering insect damage. Watch for insect damage within the seeds themselves.

WHEN TO PICK THE SEEDS

All seed should be thoroughly ripe before harvesting. Seed gathered a short time before maturity is not necessarily infertile, although invariably its vitality is impaired and it produces weak and inferior seedlings.

It is therefore very important to make sure that the seed you are harvesting is properly mature.

Seeds ripen first at lower elevations and south and west slopes, later at higher elevations and north and east slopes. Maturity may be reached several weeks earlier on hilltops than in nearby bottoms, due to local frost pockets.

In most cases you will be able to tell maturity through some visible indicator such as ripe colour, firmness of fleshy fruits, drying of cone scales or bract, external or internal appearance of the seed itself. Here are a few general guidelines.

In some species, such as oak, hickory, ash and maple, the colour of the fruit is indicative of ripeness. In other species, as in most conifers, the colour of the seed indicates ripeness. In the latter case, it is often desirable to begin gathering the fruits while they appear green because, if delayed too long or until they begin to change colour, a large part of the seed may be lost while harvesting.

Watch squirrels, rodents and birds for indication of when seed is ripe.

To determine the ripeness of conifer seed, you will usually need to make cutting tests to examine the seeds. As the seed matures, the seed coat usually changes colour and the kernel loses its soft, milky characteristics and becomes firm.

It is easy to determine ripeness of fleshy or pulpy fruits from the colour and softness of fruit.

For many species, a common indicator is the natural falling of nuts, or release of seeds. For heavy fruits, such as walnut, oak, hickory, beech, chestnut, etc. the first fruits to fall are invariably wormy or otherwise inferior, and they should not be collected.

You will always be able to find variations within each lot of seed and also between lots of seeds from different trees (of the same species). Usually the darkest, plumpest, largest seeds are of the highest quality. Seeds with wrinkled or cracked seedcoats are generally lower in quality. Worm-holes are self-explanatory.

Cutting open the seed and examining the interior is also a quality check. Interiors which are shriveled, discoloured, abnormally soft, rancid, or which have spots on the endosperm or embryo are generally dead or of poor quality. Most seed interiors are white, with the exception that most pines are yellow, and in the maple, the embryo is green.

The heaviest seed is the best seed.

The best seed grows at the top of the crown and on the ends of the side branches. Obtain these if possible.

Squirrel seed hoards can be lightly raided for seed, if they have already beaten you to it. And you will get good quality, since the squirrels have a very good nose for which are the best cones or nuts.

Large seed within a given species has greater germination power and produces more vigorous seedlings, usually becoming the dominate trees.

SEED CLEANING

Here are some general tips. Improvise your own equipment and methods.

Fleshy Fruits

Fleshy fruits include the berries, drupes, pomes, and those with seeds enclosed in a fleshy aril as in Taxus. Processing involves macerating the flesh, separating the seeds with copious use of water, drying and cleaning. Processing should be started soon after collection to avoid damaging fermentation. Moist fruits and those crushed in handling are most apt to ferment. When some storage is unavoidable, fleshy fruits should be spread in thin layers on the floor of a cool, well-ventilated room or shed and stirred frequently to prevent heating or molding. Short periods of storage may serve to break down the flesh through de-composition or the action of insects such as fruitflies. (Phagoletis spp.)

Oscillating screens or vibrators are most commonly used for removing twigs, leaves and other debris from among fleshy fruits. Such material can also be removed by flotation.

Seeds of species with thin fleshy coverings are sometimes dried and planted with skins intact. After initial cleaning or washing, such fruits may be spread out on sheeting or in trays and dried in the sun or in a warm room. Occasional stirring or turning is helpful.

Flesh may be loosened by hand, simple equipment, improvised

Species	Number of clean seeds per pound	Species	Number of clean seeds per pound
White pine	26,800	Shagbark hickory [1]	90
Western white pine	18,750	Pignut hickory [1]	210
Sugar pine	2,510	Mockernut hickory [1]	113
Red pine	61,420	Cherry birch [1]	488,400
Scotch pine	68,400	Yellow birch [1]	424,600
Yellow pine:		Paper birch [1]	711,680
California	9,340	Beech [1]	1,440
South Dakota	12,900	Chestnut [1]	162
Arizona	15,680	White oak [1]	208
Pitch pine	68,200	Swamp white oak [1]	168
Jack pine	108,200	Chestnut oak [1]	184
Lodgepole pine	83,000	Red oak [1]	128
Loblolly pine	38,160	Pin oak [1]	384
Longleaf pine	9,600	Scarlet oak [1]	264
European larch	71,400	White elm [1]	94,600
Red spruce	131,400	Hackberry [1]	2,680
Norway spruce	59,400	Osage orange	12,140
Sitka spruce	295,400	Cucumber tree	3,140
Engelmann spruce	178,200	Tulip [1]	18,560
Douglas fir	41,260	Sycamore [1]	168,400
Hemlock	194,200	Sweet gum [1]	176,800
Western Hemlock	502,400	Black cherry [1]	4,620
Balsam fir	43,800	Honey locust	2,840
White fir	11,120	Black locust	26,400
Silver fir	8,260	Sugar maple [1]	7,160
Bald cypress	9,240	Red maple [1]	18,420
Bigtree	124,000	Box elder [1]	12,760
Redwood	162,200	Basswood [1]	5,950
Incense cedar	11,480	Dogwood [1]	4,180
Arbor-vitae	284,300	Black gum [1]	2,840
Western red cedar	324,000	White ash [1]	6,240
Red cedar	17,640	Black ash [1]	2,960
Black walnut [1]	34	Catalpa	19,600

[1] The whole or a part of the fruit is sown with the contained seed. The count applies to the fruit or the part of the fruit that is usually sown with the seed.

Chart by James W. Toumey

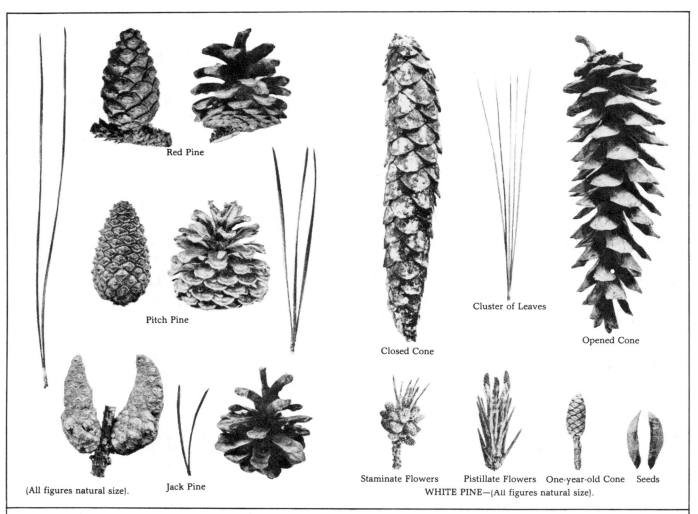

Red Pine

Pitch Pine

Jack Pine

(All figures natural size).

Closed Cone

Cluster of Leaves

Opened Cone

Staminate Flowers   Pistillate Flowers   One-year-old Cone   Seeds

WHITE PINE—(All figures natural size).

From The Forest Trees of Ontario. *Available from the Ontario Ministry of Natural Resources, Division of Forests, 50 cents.*

devices, or specially designed cleaning machines. The choice of method will depend upon the kind and quantity of fruit to be cleaned and the labour and equipment available.

Small lots of fruit are usually macerated by hand. The flesh is hand squeezed, or mashed by a wooden block, rolling pin or fruit-press. Alternatively, flesh may be macerated by rubbing it against or through a screen. If screens are superimposed with the lowest one of a mesh sufficiently small to contain the seeds, a stream of water can be used simultaneously to carry pulp away.

Cones

Seeds of most cones are obtained by drying cones to open them, shaking seeds out, separating seeds from cone scales and debris, loosening seed wings, and finally separating clean full seeds from wings, dust, empty seeds and other small particles.

Quality of conifer cones is often evaluated by estimating number of good seeds present in several representative cones that are sliced lengthwise with a sharp knife. Cones of cedar (Thuja), Douglas firs (Pseudotsuga), hemlocks (Tsuga), pines (Pinus), and spruces (Picea) are generally sliced through the centre; for true firs (Abies), the lengthwise cut is made ¼ to ½ inch to one side of centre. Incense-cedar (Libocedrus) cones can be cut across the axis ¼ inch above the base. Number of cones to sample varies with accuracy desired and consistency of seed content. Sampling of four or more typical cones taken at various sides and heights of each tree to be picked has been recommended for western conifers. A variety of commercial and home-made mounted knife assemblies have been developed for safely and speedily cutting through the tough woody cones.

In a cone sliced through the

centre, the normal seeds that are visible on one cut surface are counted. Underdeveloped seeds at the top and base of the cone are not included. A good average seed count on the cut surface varies by species. Good true fir cones have 50 per cent or more full seeds; if evaluated in the same way, pines should have 75 per cent. Minimum acceptable seed counts per cone may vary from year to year depending on seed supply and demand.

Dry Fruits

Some fruits of this group are collected when fully dry, e.g., maples (Acer) and ashes (Fraxinus). They may require cleaning but little else prior to storage. Other dry fruits may require drying and one or more additional processing steps. Dust masks need to be worn when processing dry seeds of many species, particularly those releasing fine hairs, e.g., sycamores (Platanus), which might be breathed into the lungs. Air-drying is generally adequate for seeds of dry fruits. In dry climates, spreading fruit in thin layers outdoors on canvas or plastic sheeting is fast and economical. In moist climates, seed must be aired for a longer period in a well-ventilated structure. Whether outside or under cover, fruits should be spread thinly to insure good aeration. Fruits of species like peashrubs (Caragana), which naturally expel their seeds when dry, require covering. A single layer of cheesecloth is usually adequate; screened containers might be constructed for repeated use. Wind dispersal of drying seeds and losses to birds and small animals must be prevented.

Extraction of dry seeds may involve removal of seeds from pod or capsule, partial or complete separation of seed from husk, removal of wings or appendages, or merely fragmentation of a fruit cluster to facilitate handling and sowing.

STORAGE OF SEEDS
Make sure seeds are properly dry before storing them away.

There are variations in the best storage conditions for different seeds; but generally, most seeds should be stored at low temperatures and low humidity. Some kinds of seeds are difficult to store for any length of time even under the best of conditions. Some of these are: ash, members of the white oak family, red and silver maple, poplars, willows and elm. As a general rule, seeds which ripen in spring or early summer should be planted soon after harvest.

SEEDS OF WOODY PLANTS IN THE UNITED STATES
Agriculture handbook No. 450. Prepared by the Forest Service, USDA 1974. This hefty book is the main source of information used in this pamphlet. It describes in detail how to collect seed of every kind of tree commonly grown in the U.S., nursery practices for growing the trees from seed, etc. etc. Available from the USDA; or from the Lawyer Nursery, Rt. 2, Plains, Montana 59859 (Lawyers gives faster delivery) $17.95 or so.

ORGANIC FERTILITY

THE SOIL ECOSYSTEM

The human race depends on the top six inches of seven per cent of the earth's surface for its survival. This, of course, is the fertile soil suitable for agriculture. This soil is a teeming universe of busy micro-organisms that feed us.

In just one gram of soil there are 20 million bacteria, 1 million fungi, millions of actinomycetes and 800,000 algae. These constitute only the major forms of micro-flora. Soil animals in that same gram consist of 1 million protozoans like amoeba, ciliates and flagellates. Snails and slugs, various anthropods, some vertebrates and the all-important earthworm make up the balance of the population. As fertility increases, so do the number and variety of soil life. The purpose of fertilizer is to enliven the soil. The premise of organic agriculture is that a healthy plant will emerge from a healthy soil. The role of mineral fertilizers is to create a mineral balance in order that soil life forms can proliferate. Once a vigorous level of biological activity is attained, the soil humus is able to feed the plants and replenish most of its mineral needs from sub-soil reserves.

This approach differs from the conventional N-P-K agricultural practice of feeding the plants directly with soluble salt fertilizers. Thus one cannot simply substitute organic fertilizers for artificial fertilizers. Organic fertilizers must be used in combination with green manures, cover crops, nitrogen-fixing legumes, and compost in a planned rotation.

There are, of course, thousands of highly successful organic gardeners who understand nothing of soil chemistry, who have never had their soil tested and yet manage to grow fine crops year after year. This can be attributed to the fact that keeping up the fertility of a garden plot is not a monumental task: supply it well with compost, leaf mould, barnyard manures and wood ashes, and things generally balance themselves out nicely.

On a farm scale, however, the challenge is greater, especially for someone inheriting marginal farmland or land which has been depleted by conventional agricultural practice. For the serious, would-be organic farmer (or even home gardener who suspects a soil imbalance in his vegetable plot), the following is offered as the briefest of introductions to soil science.

Agriculture in North America has become largely dependent upon annual infusions of commercial mineral fertilizers, but with good farming practices of crop rotation, composting, surface tillage and re-cycling of all organic wastes, a healthy balanced soil rich in

humus can be maintained without importing minerals from outside the farm. However, few soils are in this condition, and it is necessary for most farmers to re-stock their soil with minerals.

In order to determine the exact mineral needs of the soil, a complete soil test or soil audit is needed. This type of test not only gives the pH and read out of the minerals present but also illustrates the percentage balance between the minerals. Fertilizer recommendations are based on the desired ratio between minerals. The quality and quantity of the organic matter and humus are also assayed. The first step is to balance the positively charged minerals calcium, magnesium and potassium.

Calcium

Calcium is a basic soil and plant nutrient needed in large quantities. The percentage of calcium should be 60 to 70 per cent while magnesium should be 10 to 15 per cent and potassium three to five per cent. This ratio was discovered by William Albrecht and has been proved effective by numerous advanced soil labs and consultants. Limestone is the best known and cheapest source of calcium. While it has been used in agriculture to raise the pH because of its carbonate content, it is even more important because of its high calcium content. Plants could not, for example, grow on a soil whose pH had been raised by sodium bicarbonate. Calcitic limestone $(CACO_3)$ contains calcium, while dolomitic limestone contains both calcium and magnesium $(CaCO_3 . MgCO_3)$. Natural phosphate rock also contains significant amounts of calcium.

Magnesium

Magnesium is the core atom in the chlorophyll molecule. Its deficiency in eastern soils often goes unnoticed or is ascribed to a lack of nitrogen. This deficiency has often been caused by years of liming with a local calcitic limestone source. If it is too expensive to bring in dolomitic limestone, magnesium deficiencies can be corrected by Epsom salts $(MgSO_4)$ or Sul-Po-Mag $(MgKSO_4)$. Epsom salts are strong medicine and should be used judiciously at no more than 100 lb/acre in any one application. Sul-Po-Mag and K-Mag are trade names for sulfate of potash magnesia which is mined as the mineral langbeinite. This mineral is also a soluble salt that contains 18 per cent MgO or 11 per cent magnesium.

Potassium

Potassium is usually supplied on organic farms in the form of carefully recycled manure. It is very susceptible to leaching and it is often lost from uncovered manure piles or urine that is not soaked up by organic matter. Granite dust and Greensand are two powdered rock sources that contain five per cent potassium. With the rising costs of transport, they are just not worth the hauling unless the source is close. Unleached wood ashes are a good source of both potassium and calcium. Sul-Po-Mag is a soluble mineral salt that contains 22 per cent potash (K_2O). It is a good mineral fertilizer for soils deficient in both potassium and magnesium. The sulfate radical (SO_4) is not harmful and is often needed in most soils while the chloride radical present in common muriate of potash fertilizers is harmful in the long run. Sul-Po-Mag is a transitional fertilizer from which the agriculturalist should wean himself after two or three years by careful management practice.

Phosphorous

Phosphorous is the major limiting factor in world agriculture. World phosphate reserves are low and the North American source comes from a small area in central Florida. Conventional phosphate fertilizers are made from phosphate rock that is treated with acids to concentrate it and make it soluble. Organic phosphate fertilizer, in contrast, is simply the crushed rock (30 per cent P_2O_5) or colloidal clay phosphate (20 per cent) which is a clay by-product of early mining efforts.

Phosphorous is a lively element that wants to combine with metallic ions in the soil to form insoluble mineral compounds. Artificial phosphate fertilizers do not remain soluble long; some is lost by leaching into streams and lakes and much becomes unavailable to plants. Plants often only recover five to 20 per cent of the phosphorous applied. Phosphorous is only available to plants in a soil where the biological activity is high, since soil life forms incorporate mineral phosphorous into their tissue, making it available on their death. The correct approach is to mix untreated forms of phosphate with manure or other forms of organic matter before application to the soil. The colloidal clay form of phosphate seems to be more available because of its fine particle size and clay nature.

Trace Minerals

Modern science is discovering that the role of trace minerals in the intricate balance of the soil is extremely important. Minerals such as zinc, cobalt and selenium are necessary to the proper functioning of soil, plant and animal metabolisms. Once again the key is balance and the biological approach is to help nature maintain the balance rather than attempt to manipulate mineral levels from bags of soluble salts.

Some soils are low in necessary trace minerals due to the nature of parent rock formations but most deficiencies are caused by continuous monocultures, lack of recycling, and imbalanced applications of soil minerals. For example, if too much calcium and potassium are applied, magnesium will be relatively low; too much calcium makes iron unavailable and high levels of phosphate drive off zinc. In some cases, trace minerals have to be added to the soil. Alfalfa, for example, needs a good supply of boron in order to function efficiently so borax often has to be added. In most cases, the application of trace minerals is not necessary. Crushed rock powders, like granite dust and natural phosphates, contain a wide variety of trace minerals. Liquid seaweed extract contains more than 60 minerals, as well as growth hormones, and can be applied as a foliar spray on plant leaves to help remedy possible deficiencies and to spur growth.

Nitrogen

Nitrogen is the largest, most expensive and ultimately the most destructive input of conventional agriculture. It is always the first on everyone's list of fertilizers. A good supply of nitrogen is essential for all plant growth, but this element is last in this list because it should come from healthy organic farming practice rather than a bag. Nitrogen, as we often forget, is a gas not a mineral and is a very elusive, highly mobile plant nutrient. This vagrant substance assumes many forms although ammoniums (NH_4) and nitrates are the most important radicals. To insure a successful crop most farms apply loads of soluble artificial nitrogen compounds. The short-range results are visibly green, but the long-range result is soil death. A good level of organic matter in a minerally balanced soil will supply adequate nitrogen. In fact organic matter management is the key to successful farming (biological or otherwise).

Manure is the best source of nitrogen. If it has to be applied raw it should be done in fall not spring. Composting animal manure with organic wastes and necessary minerals is, however, the best method of creating soil fertility. As well as supplying vital humus and needed nitrogen and minerals, compost also inoculates the soil with a myriad of helpful life forms.

Growing nitrogen-fixing legume crops like alfalfa and clovers is an effective and cheap way to supply nitrogen. Tilling in any green plant growth adds nitrogen to the soil.

Supplementary forms of bagged nitrogen are leather wastes (10 per cent) and bloodmeal (13 per cent) while fish emulsion (four per cent) can be added to the soil or diluted and sprayed on plant leaves.

In our own organic fertilizer business, we come across frequent challenges that require the occasional ability to compromise in the short run to achieve good soil in the long run. One recent farm analysis showed, for example, an extreme potassium deficiency that had to be remedied before alfalfa could be made to do well. In explaining the situation to the farm owners, my associate Bart Hall-Beyer made the following observation, which all of us would do well to remember in discussing organic fertility programmes:

"Ideally, one would like to avoid the use of 'chemical' fertilizers, and after a few years this should be possible to a great degree. In the meantime, feeding the crops is important, as is flexibility in general. Many beginning farmers have stuck to their 'organic' principles and ended up as bitter failures back in the city, a fate which does no one any good. It is important to stress, however, that it is the soil, and the life therein, which is the basis for a sound and sustainable agriculture. The farmer who chases the dollar and ignores the soil does so at the peril of the long term stability of the whole farm."

—*Joe Smillie*
Sawyerville, Quebec

EATON VALLEY AGRICULTURAL SERVICES

Box 25
Sawyerville, Quebec J0B 3A0
(819) 875-3676

Joe Smillie & Co. offer consulting services on soil fertility as well as non-chemical programmes of pest management. His booklet "Soil Fertility" ($1.00) is highly recommended as a short introduction to organic soil management.

Fertilizer Prices (1979)
Sul-Po-Mag $165/tonne or $12/100 lb.
Dolomitic Limestone $60/tonne or $3/100 lb.
Colloidal Rock Phosphate $105/tonne or $4/50 lb.
"Sea Mix" Seaweed/Fish Concentrate $400/44 gals. or $14/gal.
"Sea Crop 16" Trace elements from seaweed to stimulate plant growth (foliar spray) $440/44 gals. or $15/gal.

Sea Crop 16—Growth Promoter

Sea Crop 16 is a liquid seaweed extract made from seaweed harvested off the coast of Maine. This stabilized concentrate has an indefinite shelf-life and a consistent analysis.

Laboratory tests show that seaweed extract contains over 60 minerals. Seaweed contains this wide array of major, minor and trace elements in a naturally-balanced form because its growth takes place in the minerally-rich sea environment. Many of these trace minerals, when sprayed on tree foliage, activate different enzyme systems and often correct mineral deficiencies.

Much research has been done on seaweed extracts. It has been determined that the active ingredient in the extract, responsible for many of these excellent results, is a growth promoting substance called "cytokinins." Cytokinins are a powerful group of plant hormones which initiate and activate basic growth processes at extremely low concentrations. It seems likely that the cytokinin content of Sea Crop 16 may be responsible for the following effects which have been noted after it has been applied to orchards as a foliar spray:

* Increase in mineral uptake from the soil into plant leaves.

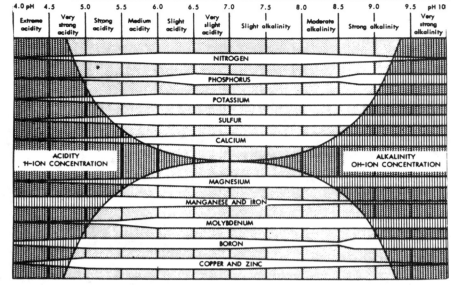

The influence of pH level on the availability of plant nutrients in mineral soils.

* Increase in protein, R.N.A. and D.N.A. content of plants. By performing this function plant vigour is increased, and thus a greater resistance to disease and frost damage occurs.

* Increases and stabilizes chlorophyll in plants which results in more efficient photosynthesis and increased sugar content.

* Increases bloom set and size of flowers and fruit.

* Improves fruit shelf-life and travelling quality by retarding loss of protein and R.N.A. after harvest.

Sea Crop 16 is used in the orchard at the rate of 1 to 1½ gallons per acre per year in four to seven spray applications. Sea Crop 16 mixes with all fungicide and insecticide sprays. Spray times vary with the season and locale but best times are at pre-pink, calyx, pink, mid-June and when buds form for the following year. Seaweed spray improves the growth processes of the apple tree, resulting in fruit of greater quality and quantity. After a few years of use the cumulative effect of liquid seaweed will be noted in increased resistance to frost damage, fungus infection, red mite infestation and insect attack. When the low cost of Sea Crop 16 is weighed against all these effects, the cost/benefit of this material to all orchardists is obvious!

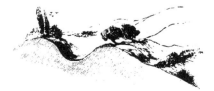

GREEN EARTH ORGANICS

Joel Holland
9422 - 144th Street E.
Puyallup, Washington 98371
(509) 845-2321

Kerry Banks of Vancouver recommends this small company's organic fertilizers. Shipping, as with any bulky agricultural product, tends to be expensive.

Offers a potent organic insect dust composed of the botanical pesticides pyrethrin, rotenone and ryania and sold under the name Tri-Excel. Also available is *Bacillus thuringiensis*, a powder known as Thuricide consisting of bacterial spores which, when mixed with water, is death on all manner of caterpillars (especially good for tent caterpillars, cabbage worms and loopers).

Tri-Excel 1 lb. $2.95; 5 lbs. $8.95
Thuricide (Bacillus thuringiensis) 1 pint $7.50
Diatomaceous Earth 5 lbs. $4.75

Green Earth Fertilizer (Blend of bloodmeal, meatmeal, bonemeal, rock phosphate, greensand, kelpmeal, beet ash and dolomite) 25 lbs. $5.50; 50 lbs. $10.95
Individual components and other organic products are also available.

GROW-RICH ORGANIC FERTILIZERS LTD.

No. 3 Highway
Oldcastle, Ontario
(519) 969-1930
Composted human sludge and

sawdust for lawns, flower beds and shrubs. Most knowledgeable horticulturists are now advising against the use of sludge products on any sort of food crop.

AGRI-SPORE INTERNATIONAL LTD.
1867 Yonge Street
Toronto, Ontario M4S 1Y5

This firm offers one product — a biological soil inoculant which is said to "accelerate the nitrogen cycle of the soil." The makers claim it helps plants develop better root systems, that it causes crop residues to decompose more rapidly and that it helps build humus. According to the label, it contains trace minerals, algae, fungi and bacteria, and 98.99 per cent water.

1 U.S. Gallon (treats 10 acres): $98.00

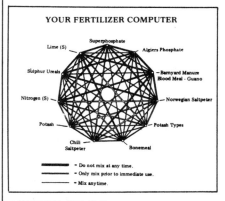

MULTI-CROP INDUSTRIES INC.
5307 Pat Bay Highway
Victoria, B.C. V8X 1S9

Source of "Multi-Crop" seaweed powder, which is not a complete fertilizer but rather a combination of minerals and trace elements. The company also offers a range of potent fertilizers and compost starters, but does not indicate how they are derived. A call to Multi-Crop resulted in an employee saying that their 20-20-20 plant food "might be the same as that sold in local garden centres."

Multi-Crop Soluble Seaweed Powder: 4 ounces $2.25 (postpaid) 1 pound $7.50
10-12-7 Compost Maker: 8 ounces $1.50 (Postpaid, good for 1,000 pounds of compost.)

BIO-CONTROLS

BENEFICIAL INSECTS

In areas of widespread insect invasion, the release of certain beneficial insects — ladybird beetles, trichogramma wasps, praying mantises — may be economically justified. In the home garden, the beneficials are more than likely to hie themselves over the nearest fence. Scientific, efficient ways of using these valuable insects should become better known in the next decade.

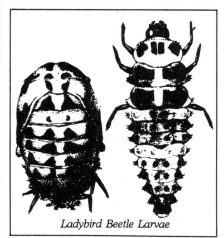

Ladybird Beetle Larvae

FOSSIL FLOWER CO.
5266 General Road Unit 12
Mississauga, Ontario L4W 1Z7
(416) 691-6029

This company offers a variety of beneficial insects, including ladybird beetles and praying mantis egg cases (write for current prices and availabilities) as well as Purple Martin houses and its own product, Fossil Flower Garden Dust. This is composed of diatomaceous earth mixed with pyrethrins (extract of the pyrethrum daisy), an effective bug killer for many garden applications.

Also available is an organic house plant insecticide and pure diatomaceous earth (harmless to humans) to be mixed with grain to prevent infestations of weevils, beetles or grain borers.

PRAYING MANTIS
Although usually found in warm climates, the European Praying Mantis, (or Stick Insect), can live in North America. The male looks just like a green stick or twig, and the female has a larger head and abdomen. Despite its very ferocious

appearance, the Praying Mantis is one of the best beneficial insects. Like other beneficial insects, they will not harm the plants in your garden because they are strictly meat eaters. When young, they feed on aphids and leaf-hoppers, and as a mature adult they eat chinch bugs, crickets, bees, beetles, tent caterpillars and many others.

The eggs are laid in masses of approximately 200 eggs, encased in a substance similar to glue, and they remain in the shrubs all winter until the young emerge in late May or early June. The adults meanwhile will die; the male after mating and the female two or three weeks after the eggs are laid.

Apply the egg cases in your garden as follows. Allow one egg case for each major shrub, or in an open area, allow four cases per ¼ acre. Run a thread through the pointed end of the case, then tie it in the shrubs or some plants that will give the young some protection. The young look just like the adult, only about the size of a mosquito. The egg case can stand all kinds of weather; freezing, rain, snow, etc. but needs protection from being destroyed.

Praying mantises are poor flyers and move very slowly. Once they are introduced to an area, they will stay as long as they can find food. They will lay in waiting in the shrubs for their prey, and you may not see them unless you look very closely amongst the leaves.

The following two sources also offer the various Fossil Flower products and beneficial insects:

THE GOOD LIFE LTD.
28 Main Street, Box 907
Montague, P.E.I. C0A 1R0
(902) 838-3393

BIANCHI '79

BETTER YIELD INSECTS
13310 Riverside Drive E.
Tecumseh, Ontario N8H 1B2

Whiteflies are a notorious problem for greenhouse owners, and, although miniscule, they can arise in white clouds of thousands of individuals and wreak havoc on certain crops. This company supplies a biological enemy of the whitefly.

The parasite called Encarsia formosa *is a small wasp. The only food of this beneficial insect is the greenhouse whitefly. No harm is done to the plants and the adults do not sting or bite humans.*

The parasites are supplied as immature stages on a tobacco leaf. Each darkened whitefly pupa contains a developing parasite. In a few days adults will emerge and move to your plants in search of whiteflies.

The tobacco leaves should be divided into 4 to 8 sections, depending on the size of the leaf, and these should be spread out in the area of the greenhouse where whiteflies are present. Although the tobacco leaf will dry up, parasites will still emerge. The lowest effective number of parasites is two per square foot. The treated area need not be the whole greenhouse.

Parasites will complete a generation in 10 days, if the greenhouse temperature is 75 degrees F. At 70 degrees they are quite a bit slower. Their numbers will increase as long as there are whiteflies available: Later, both whiteflies and parasites will persist in low numbers. Look at the under surface of the leaves to see what numbers of developing parasites there are. Normally, the per cent of parasitized whiteflies fluctuates between 50 and 80 per cent. You may also see the very small black and yellow adult parasites on the leaves. Even when parasites are working in the green- house, there may be brief periods when whitefly adults seem abundant. This reflects the time lag between a whitefly increase and a resulting

MAJA IMPORT EXPORT
R.R.2
Rock Creek, B.C. V0H 1T0
(604) 446-2315

SAFER AGRO-CHEM LTD.
5271 Old West Saanich Road,
R.R.3
Victoria, B.C. V8X 3X1
Anyone with an orchard or fruit trees should know about this new biodegradable insecticidal soap developed by a B.C. entomologist. The maker claims that it is effective against spider mites, scales, loopers, ants, fleas, mealybugs and aphids. Honeybees, ladybird beetles and parasitic beneficial wasps are said to be minimally affected. Four fluid ounces of the concentrated soap makes a gallon of spray, while the four litre container is

enough to make about 40 gallons of spray.

C. A. CRUICKSHANK LTD.
1015 Mount Pleasant Road
Toronto, Ontario M4P 2M1
(416) 488-8292

PERMA GUARD: The revolutionary new concept in insect control. A totally natural product containing Diatomite and Pyrethrins in an easy-to-apply dust. It is

parasite increase. The number of whitefly adults should drop sharply within a week.

Parasites are killed by most insecticides.

ORGANIC DEER CONTROL

I am an organic gardener, or, at least, a low-technology gardener, preferring non-poisonous insecticides or hand-removal to high impact toxins. My arsenal against pests contains store-bought *Deritox* (derris root or rotenone, not poisonous to warm-blooded creatures) which I use on the cabbage caterpillars and potato bugs if they become troublesome. The flea beetles and the cutworms get dusted with wood ashes or ground limestone, the corn borers and earworms get purged with mineral oil, and the slugs get ignored. None of these pests has ever done much harm to my gardens anyway.

Then came 1976, The Year of The Deer.

When we moved to this new home we were foolishly pleased at all the deer activity in the woods.

Come July, however, we weren't pleased when these creatures ate the corn — every stalk — down to the ground, sampled and trampled the beans and nibbled the salad. Last summer when the first hoofprints and chewed bean bushes appeared we tried a repellant out of folklore. (Home remedy Number Two involved camping out among the corn stalks with a strong flashlight, a loaded rifle, and would have resulted in neat packages of illegal venison in the freezer).

The homemade deer repellant consists of buckets of rags placed strategically around the garden. Into these the contents of chamber pots are emptied at intervals. The deer stay away. Considering that pails of aging urine are not exactly socially acceptable, I am glad that the garden is some 50 yards from the house. Visitors, often tender suburbanites, being given a tour of the "estate" always ask (sniff) what is in the buckets. We respond discreetly, but honestly, "Oh, deer repellant."

Theory: The strong human smell of urine marks the territory as off limits to herbivores. I have heard, though, that the sweat and urine of strict vegetarians smells different from that of us carnivores. (Plains Indians would abstain from meat for a month before setting out to capture wild horses in order not to spook them.) So maybe the vegetarians in the crowd will have to borrow the more threatening contents of their meat-eating neighbours' chamber pots.

—*Molly Miron*
Upper Kennetcook, Nova Scotia

WINGED FRIGHT (FOR MOSQUITOES)

In the bug infested hinterlands of this great country, beyond where government helicopters drop their annual cargoes of mosquito-mauling dragonflies, a small fraternity of bird lovers has found the symbiotic way to swatless evenings. These are the purple martin lovers.

Purple martins *(Progne subis),* the largest members of the swallow family, eat mosquitoes by the thousands every day. They also live in colonies which multiplies their collective consumption into the millions. They like living near humans. As well as all this, "purple martins are beautiful, extremely graceful, interesting in their family behaviour, and clean," says J.L. Wade, North America's foremost martin authority and founder of Trio Manufacturing Limited which specializes in building martin houses. "In addition, they seem friendly and curious about their human associates. Persons who attract martins invariably become intrigued with them."

Before North America was settled by white people, English sparrows and starlings; purple martins nested in hollow trees and Indians sometimes hung gourds to house extra families. Early colonists (human) put up large wooden martin houses which held entire colonies (martins) but they required a lot of maintenance and were easily invaded by starlings and sparrows.

Then along came J.L. Wade of

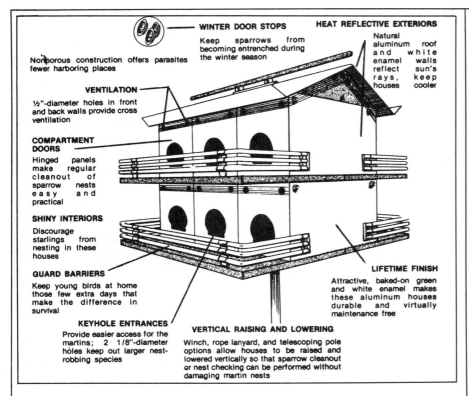

WINTER DOOR STOPS
Keep sparrows from becoming entrenched during the winter season

HEAT REFLECTIVE EXTERIORS
Natural aluminum roof and white enamel walls reflect sun's rays, keep houses cooler

Nonporous construction offers parasites fewer harboring places

VENTILATION
½"-diameter holes in front and back walls provide cross ventilation

COMPARTMENT DOORS
Hinged panels make regular cleanout of sparrow nests easy and practical

SHINY INTERIORS
Discourage starlings from nesting in these houses

GUARD BARRIERS
Keep young birds at home those few extra days that make the difference in survival

LIFETIME FINISH
Attractive, baked-on green and white enamel makes these aluminum houses durable and virtually maintenance free

KEYHOLE ENTRANCES
Provide easier access for the martins; 2 1/8"-diameter holes keep out larger nest-robbing species

VERTICAL RAISING AND LOWERING
Winch, rope lanyard, and telescoping pole options allow houses to be raised and lowered vertically so that sparrow cleanout or nest checking can be performed without damaging martin nests

---

Griggsville, Illinois, whose researches developed the modern enamelled aluminum house. He insists that "the only way to attract martins is to put up a house. Once they accept it, they will return faithfully year after year unless some tragedy overtakes them during migration. Many colonies are more than 50 years old and consist of more than 100 pairs, but typical colonies range from a few pairs to 20 or 30 pairs. The size to which you build your colony depends not only on the martins but on your own neighbourhood and desires."

He says that "martins are deserving of the best houses man can provide. Houses should be easy to keep clean inside and out, cool, parasite resistant and, above all, must have guard rails. Martins are too valuable to use as cat food," Wade says, "and it is inhumane to put up a house without guard rails and other proper design features." The guard rails prevent immature birds from inadvertently falling out before they can fly properly.

Almost any sufficiently buggy open area in North America, except the Rocky Mountains, can host a colony of purple martins. They don't like mountains, dense forest or downtown cities because of the high speeds at which they

cruise while hunting. They eat almost all flying insects, except that they don't seem to bother worker bees. Some beekeepers have martin colonies without any trouble.

Since the martins like to have their relatives nearby, a martin house in a new area must have room for at least 12 families. But once they establish themselves in a neighbourhood, it is easy to find tenants for the smaller, eight-family houses nearby.

Trio Manufacturing Limited is "the world's largest builder of purple martin houses" and is located in Griggsville, Illinois, U.S.A. 62340. Prices range from $48 to $288. The Nature Society there also publishes *Purple Martin News* at 50 cents a copy or $6.00 per year, and J.L. Wade's 240-page *What You Should Know About the Purple Martin*, $3.25 plus 25 cents postage and handling.

Trio Martin Houses are available in Ontario through:
NEWLAND'S FLOWERS LTD.
288 Talbot Street West
Leamington, Ontario N8H 4H4
(519) 326-4491
and
WOOD 'N' ENERGY
MacDonald's Corners, Ontario
(613) 278-2023

—David Creighton
Maberly, Ontario

HYDROPONICS

Hydroponics is the culture of plants without soil, feeding them with a nutrient solution that is, in most cases, not at all organic. Nevertheless, a fresh salad of tomatoes, buttercrunch lettuce, scallions and just-cut tarragon can vastly improve one's outlook on a mid-winter night. Despite the fact that their growth comes out of a jar of fertilizer, hydroponic vegetables *taste* great and should be free of pesticides.

It is possible to use a home-mixed organic solution but the odours that develop compare unfavourably with the aroma of an aquarium of dead fish. (No problem in a greenhouse or heated porch.) Otherwise, one can grow tomatoes in the kitchen with the only intrusion being the glow of the lighting unit and the gurgle of the nutrient pump.

Anti-hydroponics gardeners say that large containers of rich soil or worm castings will produce vegetables just as well as a hydroponic set-up—provided there is ample light. The whole subject of indoor vegetable culture is still in the horticultural Dark Ages.

FUN WATER GARDENS
1134 Yonge Street
Toronto, Ont. M4W 2L8
(416) 922-7798

Free literature. This is the leading manufacturer and retailer of home hydroponic systems in Canada. Source for complete units, as well as fluorescent light units, pumps, timers, plant food, growing medium and hydroponic literature.

Those who become hooked on hydroponics seem invariably to find cheaper ways of building systems and/or locating components, but many have started here.

Single Soilless Garden (Includes tank, pump, irrigation tubes, growing medium, instructions and accessories): $64.95 ($6.50 shipping not included.)

Two-Foot Growlight Fixture & Stand $59.95 (plus $4 shipping)

Hydroponic City Green Plant Food $4.25/lb.

CANADIAN HYDRO GARDENS LIMITED

411 Brook Road West
Ancaster, Ontario L9G 3L1
(416) 648-1801

Pre-fab and do-it-yourself hydroponic growing kits for the home.

SPECIALTY GARDENS LTD.

90 Earlton Road
Agincourt, Ont. M1T 2R6
(416) 291-2370

Mail order family business offering home systems, supplies and information on hydroponics.

APPLIED HYDROPONICS OF CANADA INC.

5322 Boulevard St. Laurent
Montreal, Quebec H2T 1S1
(514) 273-1550

Manufacture and sell a small hydroponic nursery and a commercial-scale herb growing unit for restaurants.

Hydroponic Nursery: $10.95
Herb Market: $1,117.00
City Green kitchen garden $24.95
City Green soilless garden $75.00

HOME HYDROCULTURE ASSOCIATION

Box 3250, Station D
Willowdale, Ont. M2R 3G6

This newly formed group offers a monthly newsletter as well as information on equipment, sources of nutrients, best plant varieties to grow and other help for hydroponic enthusiasts.

C.A. CRUICKSHANK LTD.

1015 Mount Pleasant Road
Toronto, Ontario M4P 2M1

4-FOOT FLUORESCENT LIGHT FIXTURE: There has been a recent surge of interest in growing plants under fluorescent light. Our 2-tube 4-foot fluorescent fixture provides the easiest and most inexpensive method of having a flourishing winter garden. Just suspend the fixture over a table or bench and you have a large growing area for starting seeds or growing bulbs and plants. Complete with white enamelled reflector. Deluxe Model, includes cord. C.S.A. approved. Price $29.50. Tubes extra—Cool White $1.95 each. Gro-Lux $5.85 each. Shipments by express only.

CITY GREEN HYDROPONICS LIMITED

7515 Bren Road
Mississauga, Ont. L4T 3V4
(416) 677-0824

City Green

Random Comment

A few winters ago I discovered the concept of hydroponics and became enthusiastically interested in it as a way of having fresh salad ingredients during the winter months despite living in an isolated rural area 10 miles from the nearest small country store. I spend a great deal of time caring for my 'forest' of house plants and was thrilled to think that some of this time could be spent growing edible produce.

The answers to many of my questions were discovered by trial and error. A trip to Fun Water Gardens in Toronto also proved very helpful. They carry City Green as well as some other hydroponics supplies, seeds and books. There you can see various crops being grown and cared for; the proprietor was most helpful in answering questions and demonstrating equipment. They reply to their mail promptly.

It is well worthwhile to visit a showroom if you are interested in getting into hydroponics. There are often displays set up in large shopping malls but the people attending them are not always adequately informed about their products or able to answer anything but routine questions. Before investing a large sum of money you may decide that much of the equipment can be adapted and made at home with a smaller initial financial investment.

In Fun Water Gardens my husband was fascinated by a $49.95 gadget for pollinating tomato blossoms. He came home and made a similar instrument for less than $5 using a door bell kit, a homemade handle and a six-volt battery. He also devised an inexpensive but effective hydroponic system using 0 pipe which is normally placed around

foundations for drainage. He sealed the ends with used inner tubes discarded by a local garage, sloped the 0 pipe slightly, and positioned the tube valves for use as a convenient method of draining the hydroponic food solution. These we filled with perlite, planted our 'garden' and for a winter contentedly grew tomatoes, lettuce, cucumbers, cabbages and beans. Our blissful state ended when we began to receive substantially higher hydro bills.

From a wrecker we had purchased two eight-foot fluorescent light fixtures each requiring four bulbs. Eight new fluorescent tubes at $4.29 each was an initial investment and these must be replaced each year if plants are to thrive. In addition we had raised the temperature in a normally cool room so that the tomatoes could enjoy the warmer environment that appeals to them.

For us, hydroponics became a hobby whose cost outweighed its advantages, so until such time as we can incorporate some form of solar heat and light we have reluctantly abandoned our winter 'farm' except for a few tomatoes which I nurture in a warm hallway under a smaller fluorescent fixture.

—*Lesley Rowsome*
Cloyne, Ontario

GREENHOUSES

GAZE FARM AND GARDEN SUPPLIES
9 Buchanan Street
St. John's, Newfoundland
A1C 5K8

MINIBRITE GREENHOUSES: Your Minibrite is built to weather a lifetime. Its top quality features include high tensile Aluminum Alloy frames; Aluminum nuts and bolts; easy assembly; stainless steel glazing clips, Puttyless glazing; Rustproof and corrosive resistance; No painting or maintenance. Dozens of satisfied users here in Newfoundland.

Height to top ridge 7 feet. Height to side eaves 5 feet. 8 ft. x 12 ft. Our most popular size $448.00; 8 ft. x 8 ft. model $328.00. Glass not included.
New Lean-to Model: *Size 6 ft. x 12 ft. $398.00. Glass not included.*
Brochures sent on request.

ENGLISH ALUMINUM GREENHOUSES LTD.
506 McNicoll Avenue
Willowdale, Ontario M2H 2E1
(416) 493-7773

Free-standing and lean-to greenhouses with curved eaves, glass glazing and bronze coloured aluminum support structure. Fourteen models to choose from, including: 8x8 foot free-standing (includes roof vents and door) $1,249; 8x8 foot lean-to (includes roof vent, louvre and door) $1,199.

LORD & BURNHAM
Box 428
325 Welland Avenue
St. Catharines, Ont. L2R 6V9
(416) 685-6573

Lifetime quality aluminum and glass greenhouses from an old line firm. They will send a fascinating catalogue and price list upon request.

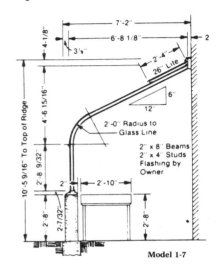

Model 1-7

Model I-7 Lean-To Greenhouse: Where space and initial investment must be budgeted tightly at no sacrifice in quality features, this slim companion to our larger vertical side, curved eave Imperials is your best buy. Note that only one end (with door) is required as this Imperial Lean-to 7 is built against two residence walls. The step-up door effect was created during construction of the brick wall. 11 feet long, double-glazed: approximately $4,000 installed.

English Aluminum Greenhouse, used as a living space and solar heat collector.

Peter Reimuller and one model in his line of wood and rigid plastic economy greenhouses.

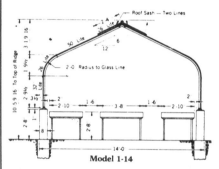

Model 1-14

Model I-14 Even Span Greenhouse:
This Imperial *Even Span 14 is one of the prettiest on-wall greenhouses we ever built, and most practical too. Straight sides expand growing room for tall plants. Exclusive new sill collects condensate, then weeps it outside. 26"-deep roof vents open to horizontal for best ventilation. 16 feet long, single-glazed only: approximately $3,300 installed.*

Solar/Window Greenhouses: *Come in many sizes, and can be installed easily. Pre-glazed panels slip together without tools, and fasten over the window with only a screwdriver. 48" x 72", single-glazed only: $285.*

All prices F.O.B. St. Catharines, Ontario.

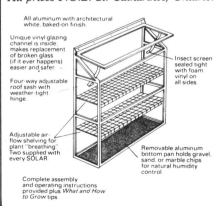

All-aluminum with architectural white, baked-on finish.

Unique vinyl glazing channel is inside: makes replacement of broken glass (if it ever happens) easier and safer.

Four-way adjustable roof sash with weather-tight hinge.

Insect screen sealed tight with foam vinyl on all sides.

Adjustable air-flow shelving for plant "breathing." Two supplied with every SOLAR.

Removable aluminum bottom pan holds gravel, sand, or marble chips for natural humidity control.

Complete assembly and operating instructions provided plus *What and How to Grow* tips.

SUNSAVER GREENHOUSES
6 Clearview Crescent
St. Catharines, Ont. L2T 2W1
(416) 684-0654

Modestly priced "Peter Reimuller" greenhouses of various configurations (including a geodesic dome), constructed of redwood framing and either 8-mil polyethylene or clear acrylic panels reinforced with fibreglass.

PEARL MIST FREE-STANDING "EIGHT"—8 ft. long by 8 ft. wide—fibreglass/Acrylic Panels. $499.95.
PEARL MIST LEAN-TO "EIGHT"—8 ft. long by 7 ft. wide—Fibreglass/Acrylic Panels $399.95.
SUN DOME I: 10 ft. diameter—Polyethylene Cover $229.95.

Electric Heater 110V $76.95
Kerosene Heater $159.95
Exhaust Fan $89.95

J. LABONTE & FILS
560 Ch. Chambly,
Longueuil, Québec J4H 3L8
(514) 651-6000

This seed company distributes five lines of greenhouses as follows:

SERRES MAYTIME (fibre de verre) Petite serre avec structure métallique et recouvrement de fibre de verre. Small greenhouse with metal frame and fibreglass covering.
No. 6208 8'x8' $499.00
No. 6212 8'x12' $699.00
No. 6216 8'x16' .... Prix sur demande
No. 6220 8'x20' .... Ask for prices
L'APPENTIS (Crittall) Bâti contre une

maison ou un mur de jardin, la serre en appentis est économique à l'achat et à chauffer. Elle peut être placée contre n'importe quel mur sauf s'il est exposé droit vers le nord. Placée contre un mur exposé au sud, la serre en appentis offre pas mal d'occasions pour faire pousser des légumes, fleurs, fruits se développeront bien.
Modèle 6'x8' (E) $595.00.

SERRES ALOUETTE: *Ces serres sont construites en fonction de notre climat; la charpente en bois (cèdre rouge) évite la condensation et la perte de chaleur; une moulure en vinyle recouvre tout l'extérieur n'est nécessaire; l'installation est facile; la ventilation automatique élimine les ventilateurs manuels; très décoratives, ces serres embelliront votre maison; elles sont offertes en blanc ou en noyer; le solin est galvanisé. Ces serres sont conçues pour vous procurer des années de plaisir.*

Built for our weather conditions. Redwood framing eliminates condensation and heat loss. Exterior completely built with vinyl moulding. No exterior maintenance required. Easy to install. Labour-saving automatic ventilation. Attractive; it will give more value to your house. Available colours: white or walnut. Galvanized flashing. Built to bring you years of pleasure. Prix sur demande. Ask for price.

SPECIFICATIONS: *Châssis tout en aluminum. Porte coulissante. Fournie complète avec toutes les parties, les éléments de fixation et les accessoires pour un montage simple et rapide.*
Les serres Crittal nécessitent peu ou pas d'entretien! Le chassis en aluminum n'a pas besoin d'être peint ou imperméabilisé et ne nécessite aucun entretien. Le seul entretien nécessaire est le nettoyage des verres de temps en temps.
Model 8'x8' (E) $695.00; Modèle 6'x8' (E) $525.00.

SERRES PIEDMONT: *Désirez-vous un jardin précoce? Installez-vous une serre Piedmont sur une partie de votre jardin au mois d'avril et commencez à récolter vos tomates au mois de juin. Enlevez ensuite et remisez la pour l'an prochain se démonte en quelques minutes. De style gotique les arches sont construites de bois laminé tel que les serres professionnelles. S'installe facilement et en très peu de temps. Recouverte de polyethylène 8 MM qui peut durer de 4 à 5 ans. Peut aussi être de verre garanti pour 20 ans. Pratique pour ceux qui désirent produire leurs propres plants à peu de frais. Dimensions 10 pieds de large X 10 pieds de long X 8 pieds de haut. En polyethylène (G) $339.00; En fibre de verre (G) $549.00.*

GARDEN RELAX
174 Torbay Road
Markham, Ontario L3R 1G6
(416) 495-7005

Polyethylene-covered greenhouses, designed in Britain and not unlike an inexpensive camping tent in structure and durability. Garden Relax claims many satisfied clients among ''smaller gardeners with smaller budgets,'' but hang on when the winter winds blow.

Greenhouse Model 10x6 feet
$229.95
Twinskin (Double wall) Option
$69.96
Fruit Cages available from Great Britain only upon special request.

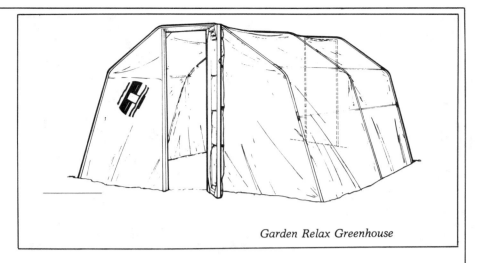

Garden Relax Greenhouse

DOMINION SEED HOUSE
Georgetown, Ont. L7G 4A2

Offers the Garden Relax models, including:

LEAN-TO GREENHOUSE: You can place it most anywhere. It needs only a space 2 feet wide, against a wall or fence, 4½ feet long, by 5½ feet high (assembled size). Ideal size to set in backyard, on patio or even on a balcony. You don't even need a soil bed. You can use pots, trays, boxes or grow-bags of earth. It adds new scope to grow things whether your garden is large, or the smallest, or if no garden at all. Bountifully productive for such small size of base dimensions. Vertical staging gives it great capacity as a coldframe or for propagating seeds, cuttings, box plants of vegetables and flowers or for production of bloom, fruit or vegetables. Provides 45 cubic feet of growing environment. The cover is tough, shatter-proof, gale-resistant, heavy-duty horticultural-quality polyethylene of same material specifications as given for Garden Greenhouse. Frame is precision-machined, ready-drilled, selected timber with interior 2-tier tubular steel staging. Front door panels provide easy access and variable degrees of top and bottom ventilations. Nothing else gives such growth potential for so little space and modest cost. Easily assembled; directions supplied. Frame, cover, screws, steel staging. $114.95. Replacement Cover. Including door panels $34.95.

F. P. HUGHES
R.R.2, Green Lane
Hawkesbury, Ontario K6A 2R2
(613) 632-4509

Instructions on how to build a pipe and plastic greenhouse: $3.00.

GASCOIGNE INDUSTRIAL PRODUCTS LIMITED
159 Rayette Road
Concord, Ontario L4K 1C7
(416) 669-1494

Kee Klamps for erecting greenhouse frameworks of standard pipe. Clamps made of strong, malleable iron, galvanized.

KEN-BAR INC.
24 Gould Street
Reading, Massachussetts 01867
(617) 944-0003

Greenhouse accessory products. Canadians will have to pay import duty on items ordered.

VENTILATED TUBING: Provides fresh air circulation and even temperature control. Our tubing is a clear 4 mil polyethylene film that is cut to custom lengths and custom punched to fan manuf. specs. It's available in 6 diameters: 10'', 12'', 18'', 20'', 24'' and 30''. Include this tubing as part of your total package.

BATTEN TAPE: For securing plastic film to wood frames. Our Batten Tape is a natural companion to our Eskay-Lite film. It saves hours of application and removal time. Simply staple every 3 or 4 inches keeping tape tight. When replacing or removing plastic, simply rip Batten Tape off along with staples. Batten Tape is a tough, white vinyl plastic strip ¾'' wide x 1/32'' thick and is available in 1000-foot spools.

ESKAY-LITE: 16 mil clear vinyl covering. Unusually clear, very small light loss. Excellent insulation. 4 year life under most conditions. A good compromise between poly and fibreglass as a cover material. Use on ends and sides for see-thru clarity. Available in 54'' x 50' rolls or 54'' x 210' rolls.

Random Comment

(Mail Order Horror Stories Dept.)
To: GARDEN RELAX GREENHOUSES
174 Torbay Road
Markham, Ontario
To Whom It May Concern:

When I finally got notice (it took exactly 66 days from order to reception!) of the arrival of my greenhouse, the first deception we found was a 50-mile car drive to pick it up. Nowhere did you tell me that the greenhouse was not to be shipped to my house. But that was just the beginning of my troubles.

Next I tried to figure out how to mount the thing from your instruction sheet. First we tried the French translation, as this is my husband's mother tongue. That didn't make much sense. So we shifted to German, which is my mother tongue. No better there. So we finally had to do with the English version, but even then it was not easy. My husband is a university professor and I am a nurse. We have built a 32-foot sailboat and a house together, but never before have we encountered such poor instructions.

In the description of the mounting steps: Where is the step showing what the foam rubber pieces are used for?

A few remarks on the material you sent:

1) There is not sufficient pressure strip supplied to cover all the

places you indicate.

2) There were not enough nails.

3) The wood of the door frames was so badly twisted as to be unusable. I had to drive to the village to buy replacements.

4) What is the use of the time-consuming job of waxing the cords? If it is indispensible, then you could have sent *waxed string* at first.

5) What is the use of the reinforcement strip? It was so badly twisted and wrinkled that it was almost impossible and very time consuming to get into the blind struts.

6) The inner and outer blind struts are so tight fitting that one has to use a hammer to get them into each other, and then they rip the plastic doorsheet and ventilator. This happened with every single one of them . . . .

7)Finally, you told me in your letter of April 9th that I would get my "twinskin" (plastic covering) two weeks later. That means tomorrow morning. I hope I will not have to make another trip of 50 miles to pick *that* up. And please do not delay, as it is now, when the nights are still cold, that I need the twinskin most.

The only thing that impressed us positively, until now, were your publicity and marketing techniques. We have seldom seen something so flimsily made for such a high price. We did not expect a few tubes, nuts and bolts, some pieces of wood and square piece of plastic to be called a greenhouse.

It would be more just and honest to speak of a do-it-yourself Kit Greenhouse. Then one would know what to expect and the price should be in accordance (not $250 for 10 feet by 6 feet).

Until now there has been very little relaxing . . . .
—*Henni Zakes*
Ham-Nord, Quebec

Organizations

CANADIAN ORGANIC GROWERS

33 Karnwood Drive
Scarborough, Ontario M1L 2Z4
(416) 957-5609

Contact: Peter McQueen. A non-profit environmental and health association composed of organic gardeners and farmers.

INDOOR LIGHT GARDENING SOCIETY OF AMERICA, INC.

c/o Mrs. Phyllis W. Banucci (Secretary)
30 Brookside Drive
Pittsfield, MA 01201
(413) 499-3076

Amateur plant growers who garden under lights. $8.00 per year membership brings bi-monthly newsletter. This group has 35 local chapters, including one in Calgary.

HOBBY GREENHOUSE ASSOCIATION

45 Shady Drive, Box 951
Wallingford,
Connecticut 06492
(203) 269-5858

Non-profit organization for non-professional greenhouse owners. Offers a chatty, bimonthly news-letter, "The Planter," primarily aimed at U.S. readers. Member-ship fee $5.00 per year.

MARIGOLDS FOR THE CONTROL OF NEMATODES
By Ralph Motsinger, Extension Nematologist & Gene Moody, Extension Plant Pathologist Cooperative Extension Service, University of Georgia

Research at the University of Georgia indicates that some marigold varieties show promise for control of root-knot nematodes under the procedures used in our experiments. There are limitations to control which will be explained later.

The growing interest in home greenhouses and increased food transportation costs from the south have created new interest in northern greenhouse research.

Varieties belonging to the French marigold group Tagetes patula have been reported to give more effective control of root-knot nematodes than varieties belonging to other groups (i.e. African or South American). Initial research was conducted with the French marigold varieties, "Tangerine," "Petite Gold," "Goldie" and "Petite Harmony." These varieties were artificially inoculated in pots with either Southern root-knot nematodes (M. incognita) or Peanut root-knot (M. arenaria) or Northern root-knot (M. hapla). All varieties gave good control of the Southern root-knot but the variety "Tangerine" gave the best control against all three species of root-knot. Other French marigold varieties not included in the test may perform comparable to those tested. Also, it should be noted that the dominant root-knot species found in home gardens in Georgia is the Southern root-knot nematode, M. incognita.

"Tangerine" marigolds and "Rutgers" tomatoes growing in the same pot were inoculated with Southern root-knot nematodes. The tomato roots were severely galled even though marigold roots were intermingled with the tomato roots in the pots. In artificially inoculated field plots, "Rutgers" tomatoes with "Tangerine" marigolds planted around them were as severely galled as tomatoes planted alone. However, where marigolds were planted solid (approximately 7" x 7"), nematodes were reduced to near zero in all plots.

Before French marigolds became heralded as a panacea for nematode control, the limitations of their use need to be explained. First, our limited tests indicate that marigolds will not prevent nematode infections when planted around annual plants in soil infested with nematodes. Marigolds did not appear to secrete sufficient toxic substance into the soil even in 6-inch pots to kill nematodes or to prevent infection of tomatoes planted in the same pot. Marigolds may act as a trap crop, allowing the nematodes to enter the roots but not allowing them to complete their life cycle. The trapped nematodes thus die without reproducing. There is some indication that this does occur. Second, our work and the work of Suatmadji in the Netherlands indicated that marigolds should be

planted as a solid crop and grown for about 90 to 120 days to effectively reduce the nematode population sufficiently to grow annual plants without treatment. Marigolds should be planted in 7-inch rows, approximately 7 inches apart in the rows so that the roots thoroughly penetrate the soil mass to exert their negative influence on the nematodes whether it be to trap them or to reduce the numbers through toxic secretions or a combination of both. Third, good weed and grass control must be maintained. Many weeds and grasses serve as hosts for root-knot nematodes. If weeds are not controlled, marigolds may be unable to suppress the nematode population. When marigolds are planted close together, they form a dense canopy which helps retard the development of weeds and grasses. Fourth, marigold varieties suppress root-knot and lesion nematodes but do not control all other kinds of nematodes. When grown as a solid planting for 90 to 120 days, however, they should suppress root-knot and lesion nematodes to such a low population level that annual flowers and home garden plantings can be made without other nematode control treatments.

Key points to keep in mind are: (1) plant one of the varieties of French marigolds, Tagetes patula; (2) plant them about 7 inches apart in the row with rows about 7 inches apart; (3) practice good weed control; (4) plant marigolds as a solid planting, and (5) let the marigolds grow the full growing season. When these points are followed, it appears that marigolds can be used to effectively suppress root-knot and lesion nematodes in the areas in which they are planted.

Books

GROWING WITH COMMUNITY GARDENS
By Mary Lee Coe
The Countryman Press
Taftsville, Vermont
$7.45, 150 pages (Paperback)

When the starry-eyed young couple, expecting their first child and just moved into the neighbourhood, installed a flower box outside the window of their West 94th Street apartment, they

could not have foreseen the consequences. Soon, boxes of geraniums and English ivy began to appear up and down the block, fresh curtains were hung, old doorknobs and knockers were polished to reveal gleaming brass and, amazingly, vandalism dropped off. The "worst block in New York's Upper West side" was transformed into a personable, colourful neighbourhood.

An optimism that plants and gardens can make a difference and change patterns of life — even in the innermost city — pervades Mary Lee Coe's new book. The optimism works only because it is balanced by an equal sense of pragmatism: The road to creating community gardening areas is not nearly so simple as hanging out a window box. Between contractors who scrape every inch of topsoil from city lots and thieves who flee with the harvest, Coe describes a series of pitfalls that would deflate the enthusiasm of all but the most dedicated gardener.

Still, gardening builds tenacity and never, since the Victory Gardens of World War II, have North American community gardens bloomed in such abundance. In Victoria, British Columbia, 160 plots were established in 1973; in three years the number had increased to 535. In a programme that began last year, municipalities in Nova Scotia could apply for grants of up to $4,000 to establish vegetable gardening areas for the landless.

Such community gardens have long been popular in Europe, where they are often known as allotment gardens or "guinea gardens" — a colloquial name derived from the practice of renting plots for one year at the price of a guinea.

Sloppy organization will spell doom for any attempt to start a new community garden project, a lesson the author learned in trying to establish a cooperative vegetable plot in the country. One member dissuaded the group from putting up fences, arguing that the very idea was "negative tripping." Four-footed pests soon discovered the garden and the whole project disintegrated.

Growing With Community Gardens provides very detailed information both for organizers and gardeners alike. Everything must be prepared — the soil, the site, and the gardener, who is sometimes required to sign a contract committing himself to a certain amount of labour each month. Although the book is geared to the United States, the experiences and problems it describes are truly universal (old-timers who persist in sneaking a little 10-10-10 into otherwise organic areas), and Coe's "sample plot for cold regions" should be suitable for most of the highly populated regions of Canada.

In all, this is a well thought-out book and a blueprint for success with new community gardening programmes.

GRAHAM CENTER SEED DIRECTORY
Frank Porter
Graham Center
Route 3, Box 95
Wadesboro, N. Carolina 28170
16 pages, $1.00

A brief, nicely presented introduction to the problems of corporate and agri-business seed breeding, along with a listing of non-hybrid seed sources, virtually all in the United States.

"Suddenly in the 1970s," writes Garrison Wilkes of the University of Massachusetts, "we are discovering Mexican farmers planting hybrid corn seed from a midwestern seed firm, Tibetan farmers planting barley from a Scandinavian plant breeding station, and Turkish farmers planting wheat from the Mexican wheat programme. Each of these classic areas of crop-specific genetic diversity is rapidly becoming an area of seed uniformity." Seed companies, governments and international aid agencies have gone into areas where traditional varieties predominate and promoted the new plants, often calling them "miracle varieties." Convinced of the "superior" qualities of the new variety, the Third World farmer or peasant ceases to grow the traditional crop. Instead, left-over seeds of the traditional variety may be used as food for the family or their animals. In a moment's time, thousands of years of crop development and seed selection become meaningless, and another variety becomes extinct.

Where thousands of varieties of wheat once grew, only a few can now be seen. When these traditional plant varieties are lost, their genetic material is lost forever. Herein lies the danger. Each variety of wheat, for example, is genetically unique. It contains genetic "material" not found in other varieties. If, because of genetic limitations which result from inbreeding, new varieties are no longer resistant to certain insects or diseases (conceivably even insects or diseases never before known to attack wheat), then real catastrophe could strike. Without existing seeds which carry specific genes conferring resistance, it may not be possible to breed resistance back into wheat, corn, or any other crop . . . .

In the end, the future of agriculture can be insured only by healthy, vibrant, small farms. The old varieties are threatened today, not because they taste bad or are nutritionally deficient, but because they do not suit the requirements of the factory farmers and the food processing industry. The California plantation owner who grows tomatoes to be shipped all over the country cannot grow the old, tasty varieties. Their skins are not tough enough. Their insides are not hard. If the old varieties are to flourish they must be, as they always have been, grown by small farmers and sold to a local market. This system of agriculture has provided sustenance to people for well over 10,000 years. It is an enduring agriculture that we tamper with only at great risk.

Seeds are a unique product of the efforts of people and nature. In seeds, culture and agriculture are linked. This bond dissolved, both are threatened. Our ancestors knew this and lived accordingly. Thomas Jefferson once professed his belief that "the greatest service which can be rendered to any country is to add a useful plant to its culture." For our generation, the challenge will be to *preserve* the useful plants we already have.

SELF SUFFICIENT GARDENER
By John Seymour
Doubleday/Dolphin
$9.95, 256 pages, Paperback

ENCYCLOPEDIA OF ORGANIC GARDENING
Edited by J.I. Rodale
Rodale Books, Inc.
Emmaus, Pennsylvania 18049
1145 pages, Hardcover

GARDENING WITHOUT SOIL
By James Sholto Douglas
H.B. Fenn & Co.
Mississauga, Ontario L5S 1A1
$6.98, 331 pages, Softcover

HYDROPONIC FOOD PRODUCTION
By Howard M. Resh
Woodbridge Press
Publishing Co.
Santa Barbara, Ca 93111
287 pages, Hardcover

THE SOLAR GREENHOUSE BOOK
Edited by James C. McCullagh
Rodale Press
Emmaus, Pennsylvania 18049
$8.95, 328 pages, Softcover

GROWING HERBS FOR THE KITCHEN
By Betty E.M. Jacobs
Gray's Publishing Ltd.
Sidney, British Columbia
$5.95, 93 pages, Hardcover

THE NEW YORK TIMES BOOK OF VEGETABLE GARDENING
By Joan Lee Faust
Quadrangle Book Co.
New York, N.Y. 10022
$6.95, 282 pages, Softcover

DOWN-TO-EARTH VEGETABLE GARDENING KNOW-HOW
By Dick Raymond
Garden Way Publishing
Charlotte, Vermont 05445
$5.95, 160 pages, Paperback

"He That Plants Trees Loves Others Besides Himself...."

Remembering a piece of English proverbial wisdom

The new car seemed just a bit too sleek as it pulled to a stop in the barnyard, and the middle-aged man who got out was, save for his construction boots, just a bit too well-dressed to be a county agent or even an implement dealer.

As a teenage summer hand, I would not be privy to the conversation — the farmer left me grinding corn for a small group of fattening hogs. The salesman — or so I judged him — pointed several times in the direction of the

nearby woodlot, and he and the farmer finally went off to inspect several tall old trees at the centre of the small woods.

After some time the stranger left and the farmer returned to help finish the grinding. It turned out that the man was a tree buyer looking for black walnut. His offer for the three or four old trees would have been enough, at that time, to put the farmer's two children through university.
The farmer did not sell the trees,

and as far as I know they are still there — a sort of living insurance policy with no annual premiums.

With quality hardwoods becoming ever more scarce, the farm woodlot is increasingly being recognized as a rediscovered resource. And, with demand for firewood suddenly reawakening, many small holders are thinking of reforesting marginal farmland.

Reforestation, in the public eye, has come to mean either MacMillan-Bloedel punching millions of seedlings back into clearcut forest land or a weekend countryman turning his farm into a Christmas tree plantation.

Neither, from a biological point of view, makes a great amount of sense. For the small landowner, especially, establishing a forest monoculture can result in disaster. Without a squadron of spray planes, he may see an entire planting succumb to an infestation of insects or disease.

A woodlot containing a variety of tree species at various stages of growth is not only better able to withstand pest problems, it is constantly regenerating itself and providing a continual source of firewood, fence posts, building timber and an occasional cash crop.

—*JL*

ONTARIO

Ontario has one of the most comprehensive programmes in the country for supplying seedlings to the public. From its seven nurseries the government distributes more than a dozen varieties which include both hardwoods and softwoods: white, red, jack and Scots pine; white, black and Norway spruce; white cedar, white ash, silver maple, red oak, Carolina poplar, black locust and black walnut.

In order to purchase seedlings from the government you must own at least two acres, excluding land occupied by structures. The minimum order is 50 trees and 25 of one species. Cost ranges from $5 for 50 trees to $10 per thousand. For delivery in early spring it is advisable to order the previous summer to ensure availability of all species.

The government provides a free advisory service and upon request will inspect your land to help determine suitability of tree species to soil type, planting methods, etc. Many books and pamphlets, including almost everything regarding woodlot management are available from the Ministry — most of them without charge.

Information and requests for trees should be made at your nearest district office of the Ministry of Natural Resources or at the main office in Toronto.

MINISTRY OF NATURAL RESOURCES

Division of Forests
3rd Floor, Whitney Block
99 Wellesley Street
Toronto, Ontario M7A 1W3
(416) 965-2785

PRINCE EDWARD ISLAND

Depending on seed availability, over a five-year period it is possible to obtain all of these varieties: red, white and black spruce, red and Austrian pine, red oak, black ash, butternut, white and yellow birch, American elm and white cedar — most of the tree species of the original Acadian forest.

After making application for seedlings, an on-site inspection will be made by the department to determine that the trees will be used for woodlot and reforestation purposes rather than landscaping. (A landscaping programme is operated under another branch of the government.)

Stock ranges from three to eight inches (larger than most seedlings) and costs $30 per thousand. This price will probably be revised downward in the future. The department also provides a planting service at $20 per thousand.

DEPT. OF AGRICULTURE & FORESTRY

P.O. Box 2000
Charlottetown, P.E.I. C1A 7N8
(902) 892-0228

NEWFOUNDLAND

Newfoundland has just begun operation of a provincial nursery and will not be producing trees until 1981. The main purpose of the nursery is full-scale reforestation of crown land but it is expected that a programme will exist for the private landowner when trees become available. For further information contact:

DEPT. OF FORESTRY & AGRICULTURE

Forest Management Branch
Confederation Building
St. John's, Newfoundland
A1C 5T7
(709) 737-3750

NEW BRUNSWICK

The provincial government in New Brunswick operates one nursery located near Kingsclear, just north of Fredericton. This nursery was set up for the purpose of growing trees for reforestation of crown land, but also sells trees to the private sector on a secondary and limited basis. Only a few species are available and all are coniferous: black and white spruce, jack and red pine (pulpwood fibre trees) and Scots pine (Christmas trees). Minimum order is 1,000 trees which sell for an average of $30 and it is not certain that there will be enough trees to fill all orders. All species are available in the spring and again in the fall.

Inquiries can be made either directly to the nursery or to the Department of Natural Resources.

PROVINCIAL FOREST NURSERY

R.R.6
Frederiction, N.B. E3B 4X7
(506) 455-6989

DEPARTMENT OF NATURAL RESOURCES

Forest Extension Service
Box 6000
Fredericton, N. B. E3B 5H1
(506) 453-3711

NOVA SCOTIA

Nova Scotia operates one nursery out of Lawrencetown and supplies seedlings to the public. Variety is limited: red, white and jack pine, and red, white, black and Norway spruce. Certain hardwoods are grown by the nursery and supplied to parks and other recreation sites but are not available to the public, since the government does not want to undercut the private nurseries. Trees are for reforestation purposes and it is obvious that the variety of tree available reflects the economic interests of pulpwood in the province.

Varieties available are red, white and jack pine and Norway spruce. Minimum order: 100 trees of any one species, price $10 for 100 to 500 trees and $20 per thousand for 500 or over. Inquiries can be made at the Provincial Forest Nursery in Lawrencetown or at any branch of the Department of Lands and Forests.

PROVINCIAL FOREST NURSERY

P.O. Box 130
Lawrencetown, Annapolis Cty.
Nova Scotia B0S 1M0
(902) 584-3400

DEPARTMENT OF LANDS AND FORESTS

Dennis Building
Granville Street
Halifax, Nova Scotia R3J 3C4
(902) 424-6694

QUEBEC

The 10 nurseries in Quebec produce over 30 million trees annually, 40 per cent of which are planted on public land and 60 per cent of which go to the private sector. Just about every variety of tree that grows naturally in Quebec is offered: balsam fir; white, red, Scots and jack pine; white, red, black and Norway spruce; sugar and silver maple; oaks, ashes and butternut. All trees are free of charge.

On-site communication with a department official is required before trees can be ordered to determine that the plantation is for the purpose of reforestation, protection of agricultural or maple bush areas, or Christmas tree production.

Contact your regional Lands and Forests office or the head office in Quebec City.

MINISTERE DES TERRES ET FORETS

Service de la Restauration
200B Chemin Ste-Foy
Quebec, Quebec G1R 4X7
(418) 643-4710

P.F.R.A. SHELTERBELT PROGRAMME

This is a federal programme operated by the Prairie Farm Rehabilitation Administration.

Apparently the lack of trees was understood quickly in the prairie provinces and as early as 1902 a nursery was set up by the federal government at Indian Head, Saskatchewan to provide trees to prairie farmers. Today this nursery annually supplies six million plants of 17 tree and shrub species to some 8,000 farmers, plus federal, provincial and municipal agencies, in the three prairie provinces. The main purpose of the programme is to provide tree material, free of charge, to farmers for use as shelterbelts and *not* for reforestation.

Originally, only native Manitoba species were produced (pines, ashes, Manitoba maple) but over the years new varieties of wind-and-weather-hardy trees have been imported and established — Siberian pea shrub, Siberian elm, Missouri cottonwood.

Although the original programme was only for landholders of 40 acres or more, it has now been expanded to include rural small holdings of one to 39 acres. However, the latter is on a second priority basis and fewer varieties of trees are offered.

Inquiries should be made directly to the nursery in Indian Head.

DEPT. OF REGIONAL ECONOMIC EXPANSION

Tree Nursery Division, PFRA
Indian Head, Sask. S0G 2K0
(306) 695-2284

MANITOBA

Manitoba operates one nursery out of Hadashville. Although aimed at producing trees for government reforestation programmes, it also supplies planting stock to the public for the purpose of tree farming or woodlot planting.

Variety is limited to four trees: jack, red and Scots pine and white spruce. Minimum order is 1,000 trees at $20 per thousand. Nursery stock is supplied under the condition that it will neither be sold as live planting stock nor used for ornamental purposes.

DEPARTMENT OF RENEWABLE RESOURCES AND TRANSPORTATION SERVICES

Chief of Forestry Services
Box 22
1495 St. James Street
Winnipeg, Manitoba R3H 0W9
(204) 786-9246

A shelterbelt programme, previously run by the provincial government, has been discontinued, and the P.F.R.A. Nursery at Indian Head, Saskatchewan supplies trees for this purpose to eligible Manitoba residents. (See the section under P.F.R.A. Shelterbelt Programme.)

SASKATCHEWAN

From the two government nurseries at Big River and Prince Albert, 11 million seedlings were produced last year. The bulk of these trees are used by the government for reforestation and parkland purposes with the remainder going as good will gestures to companies and Boy Scout groups. Requests for trees from private landowners for use as Christmas trees or woodlot improvement have been on the rise and the government plans to step up production.

Limited quantities of seedlings will be available this year for spring planting at $50 per thousand. Varieties include: white spruce, jack pine, Scots pine,

Colorado spruce, elm, ash and Manitoba maple.

DEPT. OF TOURISM AND RENEWABLE RESOURCES

Forestry Branch Room 300
Provincial Office Building
49 - 12th Street East
Prince Albert, Sask. S6V 1B5
(306) 763-6434

ALBERTA

At the moment, no programme exists in Alberta to distribute seedlings for use in woodlots. Much of the land in Alberta is open farmland and the Provincial Tree Nursery at Oliver, Alberta only supplies trees for shelterbelt purposes.

Up to the present, there has been little demand for seedlings from woodlot owners, but officials say that as economic conditions change, a programme could be implemented. Questions regarding future plans and the shelterbelt programme should be addressed to:

DEPT. OF AGRICULTURE

Plant Industry Division
601 Agriculture Building
9718 - 107th Street
Edmonton, Alberta T5K 2C8
(403) 427-5372

BRITISH COLUMBIA

Despite the fact that the B.C. Forest Service operates 15 nurseries throughout the province, it does not have a programme for distribution to the general public. Trees are big business in B.C. and, through an agreement with the lumber companies who provide the seed, these nurseries are kept busy producing 30 to 40 million seedlings per year for reforestation of Crown and private lands. This figure is soon expected to rise to 90 million but is still peanuts compared to the 500 million produced each year in Scandinavia for the same purpose. The federally operated Pacific Research Centre in Victoria is trying to aid the operation by researching ways to automate the nursery system — trees on conveyor belts and more.

B.C. FOREST SERVICE

Information Services
(Reforestation)
Parliament Buildings
Victoria, B.C. V8V 1X5
(604) 387-5985

UNITED STATES

As in Canada, the distribution of planting stock is handled by the state rather than the federal government. Also, as in Canada, the extent and quality of each programme varies widely from state to state, along with prices and stipulations. In some states no programme of distribution is offered at all.

Generally, to avoid competing with private nurseries, state policy requires that trees be used for reforestation, watershed protection, wildlife shelter, etc. and not be sold on the open market.

For the situation in your area, contact your local State Forester:

ALABAMA:
513 Madison Avenue
Montgomery 36130

ALASKA:
323 East Fourth Avenue
Anchorage 99501

ARIZONA:
1624 W. Adams
Phoenix 85007

ARKANSAS:
3821 W. Roosevelt Rd.
P.O. Box 4523, Asher Stn.
Little Rock 72214

CALIFORNIA:
Resources Building
1416 Ninth Street
Sacramento 95814

COLORADO:
Colorado State University
Fort Collins 80523

CONNECTICUT:
165 Capitol Avenue
Hartford 06115

DELAWARE:
Drawer D
Dover 19901

FLORIDA:
Collins Building
Tallahassee 32304

GEORGIA:
P.O. Box 819
Macon 31202

HAWAII:
1151 Punchbowl Street
Honolulu 96813

IDAHO:
State Capitol Building
Boise 83720

ILLINOIS:
R.R.5
Springfield 62707

INDIANA:
613 State Office Building
Indianapolis 46204

IOWA:
300 Fourth Street
Des Moines 50319

KANSAS:
2610 Claflin Road
Manhattan 66502

KENTUCKY:
618 Teton Trail
Frankfort 40601

LOUISIANA:
P.O. Box 1628
Baton Rouge 70821

MAINE:
State Office Building
Augusta 04333

MARYLAND:
Tawes State Office Building
Annapolis 21401

MASSACHUSETTS:
100 Cambridge Street
Boston 02202

MICHIGAN:
P.O. Box 30028
Lansing 48909

MINNESOTA:
Centennial Office Building
St. Paul 55155

MISSISSIPPI:
908 Robert E. Lee Building
Jackson 39201

MISSOURI:
2901 North Ten Mile Drive
Box 180
Jefferson City 65101

MONTANA:
2705 Spurgin Road
Missoula 59801

NEBRASKA:
201 Miller Hall, East Campus
University of Nebraska
Lincoln 68583

NEVADA:
201 South Fall Street
Carson City 89701

NEW HAMPSHIRE:
Box 856, State House Annex
Concord 03301

NEW MEXICO:
P.O. Box 2167
Sante Fe 87501

NEW YORK:
50 Wolf Road
Albany 12233

I DON'T KNOW FRANK, MAYBE THE TREE'S SICK...

NORTH CAROLINA:
Box 27687
Raleigh 27611

NORTH DAKOTA:
N. Dakota State University
First & Simrall Avenue
Bottineau 58318

OHIO:
Fountain Square
Columbus 43224

OKLAHOMA:
122 State Capitol Building
Oklahoma City 73105

OREGON:
2600 State Street
Salem 97310

PENNSYLVANIA:
109 Evangelical Press Bldg.
Third & Reily Streets
Harrisburg 17120

RHODE ISLAND:
Box 545, RFD 2
North Scituate 02857

SOUTH CAROLINA:
P.O. Box 21707
Columbia 29221

SOUTH DAKOTA:
Sigurd Anderson Building
Pierre 57501

TENNESSEE:
2611 West End Ave.
Room 302
Nashville 37203

TEXAS:
College Station 77843

UTAH:
1596 W. North Temple
Salt Lake City 84116

VERMONT:
State Office Building
Montpelier 05602

VIRGINIA:
P.O. Box 3758
Charlottesville 22903

WASHINGTON:
Olympia 98504

WEST VIRGINIA:
1800 Washington Street East
Charleston 25305

WISCONSIN:
Box 7921
4610 University Avenue
Madison 53707

WYOMING:
Capitol Building
Cheyenne 82002

PRIVATE NURSERIES

KEITH SOMERS TREES
10 Tillson Avenue
Tillsonburg, Ont. N4G 2Z6
(519) 842-5148
Organically oriented nursery with good prices and an impressive variety of trees and shrubs, including sugar maple, Lombardy poplar, Russian olive, Chinese elm, grey dogwood, Arctic willow, hemlock, moose maple, wild black cherry and black ash.

Hard Maple (2 yr. old):
$15 per 100
White Birch (2 yr. old):
$25 per 100
Wild Gooseberry:
35 cents each
Serviceberry (12 inch);
$1.00 each
Beechnut (2 yr. old):
$1.00/2 trees
Pussy Willow (4 yr. old):
$2.50 each

MUSSER FORESTS
Indiana, Pennsylvania 15701
(412) 465-5686
Ships anywhere, good source of nut trees, hardwoods, ornamental shrubs.

Red Oak (8 to 12 inch):
$35 per 100
Green Barberry (6 to 12 inch):
$30 per 100

(See additional listings under Seed Sources for nurseries that offer fruit and nut trees.)

BOOKS

TREES OF NORTH AMERICA AND EUROPE
By Roger Phillips
Pan Books
Distributed in Canada by:
Collins Publishers
100 Lesmill Road
Don Mills, Ont M3B 2T5
$10.95, 244 pages (Softcover)
Mr. Phillips thanks one Tim the Tree Climber, as well he should, considering that the subsequent 200 pages contain more images of fresh tree materials — cones, leaves, bark, buds and silhouettes — than have ever been gathered between two covers. Without doubt the most beautiful tree identification book ever produced, this volume is filled with high quality photographic images — crisp, colour-true macrophotos on pleasingly neutral backgrounds.

Common names, however colourful, (Clammy Locust, Fluttering Elm, Stinking Cypress) are kept in hand by an unflinching Latin nomenclature, while the layout sets a new standard in biological presentation. It is, in fact, a photographic key to tree identification, the result of the author's frustration at the difficulty in using more academic text and field books.

"My innovation," says Phillips, "is to do visually what they have done verbally: if you can see the leaf you do not need to know whether it is lanceolate or oblong lanceolate, you just look at it and compare it with the photograph, and if it is too broad or too narrow, you pass on to the next leaf or page of leaves."

It must be pointed out that the geographical aspects of the book's title are misleading, since items as disparate as the Golden Rain Tree of India, the South Australian Snow Gum and the Patagonian Cypress — whole new sets of windows on Nature's cathedral are wedged among our North Atlantic flora. (This is a British book, and one suspects that the very same volume, but with a different cover, can be found in the better book shops of London. It would be called *The Trees of Europe and North America.*) A more apt title, perhaps, would be *Trees For Temperate North America and Europe.*

The extent of the geography covered leads to the only real failing of the book, since readers in areas of severe frost or marginal fertility will fail to learn from it whether the glorious East Himalayan Spruce or the Japanese Big-Leaved Magnolia will make it by their pond in Burnaby, British Columbia or Penobscot, Maine. Perhaps we shall never know.

God's proving ground is very well illustrated by facing pages of 28 different oak leaves. These begin to creak open the mysteries of that world-wide genus. (When the book is closed, *Quercus rubra* from our own backyard noses up against Mirbeck's Algerian Oak.) Considering that a book the size of Mr. Phillips' could be devoted to oaks alone, one has to be impressed with his editorial audacity and his patience in collection.

Organizing 2,000 or so tree parts — all in mint condition — is a chore for passion and scholarship. Fortunately the author and his arboreal friends live in southern England where imperial collectors and benign climate have implanted more varieties than could be found in all of Canada. Now, for a reasonable price, even an unwoodsy reader can scrunch down with the Pines of Aleppo, the Red Snake-Bark Maple and a hundred other wonders which our curiously monotonous culture has neglected. Highly recommended.

— *Josef Reeve*
Golden Bough Tree Farm
Marlbank, Ontario

FOREST FARMING
By J. Sholto Douglas and Robert A. de J. Hart
Rodale Press
Emmaus, Pennsylvania 18049
199 pages, Hardcover $8.95

Rather academic introduction to the notion that farming need not be confined to field and row crops. Not much of practical use for northern landowners, but this should be essential reading for food futurists.

FOREWORD By E.F. Schumacher
Ten years or so ago I received, most unexpectedly, a letter from America, sent by Richard B. Gregg. It couldn't be the Richard Gregg, friend of Gandhi and author of a number of books which I had read with great benefit to myself? Well, it was. The letter was very simple. It said: 'Gandhi used to say: "When you cannot make constructive use of your books any more, give them to someone who can." I am an old man and cannot do much any more. I have looked through my library and have picked out a number of books which will be more use to you than they are to me now. May they help you in your work,'—or words to that effect. A few weeks later, a book parcel arrived and there they were, exceptional books, marvellous books, books which I should never have found myself (except for people like Richard Gregg!). Among them was one with the title Tree Crops— A Permanent Agriculture, *by J. Russell Smith.*

I confess, I did not read this one right away. Its subject seemed to me too remote and, I admit it, too improbable. But eventually I did read it, and it made so much sense to me that I have never been the same since. It made sense, because it did not merely state that 'civilised man has marched across the face of the earth and left a desert in his footprints'—a remark I had found confirmed in innumerable places throughout the world; no, it did much more than that: it showed what could be done and what should be done. Most improbably (as it seemed to me) the answer had been there all the time and was still available to us: Agriculture is for the plains, while silviculture is for the hills and mountains. When the plough invades the hills and mountains it destroys the land . . . .

Just as efficient agriculture depends on human ingenuity and work—in finding the best methods of cultivation, in plant breeding, and so forth—so an efficient silviculture depends on just the same kind of effort. Without the effort, nothing much can happen . . . .

I do not think the authors of this book overstate their case when they say:

'Of the world's surface, only eight to ten per cent is at present used for food production . . . . With the aid of trees, at least three quarters of the earth could supply human needs, not only of food but of clothing, fuel, shelter and other basic products.'

NATIVE TREES OF CANADA
By R.C. Hosie/Dept. of Fisheries and the Environment
Information Canada
Ottawa, Ontario K1A 0S9
Softcover, 380 pages
$6.00 in Canada
$7.20 elsewhere

The classic Canadian field guide: thorough, easy to use and profusely illustrated with black and white photographs.

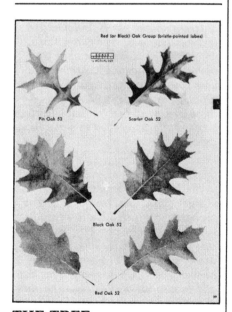

THE TREE IDENTIFICATION BOOK
By George W.D. Symonds
George J. McLeod Ltd.
73 Bathurst Street
Toronto, Ontario M5W 2P6
Softcover, 272 pages

An almost totally pictorial guide that should please those who find other tree field guides too complex. Just as true mushroom lovers can't get by with a single identification guide, tree people will find this a useful complement to most other field guides and reference works.

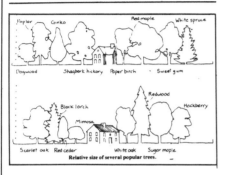

TREES FOR THE YARD, ORCHARD AND WOODLOT
Edited by Roger B. Yepsen Jr.
Rodale Press, Inc.
Emmaus, Pennsylvania 18049
Hard and Softcover, 305 pages

Good introductory guide to tree culture for the small farmer or homeowner. Chapters on propagation, pruning, woodlot management, fruit and nut trees, selling timber and orcharding.

PLAN BEFORE PLANTING
How do you orchestrate trees with different shapes, sizes, colours and textures into a pleasing, functional whole? Start with a sketch of your home and grounds. Determine the uses you will make of various areas around the home and how large those areas need to be. Lay out the traffic patterns needed to serve those areas.

If you are building a new home, go through the same exercise, but plot in the location, species, size and vigour of any trees on the site. You probably won't be able to save all the trees on your property, but if a tree is worth saving, your cost and work involved in protecting it may be well spent. Good shade trees can add thousands of dollars to the value of residential property, and yet most contractors bulldoze the land bare and start from scratch. The U.S. Forest Service reports that, on a half-acre lot, the first six-inch-diameter tree adds $300 to the appraised value of the property, the tenth adds $200, and the twentieth, $100. Trees can contribute as much as 27 per cent of the appraised land value.

Booklets/ Publications

Information Division
Canadian Dept. of Agriculture
Ottawa, Ontario K1A 0C7

Fruit Tree Propagation,
Publication Number 1289

INARCHING
The orchardist often has to contend with injury to the below-ground portions of orchard trees caused by pine mice. The bark may be completely eaten off the main anchor roots for several inches below ground level, which makes bridge grafting impracticable. Root killing is caused also by unfavourable environmental conditions during the winter months. In such cases the tree would die within a year if left in its injured state. Fortunately, trees damaged in this way can be saved, and will eventually be none the worse for their injury. By inarching the tops of small seedling trees into the trunk of an injured tree, a completely new root system is provided. This is done by planting seedlings around the base of the injured tree in the very early spring, and later, by grafting the trimmed tips of these seedlings into the healthy tissue above the injury. Trees that have been injured by grass fires can be saved this way.

Inarching is best done in the spring just as soon as the bark slips easily, or when the young leaves are showing. However, the operation can be done any time before early summer when the bark is slipping.

MANITOBA DEPT. OF RENEWABLE RESOURCES & TRANSPORTATION SERVICES
Box 22, 1495 St. James St.
Winnipeg, Manitoba R3H 0W9

"just a bunch of trees": Booklet designed to make young children aware of trees and their complexities.

SUCCESSION
"This here ocean of dust and gravel that we call a farm ain't never gonna grow nothing Ma; let's move on."

Ma and Pa McMud have left their fields, stripped of vegetation, exposed like an unprotected sore. But the unrelenting forces of nature have already started a series of events that will, in time, heal the wound, and win the land back to the forest.

This incredibly complex process is called Plant Succession. *Its stages are predictable and inevitable.*

At first, nothing appears to be growing on the abandoned fields of the McMud farm. But the soil is teeming with life: microscopic protozoa, soil fungi, earthworms and mites. Dormant weed seeds sprout, and quickly grow, providing food and shelter for mice, gophers, and armies of invading insects. Horned larks, meadowlarks and red-winged blackbirds arrive to harvest a bounty of weed seeds and bugs. Dead plant and animal matter is reduced to humus by a procession of tiny grotesque creatures and bizarre microscopic plants.

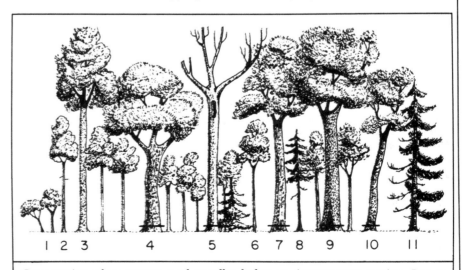

Cross-section of an uneven-aged woodlot before an improvement cutting. Proper woodlot management calls for trees 4, 5, 7, 9, and 10 to be cut.

Plant Succession: From Dust Bowl to forest in 20 years, with luck.

As one year slips silently into the next, still other life-forms invade the field. Grasses help establish new patterns of water distribution and retard soil erosion. Small bushes and tree seedlings rise up and soon begin shading out the original growth. Unfamiliar shapes appear; owls, foxes, coyotes, sharp-tailed grouse, song sparrows, skunks and badgers.

After 5 or 6 years, large shrubs share the land with small aspen trees and wolf willow.

White-tailed deer, ruffed grouse and snowshoe rabbits thrive in the lush young foliage.

In 20 years the forest canopy is well established. The changing vegetative environment is no longer attractive to sharp-tailed grouse, meadow mice or vesper sparrows. They move out, but their place is taken by squirrels and great horned owls.

ONTARIO MINISTRY OF NATURAL RESOURCES
Whitney Block
99 Wellesley Street W.
Toronto, Ontario M7A 1W3

The Farm Woodlot (50 cents)

Facts To Be Considered In Woodlot Management

Knowledge of certain forestry terms and concepts helps in understanding woodlot management.

1. Trees are a crop. They come to maturity and then decline in value, and eventually die.

2. Trees will usually seed and restock an area if it is protected from fire and livestock.

3. A woodlot without young growth is like a community of old people—it will die out.

4. Close spacing is necessary in young stands so that trees with long stems or trunks free of side branches may be grown.

5. A tree requires more space for its crown and roots as it increases in size. It secures this gradually by crowding out adjacent trees.

6. The thinning of dense stands aims at concentrating the production of wood on the more valuable trees.

7. The various tree species differ in their soil, moisture and light requirements.

8. There is a great difference in the commercial value of the species, those of least value being known as weed trees.

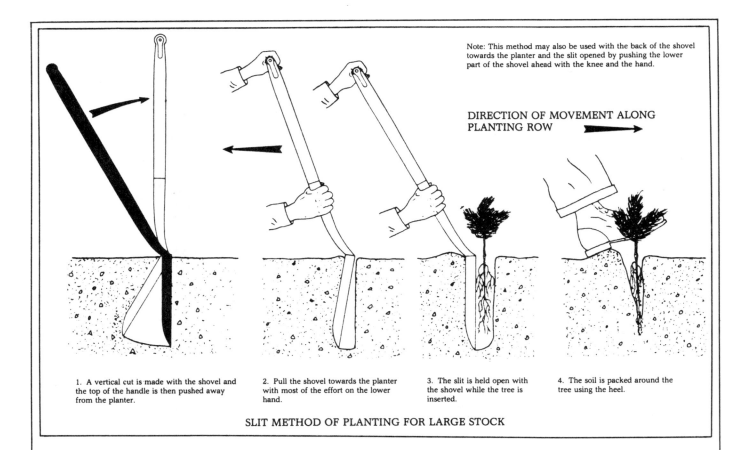

Note: This method may also be used with the back of the shovel towards the planter and the slit opened by pushing the lower part of the shovel ahead with the knee and the hand.

DIRECTION OF MOVEMENT ALONG PLANTING ROW ▶

1. A vertical cut is made with the shovel and the top of the handle is then pushed away from the planter.

2. Pull the shovel towards the planter with most of the effort on the lower hand.

3. The slit is held open with the shovel while the tree is inserted.

4. The soil is packed around the tree using the heel.

SLIT METHOD OF PLANTING FOR LARGE STOCK

9. *A wood crop does not require ploughing, cultivating, fertilizing and the provision of seed as other farm crops do, and this should be considered when comparing financial returns of other farm crops with those from the woodlot.*

10. *It takes between 60 and 120 years to grow a tree to maturity. Landowners, therefore, should consider carefully their value before deciding to sell or destroy the remaining woods on their farms.*

11. *Trees can be cropped periodically due to differences in age classes, thinnings and intermediate cuts.*

12. *Trees that can stand much shading and competition are said to be "tolerant," while those that stand little shade are called "intolerant."*

The concept of tolerance has a practical application. For example, it would be inadvisable to attempt to plant red pine in a young stand of sugar maple and beech. Red pine could not stand the shading by the hardwoods, and would gradually die out.

13. *Individual trees and timber stands are commonly classified on the basis of tree diameter measured at breast height (4½ feet above ground) as follows:-*

seedling—less than 1″
sapling—1″-4″
pole—5″-9″
small sawlog—10″-14″
medium sawlog—15″-19″
large sawlog—20″ and over

Relative Shade Tolerance

Tolerant
basswood
beech
ironwood
sugar maple
balsam fir
black spruce
hemlock
white cedar
white spruce

Intermediate
black ash
red oak
white ash
white elm
yellow birch
white pine

Intolerant
aspen
black cherry
black walnut
red maple
jack pine
red pine
tamarack
white birch

The Forest Trees of Ontario (50 cents)
Hardwood Trees of Ontario (50 cents)

Forest Tree Planting
The Planting of Hardwood Trees and Shrubs

Hardwood Planting on Cleared Upland Sites

The most important single factor in the establishment of successful hardwood plantations is the selection of a species suitable to the planting site. Most hardwood species are very demanding in their site requirements. For satisfactory growth, upland hardwood species require a deep, uneroded, fertile, moist but well-drained soil. In southern Ontario, good hardwood sites will usually be found: along creeks and streams, on lower slopes and in depressions where topsoil has accumulated, in abandoned orchards or gardens, and in agricultural fields where the topsoil is at least 18 inches deep. Areas of dry, exposed slopes and ridges or shallow topsoil over heavy, compacted clay or bedrock should be avoided.

In order to minimize damage by rodents and small mammals,

hardwood plantations should not be located adjacent to grassy areas, old windrows and young conifer plantations. Rabbit damage will usually be quite heavy adjacent to young conifer plantations and natural cedar stands.

ENVIRONMENT CANADA, FORESTRY SERVICE
Ottawa, Ontario K1A 0H3

Forestry Lessons
Publication Number Fo42-169

An Introduction to Christmas Tree Growing in Canada
Publication Number 1330

Today's accent is on the production of quality Christmas trees. Failure to appreciate this point may lead to a stand being rejected by a buyer, or worse, a retail lot that is still heavily stocked on December 26. The stand that is passed over may eventually yield pulpwood or other products, but in the Christmas tree business there is nothing more financially final or forelorn than cut but unsold trees on the day after Christmas.

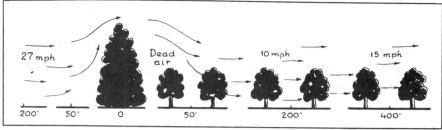

Windbreaks should be 50 to 75 feet from the nearest orchard row. They reduce wind force effectively, but can cause an area of dead air if not pruned up from the ground.

ONTARIO MINISTRY OF AGRICULTURE & FOOD
1200 Bay Street
Toronto, Ontario M7A 1A5

Nut Culture in Ontario
Planning and Planting the Orchard
Windbreaks. *It is usually wise to protect the orchard from damaging winds, at least on the side exposed to prevailing winds. On exposed sites windbreaks should be planted. However, woods or dense solid windbreaks will cause a pocket of dead air on their leeward. Windbreaks, therefore, should be 50 to 75 feet from the nearest orchard row, and kept free of branches from*

4 to 5 feet from the ground to let the air move through. Woods or solid shelter belts can be opened by cutting 75-foot swaths at about every 100 yards. Remember that wild trees of Malus and Prunus, as well as hawthorn and mountain ash, can harbour orchard insects and diseases.

NOVA SCOTIA DEPARTMENT OF LANDS AND FORESTS
Dennis Building,
Granville St., Box 698
Halifax, Nova Scotia B3J 2T9

Reforesting With Conifers In Nova Scotia.

Selling The Nineteenth Century — By Catalogue

Every Tuesday morning, after they've milked their 17 cows and done their other chores, Elmo and Mark Stoll hitch up their wagon and drive their team of horses the 10 miles or so into Aylmer to attend the Ontario town's weekly flea market.

Reminiscent of peddlers of another century, the young farmers' wagon is loaded down with cedar chests, cider presses, sausage stuffers, knives, steam juicers and a variety of other household gadgets and necessities. But, contrary to what some might think, the bearded men in their wide-brimmed dark hats, grey-blue collarless shirts and suspender-held trousers are not an anachronism; they are Amish Mennonites bringing to market a part of their life style for customers wanting to replace modern mass production gadgetry with household appliances of a more substantial nature.

Thirty-five-year-old Elmo, the elder of the two brothers, explains simply that with a growing number of people seeking alternatives to plastic and built-in obsolescence, they felt there was a need for a company which could provide time-tested technology in the new conserver era.

"A lot of our items we are familiar with because we are Amish and have been using them for generations," he says in a low soft voice that hints of a Pennsylvania Dutch accent. "Once we find out what our customers need, we use our knowledge of what is best to help them."

The Authentic Amish Open Buggy, designed along traditional lines but with modern improvements, including Timken bearings and rubber tires. Price: $1,199.

It was on that basic premise that the two men formed *The Pioneer Place* in April of 1979. While their trips to the market are a regular part of their business, most of their efforts are aimed at mail order.

Housed in a driving shed and a few extra bedrooms on the second floor of Elmo's large but modest grey, insul-brick farm house, the business is so low-key that its exact location is known by few people outside of the neighbours who make up the brothers' Old Order Amish meeting (congregation).

Although many of Aylmer's residents are familiar with the Stoll wagon at the weekly flea market, few seem to have heard of *The Pioneer Place*. For a visitor seeking directions, there is little help beyond a very general wave of the hand to the northeast, with the advice that "it's out where the Mennonites live . . . somewhere."

Elmo appreciates his anonymity and, although he is not secretive, the fact that the whereabouts of the farm is little known suits his purposes well.

"I enjoy selling things but having a store doesn't jive with our life style. Two years ago (1977) we had a small stove business called *Countryside Stoves* but it just didn't work out. We were interrupted at mealtimes, late at night, on Sundays . . . .

"People would come around and not watch their language and my boys would say 'Why did he say that?' So after four months we sold out to our competitor . . . We had to separate our home from our business so we sold out — for a conflict with something we valued more."

The stove business, while short-lived, was a financial success, starting as it did during the early days of the wood stove revival, and now, with *The Pioneer Place*, Elmo seems to have come in once again at an opportune time with another common sense retail operation.

In the first four months alone, the Stolls received inquiries from 500 potential customers — each one accompanied by two dollars for a catalogue. By running the business as a mail order house they hope to avoid the previous problem of exposing their two young families to daily interaction with people whose values are so different from their own. In fact, dealing with customers by mail is almost a necessity given the Amish eschewal of such basic business conveniences as telephones, electricity and automobiles.

Sitting on one of the straight back chairs that furnish his living room with its bare hardwood floor and undecorated walls, Elmo slowly rubs his beard, his blue eyes deep in thought, as he talks of his hopes for the future.

"We don't want to be a big business and we won't be a big business. We're trying to build the Amish community with *The Pioneer Place* but it has to harmonize with our way of life."

While some entrepreneurs would argue that the markups are too low to compensate the Stolls for their time, Elmo feels that it is important to give customers good prices and service in order to firmly establish the operation. As it grows he can spread the benefits to others.

In its first year, the business has already acquired the services of a few family members and neighbours. One hundred locally made cider presses were stockpiled for the fall harvest. One of Elmo's brothers-in-law was pressed into service making rocking chairs from hickory shoots sent up by an uncle in Iowa while Abner, a brother, imports pre-cut cedar chests from Tennessee and assembles them as orders come in. Caleb, the eldest of Elmo's five children, helps in the evenings by reading customer letters.

Most of the company's work is done around the dining room table at the end of each day. Says Elmo, "We don't watch T.V. or go to movies. We've got to do something and so we do this. We enjoy it."

But if the store is important to his immediate family now, he hopes it will eventually help the Amish community as a whole. The inflation of recent years is affecting the Amish no matter how isolated they try to remain, and for a group of dairy farmers who cannot accept marketing board subsidies or government pensions, several small cottage industries could become an important source of income.

"Land prices are fantastic here — $2,500 an acre — and we need some money to survive. We aren't going to work at Ford so we hope to employ our people in manufacturing of a suitable kind."

For the moment though, Elmo and Mark Stoll are content with selling the goods they've known all their lives to people who, for the first time, are seeing them as more than just quaint collectables.

Prices seem reasonable but, given the relatively unusual nature of the goods, it is hard to say just how low they are.

Cider presses are $99.50; coffee mills, $16.00; and a traditional Amish open buggy, $995.00.

So far business has gone fairly smoothly, running as it does on the Stolls' good will and common sense, but there have been a few miscalculations. Interest in buggies has been surprisingly low and a large stock of *Grinderoos*, a baby food grinder standard in most Amish homes, has hardly moved at all. With a grin, Elmo shrugs off the *Grinderoo* surplus to experience.

"I guess most families prefer their blenders. No doubt we will have to replace some items with others as time passes. If someone else makes a product and can supply it at a good price, we will leave them to make it.

"However, if there is a need we will fill it."

—Frank B. Edwards

Amish hickory rocking chair, available in two sizes: Child's rocker $85.00, Adult rocker $99.00. Combination fruit press and grinder made of pressure-treated pine: $189.50 complete.

GENERAL MERCHANTS

THE PIONEER PLACE
Route 4
Aylmer, Ontario N5H 2R3

Everything from showroom-new buckboard wagons to composting toilet systems. Also: leather harnesses for workhorses, cream separators, wood stoves, solid oak barrels.

THE BELL CORN SHELLER: This Corn Sheller, designed for dry ear corn and walnuts, is easily operated by hand crank. Made of first quality cast iron for longer life and painted with a rich non-toxic red finish. The Bell Corn Sheller quickly attaches to barrel or box by clamps designed into each unit. Shells easily and clean, depositing corn in box or barrel to which it is fastened. Cob ejector and tipping attachment included. Spring adjusts to fit all size ears. Capacity 10 to 15 bushels per hour. 8¼" picker wheel. Weight: 20 lbs. $59.95

COUPE: Wheels are 38 inches and 48 inches with steel tires and a wheel base of 64 inches. The seat is 44 inches wide, with a fold down child's seat. A comfortable ride is insured by a full elliptic suspension. Complete with 12-volt electric lights as standard equipment, battery and charger included, also pole. Made by Lincoln Buggy Works (U.S.) $9,650.

LIGHT ROCKAWAY: The wheels are 32 inches and 44 inches with steel tires. This wagon has a strong but light frame and is well suited for family use. This wagon comes complete with roll-up curtains and an optional lighting system. It comes finished in green and is a very attractive wagon that we are pleased to be able to offer. Comes complete with shafts, but pole also available at extra cost. Lincoln Buggy Works. $3,950.

AMISH OPEN BUGGY: Same type as 50 years ago, but with Timken Bearings. Steel or rubber tires, complete with shaft. $1,199.

SINGLE CUTTER: Here is an item that hasn't been built for years, available once

again. Built in Canada, and just the thing for winter travel in an old-fashioned way. $1,195.

HOES:

These hoes have the heft and feel of the old-fashioned quality tools they are. They come with handles that are easy to install. Only No. 270 comes without a handle.

Pointed Two-prong No. 105 $7.00
Square type No. 95 $11.00
Light-weight square-pointed No. 270 $6.50

OLD FASHION WHITE MOUNTAIN WOODEN MIXER: Smooth native pine bucket bound tight with strong steel hoops. Sturdy cast iron handle and gears. Easy to operate, easy to clean. Makes 1 to 3 loaves with no hand kneading. Wholesome recipes and instructions included. A quality breadmixer! Weight: 8 pounds. $63.50

BLOW hand churn: Model N-40 4-qt. capacity, wooden paddles, heavy-duty glass jar. $57.50

HIGH GRADE WASH BOILERS: Good for use in canning; will fit over two

burners. Holds almost 10 Imperial gal. Length 22", width 12", depth 13". Copper $32.50—Galvanized $19.50

SAUSAGE STUFFER: Lard-Fruit Press:
Three machines in one. A Sausage Stuffer, Lard Press and Fruit and Vegetable Press. Available in Non-Toxic Black or with Iron cylinder, plates and spout holder tinned. 8 qt. $170.

CUMBERLAND GENERAL STORE
R.R.3
Crossville, Tennessee 38555
(615) 484-8481

North America's largest mail-order general store, Cumberland, calls its 250-page catalogue a "Wish & Want Book." Filled with items that the average person would have considered long extinct. Delivery time can be slow, but Cumberland accepts Canadian orders if accompanied by postal money order in U.S. funds (or VISA card—these people are not unsophisticated in the ways of marketing). Send $3.00 for catalogue.

SARVEN PATTERN WHEELS: Buggy and Light Wagon Wheels — for sizes 32" thru 42" x 1" wheels. In white. (Finished & sanded.) Moulded hub of malleable steel. Hubs come with ¾" drilling. Can be bored for most axle boxes of roller bearing type.
For sizes 32" thru 42" x 1" wheels without tire. Shipping wt. 32 lbs. $76.00
For sizes 32" thru 42" x 1" wheels with 1/8 x 1" steel tire. Shipping wt. 35 lbs. $90.00
For sizes 32" thru 42" x 1" wheels with channel & rubber tire. Shipping wt. 39 lbs. $112.00
Wheels shipped freight collect FOB Crossville, TN. 38555

TIRE BOLTS: Tire bolts with nuts. Order according to size. Shipping wt. 8 oz. ea.
3/16 x 1¾" $.25
3/16 x 2" $.30
3/16 x 2¼" $.35
¼ x 3" $.45

PORCH SWING: Complete old fashioned. Bring back those childhood memories of sleepy summer days, Fourth of July parades, big frosty glasses of lemonade, and tall shade trees—when your most favourite place to be was sitting in the front porch swing, swaying gently in a cool breeze. This one-time-prominent but now-forgotten lounge furnishing is available once again. It's solid hardwood with tenoned joints and contoured seat, and comes complete with ceiling hooks and chain (4½' leaders and 2½' branches). The four-foot swing is shipped with back and arms folded flat (they are easily positioned and locked into place with two carriage bolts and wing nuts). Shipping wt. 35 lbs. $31.98

SQUIRREL NUT CRACKER: Cast iron, nickle plated for durability. Breaks the shell, not the kernel. Adapted to all popular table nuts, especially pecans. Quickly mounts on table or counter. Shipping wt. 3½ lbs. $11.95

CHEMICAL INDOOR CLOSET: Our Sanitary Chemical Toilet assures every dwelling convenient, healthful sanitation. It is the best indoor toilet of its type. The Sanitary Toilet brings low cost comfort and convenience to homes, farms, schools, trailers, summer cottages and camps. Ideal convenience for elderly or sick people.

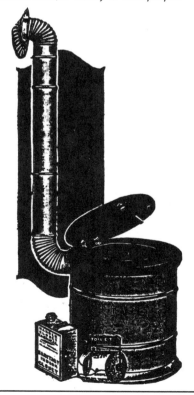

Simple to maintain. After installation, pour into the receptacle two gallons of water and one-half pint of liquid chemical. The receptacle is then usable for approximately one week. Capacity 6 gallons, diameter 15¼", height 15½". Shipping wt. 28 lbs. $59.00

Complete: Includes white enameled sheet steel cabinet, six-gallon galvanized steel receptacle, plastic seat and cover (ebony colour), 4 feet of 3" vent pipe, 2 elbows, 1 quart liquid chemical, wall finish collar and thimble for the chimney.

Liquid Chemical for Indoor Closets: Approximately a 4 month supply. In 1 gallon tin cans. Shipping wt. 13 lbs. $14.91

WASHBOARDS Maid-Rite Brass: Standard Family Size. Spiral crimp. Special rolled heavy spring brass. Supported by a five truss rod, open back. Sanitary front soap drain. Cross rails flush with rubbing surface. Fully mortised especially at the head which is "lock cornered." Washing surface 10-7/8 x 11. Shipping wt. 6 lbs. $7.50

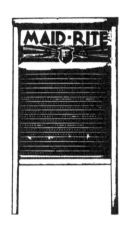

SEED SOWER Improved Little Giant: Double feeds, sows any kind of seed that can be broadcast. Easily adjusted for any amount per acre. Oscillating feed plate. Automatic feed shutoff. Wide shoulder strap. Painted hardwood base measures 7 x 14½ inches. Four section distributing wheel is 10½ inches in diameter. Adjustable feed with spring stop. Self-agitating feed plate. ½ bushel capacity. Shipping wt. 5 lbs. $21.29.

BERRY HILL LIMITED
75 Burwell Road
St. Thomas, Ont. N5P 3R5

Berry Hill is distinguishing itself with prompt service, quality goods and an increasing number of items aimed at part-time or small-scale farmers. (See *Livestock* section, also.)

SOLARVENT AUTOMATIC GREEN-HOUSE VENT: The Dalen Solarvent Automatic Greenhouse Vent is used to open a greenhouse ventilating window to prevent excessive heat buildup within the greenhouse. It will open a standard 2 foot (61 cm) square, double strength glass, aluminum framed window approximately 7½" (19 cm). It opens and closes automatically as the temperature changes between 65 degrees F (18C) and 75 degrees F (24C). These temperatures are measured at SolarVent; bench temperatures will be somewhat lower.

The SolarVent can be used on any ventilating window which does not exceed 9 lbs. (4 kg). Windows which exceed this weight may be made to operate by using the counterbalance spring accessory (SV-300). The ventilator is mounted to the cross member at the bottom of the window and lifts at the centre of the bottom of the window frame for excellent stability. It is protected by two overrun springs which prevent the unit from being damaged if the window is forced closed, buffeted by the wind, or inadvertently locked. SolarVent may also be adapted to cold frame sashes and other uses. $32.75

LIVE ANIMAL TRAPS FOR PREDATOR AND PEST CONTROL. The Tender Trap is widely used by gardeners, bird raisers, and homeowners to capture nuisance animals without harming them. All Tender Traps are made of sturdy wire mesh galvanized for long life. All models can be easily set without reaching into the trap. Their light weight and handy carrying handle enable them to be easily carried in one hand. Wide opening spring-loaded doors stay closed even if trap is rolled over by the captured animal. Complete with baiting instructions.

Folding Tender Trap: Repeating Bird Trap 28¾" x 12½" x 12". Birds. $29.75

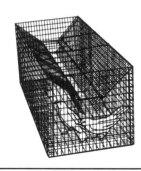

Tender Trap: One Door Set 40″ x 12″ x 12″. Fox, Dog, Armadillo, Bobcat, Large Raccoon, Opossum, Porcupine. $57.70

NORTHERN HARD ROCK Old Fashioned Butcher's Work Table: *Genuine butcher's cutting and chopping table 2¾″ thick. Solid hard rock maple top on heavy-duty wooden legs. Available in 34″ working height 4′ to 12′ long, 24″, 30″ and 36″ wide. Years of rugged service built into these sturdy tables. Made to last as in grandfather's day. $357.95—$882.95*

CHERRY PITTER: *Authentic old-fashioned cherry pitter. Is handier than you believe possible for removing pits from cherries without crushing fruit. No springs. Positive action. Easy to operate. Has plunger finger guard. Cast iron, tinned inside and out. $49.95*

EARTHWAY SPADE POTATO PLANTER: *Takes the backache out of planting potatoes! The EarthWay Spade Potato Planter gets the job done quick and easy. Simply insert planter into ground, push forward to release the seed potato, cover with your foot and you're ready to step off the next planting. That's all there is to it! Made entirely of corrosion-resistant materials. $19.55*

WHITE MOUNTAIN ICE CREAM FREEZERS: *Improved Triple Motion.* (with crank) White Mountain freezers are scientifically constructed, based on over 100 years' experience; the highest quality ice cream freezers manufactured. Triple

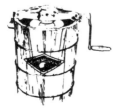

Motion freezers; three-gear drive; simple, sure and smooth operation. Makes the best, smoothest ice cream; a long-life, top quality freezer.

Materials: *Tubs: selected N.E. Pine; Can: steel charcoal tin plate; Mixers: cast-iron tinned, fitted with self-adjusting beechwood scrapers; All metal parts in contact with mixture coated with pure tin. Fixtures: cadmium plated. Finish: handsome maple.*

2 qt. $84.50
4 qt. $87.50
6 qt. $108.50
8 qt. $183.90

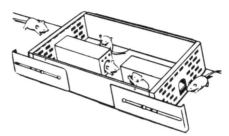

KETCH-ALL MOUSE TRAP
Catches 15 to 18 mice in one night
Winds up like an alarm clock
Completely automatic

The handiest trap ever invented. One winding sets it to catch 15 to 18 mice. Trapped mice attract others. Need be checked only every second or third day. Not necessary to touch mice. Dip trap in pail of water and destroy them. Easy to set. Simply slide off top and place bait in sealed compartment where it cannot be destroyed. Mice enter trap from side. Rigidly constructed of heavy-gauge galvanized steel. Size, 9″ deep, 7″ wide, 5½″ high. $19.95

FRUIT GRINDER: *Here's a useful item constructed of cast-iron cutters and finished hardwood side boards and hopper. This Bell Fruit Grinder will make easy work of apples, peaches, potatoes, grapes, carrots and other fruit you grind in your home. The unit is 24″ long, 13″ wide and 12½″ high. $144.50*

FRUIT PRESS: *Here's a practical, useful tool for rural or city homemakers. C.S. Bell's 8-quart capacity fruit press is constructed of natural finish oak wood with cast-iron cross piece and basket hoops painted a rich satin black. The unit has a 12″ square base and is 19″ high. It can be easily assembled and disassembled for cleaning. $87.25*

IN-TEC EQUIPMENT CO.
Box 123, D.V. Station
Dayton, Ohio 45406
(513) 276-4077

Growing inventory of intermediate technology items for the farmstead. Ships to Canada, usually by bus. Payment must be made in U.S. funds and freight charges are not included in any of the listed prices.

SEED & GRAIN CLEANER AND GRADER: *Vac-A-Way removes dirt, chaff, stems and unwanted weed seeds, at the same time separating the cleaned seed into two grades, if desired.*
Hand Operated Model $209.95
Motor Driven Model (Without Motor) $219.95

MIDGET II THRESHER: *Recommended for wheat, rice, barley, beans, peas, sorghum, millet and other grains. Threshes up to 1 ton per hour. British made. Prices on request.*

GAUBERT FEED & FLOUR MILL: *Comes with 10-pound flywheel and yields about 25 lbs. of animal feed per hour, or 10 lbs. of flour (by hand). Adding a small motor trebles the output. $139.00.*

DIAMANT GRINDING MILL: *Internationally praised hand or motorized mill for grinding wheat, corn, rice and other grains into feed or flour. Output, by hand, is about 15 lbs. of flour per hour or 40 lbs. of kibbled grain. With motor, 40 and 110 pound yields respectively. $209.95*

CABBAGE SLICER: *Wooden slide box with stainless steel blades for making quantities of sauerkraut or cole slaw. $35.95*

SPAGHETTI/NOODLE MAKER: *$43.50*

THE PANTRY
THE RURAL ROOT
Bradalbane, P.E.I. C0A 1E0

Cast iron makes a comeback: cookware, trivets, match holders and lamp brackets, as well as coffee mills and other utensils. Price does not include shipping.

WHY CAST IRON?
Back in the early days of our Country and on to the days of our own Grandmothers, enviable reputations in the culinary arts were built in our kitchens. The cast-iron utensils certainly helped. Cast iron can hold and distribute heat in an even fashion that cannot be matched by any other cooking tool. In addition to the superb food,

medical authorities feel that the reason "iron deficiencies" were unheard of years ago could well be the fact that enough iron automatically got into our systems by virtue of the cast-iron cookware commonly used in food preparation. The desirable aspects of these pots and pans are so impressive that today their use is broadly recommended by many cooking schools. We heartily endorse these recommendations.

Rooster Trivets—*Sold as a pair. Satin black finish. 11½" high. $15.00/Pr.*

Matchholder—*7" high. Satin black. $8.50*

Cornstick Pan — *7 stick $6.85*

Apple Parer—*Constructed of cast iron with nickle plated cutting blades and holder. Fastest way to pare, core and slice one apple or several bushels in one operation. Clamps to table or counter top. $22.50*

Wall Bracket—*Extends 11" from wall. Bowl diameter at base is 3½". Finished in satin black. $9.50*

NEW ENGLAND CHEESE MAKING SUPPLY CO.
Box 85
Ashfield, Mass. 01330
Suppliers of the pricey, but well-made Wheeler Cheese Press, as well as such cheesemaking supplies as rennet, dairy thermometers, cheese pots and various cultures for exotic cheeses.

THE WHEELER CHEESE PRESS: *Beautifully hand-crafted from hard maple and stainless steel, this press is designed as a table-top model (it even has rubber feet to protect your table) for the home cheesemaker. The stainless steel mould makes a 3 to 4 pound cheese. Ingenious stainless steel locks at the tops of the shafts hold the pressure bar firm at whatever pressure you set by pushing down with hand pressure. Gauge shows you how many pounds of pressure you are using, up to 50 pounds.*

Once you have experimented with some of the other moulds in our catalogue, we feel sure you will want to graduate to the Wheeler Press, which will enable you to make an enormous variety of hard cheeses—including Swiss, gouda, cheddar, caerphilly and many, many more.

Included with the Wheeler Press are recipes for farmhouse cheese, caerphilly and gouda. Also included is a copy of The Home Dairying Book *which has time-tested recipes and instructions for cheddar, cheshire, edam and many more delicious cheeses. $100.00*

CAMEMBERT CHEESE KIT: This kit contains a polyethylene camembert cheese mould, 12 cheese rennet tablets, one yard of cheese cloth (butter muslin) and a 15 gram bottle of white mould (penicillium candidum). Also included is a copy of Lue Dean Flake's book Kitchen Cheesemaking. *$17.75*

COULOMMIERS CHEESE KIT: This kit contains a traditional French Coulommiers mould made of 2 stainless steel hoops which lock together. The mould is 6 inches high and 4½ inches in diameter and will make a delicious 1½ pound soft cheese.

Also included are 2 hand-sewn cheese mats for draining the cheese, 2 hardwood cheese boards 6"x6", 12 cheese rennet tablets, a recipe for coulommiers cheese and a copy of The Home Dairying Book. *$24.95*

Blue Cheese Culture $4.00
Camembert Culture $4.00
Swiss Cheese Culture $7.50

AMBASSADOR UNIVERSAL
Box 339
Acton, Ont. L7J 2M4
(519) 853-0311

Vita-Mix juicer and cider press, Champion juicers, solar food dryers, bee pollen from England, plastic bean sprouting kits and other health food accoutrements.

DOMINION & GRIMM INC.
8250 - 3 ieme Avenue
Parc Industriel
Ville D'Anjou
Montreal 437, Quebec
(514) 351-3000

Canada's largest supplier of maple syrup making equipment, geared mainly to commercial producers.

Their least expensive syrup evaporator is the "Junior" which measures two feet by six feet, includes both a boiling and finishing vat and can handle upwards of 50 taps. Model 92 has only one pan, but sells for the price of $375 (looks like it would serve nicely as a small-scale evaporator).

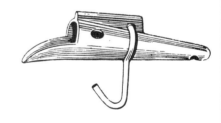

Junior Evaporator: $1,450
Royal Spiles: $38.50/100
Grimm Galvanized
Bucket Covers: 50 cents each
2-Gallon Used Aluminum
Pails: 75 cents each
Syrup Densitometer: $4.75 -$13.00
Sugar Moulding Table & Moulds: $25

Catalogues in either French or English.

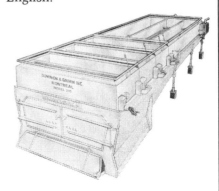

COOMB'S MAPLE PRODUCTS, INC.
Jacksonville, Vermont 05342
(802) 368-2345

Homemade evaporators designed for backyard syrup makers (evaporating pan atop barrel stove).
Home Syrup Evaporator: $190 (shipping and duty extra)

McFAYDEN SEED CO. LTD.
Box 1600, 30 - 9th Street
Brandon, Manitoba R7A 6A6

McFayden, a division of McKenzie Seeds, is now developing a mail order general store, primarily oriented toward the country kitchen and stocked in large part by items from the Garden Way people in Vermont. Also offer woks, oriental cooking utensils and seeds for sprouting.
Pressure Canner (holds 10 pints, 7 quarts or 12 No. 2 cans) $89.95
Steam Juicer, Aluminum $65.95
Steam Juicer, Stainless Steel $89.95
Equi-Flow Dehydrator Kit (10-tray model) $229.95
Garden Way Carts from $109.95 to $229.95
Garden Way Squeezo Strainer $49.95
(With two accessory screens) $65.95

THE RICHARD S. KUTAS COMPANY
181 Military Road
Buffalo, New York 14207
(716) 876-5521

Rytek Kutas has been making sausage for 25 years, and it shows: his catalogue and book are fascinating and obviously the work of an expert. (Included are recipes and ingredients for making Braunschweiger, Thuringer, Italian Hot Sausage, Genoa Salami, Pepperoni, Leberkase, Pastrami and many others). Mr. Kutas is a believer in the use of sodium nitrate-sodium nitrite, so anyone concerned about these additives will have to pick and choose among the supplies and equipment.
Sausage Stuffer: $64.95
Natural Hog Casings: (enough for 100 lbs. of sausage)
Deluxe Kit $129.00
Special Kit $79.95
Great Sausage Recipes and Meat Curing 227 page book, comb-bound paperback $6.95

INTERNATIONAL MAGIC KITCHENS LTD.
8171 Main St.
Vancouver, B.C. V5X 3L2

Canadian distributors of the Equi-Flow food dehydrator and the Golden Grain Grinder. Available in three sizes — five tray, 10 tray and 20 tray. Flexalon sheets, recipe book *Dehydrating For Food and Fun* also sold.

Equi-Flow Food Dehydrator:
5-Tray Unit: $149.50
10-Tray Unit $229.50
20-Tray Unit $429.50

Golden Grain Grinder: $429.50

AGRI-RESOURCES
R.R.3
Napanee, Ont. K7R 3K8
(613) 354-4694

Source of the expensive, German-made Schnitzer kitchen flour mill. Produces fine, stone-ground flour at the rate of 4 oz. per minute. The distributor claims "grinding is not hard, because of the long handle and roller bearings. This machine will last a lifetime." R. Cieremans, the proprietor of this business, will answer inquiries only from those seriously intent on buying one of these mills.

GREAT NORTHERN DISTRIBUTING CO.
325 West Pierpont Avenue
Salt Lake City, Utah 84101

Long list of grain mills, steamers, juicers, grinders and other kitchen paraphernalia at discount prices.

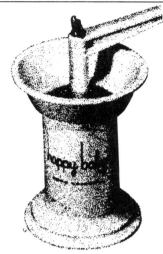

EARTH FOOD DISTRIBUTORS LIMITED
4102 - 49th Street
Wetaskiwin, Alberta T9A 2K1
(403) 352-7770
Champion juicer (Alberta only) $229.00
Water filters, portable and not $4.95 to $49.95
Baby food grinder $8.95

PURE WATER CANADA
Box 1134, Station A
Windsor, Ontario N9A 6P8
(519) 969-3461

Recent studies seem to indicate that "hard" (mineral-rich) water is good for one's health, and that it may even help in the prevention of heart disease. Nevertheless, those seeking to purify their drinking water (either of city-injected chemicals or contaminants from the well) may find this company's line of stainless steel distilling units of interest. The smallest yields 3 gallons every 24 hours and sells for $397.

CAVENBY PRODUCTS
Box 331, Station Q
Toronto, Ontario M4T 2M5
(416) 489-3778

Finnish-made water filters that

screw onto the kitchen tap. Claimed to extract "chlorine and bad taste" from drinking water. Filters last about three months. Prices on request.

AQUA-VIE DISTILLATION CENTRE
1259 Avenue Greene
Montreal, Quebec H3Z 2A4
(514) 937-7642

Numerous models of water distilling units, from simple kettle distillers ($49.95) to high capacity models at $495.

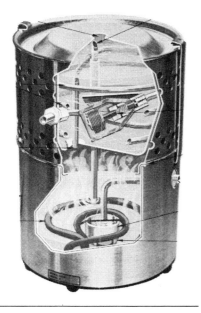

HEALING ARTS BOOK SERVICE
Box 579
Thornhill, Ont. L3T 4A2
(416) 226-6987

Mail order sales of "Footsie Rollers," water distillers, filter straws and books on natural healing.

LIVESTOCK EQUIPMENT

KETCHUM MANUFACTURING SALES LIMITED
396 Berkley Avenue
Ottawa, Ont. K2A 2G6

Is your prize cow in need of a brassiere? Your Newfoundland in need of a new dog cart harness? Could you use a six-foot shepherd's crook or, perhaps, a set of genuine tuned Swiss cow bells?

Ketchum's is the source of these and some 1,300 other items for raisers of livestock (cattle, sheep, swine, poultry, horses and dogs). Their 52-page catalogue (available in English or French) lists all manner of practical items for the husbandman and far exceeds the inventory of any local farmer's co-op or supply house.

Ketchum's has been in business since 1913, when Z.C. Ketchum began manufacturing tamper-proof numbered ear identification tags for livestock. These tags still occupy the front pages of the catalogue, decades after Ketchum's death, when his 18-year-old daughter took over the fledgling company. Now Mrs. Percival is in her late seventies, and she is still President, but the day-to-day management of Ketchum's business and its 65 employees is in the hands of Claude A. Lalonde.

"We have been going on trust when shipping to individuals," Mr. Lalonde says. "If a customer in Argentina wrote to us out of the blue, we would send him the product he asked for, and we would request him to remit the cost. We are 99 per cent successful doing that."

Dog supplies and grooming aids are Ketchum's fastest growing line, with even dog harnesses selling well just before Christmas. Many of the more unusual items sell in surprisingly large quantities, simply because there is no competitor to be found. They sell, for example, some 200 shepherd's crooks per year.

Farmers and livestock hobbyists can find most of what they need in the Ketchum catalogue, including veterinary supplies and feeding and watering equipment in all sizes and for all animals.

They have electric heating cable for frozen pipes, mailboxes, incubators for 50 chicks (or 80 quail or 65 pheasants, if you like) cattle oilers, infra-red brooders, all types of halters and saddles and even a wind-driven pond agitator, which is designed to keep water open in your pond for livestock or wildlife, while stimulating aquatic life as well. They have humane traps for birds, turtles, rodents and canines, they have magnets to put in your cow's stomach, they have . . . . well, 1,300 different items for the farmer and homesteader.

—Hank Reinink
Yarker, Ontario

TAMM CANVAS UDDER SUP-PORT: *Protects your good cows before and after calving. Helps prevent broken udders. Used also for shipping. Adjustable for snug fit: unbuckles for milking. Heavy web straps and strong waterproof canvas bag. Ideal for compresses and poultices. Available in four sizes.*
Small, 900 to 1,100 lbs. $59.85
Medium, 1,100 to 1,600 lbs. $59.85
Large, 1,600 lbs. and over $59.85
Extra large, for cows with extremely large udders $63.50

No. EW-12-CSA Egg Washer   No. 2380 Egg Basket

EGG WASHER: *$66.40*
EGG BASKET: *$5.50*

50-EGG INCUBATOR: *$55.15*
Observation Window
Adjustable Thermostat
Enclosed Heating Element
Humidifier Pan
Pilot Light
Control Guard
Insulated Throughout

BULL-POINT MARKER
(For Heat Detection)

For more accurate heat detection, higher conception rates and greater profits from your A. I. programme. Designed to fit under the chin of a surgically altered bull, the spring mounted steel ball marks cows in heat with the specially formulated Bull-Point marking fluid. (Works on the same principle as a ball point pen.) The Bull-Point marker has steel buckles with strong nylon straps for easy adjustment

and long life. The stainless steel ink reservoir holds about 10 fluid ounces of marking fluid, enough for 50 to 60 mountings, or 25 to 30 cows, depending on the mating characteristics of the individual bull. Only the Bull-Point marking fluid should be used as it is formulated to adhere to the ball and resist drying, retaining its fluid properties for long periods after exposure to the air.
Bull-Point Marker—$50.75

EGG SCALE: *The attractively streamlined "Jiffy Way" Egg Grading Scale has a Four-Colour Zone Dial which doubles grading speed. You see the correct weight instantly, at a glance. Elimination of springs, and use of adjustable screw levelling device, assures accuracy. $9.00*

MUSICAL SWISS BELLS For Cows and Sheep: *This pattern is the famous Siagne Legier Bell, which originated in Switzerland. These bells produce a very pleasing harmonious tonal quality on herds of stock. Sold individually without straps.*

2¾" diameter $3.95
3" diameter $4.55
3¼" diameter $5.10
3-7/8" diameter $8.00
4-7/8" diameter $13.75
6" diameter $26.85
Above bells Ontario tax exempt to farmers.

POULTRY KILLING CONES: *Three sizes of poultry cones, made of 26-gauge galvanized steel. Prevents bruising of wings when birds are being prepared for dressing.*
Broiler size $2.95
Chicken size $4.25
Turkey size $5.15

BERRY-HILL LIMITED
75 Burwell Road
St. Thomas, Ontario

In addition to its kitchen and horticulture catalogue, Berry-Hill publishes a larger listing of equipment for farmers and game bird raisers.

LAYING NESTS AND CAGES:
Berry-Hill offers the largest selection of metal laying nests available to the poultryman.

Manufactured of 28 gauge galvanized steel for long life, removable bottoms for easy cleaning, and plastic coated wire trays for long life. Plenty of ventilation, pitched roofs to prevent roosting, folding perches and no sharp edges. Easy assembly with new pinch grip fasteners. Provide one hole for each five hens. Various sizes for different breeds. Prices range from $70 to $150.

HEATED FOUNTAIN BASE:
Automatic electric fountain heater base. Fits any fountain. Thermostat keeps water at 50 to 55 degrees. Operates only when temperature is below 50 degrees. 100 watt element guaranteed for 1 year. $28.75

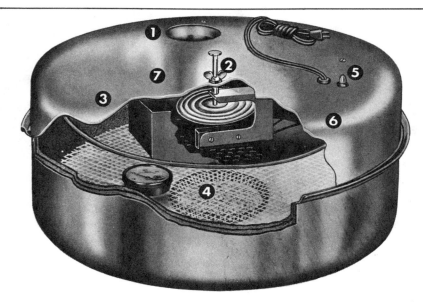

1. Observation Window 2. Adjustable Thermostat 3. Enclosed Heating Element 4. Humidifier Pan 5. Pilot Light 6. Control Guard 7. Insulated Throughout

Pheasant Spectacles: *Opaque plastic spectacle-like devices when attached to their beaks restrain hostilities in pheasant and similar sized birds. Particularly beneficial in the breeding season to handicap the aggressive males. Gives the hens and lesser males a running chance. Birds can still eat, drink and breed but are tamed down. A plastic pin is furnished for inserting through the spectacle and nostrils of each bird. When need is past, the spectacles may be removed by snipping the pin off on one side.*

$10.50 per 100

Little Giant Dog Waterer: *Patented waterers are rigidly built of brass and non-rusting metals. The bowls are tough, long wearing, molded plastic. There are no floats, gadgets or special devices to get out of order.*

Water flows automatically when the water drops below the desired level and shuts off automatically when the bowl is re-filled.

The Little Giant waterer is easy to install. The 850 kit is ideal for the home. It can be installed in minutes by securing to the house with four screws.

$20.85 each

K.G. JOHNSON LIVESTOCK EQUIPMENT LTD.
Box 209
St. Jacobs, Ont. N0B 2N0
(519) 664-2277

All manner of equipment—stalls, pens, heatfeeders—for commercial pig raisers. A few items of interest to the one-sow farmer.

Lixit Hog Watering Nipple Valve $6.95

FANCIERS' SPECIALTY COMPANY
Paris, Ontario N3L 3E3
(519) 442-4038

The pigeon breeder's supply centre, with incubators and other equipment for poultry raisers and an extensive supply of mail-order books on animal husbandry.

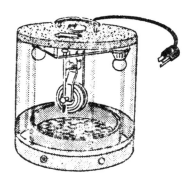

LYON TRANSPARENT HEN: *Sets 20 eggs. Complete visibility from all sides. Comes complete. 115 volt. $64.00 postpaid.*

ANIMAL SCIENCE: *By M.E. Ensminger. One of the most comprehensive and useful animal husbandry books ever published. Seven chapters on beef cattle, nine on sheep and goats, six on swine, seven on dairy cattle, nine on poultry, six on horses, eight covering general practices and principles.*
$25.50

DIAMOND FARM ENTERPRISES
R.R.3
Brighton, Ont. K0K 1H0
(613) 475-1771

Trace element minerals from seaweed for addition to livestock rations.

KETCH-ALL AUTOMATIC MOUSE TRAP
Kness Manufacturing Co.
Albia, Iowa
Available at seed and feed stores or from Berry-Hill.

Our cat happens to be a good mouser, an enterprising hunter, but she catches most of her prey —mice or otherwise—outside and transports it in either for approval or simply to chase it again before closing in for the kill. We must have the most rodent-free back 40 in B.C.

The same is not true of our house. Recently, we returned to "the place" after several months in the city. We and said cat were in the process of de-creaturizing the corners. The cleanup was not dull. We uncovered a dryer vent full of what our three-year-old pointedly refers to as pack rat poop; oven insulation riddled with mouse nests; a small trail of dried blood from which we have yet to find a corpse.

At night it was no longer a case of being lulled to sleep by the wind and the occasional owl in the tamaracks. Rather it was the rustle-scratch-nibble of multi-beasts and the crashing of the cat as she pounced amid pots and pans and unpacked piles of boxes. She was becoming neurotic trying to keep up with the traffic.

We knew we had to resort to something, but preferred not to buy what would be for us a five-year supply of poison seed. With children, we don't like it around at all. So we invested in the Ketch-All Automatic Mouse Trap.

If one of your concerns is childrens' fingers, this trap is safer than the regular mousetrap. It is approximately the size of a shoe box. It does catch mice. It's bloodless. It doesn't need bait. But one little hint. Peanut butter is a great lure. We place an open jar containing a slathering of peanut butter against one entrance. The

mouse enters the opposite opening to get to the p.b. and triggers the spring which whips him into the holding area. He's trapped but still alive and if you don't want to drop him into a bucket of water you can take him (or them) down the road to freedom. Another hint: check the trap regularly. It isn't pleasant finding a 10 days' supply: as advertised, the trap will accommodate 15 mice at one setting.

Buy one at your local feed and seed store for less than $20.00. It's worth the money.

We now own two. They've been operating steadily and with great success. The cat is back to normal—outside bringing the creatures in—and we're sleeping peacefully all through the night.

— *Betsy Briery*
Sirdar, B.C.

THE GARDEN

W-W GRINDER INC.
Box 4029
Wichita, Kansas 67204
(316) 838-4229

Last summer we purchased a shredder-grinder, a W-W model 5-20-N with optional centre-feed opening for large branches. The price was about $360 U.S.; there was no customs' duty or tax to pay, just a few dollars shipping charge from the Canadian border. We were surprised both by the performance and versatility of the machine, and also by the fact that none of our neighbours or friends in the semi-rural area where we have our summer cottage (Ile Perrot, Quebec) had even heard of such a device.

Powered by our 14 hp garden tractor, the W-W reduced a honeysuckle hedge, eight feet high and 300 feet long into shredded mulch in about six hours. Had the branches been reasonably straight, we would have undoubtedly finished sooner; as it was, the machine always seemed ready to accept branches faster than they could be fed in.

When we first wrote to W-W Grinder Inc. (Wichita, Kansas) they sent us a list of their Canadian customers—less than two dozen names. The serial number on our machine also indicates that less than 100 of that particular model—suitable for use with any garden tractor with 8 hp or more—have been manufactured.

— *Ron and Ellen Dean*
Ottawa, Ontario

Shredder-Grinder with electric motor $314 (U.S.)
Shredder-Grinder with 3 hp gas engine $299 (U.S.)
Shredder-Grinder less power $199 (U.S.)

HOMESTEAD EQUIPMENT
Box 339
Acton, Ontario L7J 2M4
(519) 853-0311

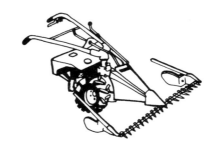

Canadian distributors of the Homesteader rotary tiller, available in a variety of sizes and capable of converting into a snow blower, sicklebar mower, or grinder; also can become a power unit for towing carts, etc. Powered by Lombardini gas or diesel engines, as are the Homesteader line of small tractors (14 to 45 horsepower). Prices on request.

TROY-BILT
Garden Way Mfg. Co. Inc.
102nd St. & Ninth Avenue
Troy, New York 12180
(518) 235-6010

Troy-Bilt has one of the best reputations among the many garden tillers, partly because of their blanket advertising, but mainly because their machines live up to the promises. Almost all

tillers are sold directly from the manufacturer to the gardener, and their mail order customer service is generally excellent. Prices are discounted in the off-seasons.
5 hp (Pony) $698
6 hp $797
7 hp $966

GRAVELY
Otto Richter & Sons Ltd.
Box 26
Goodwood, Ont. L3P 1M4
(416) 294-1407

Richters are the Canadian distributors for the Gravely line of garden tractors. People who own Gravely machines usually swear by them—the walking tractors take a variety of useful attachments and the quality is high—as are the prices.

Garden tractors (without attachments) $1,620 to $4,557

PRECISION VALLEY MFG. COMPANY
Chester Road
Springfield, Vermont 05156
(802) 885-5576

Offer the Yellowbird and Groundhog lines of rear-tined tillers and cultivators.

ARIENS CANADA LTD.
5124 Ashland Drive
Burlington, Ont. L7L 3H2

Manufacturers of outdoor power equipment, including garden tillers, riding mowers, 8 to 18 hp tractors, 2 to 10 hp snow throwers.

2 hp tiller $160.00
4 hp tiller $339.95
7 hp tiller $900.00

ALLSAW COMPOSTER
c/o Peter Carlow
87 Risebrough Ave.
Willowdale, Ont. M2M 2E2

or
G.G. Mambley
9 Calais Avenue
Downsview, Ont. M3M 1N3

Year-around composting unit that has proved successful for eight years in an urban environment, allowing decomposition of household garbage without offensive odours. Simple design, using wooden, insulated box.

ROTOCROP CANADA LTD.
361 King Street E.
Toronto, Ont. M5A 1L1
(416) 368-5769

Three types of modular plastic composting bins, including a high bulk model for making leaf mould. Write for prices.

INTERNATIONAL IRRIGATION SYSTEMS
Box 1133
St. Catharines, Ont. L2R 7A3
(416) 688-4090

Trickle irrigation is the latest thing in the agribusiness world, especially among row crop operations in the dry southwestern United States. Essentially what this consists of is a network of porous plastic tubing that is buried near the roots of plants and that exudes water pumped through at low pressure.

The advantages are: greatly increased savings of water (50 per cent over sprinkler systems, according to Dupont which manufactures the *Viaflo* tubing), decreased loss by evaporation and less pollution caused by run-off. The tubing is chemically inert and will not rot.

The drawback is that the tubing must be covered by soil or mulch to avoid sun-caused deterioration. This firm offers all supplies, as well as a home garden kit that will water four rows totalling 100 feet in length.

IRRIGRO Trickle Irrigation Kit $12.95

DOMINION SILO INC.
C & W Drive
Bridgewater, Virginia 22812
(703) 828-6454

Hand garden ploughs and cultivators: $15 to $21. Shipping extra. Minimum order of 20. Will ship to Canada.

Model 220
HIGH WHEEL Garden plow
Selected oak handles 4 ft. long 24"
x 1¼" steel wheel

W.H. PERRON & CO. LTD.
515 LaBelle Blvd.
Laval, Quebec
(514) 332-3610

No. 1 Mouss Seeder, for vegetables. Price $159.95

Precision Garden Seeder, opens soil, spaces seeds, plants, covers seed and packs soil in one easy operation. Will handle most common garden vegetable seeds (except cucumbers and melons). Price $45.95

FARM TOOLS

SURPLUS TRACTOR PARTS CORP.
Box 2125, 3215 W. Main Ave.
Fargo, North Dakota 58102
(701) 235-7503

We all get, and give, imperfect technical information from time to time. But this bit of misinformation had me furious. I needed that Ford 9N tractor which was laid up with no brakes—no brake linings either.

A failing oil seal had allowed oil to reach the brake shoes. I intended to wash the shoes with gasoline but a neighbour strongly advised, ''The pros burn the pads. That way you get rid of even the deep down oil. The brake shoe will be as good as new.''

I remembered the conversation as I balefully looked at the freshly burned shoe and bits of brake lining which crumbled and blew away in the wind.

New brake linings were definitely in order and the questions of speed of delivery and cost were uppermost in my mind. Surplus Tractor Parts Corporation of Fargo, North Dakota had a set of four brake linings with rivets for a total cost of $14.00 (U.S.) with 10 to 14 days for delivery. The Ford dealer could deliver the next week but could only supply bonded brake shoes at $14.00 each for a total cost of $56.00.

As I had more time than money Surplus Tractor Parts Corporation got my order.

I have ordered seals, pistons, rings and sundry other parts and have always found the company to be prompt, inexpensive and courteous—even telephoning when they cannot fully fill an order.

Farm tractor parts enter Canada duty-free—a plus—but the depreciated Canadian dollar does somewhat reduce the savings.

Surplus Tractor Parts Corporation supplies new and used parts for wheel and crawler tractors. Although I see no parts listing for the newest Japanese and European tractors, the listing is certainly complete for North American makes, including discontinued brands. Shop manuals are available as are results of the exhaustive tractor tests done in North Dakota on all tractors over the last 10 years—a great way to shop and compare before buying.

I can't say if the brake linings I received stand up to burning any better than the old bonded shoes and linings. The new seals haven't let any oil through to the linings to necessitate a test.

When I need parts, regardless of the cause of failure, Surplus Tractor Parts Corporation with its economy and service is always considered. The catalogue costs $1.00.

—*Larry Brierley*
Sirdar, B.C.

WD40 PRODUCTS (CANADA) LTD.
Box 220
Etobicoke, Ont. M9C 4V3
(416) 622-9881

I have used this spray lubricant despite the aerosol container, and it works. Helps loosen stuck and rusty metal parts.

—*David Archibald*
Camden East, Ontario

ELFENCE CONSULTANCY LIMITED
R.R.1
Belwood, Ont. N0B 1J0
(519) 843-5817

Twenty-page mimeographed booklet on erecting and maintaining electric fencing, both portable and permanent. Most shocking of all is the price: $4.95

Economic realization has forced farmers all over the world into re-evaluating their fencing methods and the end result has been an upsurge in the building of permanent electric fences.

Unfortunately, because so much emphasis has been made on the cheapness of this type of fencing, "cheap fences" are what we are getting and already many badly designed and constructed fences tend to bring electric fencing into disrepute. If the farmer is going to reap the real advantages of going electric, he must firmly fix in his mind that there are no shortcuts to effective permanent electric fencing

in the same way as there are no real shortcuts in conventional fencing. The farmer, when he sets out to build an electric fence, should have in mind that it is to be permanent, that he does not want to do it again, that he is building a relatively maintenance-free tool to control his stock and pasture and that only the best components and workmanship make the best fences.

ROKNICH PROD. INC.
Box 311
North Chicago, Illinois 60064
(312) 336-3773

Belt fencing—one answer to the problem of horses chewing fence rails. Free brochure available.

ERIE IRON WORKS COMPANY LTD.
99 Edward Street
St. Thomas, Ont. N5P 1Y8
(519) 631-6680

Wheelbarrows and parts including the "Ballbarrow" shown.

POLARIS IMPORT AND DISTRIBUTION
Box 3513, Station B
Calgary, Alberta
(403) 283-1542

How to reach the best apples, which always seem to grow near the top of the tree? This manual fruit hooker and catching bag

assembly solves the problem when attached to a long pole.
Model A (Gentle picker) $7.95
Model B (Built-in sharp cutting edge) $12.95
Handle extension (to connect two poles) $6.95

GUZZLER PUMPS

This Canadian-made, hand-operated pump is designed for emptying boat bilges, but it is capable of serving many other functions. We're using it as a cistern pump and have found it has many advantages over the familiar green clunker.

Most important, the Guzzler can push water as well as pull it—both the inlet and the outlet can be fitted with flexible plastic pipe. So while a conventional cistern pump can deliver water to only one spot, this one can be used to fill an overhead tank that supplies several different faucets (and maybe even a solar or stove-jacket hot water system). Yet the pump itself can still be downstairs where it'll be needed for big jobs like laundry.

This push-as-well-as-pull feature has another advantage as well—you don't have to mount the Guzzler directly beside the kitchen sink. Cistern pumps *must* be enshrined in the most valuable work space in the kitchen. And they have a remarkable talent for getting in the way of fast-moving dishes, tea pots and elbows. With a short outlet pipe attached, the Guzzler can bring water to the sink, yet be mounted out of the way.

The Guzzler is also self-priming, easier to operate than a cistern pump, quieter, smaller and generally more pleasant to live with.

This is not to say, however, that it has no faults. The most serious difficulty involves the valves—after only about a week of use they started to stick open, and the pump wouldn't work at all. It turns out that the valve flappers were being pushed beyond their normal travel point and lodging in the pump's water passages. Though each flapper is fitted with a rigid plastic disc, presumably to prevent this very occurrence, the disc is too small to do the job. We solved the problem by adding a sheet metal disc to each valve assembly. Cut the same size as the flapper, and carefully smoothed to eliminate sharp edges, it is stiff enough to resist the pump's suction and keep the flapper where it belongs.

The Guzzler comes in three sizes rated at 12, 15 and 30 gallons per minute—but these figures are optimistic. Our 15-gallon model actually delivers about five gallons a minute (through a lift of six to eight feet). And though it's supposed to pump a gallon in five strokes, in reality 12 strokes are needed. We find this capacity sufficient for our needs, though.

Other features claimed by the Guzzler: 15-foot lift or delivery head, non-corrosive, unaffected by detergents and many solvents, can handle sludge, slurries and small stones. Cost: $28.95, $33.95 and $94.95 for the 12, 15 and 30 gallon models respectively.

Available from Princess Auto (a gold mine of mail order motors, gizmos, parts for farmers and mechanics) Box 1005, Winnipeg, Manitoba R3C 2W7.
—*Bernadine Roslyn*
Wilno, Ontario

DEEP ROCK MFG. CO.
Industrial Park
Opelika, Alabama 36801
(205) 749-3377

Manufacture the widely advertised "Hydra-Drill." Read the introductory material and guarantee carefully before ordering. This lightweight tool

cannot replace professional equipment in certain types of drilling conditions.

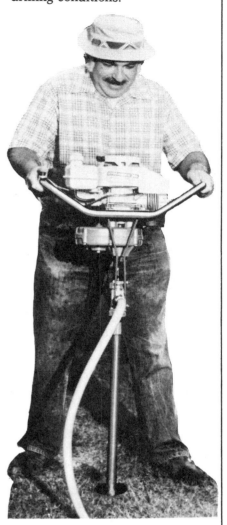

SMITH'S INDUSTRIES
105 Scarsdale Road
Don Mills, Ontario
(613) 447-7291

Electrical aerators for small ponds.

MONARCH IND. LTD.
889 Erin Street
Winnipeg, Manitoba

A large variety of pumps—hand pumps, jet water systems, deep well pumping units, centrifugal pumps, fire fighting units, sump pumps and hydraulic cylinders.

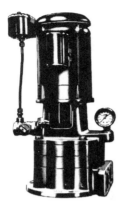

CHAIN SAWS

Like many people, we began homesteading with a strong dislike for chain saws. They're noisy, dangerous, and you remain hooked into combustion engines, gas, oil and all that. But we quickly found ourselves making an almost full-time job of wood cutting. Then a helpful neighbour offered his chain saw services for an afternoon. We were hooked.

Beginners generally look at chain saws by bar size. Cubic-inch displacement of the engine is more important, as that gives you an idea of the power and approximate weight of a saw. Generally speaking, chain saws can be divided into four categories: Mini, Light, Medium and Pro.

You can do a lot of work, with even a small mini-saw, if you're very careful, and keep the chain sharp. I've cut 24-inch oaks with a 2 cu. inch Stihl 020 AVP. I would only have a chain saw with "AV": anti-vibration, shock-mounted

handles. It's also a good idea to wear ear protectors, a hard hat in the woods, and a face shield or goggles for working overhead or ripping.

An excellent book on buying, using and maintenance is *Barnacle Parp's Chain Saw Guide* by Walter Hall (Rodale Press, Inc. 1977). For in-depth saw service Hall recommends: *Chain Saw Service Manual* (Kansas City, Mo. Intertec Publishing Corp.).

—*Drew Langsner*
Marshall, N.C.

ZIP-PENN CO. LTD.
188 Stronach Cr. Box 5877
London, Ontario N6A 4L6
(519) 455-3552

ZIP-PENN CO.
Box 179
Erie, Pennsylvania 16572

Everything for the amateur and professional chain saw user. Replace chain, guide bars, manual and motorized sharpeners, wedges, parts, protective clothing. Free catalogue. Highly recommended source.

CHAIN SAW MILLS—Alaskan MK III:
Turns any chain saw into a portable saw mill. Clamps on to bar. No holes to drill. New frame design produces precision dimensioned lumber in thickness from ½" to 12". Comes complete with instructions. Available in 2 adjustable sizes:

24" Mill $123.95
30" Mill $129.95

Mini Mill: Simplified, low cost lumber mill attachment for use with mini and lightweight saws. Clamps on to guide bar. No holes to drill. Has no moving parts. Weight only 5½ lbs. Comes complete with instructions. $74.95

Ripping Chain: This type of chain is especially designed to make ripping cuts and will give you best results with both mills shown above. It is especially recommended for the Alaskan MK III. It is made on special order in 3/8", .404" and ½" pitch.

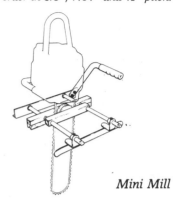

Mini Mill

Chain Saw Safety Leggings and Chaps:
Helps prevent chain saw accidents. These protective leggings and chaps contain ballistic nylon which is designed to take the first shock of an accidental hit with a saw chain. It slows down the cutting action, giving the user time to react. Lightweight, adjustable, in choice of legging or chap style.
Leggings: $33.95 pr.
Chaps: $33.95 ea.
Replacement Pads $11.50 pr.

GRANBERG INDUSTRIES
7810 Express Street
Burnaby, B.C. V5A 1T4
(604) 420-5434

Chain saw equipment, especially sharpening tools and Alaskan chain saw lumbermill units.

PIONEER CHAIN SAW SALES CORPORATION
775 Neal Drive
Peterborough, Ont. K9J 6X7
(705) 748-5333

Popular Canadian-made chain saws.

TYPE	DISPLACEMENT CU. INCHES	BAR IN INCHES	DRY WEIGHT
Mini	1.6 - 2.6	10 - 16	6 - 10
Light	2.7 - 3.7	14 - 20	10 - 13
Medium	3.5 - 5.0	16 - 24	12 - 16
Pro	5.0 - 8.5	16 - 72	16 - 26

USES

(Mini) Limbing, carpentry, log cabin, easy felling
(Light) All-around light work
(Medium) Most anything
(Pro) Hard, heavy work

Husqvarna Clearing Saw

BUCCANEER IND. LTD.
520 Lafleur Street
Lachute, Quebec J8H 3X6
(514) 562-8551 or 562-5201

Husqvarna chain saws and brush clearing tools. This distributor offers an excellent series of how-to booklets on forestry techniques.

McCULLOUGH OF CANADA LIMITED
6338 Viscount Road
Malton, Ont. L4V 1H4
(416) 677-5086

Either the Ford or Chev of chain saws, depending on your locale and point of view.

JOHN DEERE LIMITED
Box 1000
Grimsby, Ont. L3M 4H5
(416) 945-9281

Chain saws and accessories.

DESA INDUSTRIES LTD.
3710 Nashua Drive, Unit G
Mississauga, Ont. L4V 1M5
(416) 678-2501

Remington chain saws and the Champion hydraulic log splitter.

SKIL CANADA LIMITED
1190 Caledonia Road
Toronto, Ont. M6A 2W6

Chain saws for backyard lumberjacks—through SKIL distributors only.

HOMELITE-TERRY
180 Labrosse Avenue
Pointe Claire, P.Q. H9R 1A2
(514) 697-5910

Chain saws and accessories.

MINI P III

The Mini P III is a very small chain saw (12 or 14-inch bar) distributed by Partner, a Swedish saw manufacturer. Since the Swedish-made full-sized Partners are good quality saws and give satisfactory service, you might expect the Mini to do likewise—even though it's not made by Partner but purchased by them from a North American manufacturer. If a company with a reputation for producing quality products puts its name on something, they're going to choose a reasonably workable machine, right?

Wrong! The Mini has proved to be an unbelievably bad purchase. Working with it is an exercise in unrelenting frustration. And dealing with the Canadian distributor (Theo Turgeon Inc., Quebec City) is not much different. Altogether the saw has done about six hours work, been repaired three times (once to the tune of $50) and caused more hassles than anyone needs.

Some people claim there is no such thing as a good small saw; others no doubt would disagree.

But even if such a machine exists, the Mini P III isn't it.

—Bernadine Roslyn
Wilno, Ontario

"Stihl" Chain Saws—Bought a *used* 031AV five years ago, have yet to change plugs or points or put $10 in repairs. It sits patiently in the basement waiting for me to give the starter rope a few pulls so it can obediently serve me. I've gone through two chains with it, cutting four winters' worth of firewood. A Rolls Royce.

— *Ken Parejko*
Holcombe, Wisconsin

HARDWARE

THE MANTLE LAMP SUPPLY LIMITED

Box 959, 145 High Street
Sutton West, Ont. L0E 1R0
(416) 722-6011

Aladdin Portable Heater

Aladdin lamps are beautiful to behold, they throw a good reading light and burn 50 hours on a gallon of kerosene. Wide range of prices and styles (brass, aluminum, amber glass bases), as well as the Aladdin "37" Blue Flame kerosene portable heater, which sets a mood of Van Johnson and late movie cohorts huddled in leather bomber jackets in a World War Two quonset hut, plotting the next morning's mission. This heater is an international classic. $140.

CREATIVE ENERGY, INC.

Box 610
Thornhill, Ont. L3T 2C0

Same Aladdin lamps. Higher prices.

BLAIRHAMPTON ALTERNATIVE

Box 748
Haliburton, Ont. K0M 1S0
(705) 754-2290

James Stainless Steel Handwasher $160.00
Wringer $70.00

A Different Operating Principle: The James Washer has revolutionized washday with its exclusive pendulum action. In many washers the clothes are never fully submerged in the water. With clothes floating on the surface or lodged in a corner, washing time is lengthened. In the James Washer the pendulum agitator sweeps in an arc around the bottom of the tub. This action keeps the tub submerged at all times. Also, hot suds are thoroughly mixed with the clothes as they are gently rolled and turned. Wash time is cut to less than seven minutes on an average washing.
Large Capacity—The James can handle up to 6 large sheets at one loading.
Ease of Use—The backward and forward stroking of the agitator arm does all. A minimum of effort and less than 7 minutes per average load.
Uncomplicated—No water pumps, electric motors etc. to cause worry and expense.
And It Works—With the wringer attachment the James is unexcelled for getting clothes clean and fresh — from delicate silks to overalls.

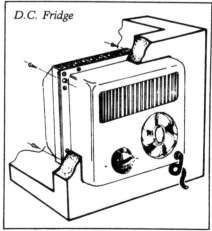

D.C. Fridge

12-Volt D.C. Fridge
In 1834 a French scientist Jean Peltier noted that when voltage is applied across the junction of two dissimilar metals, heat is removed from one of the metals and transferred to the other. This "Peltier effect" is the basis of "Thermoelectric" refrigeration. Solid State Thermoelectric

modules are capable of transferring large quantities of heat when connected to a heat absorbing device on one side and a heat dissipating device on the other. Unifridge's large aluminum cold fins absorb heat from the inside of an insulated ice chest and the thermoelectric modules transfer it to heat dissipating fins outside the chest, where a small fan helps disperse it into the air. The fan and shroud on the cold fins circulate the air.

ENERGY ALTERNATIVES

2 Croft Street
Amherst, Nova Scotia
(902) 667-2790

NOVA ecological shower heads $12.95 and $17.95
MK100LV energy-saving faucet aerator $2.00

The NOVA provides as forceful, effective and pleasant a shower as a conventional shower head, but it uses only 2.1 gallons of water per minute compared to the usual 5 to 8 gallons of water per minute.

A family of 4, each showering for only 5 minutes per day, will save up to 3,000 gallons of water each month by replacing a conventional shower head with the NOVA. If they heat with oil, they will save up to 31½ gallons of fuel oil per month; if they heat with gas, they will save up to 4,000 cubic feet of gas per month. The most significant savings are not in water and sewage costs, but in fuel required to heat the shower water.

"First year savings (with 2,000 NOVA units) at current oil prices ($.40/gal), should come to $172,000. That breaks down to $28,000 for water, $14,000 for the water that doesn't go down the sewers, and $130,000 in fuel savings for the water which was not heated."
—*University of Massachusetts*

MILL VALLEY PRODUCTS

R.R. 4
Stirling, Ont. K0K 3E0

Another distributor of Aladdin products, as well as the Stickler wood splitter and other products.

Random Comment

DISSTON CORDLESS ELECTRIC SHEARS

This may seem weird to fellow energy-intensive farmers, but my favourite garden tool is my rechargable hand-clipper: *Disston Cordless Electric Shears, Model EGS-7B,* charger type "D." Bought at a local hardware store for about $10, the little machine has seen me through four seasons now with nary a wobble or dulling of its cutting mechanism. A marvel for mowing down my herb garden weeds, it also performs yeoman service in the asparagus patch, where it clips pesky grasses most carefully around precious stalks without disturbing their roots, as cultivation or yanking the mothers tends to do. It's great, too, for keeping pristine those hard-to-get-at places along fence lines, between posts and under split rails, where the grass grows always greener and maddeningly lush. I've even been caught using it along my vegetable rows, where one can sneak it under good leaves and cut prickly weed stems or deep-rooted intruders to the quick in short order.

My husband claims the clackety tool is my therapy. There's some truth there. Clean plots, earned by a half an hour a day's devotion to this handy clipper, are far more therapeutic than a wrack of weed-tugged soil and the resultant blistered fingers.

Now, if I could just figure out how to make the thing run on solar, my conscience would be as clean as my rows. In the meantime, I'll take the few watts it needs for recharging rather than electrified kitchen frills any time. Scythes and hand shears have their place, but MY farm energy must be included in the balance too.

—*Joan Wells*
Spray, Oregon

THE POWER STRIPPER
The Mail Store Limited
312 Rexdale Blvd.
Toronto, Ontario M9W 1R6

Ever wondered what those hyped-up kitchen gadgets and off-beat tools are like that you see occasionally fanfared on half-page ads in the weekend supplement papers? Me too. Well, I took the plunge and found out after my eye caught the Power-Stripper ad, since I was trying to discover a way of removing the mould-stained layer from logs inside my house. What happened after I sent in my cheque for two Power-Strippers (the coarse and fine models) was: precisely nothing. A follow-up threatening letter brought me a reply which said they were all out of strippers due to the great success of their ad campaign. I was told to have patience and the tools would arrive. A month later, they did.

The Power-Stripper fits any ¼-inch drill, and is a variation of the rotary wire brush. Its "bristles" are hardened steel wire, one-sixteenth (coarse model) or one-thirty-second (fine) of an inch thick, which are hinged where they attach to the rotor, giving the "bristles" more splaying effect than a regular rotary wire brush. I quickly found the tool was no good for cleaning up the logs, but it has been put to several other uses so far with mixed success. As the ads say, it's at its best stripping old, cracked, peeling paint from woodwork—especially hard-to-get-at door and window mouldings (it won't crack the glass) and carved furniture. It does no more or less than a hand-powered wire brush would, but with considerably less effort. (But considerably *more* teeth-gritting tension: With those unguarded steel fingers whirring at 1,750 rpm close to your hands, it's a potentially dangerous tool. Most of the instructions are block-type warnings to wear safety goggles and a face-mask against lead-paint dust.)

I found the heavy-duty (coarse) model useful in removing uncured cement from masonry and a metal fire hood, and also good for getting paint off metal. Overall, I'd give it an eight-out-of-ten for paint-stripping and a five for the other jobs they recommend it for. A wire brush would do most other things as well. But before you send money to The Mail Store, I'd find out if they've got in another shipment from Taiwan.

—*Frank Appleton*
Edgewood, B.C.

THE DASHER CHURN
Compared to the modern crank-operated butter churn, with its smoothly spinning paddles, the old-fashioned crock-and-dasher may seem jerky and inefficient. But now that I've tried it I'll never crank-churn butter again. That up-and-down motion causes more splashing than a rotary action does, so the butter comes faster. And it actually takes less effort than cranking. Maybe a lot of the energy that goes into turning the crank gets lost in all those gears.

But the main problem with a rotary churn is the circular motion your hand makes. It tends to slide the churn back and forth across the table so the other hand is needed to hold it in place. With a dasher, the motion is all up and down and the cream's own weight is enough to hold the churn steady. This means the butter-maker has one hand free to hold a

book, a cup of tea, a harmonica, or whatever dull-job amusement he prefers.

Stand-up crock churns are still being manufactured and some hardware stores carry them. But it's easy to make a smaller model out of a plastic pail. The pail's size can vary according to your needs, but it must have a tight-fitting lid. A gallon ice cream container is good for small amounts of cream (up to two quarts) or a 10-kg. peanut butter pail can be used for larger quantities (up to one gallon).

To make the churn you put a hole in the pail's lid and reinforce it with plywood. The cross-shaped dasher is made from two lengths of one-by-two inch or half-by-one-inch softwood, affixed to a hardwood dowel handle. The dowel can be anywhere from three-eighths to one inch in diameter, depending on how much cream it will have to move—and how vigorously.

And now the details.

Cut two lengths of softwood slightly shorter than the inside of the bottom of the pail. Sand them smooth and round the sharp edges, then drill a hole in the exact centre of each—about one-eighth inch *smaller* than the dowel you are using.

Whittle down one end of the dowel so it will fit in the holes. (To mark the dowel, scribe a circle on its end with the auger bit you used to drill the holes.) Shave down about a two-inch length so both pieces of the dasher can fit on the handle. Make a saw cut across the end of the dowel so it can be wedged.

Put on the dasher pieces so they fit securely and insert a hardwood wedge into the saw-cut to hold the whole thing together. Cut off the short length of dowel that sticks out past the dasher.

Now make a hole in the centre of the pail's lid just slightly larger than the dasher handle. Cut two small pieces of thin plywood and drill them too. Position the plywood on either side of the plastic lid so all three holes line up. Screw the two plywood pieces together through the plastic. This reinforcement is needed so the

dasher's movement won't tear the lid.

Assemble the three parts of the churn, add cream, and get comfortable. Then churn till butter happens. With the lid and dasher removed, the pail makes an ideal container for washing and working the butter.

—Bernadine Roslyn
Wilno, Ontario

OF SHELLERS AND STRAINERS
Burpee Seeds
Warminster, Pa 18991
Shelling peas by hand can be enjoyable if you and a friend share the task, but can also be mortally tedious if you have two small children and other farm and domestic chores to do. Since I do not find it convenient to spend an afternoon shelling peas and lima beans, I looked for a pea sheller last spring and finally found an electric frencher/sheller listed in the Burpee Seed Catalogue. I paid approximately $16.00 Canadian funds and $4.50 duty. This price does not include the motor—the frencher/sheller attaches to the motor of an electric hand mixer or a variable speed drill (800 rpm max.).

The instructions suggest either to pick a day or two before shelling or boil the peas for one to one and a half minutes before shelling to remove excess moisture and allow for more efficient shelling. I did not want to do either, so I tried shelling them immediately after picking and most of the peas got mashed.

Now I have reverted to hand shelling enough peas for dinner so I don't have to cook them twice, but for freezing I boil the peas for the recommended one and one half minutes then immediately cool in cold water for another one and one half minutes. I do not blanch the peas again after shelling for freezing. The frencher/sheller, if used properly, is a good investment for those who love peas and lima beans.

I also purchased a Victorio Strainer from Burpee over five years ago. It has definitely proved a time saver in canning apple sauce and tomatoes. I can put up about three times as much apple sauce using the Victorio Strainer as compared to using a hand cone-shaped strainer, and making tomato sauce or juice is a breeze. No need to peel or core the apples. Just cut the apples in rather large pieces and add enough water to prevent scorching. Keep the pot covered when you're not stirring because the hot sauce does splatter. Once the apples are soft they're ready to be put through the Victorio Strainer. The apples are strained while the skins and seeds are expelled. To make tomato sauce or juice, cut fresh, washed tomatoes in quarters and put through the strainer before cooking. The Victorio Strainer can also be used for baby food, creamed soups, seedless jams and jellies, pie fillings and mashed potatoes. There is no electric motor and very few small delicate parts to give you trouble. (From McFayden, Garden Way, Pioneer Place and others, $29.50).

—Dianne Baker
Tatamagouche, Nova Scotia

GETTING CULTURED
For a yogurt maker who has incubated batches of yogurt on a succession of apartment house radiators, back burners and finally on the edge of the homestead wood cookstove, an electric automatic yogurt machine is an incredible luxury somewhat akin to colour television and dishwashers. Naughty but nice.

If you can excuse the fact that an automatic yogurt maker plugs into a wall socket, however, there are advantages to a model like the Contempra/Braun Automatic which is available in the U.S. and Canada. Currently list priced at $36.95 in Canada and about $10 cheaper in the U.S., the machine turns off the heat automatically. The yogurt is prepared in six neat little cups which won't become contaminated with random bacteria as the days pass. You still have to heat up the milk in a separate container.

The unit comes with an introductory package of excellent freeze-dried culture with a recipe book and complete instructions along with a year long guarantee. A non-automatic model retails in Canada for $26.95. (In Canada, actual selling price is often lower than list.)

In Canada:
Braun Natural Yogurt Maker
3269 American Drive
Mississauga, Ont. L4V 1B9

(not available from mfg., sold through major dept. stores and hardware store chains)

In U.S.:
Contempra Industries Inc.
371 Essex Road
Tinton Falls, New Jersey 07753
—*Sharon Airhart*
Corbeyville, Ontario

ZEN AND THE ART OF BLASTING

BLASTER'S HANDBOOK
Published by Canadian Industries Limited, available at C.I.L. branch offices in 20 towns and cities across Canada
$12

For those with stumps to remove, trenches or ditches to be dug, or boulders broken, I strongly recommend blasting for consideration. Having several pounds of high-explosive going off in your backyard may not sound very peaceful and organic, but it really works, I swear. And the side effects can be minimized. (I did less damage to my place using dynamite than some amateur bulldozer operators I've seen.) For dealing with situations like shelving bedrock across a water-line trench it is an unparalleled tool. For small jobs it is far cheaper than hiring a Cat, and so

much less effort than any hand-labour scheme you can dream up.

Getting this tool to do what you want, eliminating screw-ups *and* keeping things safe all come together at a certain point, and to learn it, I spent one spring teaching myself Zen and the Art of Blasting. Don't laugh. It's also a discipline—a very serious discipline if you don't want to hurt yourself and others. I decided this was a serious business—I'd really better learn all about it. With a hillside of stumps, a box of 40 per cent Forcite, some fuse and caps, I settled down with a copy of C.I.L.'s *Blasters' Handbook* and read it through before touching a single stick.

Actually, I found the book interesting reading. The simple elegance of Nobel's invention is easily visualized—at detonation your stick becomes a rapidly-expanding bubble of gas, plus a shock-wave. Simple enough. Learning how to *place* that bubble for maximum effect, and *how big* to make it is where the subtleties come in, and make the difference between sloppiness (read *danger*) and success. You actually do get into the mystique of balancing massive forces, as you stare at the buttress of roots surrounding the stump, and try to guess just the right location and angle of your charge, and its size. You step back, note if it's a pine, fir, cedar or cottonwood, see how old it is, adding a stick for certain species, subtracting a stick if rot has set in. You also pick your season—early spring is best.

My ''perfect shots'' were when the stump was *not* blasted into the sky, but lay on its side, usually split, and a bit of wrestling brought the pieces out. They weren't *all* like this, but my technique got better with experience, and I never even came close to having a disaster. The *Blasters' Handbook*—at 460 pages—tells you more than you would ever want to know about the science and practical application of blasting, but every situation is unique, and the onus is on you to get absolutely focussed on what you are trying to achieve and how you'll do it. I found the learning to be fun, and since this is serious, I'll say nothing about the tremendous adrenalin rush you get in the final count-down seconds.

There's also a Blasters' Booklet issued free by C.I.L., which gives all the essential information required by the backyard blaster. The *Blasters' Handbook* has tripled in price since I got mine in 1966, but if you decide to get into it, your money will be still well spent on this bible of blasting. Read it first. It's part of the discipline.

—*Frank Appleton*
Edgewood, B.C.

FORGOTTEN IMPLEMENT?

Harrowsmith seems to have neglected one very basic and extremely useful tool for big jobs like splitting rocks or pulling stumps. It is called *Dynamite*. CIL and Dupont both manufacture it in Canada and provide helpful information. Take some instructions from an old-timer who has been using the stuff for 50 years; his credentials must be good if he is still around.

Dynamite itself is not very sensitive, but it must be kept well separated from blasting caps. Fuse is relatively cheap—use lots so you don't have to hurry once it is lit. Buy only what you will use up promptly. Keep in mind that you are not allowed even *one* serious mistake. But it does jobs that cannot be done by one man with any other tool available.

—*Nyla N. Maurer*
Bolton, Ontario

In Praise Of The Good Husbandman

"Give him five acres, to live and rear his family on, and you will soon find it supporting a very rich flora and fauna."

The world can support a certain number of vegetarians, but for reasons that I shall now set forth I don't believe it can support a population which is all, or nearly all, of this persuasion. The non-vegan vegetarian I think we can discount, that is if he is a vegetarian on moral or ethical grounds alone. If he just doesn't eat meat because he doesn't like it, that is his own business entirely: after all plenty of people don't like boiled turnip and nobody else worries about it. But the man who takes a high moral attitude about not eating meat, and eggs, drinks milk or eats butter or cheese, wears leather or wool, just does not have to be taken seriously at all. A cow won't give milk unless she has a calf every year, and every other calf she has, on average, is going to be a bull.

What do you do with the bull? Let it starve to death or feed it until it dies of old age? If you do the latter your five acres soon aren't going to be supporting anything else except bulls—and it won't support them

for long. We have only to go to the parts of Hindu India where they really don't kill cattle, and have no export outlet for them, to see what happens there. The children starve while walking hat-racks wander about picking up any bit of stick they can eat and eventually provide the vultures with poor pickings indeed.

You can't hatch eggs to provide yourself with hens to lay more without hatching out as many cocks as hens. What do you do with the cocks? If you keep sheep to shear, your sheep will breed, unless you are very careful — or would you allow castration, vegetarian?

As for the vegan (a vegan will eat no milk or eggs besides, of course, no meat), a vegan world cannot really suffer any large animals to live at all. If I become a vegan what would I do with the two sows I have got in my sty now? Do I feed them until they die of old age — not letting them breed of course? Or do I turn them loose to roam the roads and get what living they can? If I do

that somebody's crops are going to suffer — if enough people do it there won't be any crops left at all. Man has a part to play in the balance of nature, and if he fails to play it that balance gets off-balance and nobody benefits at all. The only possible way in which, in a vegan country, we could suffer large mammals to share the same country as ourselves and go on flourishing would be to import large predators to control them. If we just let loose all the cattle, sheep and pigs that we have now, what does any vegan think would happen? What is the alternative to letting them loose?

Well, kill them all, or castrate all but one or two of the males and let all but a few zoo specimens die out.

I have never heard any answer to any of the above arguments and I am quite sure I never will, because there are no answers. As for the non-vegetarian whom the self-supporter is bound very often to meet who, with his legs under your table, a knife and fork in his hand,

and tucking away happily into his share of a shoulder of mutton, says: 'Ugh! How on earth can you bring yourself to kill a poor sheep!' — well, the only answer to him is to take his plate away.

The good husbandman is not the tyrant of his piece of land, but should be the benign controller — and part of the biosphere himself. He is an animal, and the fellow of his sheep and his pigs—and of his grass and his cabbages too: hasn't it now been proved that all life on earth derived from one cell? Take a five-acre piece of wilderness, or a five-acre stretch of a barley-prairie, and there is really very little life on it at all — very little of the higher forms of life at least. Give that five acres to a true husbandman, to live and rear his family on, and you will soon find it supporting a very rich flora and fauna. The application of the intelligence that only man has is beneficial to the other life forms, but for this, man must be free to harvest and control, not only among the plants, but among the animals too.

So while I would never try to persuade any vegetarian to become a carnivore I would never become a vegetarian myself. The vegetarian cannot share his holding with other large mammals. I don't think I have the right to be so exclusive.
—*John & Sally Seymour*
Farming for Self-Sufficiency
Schocken Books, New York
250 pages, Hardcover $9.00

BEES

Beekeeping, as with most of life's more complicated rituals, is best learned at the elbow of a master. Failing that, thorough study of one or more of the basic texts, becoming familiar with the mail order catalogues and visits to working apiaries can launch a small-scale bee yard. Many experienced beekeepers counsel rank beginners to buy a pair of colonies from a reputable local beekeeper and make the most of the free knowledge he should be willing to impart.

More advanced beekeepers (both amateur and those with cottage honey businesses) and beekeepers with woodworking skills will find contributor Michael Shook's views under the Random Comment Section at the end of this chapter to be of interest.

Those who, for one reason or another, choose to buy new equipment and fill it with package bees are advised to be well prepared for the arrival of the packages. The general rule is that bees can survive only nine days from hive to hive, and the beekeeper who cannot install arriving packages immediately may be off to a poor honey year (if not total failure). A package of bees, it should be pointed out, usually contains from two to five pounds of living bees or 8,000 to 20,000 or more individuals. Managed properly, their numbers will increase dramatically within weeks. This is not, as more than one newcomer to the countryside has learned, a husbandry venture on the same level as, say, bringing home a pair of laying hens. Bees require intelligent care and involved management, but, of course, therein lies the prime reason for acquiring them in the first place.

Beekeeping Supplies

B.C. beekeepers were a little perturbed when Hodgson's Bee Supplies (7925 - 13th Avenue, New Westminster, B.C. V3L 4Y6) slid into receivership in 1978. Apart from being *the* beekeeping store in B.C. for as long as anyone could remember, Hodgson's was the only outfit in the province making beeswax comb foundation. My own mail order requests to Hodgson's somehow got forwarded to something called Can-Am Bee Supplies (P.O. Box 2221, New Westminster, B.C. V3L 5A5) which turned out to be a new company Hodgson's manager Bob Bird had started after flying the old coop. (For its minute size, the B.C. bee supplies' game has all the manoeuvrings of Weston, Thomson and The Bay.) *Now,* the word is that Hodgson's is going to be back in business soon. But for those out West who are wondering where their next super is coming from there's still lots of choice.

Many of those listed below are

small outfits, operating out of their own homes, and in some cases charging too much for slow-moving items. Write for prices first if you're mail ordering. Some do not handle large, high-priced items such as extractors.

R. BARKER
6200 No. 4 Road
Richmond, B.C. V6T 2T9

Basic bee supplies. Handles plastic comb foundation.

COOPER BEE SUPPLIES
7942 - 208th Street, R.R.8
Langley, B.C. V3A 604

Basic hobbyist equipment.

THE HONEY POT
Cleveland Ave., Box 1430
Squamish, B.C. V0N 3G0
(604) 892-5757

Hive equipment only.

MODERN BEE SUPPLIES
10952 - 120th Street
North Surrey, B.C.

DADANT AND SONS INC.
Hamilton, Illinois 62341
(217) 847-3324

In contrast to many beekeeping catalogues, Dadant's is clearly written, full of details for the beginner, yet with the sophisticated lines of equipment and supplies required by professionals. To reduce freight charges, Dadant has nine shipping points throughout the United States and routinely supplies Canadian customers.

ALTASWEET HONEY
16650 - 111th Avenue
Edmonton, Alberta T5M 2S5

Handles everything. Prices generally similar to those of B.C. suppliers, but some items are cheaper.

—*Frank Appleton*
Edgewood, B.C.

HODGSON BEE SUPPLIES LTD.
Box 297
New Westminster, B.C.
V3L 4Y6
or
7925 - 13th Avenue
Burnaby, B.C.
(604) 521-2606

Hodgson's—despite the turmoil —still seems to be *The Name* in B.C. beekeeping circles. The company has been giving excellent service to B.C. apiarists for over 45 years.

The catalogue, free for the asking, is a marvel for beginners. It does not assume you know what you're doing, and the first eight pages are devoted to describing each piece of equipment a beginner needs to set up shop. Pictures and handy hints are liberally sprinkled throughout the whole catalogue.

Mrs. Audrey Ford is the lady in charge of taking orders and she is most helpful. She has an almost encyclopedic memory, and can usually give any amount of help a beekeeper would require.

Their equipment is top-notch and

is shipped out the same day they receive your order.

—*Mary Ann Robertson*
Quesnel, B.C.

AGRI SUPPLY
101 - 1959 East Trans-Canada Highway
Kamloops, B.C. V2C 4A2

A new beekeeping supply, Agri Supply, has been formed in Kamloops. Manager Jay Ross has been in the business for three years and the place has definite advantages for beekeepers living outside the lower mainland of B.C.

His catalogue is complete, and equipment is easy to find, as opposed to some other catalogues in which finding the piece of equipment you need is an adventure in itself. Everything for the apiarist is listed in alphabetical order under main titles—from "Beekeeping Books" to "Pollen Substitutes."

The price list is a bit of a nuisance. It's coded, corresponding to catalogue equipment numbers, and is listed on a separate sheet of paper. For instance, to find a "cutting blade" for G238WW and GA 128XX (listed on page 5) you read that it sells for A128ZZ. Turn to the price list, find A128ZZ in the section called page 5 and see that it costs $1.75. Ugh. Obviously the separate coded price list cuts down on the yearly cost of printing a whole new catalogue to keep up with inflation, but it is a little confusing.

The cost of Jay's equipment, however is very reasonable; sometimes dollars cheaper than you can get anywhere else. For instance, *The Hive and the*

Honeybee book from him is $12.95 and from the huge rival supply house it is $17.70. Postage rates are more reasonable than the lower mainland supply, depending, of course, on where you live.

Jay will ship anywhere in Western Canada and will do so by the cheapest possible means, including Greyhound. Orders for his free catalogue should reach him in the late fall to guarantee your receiving it.

– Mary Ann Robertson
Quesnel, B.C.

EDWARD JAMES
R.R.1
Sayward, B.C. V0P 1R0
(604) 282-3706

Raises and sells queen bees, but no package bees. $6 per queen bee, postpaid. Correspondence is welcomed.

NORTH PEACE APIARIES LIMITED
R.R.1
Fort St. John, B.C. V1J 4M6
(604) 785-4808

Unpasteurized honey and pollen for human consumption and bee feed.

W.A. CHRYSLER & SON
1010 Richmond Street
Chatham, Ontario
(519) 353-0486

Old line (the catalogue appears not to have changed in 30 years) apiary supplier, offering a complete selection of traditional equipment and hive components of their own manufacture (Ontario White Pine).

COOK'S BEE SUPPLIES
91 Edward Street
Aurora, Ontario L4G 1W1
(416) 727-4811

Unillustrated catalogue of basic beekeeper's supplies. Free price list.

F.W. JONES & SON LTD.
Box 1230
Bedford, Quebec J0J 1A0
(514) 248-3323
or
68 Tycos Drive
Toronto, Ontario M6B 1V9

(416) 783-2818

Free price list of beekeeping equipment and supplies.

MARIOARA APIARIES
129 Ossington Avenue
Toronto, Ontario M6J 2Z6
(416) 536-6120

Packaged bees in season, queen bees, beeswax, honey, pollen, equipment, books. Price list free.

BENSON BEE SUPPLIES
Box 9
Metcalfe, Ont. K0A 2P0
(613) 821-2797

Retail and wholesale source of: comb foundation (beeswax sheets), wooden supplies, extracting equipment, containers, retail and wholesale sheets of coloured beeswax for rolling honeycomb, candles.
Package bees imported:
$25.15 basic hive
$120.50 for five

NOVA SCOTIA DEPT. OF AGRICULTURE
Mr. Lorne Crozier, Apiarist
Horticulture & Biology Serv.
Box 550
Truro, Nova Scotia B2N 5E3

In Nova Scotia, the provincial apiarist annually organizes the importation of queen and package bees from Florida, California and Texas, via Quebec. Packages arrive by truck and parcel post during April and May, with queens available by mail into October.
2 lb. packages (Italian & Caucasian Bees) $23.00–$24.30
3 lb. packages $29.25–$31.00

MARASAN HONEY LTD.
890 Denison Crescent
Ottawa, Ontario K2A 2N5
(613) 729-9981

Mark Hopkins, former president of the Ontario Beekeepers' Association, offers package bees throughout eastern Canada and the northeastern United States.

THE A.I. ROOT COMPANY
Box 706
Medina, Ohio 44256
(216) 725-6677

Full service, large apiarists' supply house.

BEEKWIP SUPPLIES
7151 Heather Street
Richmond, B.C.

IAN'S APIARY
33680 Arcadian Way, R.R.3
Abbotsford, B.C.

POOLE'S BEE SUPPLIES
5787 Bell Road, R.R.1
Matsqui, B.C. V0X 1S0

Make their own wooden equipment. Try them for frames and supers.

WALTER T. KELLEY CO.
Clarkson, Kentucky 42726
(502) 242-2012

I highly recommend this company—prices lower and quality as good or better than the other two big catalogue suppliers.

—Ken Parejko
Holcomb, Wisconsin

SUNSHINE BEE CO.
Box 1
Fanson, Wyoming 82932
(307) 273-9371

Relatively pesticide and herbicide-free pollen from dandelion, willow, Russian olive, thistle, milkweed, several clovers, grasses, alfalfa, rabbitbrush available cleaned for human consumption and uncleaned for bee feed. Further information available if you send a self-addressed, stamped envelope.

ONTARIO MINISTRY OF AGRICULTURE & FOOD
P.W. Burke
Dept. of Environmental Biology
University of Guelph
Guelph, Ontario N1G 2W1
(519) 824-4120 ext. 2477

Extension courses, regulatory services in beekeeping.

CAN. BEEKEEPING
Orono, Ontario L0B 1M0

A monthly trade magazine of the beekeeping industry in Canada.

THE AMERICAN BEE JOURNAL
Hamilton, Illinois 62341

Lively monthly magazine for professionals and serious amateur beekeepers. $8.00 per year, $10.00 to Canada.

GLEANINGS IN BEE CULTURE
A.I. Root Company
$5.50 per year

Gleanings in Bee Culture carries more articles of interest to the hobbyist than the other periodicals, which cater to the commercial beekeeper to a greater extent. All carry a great deal of advertising and can put the beekeeper in touch with additional sources of bees and equipment.

GOATS
Capsulized capriculture:
Don't buy that goat (yet)

You want to buy a goat? Something in your psyche has gone *bo-ing* at the sight or thought of one of these gentle, friendly animals. Or you are a practical soul and want a healthy and convenient source of dairy products. You may be turned on by the sleek flop-eared Nubians, the deerlike quality of Alpines or Toggenburgs, the sturdy down-home practicality of the Saanens or the outright uniqueness of the earless La Mancha. Whatever your desires, there is a goat out there somewhere for you.

But just a minute. Before you grab your purse or wallet and go dashing out at the first newspaper ad, give yourself a small education about what you will be looking at and perhaps buying. Goats come in all shapes and colours, and also

in all levels of production, health and personality. Unfortunately, many people buying a goat for the first time, end up with a poor animal, and become convinced that goats are not for them. With a bit of prior education, this need not happen and you will embark on a happy life involved with goats. They are treacherous little beasties. They can wangle their way into your heart as fast as a dog or cat, but unlike keeping a housepet, most people embark on goat ownership with the idea of milk production. To be saddled with a lovable old dear who gives less than a quart a day or has continuous bouts of mastitis is heartbreaking.

First, when embarking on a goat shopping expedition, make up your mind whether you want a purebred or a grade goat. There are advantages to each. A grade goat is usually cheaper than a purebred and many grade does have very good milk production records. If you are interested in only one or two goats to provide milk for your family at an

economical price, this may be the best choice. However, there are several things you should think about before deciding on a grade doe. She may not hand on her good milking qualities to her offspring. If you are interested in successive generations of offspring, you may wish to buy a purebred. Even if you do not wish to develop your own herd, you must have offspring. The goat must be bred every year in most cases in order to produce milk. Nature did, after all, design her to provide milk for her babies. So you will have little ones. The fact is that purebred kids sell for much higher prices than grade kids.

If you are interested in a purebred, you will probably have read something about the various breeds. There are five main breeds of dairy goat. The Nubian is fairly large, comes in any colour, and has long pendulous ears and a roman nose. Nubians are the Jersey cows of the goat world; they do not produce quite the volume of the other breeds, but the milk has a very high butterfat content. If you have close neighbours, it would be well to keep in mind that this breed has the loudest voice.

The La Mancha is distinguished by its lack of external ears, although many have very short ones. They come in any colour.

The Saanen is a medium to large goat with erect ears and comes with a white or cream coat.

The French Alpine is large and rangy, a deerlike animal with erect ears. There are several colour variations of dark and light pattern.

The Toggenburg is medium-sized and sturdy. It has white markings on a fawn to chocolate background. It has erect ears.

Having decided what animal you are interested in, you are now ready to go shopping, right? Wrong. Purebred or grade, you can still come out the loser in a deal. You are at the mercy of the seller when it comes to the records of milk production, health and personality. Most breeders are honest and will evaluate faults and this will be reflected in the price, but there are a few unscrupulous people who will unload anything on a trusting buyer. Your best bet, of course, is to enlist the help of someone knowledgeable about goats to accompany you and inspect any prospective buys. I strongly advise this course. However, if you know no one, you can still make a pretty good guess as to the quality of an animal before you part with your money.

Your first concern will be the health of the animal. Look at the whole herd. Do they all seem pretty healthy and active? Are any of them coughing severely? Do they appear to be well cared for? Look at the animal you are interested in. She may seem a little scrawny to you. Pay that no mind. This is what is known as ''dairyness.'' A good goat will put all she has into the milk pail. I would advise against an overly fat animal. She may be a poor producer and you will most certainly have problems with breeding and health later. However, you do not want an animal that is skin and bone either. That would indicate health

problems. A good goat should be lean. She should look sleek and bright eyed. Are her hooves trimmed? If she is wearing miniature skis it indicates a lack of care. Her legs may have been thrown into an awkward position. Hooves can be trimmed down if the animal seems healthy otherwise and the legs do not seem damaged. Check her udder. In fact check several udders so you know how a healthy one should feel. A healthy udder, when milked out, should be small and fairly tight to the body. Of course no goat is perfect and some udders are more pendulous than others. A very pendulous udder is to be avoided, as it lends itself to injury. The udder should feel soft, but there will be masses of tissue (the milk glands) inside. Hard lumps are an indication of mastitis, or scar tissue from an earlier infection. An extremely lopsided udder is another indication of a past mastitis infection. I say ''extremely'' because a goat with one kid may have a slightly lopsided udder, due to the uneven demand, and some goats seem naturally to milk a little more from one side than from the other. Try milking your goat. Does she stand easily or jump all over the landscape? A jumpy doe can be calmed down, but if you are a beginner at the business she is probably not for you. It would be too traumatic for both. Does the milk come out in a good single stream? Some goats have extra teats, or double openings and these should be avoided. Lastly, taste the milk. Most goats give very good milk, but there is the odd one who gives an off-flavoured product and you don't want to be the one drinking it.

Check over your prospective buy for any lumps or abscesses. There is a very serious disease which manifests as abscesses. If your goat, or any in the herd, has them you could be buying a load of trouble.

A good goat should have no horns. She will either have been born polled, or will have been dehorned shortly after birth. Horns are dangerous weapons, and the goat will be tempted to use them on other goats. She may not use them purposefully against you or your family but even a casual toss of the head could catch you in the stomach or a small child in the face. Horns have no place on a dairy goat. Unfortunately, removing them from an adult goat is a fairly serious operation.

So now you have found a goat. She is bright eyed, alert and friendly. She stands well on her feet, and not back on her hocks. She has a large deep barrel, a straight topline, and a good wide stance when viewed from the back. Her udder is tight to her body and soft when handled. The seller has her papers ready to be transferred, along with records of her production since she freshened. It looks as if you have found your goat.

—*Kathryn A. Sinclair, Winterburn, Alberta.*

ZYGOTE FARM
R.R 3
Maberly, Ontario K0H 2B0
(613) 268-2800
David and Anne Creighton

When I moved from the big city onto an old Lanark County farm 11 years ago, I left behind all the rat race pressures which kept me on the go all the time and eventually found myself looking around for something to get me out of bed in the morning. A milking goat turned out to be the answer. But to give milk a goat must have kids every spring and 11 years later we have 50 to 75 registered and recorded French and Canadian Alpine dairy goats, plus accessories, and can get out of bed pretty well automatically under any conditions.

The goats provide us with milk,

cream, butter, yogurt, various cheeses, ice cream, meat, hides, the finest manure, irreproachable companionship, a healthy constitution and a ready topic of conversation in any social circle. And they're quite valuable nowadays too, providing much of our farm income.

Registered and recorded French and Canadian Alpine dairy goats and meat bucks for sale in season. Registered buck service. Consultations by appointment, visitors welcome. Members of CGS, ODGS, OVGC and EOGF.

HALCYON FARM
R.R. 3
Denfield, Ontario

Dan Baran and Phillippa Cranston-Baran operate Canada's leading goat milk dairy. Alpine, Nubian, Saanen and Toggenburg production-selected stock for sale.

WINWOOD DAIRY GOAT FARM
Box 3144
Langley, British Columbia
(604) 530-7738
Michael Cassidy

Registered Nubians, LaManchas and Alpines, shipped anywhere.

SANCTUARY FARM INC.
Chantry Rd., R.R. 1
Toledo, Ontario K0E 1Y0
(613) 275-2316

Kay Jay purebred, registered Nubian goats for sale, $150. Stud services.

CONRAD LOAN
R.R. 5
Kemptville, Ontario R0G 1J0
(613) 258-2826

Saanen goats, wild turkeys, Khaki-Campbell ducks.
Goats:
Recorded grade kids $125
Purebred kids $200
Wild turkeys:
Eggs $ .50 each
Poults $2.50 each
Khaki-Campbell ducks:
Eggs $ .50 each
Ducklings $1.25 each
Ready-to-lay females $4.50 each

HEART'S DELIGHT
22030 Telegraph Trail, R.R. 6
Langley, B.C. V3A 4P9
(604) 530-4225

Registered Angora goats from Texas. Romney sheep—registered from New Zealand imported stock.
Registered dairy goats: Toggenburg, Saanen, Nubian
Angora kids $150 to $175
Romney lambs $100 to $125
Dairy kids $75 to $125
Wool fleeces $2/lb.
Mohair fleeces $4/lb.

TAURUS ENTERPRISES
Box 26, R.R. 1
Shanty Bay, Ontario L0L 2L0
(705) 728-1116

Dairy goats—registered Alpine and Nubian. Breeding stock available.
Does $200 and up
Bucks $125 and up
Design and/or construction—goat housing and equipment. Pre-cut kits available where practical (eg. milking stands, disbudding boxes, etc.).
Will consider barter offers.

BRANDY CREEK FARM
R.R. 1 (3 rang nord)
Valcourt, Quebec J0E 2L0
(514) 532-2300

Harold and Margrit Multhaupt breed registered Angora goats and sell breeding stock and Mohair (raw)
Adult Mohair $3.75—$4.50/lb.
Kid Mohair $5/lb.
Angora goats (females) $250
(males) $250 and up

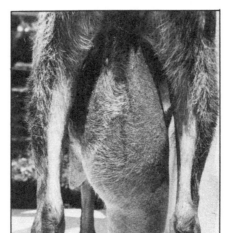

DONELDA ACRES
R.R. 1
Inverary, Ont. K0H 1X0
(613) 353-2844
The Turners

Goats—Purebred and grade Toggenburgs and Alpines.
Stud service.
New Zealand white rabbits
Young does $18
Young bucks $25
Banty chickens $2—$3.

GEORGE AITKENHEAD
R.R. 2
Durham, Ont. N0G 1R0
(519) 369-5163

Nubians and Saanans—registered. Registered weaned kids— $125—$200
Stud services.

ONTARIO DAIRY GOAT SOCIETY
c/o Mrs. Marilyn Baine
R.R. 1
Millgrove, Ont. L0R 1V0
(416) 659-7347

Publish the bi-monthly newsletter *Browse*, with news of shows, sales and goat husbandry, extensive breeders' directory, and stock available from across Canada and the U.S. Membership (includes newsletter), $8.00/year.

DAIRY GOAT JOURNAL
Box 1808
Scottsdale, Arizona 85252

Subscription $9 per year. Add $2 outside U.S.A.

DAIRY GOAT GUIDE
Hwy 19 East
Waterloo, Wisconsin 53594

Subscription $7 per year. Add $2 outside U.S.A.

UNITED CAPRINE NEWS
Box 27
Leakey, Texas 78873

Subscriptions $4 per year. Add $2 outside U.S.A.

ALBERTA GOAT BREEDERS' ASSOCIATION
c/o Ruth Mausolf
R.R. 6, Site 6, Box 16
Edmonton, Alberta
T5B 4K3
(403) 973-3777

A very active association throughout Alberta. *Slant,* a bi-monthly publication, is edited by Ruth Mausolf. This magazine is considered to be one of the best goat association magazines in North America, and is mailed to many subscribers in Canada, the U.S. and overseas. Mrs. Mausolf will send a sample copy of the magazine to anyone requesting it. Mrs. Mausolf is also a bottomless source of information on any aspect of dairy goat husbandry.

—Kathryn Sinclair
Winterburn, Alta.

ALBERTA GOAT INFORMATION CENTRE
c/o Mrs. Brigitte Wooley
Box 89
Kingman, Alberta T0B 2M0
(403) 672-7372

Information service for goat owners, with free pamphlets about goat raising. They will answer questions from goat owners. Free Booklet ''A General Guide to Feeding & Management Practices of Dairy Goats in Alberta'' will be sent upon request.

SHEEP

SHEEP CANADA MAGAZINE
Spruce View, Alta. T0M 1V0
(403) 728-3600

News and information for those who raise sheep, with an emphasis on newcomers to sheep husbandry and to family farm operations. Good source of breeders names, including kennels specializing in Border Collies and guarding dogs, such as Komondors and Great Pyrenees. $5.00/yr. ($7.00/yr. outside Canada.) Quarterly publication.

BLACK SHEEP NEWSLETTER
28068 Ham Road
Eugene, Oregon 97405
Subscription rate $4.00/yr.
4 issues, plus annual directory
Classified ads free

The *Black Sheep Newsletter* is a small quarterly of special value to

sheep raisers interested in the spinning and weaving aspects of wool production as well as to those craftspeople who work with wool. The newsletter proposes to ''serve as a tool to educate both sheepman and spinner to each other's needs'' and ''to encourage good craftsmanship at all levels from the rearing of good lambs to their fleece and to the finished woven or knitted product . . . .''

—Louise Langsner
Marshall, N.C.

WINDOVER FARM
R.R.1
Orangedale, N.S. B0E 2K0
(902) 756-2403

Mrs. Jodie Sanders operates this unique Atlantic Shepherding School, conducting weekend courses on all phases of sheep husbandry.

NATURAL COLOURED WOOL GROWERS ASSOCIATION
The NCWGA was established to fulfill the needs of sheep breeders developing coloured wools for spinners and weavers. Emphasis is on the breeding of quality animals, producing quality wools, maintaining adequate records, and marketing. NCWGA has a flock

registration programme in regions throughout the U.S. and Canada and recently launched a newsletter. Membership fee is $10.00.
For information write:
Secretary
Lorry Dunning
Route 1, Box 2382
Davis, Ca 95616

—Louise Langsner
Marshall, N.C.

Hide Tanning

MAISON D'APPRET CARCAJOU ENRG.
19 Avenue Roy
Lanoraie, Quebec J0K 1E0

ATLAS FUR TANNING
Blyth, Ontario

Supplies

KETCHUMS OF OTTAWA
396 Berkley Avenue
Ottawa, Ontario K2A 2G6

Covers large and small animal equipment. (Free catalogue available.)

ARNOLD NASCO LTD.
58 Dawson Road,
Guelph, Ontario N1H 6P9

Large and small animal equipment. (Free catalogue available.)

AMERICAN SUPPLY HOUSE
P.O. Box 1114
Columbia, MO 65201

Sheep and goat equipment. (Free catalogue.)

HOEGGER SUPPLY CO.
Box 49009, Dept. S
College Park, GA 30349

Sheep and goat equipment. (Free catalogue.)

SHEEPMAN SUPPLY CO.
P.O. Box 100
Barboursville, VA 22923

Sheep equipment
(Free catalogue.)

BOVINES & EQUINES

Our long-time dream had been to raise beef cattle, and when, six years ago, we started clearing our 274 acres of woodland, we began to realize that we would need a very hardy breed of bovine to forage on woodland meadows; sturdy animals that could navigate swampy areas, withstand the deer-fly season in summer and the cold of early winter.

We spent three years clearing land, building our house and barn and engaging in a breed search that led us finally to the Galloway. Originally from the Mull of Galloway in southwest Scotland, the Galloways are everything we had hoped for. They forage on all types of wild grasses and weeds and helpfully enjoy the young poplar, birch and maple suckers and raspberry canes that grow profusely on newly cut land. This has the added advantage of keeping the land clear until we can remove the stumps. Steers of other breeds sometimes sprain their ankles in the rough pasture land, but neither the Galloways nor the Galloway crossbreeds seem to suffer in this way. Our dual-purpose Shorthorn milk cow has to be kept in during the height of the fly season in June and July, for she gets badly bitten even after using the oiler. The longer shaggy coat of the Galloways, which the crossbreeds inherit, protects them quite well from the flies. Then in November when the wet areas turn into iceponds, these clever cattle walk over the slippery areas without missing a step. On bitterly cold days they are not found with their backs to the brisk winds or huddled by the barn but up in one of the little cleared areas in the woods, high and dry, enjoying the sun, sheltered from the wind. Above all, they grow and gain weight fast on this routine, and Galloway carcasses have recently been winning important exhibitions for their large loin-eye meat quality.

Although we have Black Galloway and Black crossbreeds, there are two other types of Galloways; Duns and Belted. All Galloways are polled—genetics prevent their horn development. The Galloways are one of the oldest registered breeds of beef cattle and we hope these hardy intelligent cows will be around for many more years to come.

Descriptive literature, names and addresses of Galloway herd owners and animals for sale are available free on request from Eastern Galloway Association, Robert Burns, Box 202, Norwood, Ontario K0L 2J0 or Canadian Galloway Association, Box 311, Blythe, Ont. N0M 1H0.

—Janet Young
Black River Bridge, N.B.

HIGHLAND North America Breeders' Magazine
Box 1831
Charlottetown, P.E.I.
C1A 7N5

Proud, prehistoric-looking Highland cattle that are making something of a comeback. This bi-monthly magazine publishes news and breeders' ads.

$7.50 per year (Canada and U.S.)

JIM AND FORLEY WELLS
R.R.3
Ashton, Ontario K0A 1B0
(613) 257-1504

Beefalo breeding stock, plus semen for artificial insemination. American Beefalo Association registered stock.
Semen: $15/ampule

WINDY RIDGE FARM
R.R.2
L'Avenir, Quebec J0C 2B0
(819) 394-2871

Mr. and Mrs. Carl Sewell. Standard size donkeys (36''—48'' high) from registered stock. Stud service $75 and board. Young stock for sale: registered weanlings $350 and up.

BRAEMOOR FARM
R.R.6
Renfrew, Ont. K7V 3Z9
(613) 432-6721

Burros: 32''—35'' high at the withers, quiet and gentle.

Females $450
Males $350

RHYNEMOOR FARM
R.R.1
Slocan Park, B.C. V0G 2E0
(604) 359-7750

Standard donkeys. Registered and guaranteed sound.

THE WORLD OF BEEF & STOCKMAN'S RECORDER
604 MacLeod Trail S.W.
Calgary, Alberta T2H 0L3
Newspaper format, monthly

One of the best sources of information about all phases of beef production, this professional farmers' paper promotes all the various breeds of beef cattle.

During the past year, articles have described herd management, R.O.P., nutritional requirements, cow calf management, bull evaluation, artificial insemination, markets, sales and many more subjects of interest to both small and large beef farmers.

Subscriptions $5 per year.

—Janet Young
Black River Bridge, N.B.

POULTRY

FREY'S HATCHERY
70 Northside Drive
St. Jacobs, Ont. N0B 2N0
(519) 664-2291

Serving small farms and small hatcheries, Frey's is a family-run business that ships chicks to all parts of Canada, including the far north. Offers 16 varieties, mostly dual-purpose. Highly recommended source. Write for catalogue.

MURRAY McMURRAY HATCHERY
Webster City, Iowa 50595

U.S. source of mail-order chicks—good variety, informative catalogue and friendly service.

COUVOIR DORVAL (1977) INC.
2941 Boul. des Sources
Dorval, Quebec H9R 4N3
(514) 684-1201

Diamond White turkey poults —80 cents each.

FLINTSHIRE PHEASANTS
R.R.1
Flinton, Ont. K0H 1P0
(613) 336-8552

English Ring-Neck pheasants—hatching eggs, chicks, mature birds.
Day-old chicks—
under 100 $1.30 each
Poults (6-8 wks)—
under 100 $2.90 each
Mature Cocks—
under 50 $7.20 each
Mature Hens—
under 50 $6.65 each

FEATHER FANCIER
Box 239
Erin, Ontario N0B 1T0
(519) 833-2208

Monthly newspaper filled with news and classified advertising for poultry, pigeons, rabbits and cavies. $7.50 per year, sample copy 75 cents.

POULTRY PRESS
Box 947
York, Penn. 17405

Free sample copy on request, $5 per year.

CAN. ORNAMENTAL PHEASANT & GAME BIRD ASSOCIATION
409 Crumlin Road
London, Ont. N5V 1R6
(519) 455-3646

Annual membership $10.00 brings monthly newsletter, including a classified advertising section that can lead one to unusual ducks, swans, geese, guinea fowl.

RABBITS

The average good rabbit doe will raise between 30 and 35 young per year. If slaughtered at four pounds of weight (fryer size), these offspring thus represent 120 to 140 pounds of meat per doe per year. This efficiency puts a beef animal to shame, and, as they say on the bunny farms, "nobody was ever kicked to death by a rabbit."

RAINBOW ACRES RABBITRY
34985 Hallert Rd., R.R.1
Matsqui, B.C.
(604) 859-6514

Rabbits, cages, equipment. Earthworms.

THE UNDERGROUND RABBITRY
Box 805, Station F
Toronto, Ontario
Ken McRae

Breeding stock available—French lops, Black Dutch. Enquiries answered when accompanied by a self-addressed stamped envelope. This rabbitry operates, almost unnoticed, in the shadow of the huge Hudson's Bay Centre at Yonge and Bloor Streets, Toronto.

BUNNYVIEW'S COMMERCIAL RABBIT INDUSTRY
R.R.2
West Montrose, Ontario
N0B 2V0
(519) 664-2701

New Zealand white rabbits for meat or fur as well as rabbit housing equipment, cages and books.

CALLOPTAN RABBITS
76 Pleasant Street
Truro, Nova Scotia B2N 3S1
(902) 893-2122

Rabbits for show or meat. Breeds—Tan, Californian, Netherland Dwarf, Satin. Average prices:
2 months old $12.
3-4 months $15—$25
Breeders $35

BARBARA OLSEN
Box 422

Hines Creek, Alta. T0H 2A0
(403) 494-2176

Purebred Angora rabbits.

ANGORABLES
Box 1417
Alliston, Ont. L0M 1A0
(705) 435-4240

White English Angora breeding stock. This farm currently also offers the wool from this breed, and exports it in quantity to a Swiss manufacturing firm which specializes in weaving it into "therapeutic underwear."

DOMINION RABBIT & CAVY BREEDERS ASSOC.
c/o Mrs. Rene Clark
25 Sommerset Avenue
Toronto, Ont. M6H 2R3

Organizes shows, offers annual breeders' directory.

EARTHWORMS

There is, in Toronto, a man who *did* become a millionaire selling earthworms, sending crews of recently immigrated women out onto golf courses at night to gather night crawlers to be sold to sport fishermen. Otherwise, those who have become rich in earthworm ranching are about as common as the chinchilla-breeder millionaires.

Nonetheless, earthworms make good companions in a rabbitry, quickly neutralizing the odorous droppings in pits under cages and producing one of nature's best fertilizers. Worm pits, for the fast conversion of kitchen scraps and garden wastes to compost, also make sense.

The following people will sell earthworm "breeding stock" and/or castings. Judge their literature for yourself.

WESTERN EARTHWORM FARMS LIMITED
Raymond, Alta. T0K 2S0
(403) 752-3840

Free brochure and information. Red hybrid earthworms and earthworm products. "Grower's Programme" package available— training, consultation, starting stock replacement guarantee.

MAPLE LEAF WORM RANCH
R.R.2
Eganville, Ont. K0J 1T0

Pure organic earthworm castings.

BUNNYVIEW COMMERCIAL RABBIT INDUSTRIES
R.R.2
West Montrose, Ontario
N0B 2V0
(519) 664-2701

Red Hybrids: $10 for 1,000

G.O. MAIN LIVEWIRE BAIT & ECOLOGY FARM
Richer, Manitoba R0E 1S0

For further information including price lists and publications:
CALIFORNIA WORM GROWERS' ASSOCIATION
Box 21922
San Jose, Ca 95151

STEVE H. BRIDGENS, EARTHWORM TECHNOLOGY
604 Greenway Terrace
Kansas City, Missouri 64113

AQUACULTURE

AQUAFARMS CANADA LIMITED
Feversham, Ont. N0C 1C0
(519) 922-2817

Live trout for stocking:
12 cents/inch for fish under 10"
$2.50 per lb. for fish over 10"
Delivery: 50 cents/km. one way
(Orders over $300, first 75 km.free.)
2 per cent discount if paid within 10 days

Also offers extensive line of hatchery equipment, including seine nets, shipping bags, rearing tubs, rearing pond liners, aerators.

EWOS GRADER: The grader can be used to sort fish in sizes from small finger-lings up to a length of 30 cm (12") in size. The grader measures 75 cm length, 60 cm width (2'5½" by 1'11½"). It comes with interchangeable screens of 5-30 mm (3/16"x1-3/16") openings. $165.00

NORTON COMPANY
1170 Blair Road
Burlington, Ont. L7M 1K9
(416) 335-0783

Distributors of Actifil, a water filter matrix material for filtering ponds, aquaculture tanks in greenhouse situations, etcetera.

Random Comment
INTEGRATED FLY CONTROL

"A cow's tail is the most expensive fly swatter in the barn," so the saying goes. A cow that is busy swishing her tail at flies doesn't eat; no feed means no milk. Flies can make life miserable for other farm livestock (and humans) and are carriers of disease germs and parasites, as well. In general, I consider flies to be bad company.

Happily, there are folks around who have put their expertise in the field of entomology to use to develop fly management programmes without pesticides. Their research has resulted in safe, effective, long-term fly control based on biological control methods.

We are in our third summer of using biological fly control and find it well worth the moderate cost, time and effort. We recommend the following methods:

1. Careful handling of manure and other fly-breeding materials, e.g. compost. Keep the barn as clean as possible. We use a deep litter system and add fresh bedding as often as needed to keep the surface dry. Manure is hauled to compost heaps daily and always covered with freshly cut grass or weeds or dry hay.

2. Pteromalids (fly parasites): These tiny, stingless wasps are the natural enemies of manure-breeding flies. They work by laying their eggs in fly pupae, the inactive stage between the maggot and the adult fly. Although pteromalids are present naturally, they do not breed as rapidly as flies, and therefore need a population boost from outside in order to control fly booms. The outside help comes from an insectary. Pteromalids are most effective if brought in *before* a fly problem develops, i.e. late spring for us, and re-established

periodically throughout the fly-breeding season.

3. Fly traps: Traps control adult flies and are an effective tool for preventing population explosions due to heat waves, rain, etc. Traps may be handmade or purchased and are baited with a non-poisonous, but very alluring bait.

Recipe: 1½ quarts luke-warm water, 1¼ cups active dry yeast, 1 Tbsp. ammonium carbonate. Combine yeast and water in a one-gallon jug, cover lightly and let stand 3-4 days at 60-70 degrees F. After ripening period is over, stir in ammonium carbonate. This stinky mixture is now ready for use. It may be stored 3 to 4 weeks.

Trapping systems are based on fly behaviour—attraction to odour, aggregations of live flies, and light. Basically, a trap is a container of bait covered with a screen funnel leading to a screened enclosure. Flies are attracted to the smell of the bait and buzzing of trapped flies. They fly into the bait, then fly up the cone toward the light and are trapped. Trap maintenance includes replenishing bait every three to five days and disposing of the accumulated dead flies. (Good chicken munchies.)

Suppliers of pteromalids, fly traps and bait, as well as valuable information and advice are:

BENEFICIAL BIOSYSTEMS
1523 - 63rd Street
Emeryville, CA 94608

RINCON-VITOVA INSECTARIES
Box 95
Oakview, CA 93022
—*Louise Langsner*
Marshall, N.C.

INTERNAL SOURCES

Everything we buy these days, from cars to houses to the food we eat, becomes more expensive as the quality deteriorates. Beekeeping supplies are no exception to this rule. Just as with houses, cars, and food, the more we can build, repair, and raise our own bees and beekeeping equipment, the cheaper and more satisfactory will be the results.

There are quite a number of suppliers of hive parts, extracting

equipment, package bees, and queens in Canada, but there seem to me to be drawbacks to many of the sources. Some are slow to respond to orders, perhaps because many of their wares are shipped in from the United States. Others are consistently inaccurate in filling orders, sending out square lids for round honey pails, as it were. Many supply wooden ware and foundation of poor quality. And all are expensive.

Of course, for the commercial beekeeper, there are few alternatives to buying standard honey containers; the South American tradition of selling honey in used rum bottles would hardly be acceptable by Canadian packing standards. But nearly everything else required to operate five or 500 colonies can be made by the beekeeper who has a bit of time, skill, and equipment at his disposal. A fully equipped woodworking and machine shop is not a prerequisite, nor is master craftsman status; time and attention to detail mean far more than fancy equipment. An old southern queen breeder once showed me the first two supers he ever made, forty odd years ago, with a jackknife and handsaw. They were still serviceable.

Few of us want to go back to the primitive level of whittling bee boxes out of logs; a bit of appropriate technology is in order. All the wooden components of a bee hive: bottom board, hive bodies, frames, inner cover, and cover can be sawn with a table saw, many out of scrap or recycled lumber, due to the small dimensions involved. The only additional operation, besides assembling the equipment, is

drilling wire holes in the end bars of the frames, which can be done with a quarter-inch hand drill. There are several books of detailed plans and instructions available.

Alternatively, one can buy one of each component from a commercial supplier to use as a pattern. Accuracy in all the inner dimensions of a bee hive is of paramount importance, as any spaces between components that are too wide or too narrow will be filled with burr comb or glued together by the bees—to the extreme annoyance of the beekeeper. A good source for wooden ware to use as patterns is Bee-Care Supplies in Brantford, Ontario.

To complete the furnishing of a bee hive, all that need be purchased are nails, frame wire, foundation, an excluder and a metal top for the cover. The first three are essential, the latter two optional. Nails must be especially thin to avoid splitting the small wooden parts; these and frame wire are rather inexpensive at any beekeeping supply house. The foundation is made by a fairly exacting process from pure beeswax, and is therefore quite expensive. F.W. Jones has a reputation for high quality foundation. Colonies can be managed quite nicely without a queen excluder, a precisely made and fairly expensive piece of metal. The customary metal cover to waterproof the hive cover can be replaced with much cheaper tar paper or roofing material, which may need replacing several times during the life of the cover.

Personal protective gear: veil, gloves, and bee suit can be sewn together in a number of imaginative designs. Everyone has to deal with his own level of paranoia regarding stings. I've worked bees with a paper bag over my head with holes for my eyes, when nothing else was available. Such garb is not recommended for long-term use, but no matter how thoroughly armoured he is, a beekeeper will occasionally get stung.

Many old time beekeepers still have the smoker and hive tools they bought back in the '30s. It's doubtful if any of today's smokers will see the year 2000, but these can be a once in a long time, if not lifetime, purchase.

Extracting equipment for use in a small scale operation can be homemade or found around the house. Several years ago *Organic Gardening and Farming* magazine carried plans for an extractor made from a barrel. A heated butcher knife can serve to uncap several supers of frames each year, and assorted tubs and pails will catch the cappings and honey as it is spun off. Anyone beginning commercial beekeeping should have toured or worked in several operating honey houses to know what type of extracting gear he wants to make or buy. Much of this equipment is available used through the classified ads of beekeeping publications.

Of course, the central component of every beekeeping enterprise is the bees themselves, and here again there are several do-it-yourself avenues available. Probably the least satisfactory means of acquiring bees is to purchase package bees from the southern States. Generally, the queens are bred for the southern climate, and often they are of poor genetic stock and/or are inadequately mated. Even if a package contains a viable queen, they are generally unable to build up to adequate strength during the short Canadian summer to produce a crop of honey. Catching swarms has given many bee-keepers their start. If equipment is prepared to house them, a swarm collected in May can produce a honey crop through the summer. An ad in a small town newspaper offering to remove swarms is quite likely to produce results.

The best and surest way of acquiring bees is to purchase established colonies from another beekeeper. Care must be taken to ensure that the colonies are of good strength and disease-free. Bees sold in any province or state must be inspected by a government inspector for American foulbrood, and a permit to sell issued. The inspector for each area can be contacted through the Department of Agriculture, and they will often have information about bees that are for sale in their area.

Once the initial colonies are purchased or established from swarms or packages, it is possible to increase the number of colonies each year by building a bit of new equipment, raising a few queens, and dividing the over-wintered colonies. This is the natural inclination of anyone struck with "bee fever," to keep on building more and more colonies until they become commercial beekeepers or their spouses leave—or both.

In order to establish a new colony, one must acquire a new queen, and again the alternative to buying the expensive southern model is to raise queens from one's own colonies. The Miller method is quite a simple way to raise the few queens that a backyard beekeeper needs. The details of this process are outlined in *The ABC and XYZ of Bee Culture*. The queens thus raised will be of better quality, since the parent colony will be adapted to Canadian climatic conditions.

So we see that, with the exception of a few metal and wax components, the beekeeper can make nearly everything involved in beekeeping, except something to put the honey in. Every commercial beekeeper knows that five hundred dollars worth of containers will hardly fill a pickup truck these days. I sell part of my honey crop at a farmers' market, and nearly every week a potential customer picks up a jar and exclaims, "Oh, do you make the honey yourself." To which I reply, "No, the bees make it." And under my breath, "But I had to buy the damned jar!" I've taken to quoting my prices as "so much for the honey plus the cost of the container," and an increasing number of jars and pails are coming back to be refilled.

Thus we can add coffee jars and ice cream pails to our list of recycled bee equipment, for these make dandy honey containers. And as the honey is spun out of scrapwood frames by our homemade extractor into a recycled honey pail, we can thank our home-grown queens for helping us take one more step

away from the great orange pyrotechnic North American success machine.

—*Michael Shook*
Bluevale, Ontario

Books

131 pages, $7.95 Paperback

Fascinating, no-nonsense approach to beekeeping. Carefully and completely documented with line drawings to illustrate hive construction and orientation, apiary management, the interior workings of the hive and the rituals of the bee. Precise, expertly written reference book for the serious beekeeper.

THE DRAFT HORSE PRIMER, A Guide to the Care and Use of Work Horses and Mules
By Maurice Telleen
386 pages, Hardcover $12.95

This book is based on the author's own extensive experience with draft animals, and on the most useful of now out-of-print publications from the twenties and thirties. It covers the essentials of buying and caring for a team, and is packed with solid advice for the beginner on using horsepower on the homestead. An invaluable back-up to direct experience and the company of "good old teamsters."

THE FAMILY COW
By Dirk van Loon
262 pages, $5.95 Paperback
Essential for anyone interested in small-scale dairying. Nova Scotia's Dirk van Loon combines good humour and thorough information to give an excellent guide to

buying a cow, feeding, breeding and managing her, and using those gallons of fresh milk.

THE HORSE
By Evans, Borton, Hintz and Van Vleck
766 pages, Hardcover $33.25

A virtual encyclopedia on horses and horsemanship with over 300 illustrations. The four principal authors are all professors of animal science with more than 100 years of experience among them. The book begins with the history of horses and goes on to cover their biology, nutritional requirements, standards for selection, breeding, diseases, training and management. A removable colour chart shows all possible coat colours.

DUCKS & GEESE IN YOUR BACKYARD
By Rick and Gail Luttmann
273 pages, $6.50 Paperback

Another of the "backyard" basic guides, this comprehensive, easily understood manual shows how ducks and geese can supplement or even provide the egg and meat supply of modest acreages. Includes pond construction, incubation and butchering. Pen-and-ink illustrations.

RAISING THE HOMESTEAD HOG
By Jerome Belanger
226 pages, $8.95 Hardcover

The author is probably North America's only publisher (*Countryside* magazine) who also raises swine commercially. He knows his subject and this book will serve as a complete guide for raising bacon on a small scale.

KEEPING LIVESTOCK HEALTHY, A Veterinary Guide
By N. Bruce Haynes D.V.M.
323 pages, $9.95 Paperback

Twenty-five years as a veterinarian has convinced the author that the great majority of farm animal disease problems are preventable. This is not a manual on how to treat sick animals, but a well-organized explanation of the nature of specific diseases and the methods of assuring the animal's good health. Horses, cows, goats, sheep and pigs are covered. Rank beginners in husbandry may find this book too technical.

RAISING SHEEP THE MODERN WAY
By Paula Simmons
224 pages, $5.95 Paperback

This highly practical book is backed up by 20 years of experience in raising sheep for wool, lamb and mutton. Includes an annual sheep-raising calendar to help beginning shepherds through the first year.

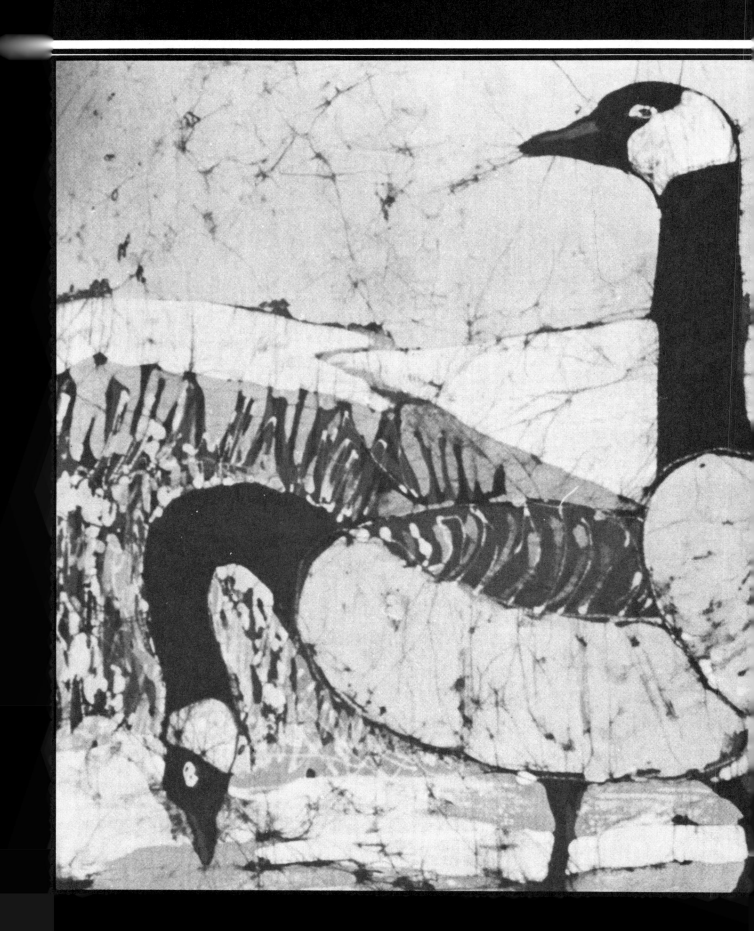

Tight Is Right

The return of crafty integrity

A new burst of energy among artisans and artists has characterized the fields of functional and decorative weaving in the last dozen years. Beginning with the free and easy stylizations of the 1960s, weaving was no longer associated only with little old ladies making floral placemats. Major fibre artists had always worked to produce tapestries or fashion fabrics or upholstery and draperies for fine homes but only recently has the art been revived by craftsmen and serious hobbyists. The revival began at the same time the revolutionary '60s brought slogans like "technique is cheap" to the craft. Practiced skill almost became a detriment.

Blobs and gobs bubbled out of wall hangings; what did it matter if they fell apart in three months or couldn't be cleaned? Eye impact was what counted and everybody, and anybody, could produce works for sale. When things settled down and the fibre dust cleared, artisans once again concerned themselves with the integrity of what they were producing, the dilettantes moved on to something new and the buying public, having cut their teeth on some pretty awful stuff, demanded craftsmanship. The slogan for the '80s: "tight is right." Technique is no longer cheap.

Through all of the ups and downs—should I say ins and outs?—of weaving in the past decade, hobbyists and professional artisans alike have spent mountains of money in search of published materials exploring their craft. It is unfortunate that the book publishing world seems jammed at about 1968; with notable exceptions, weaving books

seem to be cheap, knee-jerk reactions to popular demands, occasionally shoddy and often over-priced. In my early eagerness to learn about weaving, I spent much more than I should have on a large collection of books. Of about 60 on my shelf, half a dozen are significantly useful.

What's wrong with weaving books? First, nearly every new book starts with an explanation of how to set up a loom, what the types of looms look like, how to make a warp, blah blah blah. I keep paying over and over for the same information. Next, most weaving books are filled with very bad photos: technically imperfect with amateur models holding or wearing weaving that you can't really see. Detail photos are often out of focus. Photographs appear of weaving that is never mentioned in the text. Prices are quite high and content is disappointingly thin.

In spite of all this criticism, there are books I like very much, books I dip into again and again and even a couple of books I don't expect to exhaust in a lifetime of weaving. These are the books I would recommend, in the order a new weaver might want to acquire them.

NEW KEY TO WEAVING, by Mary Black, Macmillan Publishing, New York, 1974. The classic of hand weaving, this book is the one you should buy if you are only going to buy one. Be prepared, though, because it isn't big and beautiful, it doesn't inspire you with examples and it certainly isn't bright or colourful. The only thing it can do is teach you how to weave, technically speaking. From there you need your own imagination and creativity.

THE WEAVING, SPINNING AND DYEING BOOK, by Rachel Brown, Alfred A. Knopf, New York, 1978. This book *is* big and beautiful and its design, clear illustrations and exceptional drawings are reason enough to buy it. It surveys all kinds of weaving techniques with extra emphasis on the Navajo weaving of the American southwest where the author resides. It is packed with the little tips and how-to's

that thrill most weavers. Even the experienced weaver will like this one.

WEAVER'S STUDY COURSE, IDEAS AND TECHNIQUES, by Else Regensteiner, Van Nostrand Reinhold, New York, 1975. **THE ART OF WEAVING,** By Else Regensteiner, Van Nostrand Reinhold, New York 1970. I tried to analyze why I like Regensteiner books and couldn't. They are very well thumbed, though, and I guess in some ways, that says enough.

A HANDWEAVER'S PATTERN BOOK, by Marguerite P. Davison, Self-Published, Box 263, Swarthmore, Pa. 1944. This handy resource book is like a cook book with all the zucchini recipes in one place; when you need to look at a particular group of weaves, when you're searching out constructions for a project, it's all right in front of you.

THE TECHNIQUES OF RUG WEAVING, by Peter Collingwood, Watson Guptill, New York, 1968. This massive volume is a must for the rug weaver, a pleasure for any weaver. Its scholarship is awe-inspiring.

KEEP ME WARM ONE NIGHT, by Ruth Burnham and Howard Burnham, University of Toronto, 1972. This book is for weavers who are entranced with that special area of early North American weaving: overshot. Hundreds of coverlets are photographed, discussed and drafted in this large book.

ON WEAVING, by Anni Albers, Wesleyan University Press, Middletown, Ct., 1965. Every other book listed concerns itself mainly with how to weave. This book explores what weaving is about. ''Tactile Sensibility'' and ''Design as Visual Organization'' are chapters of particular interest.

These books are the best I've found but it is important to me that in weaving, now, as for 200 years in North America, the best information comes from the notebooks of other weavers. It's almost a good thing we are forced to get together with others in the same craft for inspiration and information—it serves to keep the art alive.

—*Sharon Airhart*
Corbeyville, Ontario

Carleton Place, Ont. K7C 3P3
(613) 257-2508

It may not look like a proper spinning wheel, but it is and it works. Neophytes reportedly find it especially responsive and easy to use.

Louet Dutch Spinning Wheel $140 kit (completed wheels on request)

HANDCRAFT WOOLS LTD.
Box 378
Streetsville, Ont. L5M 2B9
(416) 826-2059

Supplies for the hand-spinner and weaver, also hand-spinning equipment such as spinning wheels, hand carders and drum carders.

Yarn sample card $4
Fibre card $5

SCHACHT SPINDLE CO. INC.
2526 49th St. Box 2157
Boulder, Colorado 80306
(303) 442-3212

Well-made hard maple looms, shuttles, spindles and other accessories. Free information, or send $2.00 for the world's most beautiful loom catalogue. The cover is an all-white embossed sculpture of a small flock of sheep. People can't resist picking up and stroking this one.

Eight-Harness Table Loom Weaving Width 20" $235

Inkle Loom (for weaving belts, trims, straps) $25

NILUS LECLERC INC.
C.P. 69
L'Islet, Quebec G0R 2C0

For more than 100 years, the Le-Clerc family of Quebec has been producing the Chevrolet of looms for Canadian and American hand-weavers. Well-constructed and moderately priced, Leclerc looms are neither the most substantial nor the most beautiful looms being built but they are the most popular, with good reason.

The Leclerc line includes everything from a new series of low-priced kits for hobbyists to a prestige model, the Colonial, which is far more substantial

Leclerc's Colonial, $660-$750

both in appearance and price. Many weavers choose Leclerc's most widely-known model, the Fanny, a folding counter-balanced loom. Its non-folding counterpart, the Mira, is probably the best investment for serious weavers, currently priced at just over $400. Weavers who will give their loom hard use should avoid the Artisat, a folding jack loom which has been extremely popular with hobby weavers because of its lower price.

—Sharon Airhart Corbeyville, Ont.

METIERS CLEMENT ENR.
941 rue Clement
St. Justin Cte
Maskinonge, Quebec J0K 2V0
Quality looms from $500 to $700.

ASHFORD SPINNING WHEELS
Box 180
Ashburton, New Zealand

These silver beech spinning wheel kits make their way around the world, with many "stockists" throughout North America. Write for address of nearest distributor.

QUARK
Box 211

Ajax, Ont. L1S 3C4

Portable four-yard warping mill. Two-yard table and three-yard floor models also available. Send for illustrated details of the full range.

ROMNI WOOLS
319 King Street West
Toronto, Ontario
(416) 368-0202

Wonderful fleeces, good range of interesting yarns, equipment and books; this is truly the spinner's store, and its old customers are happy ones.

SUE-SAM PRODUCTS
210 Randall Street
Oakville, Ont. L6J 1P5
(416) 844-3759 or 827-6474

Family business producing looms and spinning wheels of their own design. Send $1.00 for catalogue.

STONECREST SHEEP FARMS
R.R.2
Elora, Ontario N0B 1S0
(519) 846-9284

White and coloured fleece: white $1.25/lb., coloured $2-3/lb. Tanned sheepskins: white $30, black $40

Yarn, Wool & Supplies

Generally speaking, yarn suitable for hand weaving is also appropriate for knitting, crochet and other hand work. But weaving fibres tend to be more interesting and most firms that carry weaving yarns offer a great diversity in sizes and colours. New Brunswick's Briggs and Little Woolen Mills have a shade they call "Fundy Fog" that weavers across this continent and even beyond have come to rely on for a certain effect in colouration that makes their work unique because of this very fibre.

The best buys are not always the least expensive yarns. Consider the use to which the handmade product will be put. Decorative textiles (hangings, banners) are to look at: colour and texture are very important in such articles, but the yarn quality is not as critical as the visual effect obtained. However, with functional items like curtains, cushions and floor rugs, it is important to choose long-wearing fibres that will stand up to the rigours of day-to-day wear and tear. With clothing and garments, fibres chosen for their construction should be easily washable, resistant to fading and shrinking, and most important of all, the yarns should *feel good* next to your skin. Scratchy, stiff, crimpy fibres are o.k. for a wall piece but who would want to sit with them wrapped around their bare legs?

Spinning, a gentle and loving skill, is making a big comeback. Most of the institutions and organizations listed under **COURSES** offer spinning and weaving instruction at beginning and advanced levels. But spinning is a time-consuming way of providing yourself with yarns for hand work. If you really want the most gorgeous yarn on earth, by all means do spin it for yourself; otherwise, you can spin yarn for special projects and use factory-spun fibres for the regular things. Items made of handspun, plant or lichen-dyed yarns that are designed for resale have to carry quite a high price to make it

worth your while. Still and all, handspun, hand-dyed yarns are the ultimate expression of aesthetic values, and stand in marked contrast to so much of today's hand work that is lacking in colour harmony and textural interest.

As for suppliers, it is amazing how many go in and out of business overnight. The following companies are, in the main, all "old and reliable," but some, as indicated, treat their mail order business with disdain. Equally surprising is the fact that some insist on not making their phone numbers or postal codes available on their promotional material! Most of the French-speaking firms have bilingual staff. Samples range in price, if not free, from 50 cents to $5.00. Who wants to mail a money order for 50 cents? A few offer the samples to you, without an initial charge, and then add that amount to your first order. A few charge first, then deduct the amount from your first order. It really does vary. Samples are essential if you order by mail.

—*Karen Casselman*
Cheverie, Nova Scotia

ABRAM'S VILLAGE HANDCRAFT CO-OP LTD.
Abram's Village
Prince County, P.E.I.
(902) 854-2096

Plant dyed, handspun yarns.

ANJA'S WEAVING SUPPLIES
Box 10, R.R.1
Chelsea, Quebec J0X 1N0
(819) 827-0742

Beautiful, but expensive, Finnish wools and linens; Finnish looms and equipment; books; samples cost.

BRANDY CREEK FARM
R.R.1 (3 rang nord)
Valcourt, Quebec J0E 2L0
(514) 532-2300

Angora goats raised for mohair. Sell mohair and goats.
Goats $300—$350
Mohair prices vary according to auctions in U.S. Sell raw mohair—preferably whole fleeces.

BRIGGS & LITTLE WOOLEN MILLS LTD.
York Mills Harvey Stn.
Nova Scotia E0H 1H0
(506) 366-5438

Moderately priced wool yarns in various plies and lovely colours; their heather shades are outstanding; samples free.

GINA BROWN FIBRE CRAFTS
2207 - 4th Street Southwest
Calgary, Alberta

Yarns and natural dyes.

WILLIAM CONDON & SONS LIMITED
203 Fitzroy St., Box 129
Charlottetown, P.E.I.
C1A 7K3
(904) 894-8712

Wool yarns for knitting, weaving, hooking, crocheting. Sample card and price list available—no charge.

CRAFT COTTAGE
7577 Elmbridge Way
Richmond, B.C. V6X 2Z8
(604) 278-0313

Dyes, mordants, yarns, books and equipment.

CREATIVE CRAFTS
4 John Street West
Toronto, Ontario
(416) 249-0732

Looms and equipment; yarns.

CURL BROTHERS SPECIALTIES LIMITED
334 Lauder Avenue
Toronto, Ont. M6E 3H8

Wide range of inexpensive yarns, including wool and cottons; their linen rug warp is excellent; service is prompt; samples cost.

CUSTOM WOOLEN MILLS
R.R.1
Carstairs, Alberta T0M 0N0
(403) 337-2221

Sell many quilting and spinning supplies, as well as providing custom carding and sewing services.

R. STEIN YARN CORP. LIMITED
Place de la Mode
5800 Rue St. Denis, Suite 303
Montreal, P.Q. H2S 3L5
(514) 274-9475

The most extensive selection of
yarns in Canada is available here;
expensive, but worth
it . . . cashmere, alpaca, mohairs
Lopi, orlon, wools, boucles . . . .
samples cost.

BARBARA OLSEN
Box 422
Hines Creek, Alta. T0H 2A0
(403) 494-2176

Purebred Angora rabbits raised for
wool. Sells breeding stock
$15—$25. Wool $15—$25/lb. Also
sells it by the ounce.

P.E.I. SHEEP FARMERS CO-OP ASSOCIATION LTD.
Box 160
Charlottetown, P.E.I.

Natural shades in wool yarns.

EARTH FIBRES
9 William Street East
Oshawa, Ontario
(416) 576-9431

Handspun and unspun fibres,
natural-dyed wool, novelty yarns,
handmade garments. Ashford
spinning wheels, frame loom
weaving and spinning.

FIBRE FACTORY LTD.
1745 Marine Dr. West
Vancouver, B.C. V7V 1J5
(604) 922-2211

Retail shop selling spinning,
weaving and knitting supplies,
New Zealand fleece, looms,
carders, exotic fibres for spinning,
traditional spinning wheels, Indian
spinners, LeClerc looms. Mail
order catalogue and samples
available.

HIGHLAND OF HASTINGS WEAVERS
R.R.1
Corbeyville, Ont. K0K 1V0

Handwoven fabric from Canadian
and imported wools, specializing
in natural fibres. Handwoven
stoles 22'' x 77'' $25 postpaid.
Fabric also sold by mail order.

Fabric samples $1 plus S.A.S.E.
Yarn samples for stoles $1 plus
S.A.S.E. Refundable with order.

LES TEXTILES DU GRAND MOULIN INC.
St. Pascal, Kamouraska Co.
Quebec G0L 3Y0

Unbleached fleece, wool yarns in
natural shades.

VALLEY FIBRES LTD.
51 William Street
Ottawa, Ont. K0A 2N0

Supplies for spinners, weavers,
macrameists (fleeces, flax, rovings,
spindles, spinning wheels, yarns,
dyes). Complete mail order
service.

THE VILLAGE WEAVER STUDIO
551 Church Street
Toronto, Ont. M4Y 2E2
(416) 964-0436

Terrific yarns . . . cottons, linens,
wools, mohairs, chenilles, raffia,
fleece, horse and camelhair;
books; looms; equipment. Service
here is prompt and friendly. Good
mail order. Samples cost.

WALTONCRAFT STUDIO
58 Dutch Village Road
Halifax, N.S.
(902) 477-6495

Mrs. Hill is practically an
institution herself; her charming
studio offers yarns, books, looms
and equipment; occasionally she
gives courses to beginners.

GERALD H. WHITAKER IMPORT
6291 - 9 Dorman Road
Mississauga, Ont. L4V 1K6
(416) 677-3464

Natural fibres—fleece, yarns—and
spinning wheels.

WILD WORLD OF HERBS
11 St. Catherine Street E.
Montreal, Quebec H2X 1K3

There's no denying that WW
offers the most comprehensive list
of plant dyes, mordants and herbs
available anywhere; however,
their mail order department is
given to delays that last for
months. They have it all . . . if
you want it, you put up with
maximum prices and spotty
service.

ISLAND CRAFTS
335 George Street
Sydney, N.S. B1P 1J7
(902) 539-6474

Moderately priced wool yarns in natural shades.

FILATURE LEMIEUX INC.
St. Ephrem, Beauce
Quebec G0M 1R0
(418) 484-2169

Moderately priced wools in various plies and great colours; prompt. Samples cost.

THE NEWFOUNDLAND WEAVERY
170 Duckworth Street
St. John's, Nfld.
(709) 753-0496

Yarns, books, looms, equipment; also have a Toronto location. Samples cost.

FILATURE SUTTON
12 Main Street
Sutton, Quebec J0E 2K0
(514) 538-3222

Wool, cotton and novelty yarns; lovely rayon chenilles; reasonable prices; samples cost.

Courses

Not all the institutions and organizations listed offer dyeing and spinning, but all give instruction in weaving. Some, like the Ontario College of Art, have credit programmes designed to lead to a certificate; others, like the Banff School of Fine Arts, offer work-intensive sessions with "names" in the textile field that appeal to craftspeople who are fairly well along in their training.

Programmes vary from year to year; instruction varies just as greatly. If you're not happy with one set-up, try another programme at another place. Costs for weaving instruction are minimal when frame or other small looms are used, higher when the studio is fully equipped with a range of floor looms and spinning wheels. You pay more for credit courses. If the credits are not important, try to find a non-credit programme or investigate "monitoring" a class.

In addition to these addresses, check with local organizations that are art and craft oriented; each province has several. Also inquire at the YMCA, YWCA and Women's Institutes.

ALBION HILLS FARM SCHOOL
Caledon East, Ont. L0N 1E0

Instruction in weaving, spinning and dyeing.

THE BANFF SCHOOL OF FINE ARTS
Banff, Alberta
T0L 0C0

Courses are short and expensive but definitive in what they offer: weaving, dyeing, design.

CANADORE COLLEGE OF APPLIED ARTS & TECHNOLOGY
Box 5001
North Bay, Ont. P1B 8K9

Weaving courses.

GEORGIAN COLLEGE
401 Duckworth Street
Barrie, Ontario

Weaving courses.

HOLLAND COLLEGE
Box 7500, Burns Avenue
West Royalty
Charlottetown, P.E.I.
(902) 894-5104

Two-year programme in weaving; extension programmes in other communities.

NOVA SCOTIA COLLEGE OF ART & DESIGN
5163 Duke Street
Halifax, N.S. B3J 3J6
(902) 422-7381

Full-credit programmes in weaving and textiles; non-credit programmes offered by Extension Services.

ONTARIO COLLEGE OF ART
100 McCall Street
Toronto, Ontario

Courses in weaving; credit towards certification; non-credit as well.

SENECA COLLEGE OF APPLIED ARTS & TECHNOLOGY
1750 Finch Avenue
East Willowdale, Ontario
M2N 5T7

Weaving courses.

SHERIDAN SCHOOL OF CRAFT & DESIGN
1460 Sheridan Way
Mississauga, Ont. L5H 1Z7
(416) 274-3685

An excellent school for all crafts—weaving, pottery, jewelry, wood, etc.

TOWER STUDIO
Box 1719
Gravenhurst, Ont. P0C 1G0
(705) 687-2575

Courses in weaving, spinning, dyeing, stitchery.

DEPT. OF YOUTH, RECREATION & CULTURAL RESOURCES
Handcrafts Branch
Box 6000
Fredericton, N.B. E3B 5H1

Offers various workshops and training programmes.

QUILTS

"Trip Around the World"—"Grandmother's Garden"—"Sunshine and Shadow"—all are names for quilt designs, bringing back memories of a time when living was slower and there were few outlets for women's creative talents.

Unlike other crafts abandoned in the wake of modern technology, there's still a tradition of quilt making among the Amish, Hutterites and Mennonites. Dacron has replaced the carded wool filling; there's more variety of fabrics available; and the designers create their own variations on traditional patterns, but the sense of heritage continues.

Quilting is a social activity among the Mennonite women in the communities of Clearbrook, Greendale and Yarrow in British Columbia's Fraser Valley. A visit for coffee is accompanied by a few stitches on the current quilt. A morning gathering of several women is an opportunity to catch

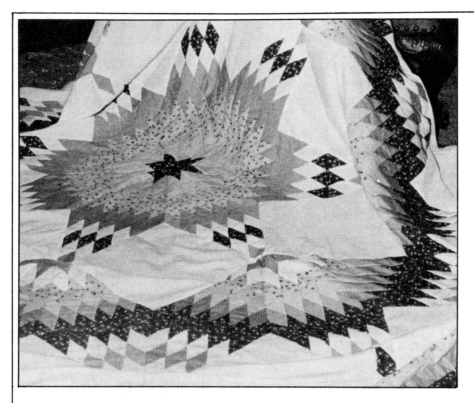

up on family news and work on a "church" quilt. The "church" quilts are projects stitched especially for the Mennonite Relief Sales held in September each year to raise funds for church mission work. These Relief Sales are colourful events—a harvest of bounty from the farmland—vegetables, fruit, honey, herbs and plants, a variety of new and used items, and the beautiful quilts which are auctioned off at prices ranging from $150 to $500.

In Yarrow it's not uncommon to see old-fashioned wool-filled comforters airing on porch railings or clotheslines, the covers (like eiderdown covers) washed and drying alongside. These comforters are constructed like huge flat pillows, a layer of soft insulating wool sandwiched between two yardages of cloth, then loosely stitched about every six inches to hold the batting in place. The covers are sometimes a plain length of fabric, or as elaborately pieced as the quilts, sewn on three sides and buttoned at one end.

Quilt designs are graphic examples of the old adage—"Necessity is the mother of invention." No scrap of fabric was allowed to be wasted; in pioneer times cloth was a precious commodity. Patterns from the early 1800s are usually either bars or diamonds, with perhaps only two types of colours or fabrics used, and almost always with the squares in the corners accenting the central square design. Wool flannel and worsted were frequently used, making heavy covers for protection from the cold in the days before central heating. The more recent quilt designs are intricate and radiantly coloured—and machine washable.

"Friendship Quilts" make very special mementos. These are made by piecing together fabric squares covered with individual appliqués and the embroidered names of the makers, and given to a cherished neighbour moving away to a new home.

The recent revival of quilt making as an art form has led to several publications on the history of quilts. Two recommended books on this subject are listed below:

300 YEARS OF CANADA'S QUILTS
Mary Conroy
Griffin House, Toronto
Paperback, 133 pages, $7.50

THE PIECED QUILT:
An American Design Tradition
Jonathan Holstein

Allows wax to saturate fabric more thoroughly
Makes squares or rectangles
Owing to its unusual shape the batik frame must be sent as a separate package. When ordering the batik frame be sure to include enough extra to accommodate a three-pound package. $6.20

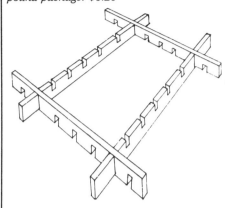

WAX THERMOMETER
A perfectly designed thermometer for a wax pan, rests on the edge and won't slip in. $1.65

POTTERY

Some years ago, when I was teaching a night school pottery class, I prepared a series of printed lessons for the students, hoping to save them the time of ploughing through the pottery texts. My "lessons" fit nicely onto just 14 pages, with lots of white space. Sometimes it's better to get started working with something and then back-track to the book learning. Traditionally, pottery was taught to apprentices who learned by *doing*.

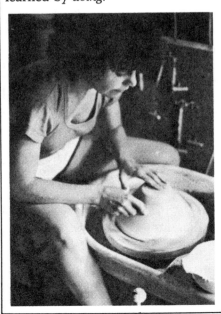

For those who want to know more about the chemistry—or the philosophy—of pottery, the following books are recommended:

CLAY & GLAZES FOR THE POTTER
By Daniel Rhodes
STONEWARE & PORCELAIN
By Daniel Rhodes
A POTTERS BOOK
By Bernard Leach
CERAMICS
By Glenn C. Nelson
MAKING POTTERY WITHOUT A WHEEL
By F. Carlton Ball and Janice Lovoos
KILNS
By Daniel Rhodes

NATURE AS DESIGNER
By Bertel Bager
(which is not about pottery at all, but an invaluable source of design inspirations.)

And if you're thinking about opening your own studio, a down-to-earth review of the economics and business end of potting is available in **STAYING AFLOAT IN MUD** by Ellen Zeiss and Ronda Green (Emily Carr School of Art, Vancouver, B.C.).

—*Paula Gustafson*
Yarrow, B.C.

STRATFORD CLAY SUPPLY LTD.
Box 344
Stratford, Ont. N5A 6T3
(519) 271-5371

Quality pottery and ceramics supplies to hobbyists, schools, clubs and professionals. Extensive catalogue, sent free.
Wood Kick Wheel Kit $112.65

PV ENTERPRISES
66 McDougall Road
Waterloo, Ont. N2L 2W5
(519) 884-1202

GREENBARN POTTERS SUPPLY LTD.
2982 164th Street
Surrey, B.C.
(604) 536-9198

Pottery supplies and equipment.

B.C. POTTERS SUPPLY
20266 Douglas Cr.

Langley, B.C.
(604) 534-8424

Complete pottery supplies and equipment.

PARAGON KILNS so easy to fire. The favourite of thousands of hobbyists just starting in ceramics and doing their own firing. Full 14-3/8" dia. x 13¼" deep. Will handle 14" plates easily. Outstanding features are a full open-hinged lid, quality insulating firebrick and heavy-duty Kanthal elements. Fires to cone 6. Extremely low operating cost. One 4-way switch with low, medium and high heats allows for complete firing control and you can fire as fast or slow as you may desire. Receptacle in kiln standard for easy plug in of collar later. With off/on pilot light above switch.
In stainless steel $179.50
In hammertone brown $169.00

ONTARIO POTTERS' ASSOCIATION
Hamilton Place
Box 2080, Station A
Hamilton, Ont. L8N 3Y7
(416) 523-8225

Pottery and Glass: An illustrated guide to the work and studios of potters and glass blowers of Ontario. Membership $15/yr. includes subscription to "Ontario Potter" which is published 5 times a year.

WOODWORKING

LEE VALLEY TOOLS LTD.
Box 6295
Ottawa, Ontario K2A 1T4
$1.00, 88 pages (Softcover)

This new Canadian offering of high quality, hand-powered

woodworking tools ranges from rosewood try squares to Brazilian Tulipwood marking gauges and jointer planes crafted of Goncalvo Alves, a tropical wood of outstanding hardness with a natural impregnation of waxy lubricants.

In between are hundreds of less exotic tools, but chosen with care for quality and usefulness. Inshaves for hollowing out bowls and chair seats, log saws, wood sculptor's tools and a hard-to-find axe-eye splitting maul head.

CROSS CUT SAWS: These cross cut saws, which are about 40 years old, came out of an old New Jersey warehouse and are in perfect condition. No longer available from current production, we were particularly pleased to find them because of their size. Although they were called ''one-man cross-cuts,'' they take a good man to use one continuously. Fortunately we also have supplementary handles so that they can be used by two people as well. Available in two styles. The Champion tooth is a bit better for felling because of the higher ratio of raking to cutting teeth. The Lance perforated tooth is better for all round use. Since our stock is quite limited on these saws, we will ship your preference on tooth pattern if we can, otherwise we will substitute the other pattern unless you mark ''cancel'' on your order. Our supplementary handle fits both saws.
4' Lance perforated tooth $44.95
4' Champion tooth $44.95
Handle $4.95

AXE-EYE SPLITTING MAUL: Most splitting mauls available have two major failings—they are awkward to use and they have a sledge eye rather than an axe eye. The awkwardness is caused by the nearly round sledge handle required and the sledge eye contributes to broken handles because of frequent fracturing just back of the head. This splitting maul is an ideal weight (at 6 lbs.) and with an axe handle makes a much, much easier tool to use. The pronounced oval of an axe handle allows the user to use the maul by ''feel'' rather than by visual checking before each swing. The much greater depth of an axe handle where it enters the maul eye also provides a very strong handle. The maul comes unhelved allowing you to select a handle length and design best suited to you. Splitting Maul $13.75.

WOODCRAFT CATALOGUE
314 Montvale Avenue
Woburn, Massachusetts 01801
$1.00 104 pages

Only rarely do you come across a catalogue so obviously done by people with a true respect and love for the things they are selling. The Woodcraft Catalogue offers tools for both the fine woodcrafter (sculpting mallets, carving knives, violin makers' gouges) and the log builder (peaveys, woodchoppers' mauls, English drawknives and froes for making cedar shakes.)

Also offered, along with all the tools needed to make them, are measured drawing plans for looms, spinning wheels, cider presses, corner cupboards and Windsor chairs. The catalogue is also an exceptional source of books on all facets of woodworking.

Random Comment

I'm not impartial about Lee Valley Tools. I read the adverts of it several times before I bit and wrote for a catalogue; it was, at least and at last, a Canadian tool-by-mail operation.

Well---

The catalogue, when it arrived (delayed by the Post Office, not by Lee Valley, as the postmark showed) was a wonder. In the first place, it is a five-colour production on slick paper, with many first-class photo reproductions. In the second place, all the goods are best of kind, or so close that it makes little difference. (A few are the ONLY ones of their kind.) In the third place, *all* conditions are plainly set out—and I may say that Lee Valley puts conditions on itself, and goes much further to meet them than is generally regarded as economically feasible in business—especially mail-order business—nowadays. So far as I am aware, Lee Valley is the best single source of uncommon, high-quality hand tools in Canada. It also sells some hardware, equally uncommon and beautiful, and collectors' items in both tools and hardware. There are a few power tools listed, but these are not obtainable anywhere else in the country and are of outstandingly high quality—the tool grinder, for example.

Lee Valley's catalogue lists the best assortment of genuine Arkansas stones I have ever seen advertised anywhere in the U.S. or Canada. I would say that this is an essential catalogue for woodworkers, including joiners, cabinet makers and instrument makers, but also for timber and log builders. (Where else can you get a broadaxe—a *good* broadaxe? Or three kinds of adze?) The catalogue itself is worth twice the price—and, in addition to the tools, is filled with straight talk on tool care, use and storage. Special supplements are issued from time to time—with no fanfare in advance—advertising, for instance, collectors' item tools or hardware. (Would you believe a *solid* brass drawer pull? Don't ask Lee for it, they'll be sold out by now.)

Let me give you my own experience: I bought a bent gouge from Lee Valley. I was delighted with it; it performed much better than I had expected —in fact, it worked as I had hoped! But I broke a chip out of the edge. Fancying that there might be a flaw in the metal, I sent it back and sent a covering letter separately. The package arrived first. Leonard G. Lee looked at the tool, deduced what I had done wrong, repaired the damage, sent it back, and wrote me a detailed letter telling me where *and why* I had gone wrong—no recriminations about my ignorance and haste, mind you, just plain fact. He also threw in some alternative suggestions. No charge.

—*Norman McKinney*
Toronto, Ontario

CRAFT DIRECTORIES

Some years ago I was involved in compiling a handbook about craftspeople in the province of British Columbia: a directory listing their names and addresses, and the crafts they made, sold and/or taught. A new issue of that handbook recently arrived on my desk and I looked forward to leafing through it. Unfortunately, my anticipation quickly turned to dismay. Instead of being a refreshed and revised edition of the original ''Handbook for Craftspeople in British Columbia'' first published in 1973, the new handbook was a retrograde version entitled "Handicraft Directory." Handicraft? I thought we'd passed that word at least 10 years ago, back in the days when earning a living as a potter or silversmith was considered a silly ambition.

Further review of the "Handicraft Directory" left me in a state of mind that could only be called utter depression. I felt embarrassed having my name listed among so much misinformation. Every page contained glaring errors. The directory could have only been revised by someone who knew nothing about the phenomenal growth of crafts during the past decade—and who also knew little of the art of editing!

But, being the eternal optimist, I decided to try to find out if other provinces published craft directories and whether they were any more satisfactory to the craftspeople involved (although, in fact, the directories are published for the benefit of tourists and other purchasers of crafts).

I wrote to each provincial government, asking for a copy of their directory if they published one, and how the information was collected and compiled. I did not receive replies from Alberta, Ontario or Quebec. My letter was returned from the Parliament Buildings in New Brunswick marked "Address Incomplete." Manitoba sent me a photocopy of the Winnipeg Yellow Pages listing "Handicrafts" (along with a very nice letter saying that a Mr. Kirk Creed was preparing a craft directory for that province—on his own initiative). That left Saskatchewan, Nova Scotia, Newfoundland and Prince Edward Island with the only interest in promoting their craft industries, but what a heartening interest it is!

PROVINCE OF PRINCE EDWARD ISLAND
Handcraft Division
Dept. of Industry
& Commerce
Box 2000
Charlottetown, P.E.I.
C1A 7N8

Prince Edward Island puts out a publication entitled "Special Attractions—Coming Events Highlights—Handcrafts." Glossy pages, lots and lots of photographs, and what appears to be a fairly comprehensive listing of craftspeople and stores selling crafts. This is a "vacationer's handbook," and as such is an excellent little publication—in both English and French.

THE SASKATCHEWAN CRAFT COUNCIL
Box 7408
Saskatoon, Sask. S7K 4J3

Saskatchewan's Ministry of Culture and Youth is in the process of preparing a handbook for craftspeople—it should be available in late 1979—but in the meantime they've established a very active Craft Council which, in turn, publishes a quarterly magazine entitled "The Craft Factor."

NOVA SCOTIA DEPT. OF RECREATION
Handcraft Section
Box 864
Halifax, Nova Scotia B3J 2V2

Nova Scotia's "Handcraft Directory" is published by their Department of Recreation on what appears to be light-brown recycled paper and contains an introduction by the Minister of Recreation which states that "The Department of Recreation is also very cognizant of the importance of serving as a catalyst to help Nova Scotia craftsmen develop a positive climate for selling their respective works . . . ." Encouraging words—and the booklet bears out the concern and awareness. There is a map showing the various counties in the province, and a short description of each craftsperson, crafts shop, and supply source in each of the counties, as well as a listing of crafts organizations and annual crafts events. The format could well serve as a model of how craft directories should be prepared.

Of course, one of the reasons this directory is so good is that a form of Handcraft Directory has

been published by Nova Scotia for over 30 years. Practice makes perfect.

HOME INDUSTRIES DIV.
Dept. of Rural Development
Confederation Building
St. John's, Newfoundland

"Crafts of Newfoundland and Labrador" is a nicely designed booklet published under the auspices of their Ministry of Tourism and Recreation and Ministry of Rural Development, and contains the enlightened statement that "Crafts, traditional and otherwise, must be taken seriously as an alternative livelihood." Interspersed among the listings of craft shops and craftspeople are brief descriptions and photographs of the how and why of some of the more traditional crafts such as Caribou skin moccasins, Spruce root baskets, and Birch brooms. Educational— and intriguing.

ONTARIO CRAFTS COUNCIL
346 Dundas Street West
Toronto, Ont. M5T 1G5
(416) 366-3551

The Ontario Crafts Council, it turns out, does exist and recently published its second edition of "The Directory of Craft Organizations in Canada" which can be ordered for the cost of $3.80. Also available are an Ontario directory and membership at $15/year.

As for the distribution of the handbooks, Prince Edward Island prints 50,000 each year; Nova Scotia prepares 75,000. (British Columbia, thankfully, published only a few thousand of the 1978 'revised' edition, and most of those were mailed to the craftspeople themselves.) It seems obvious, however, that if the former two provinces with a relatively small craft industry can justify the need for large printings of their craft directories, then some of the more populous provinces might be wise to reconsider the marketing needs of their own craftspeople and distribute craft directories worthy of the name.

—Paula Gustafson
Yarrow, B.C.

Good Food, Unlimited

An introduction and a modest proposal

I recently sat through a live performance by the now mass-marketed Wild & Crazy Guy, Steve Martin, in which he described his new neighbours, who were, as he put it, "into cannibalism."

Not wanting to alienate these newcomers, Martin said he was considering taking up the practice himself . . . hastening to add that, "Of course, I would only be into eating vegetarians."

The natural food business, despite earlier predictions of its fleeting trendiness, is alive and well because, like Steve Martin's comic ego, more and more of us like to know what we are getting in the food we buy. While we continue to hear cries of "rip-off" and while people continue to wrangle over the definition of "health

food" or "natural food," the fact is that the number of alternative food stores, co-ops and restaurants is growing in Canada. If, for some of us, the health food outlet is not the brains of a more holistic way of life, it is at the heart and, most certainly, the stomach of it.

One proof of the spreading appeal of better foods is the appearance, from huge corporate entities, of whole grain cereals and other "health food type" products. They have done particularly well with granola bars in the supermarkets as well as school cafeterias. There is, however, more to healthful eating than Crunchy G.

The following source listing represents only an introduction to alternative food outlets in Canada, focussing on those which deal in mail order, the major distributors

and umbrella groups under which many local food cooperatives exist, as part of a growing network of non-supermarket-food sources. Simply by thumbing through the Yellow Pages and checking bulletin boards in sympathetic public places, the reader should be able to discover the presence of local co-ops, health food restaurants and natural food stores.

The latter range from homey, cottage industry, bring-your-own-container shops to high powered commercial retail businesses, replete with fluorescent WHEAT GERM ON SALE THIS WEEK! signs. Commercial chains such as Farefax and the Health Shoppe differ drastically from the cooperatively run store, where members scoop, bag and weigh their own purchases, and, in some cases, even handle cash exchanges in the store. The difference is even more marked than, say, the gap between Becker's and the old country general store. The number of natural food stores varies greatly from province to province, with a preponderance on the western side of the cordillera. British Columbia's reputation for having a healthy environment is certainly reflected in the number of such shops, and the names there have a flavour that is distinctly western (e.g. Triple Jim's Fruit Stand and Natural Food Store). Many of the outlets in Alberta are located in strip plazas, and many prairie stores are fronts for bible and religious centres.

Even if they seem to roll up the streets in St. John's before the sun sets, there is still Mary Jane's, the foremost natural food outlet in Newfoundland. In areas without ready access to a shop, there is always Canada Post, and many stores will arrange mail order service.

Food co-ops, despite false starts and failures in many places, continue to grow in number, strength and in the types of members they attract. The number of communities or regions having active co-ops seems likely to increase in the near future, with prospects of even more troubled economic times. Although some observers feel a slight optimism about the growing number of unadulterated food choices in the supermarkets, the huge chains continue to increase profits while both the farmer and consumer suffer.

Co-ops vary from disorganized and maddening to deal with, to extremely vital groups which not only provide their members with fair-priced sustenance but also encourage social interaction and an exhilarating *esprit de corps*. Substantial savings can be had in bulk purchases of grains, nuts and beans, and co-ops are often the sole source for hard-to-find "all natural" yogurt and other products, especially in rural areas or small towns.

For those who live beyond the influence of retail outlets or co-

ops, or if the local alternatives prove unsatisfactory, there is always the mail order distributor or the large food outlets that are worth a long drive for stocking up on bulk items.

The listings which follow are only part of what I hope will become a truly comprehensive directory of all natural food outlets in Canada, as well as those which are North American in scope. People interested in contributing information to this effort and who have first-hand knowledge of specific reasturants, shops, distributors and co-ops are invited to write me at the following address:

Canadian Natural Foods Directory
c/o The Harrowsmith Sourcebook
Camden East, Ontario K0K 1J0
—*Michael Schultz*
Gormley, Ontario

MAIL ORDER NATURAL FOOD STORES

COLLECTIVE RESOURCE AND SERVICES WORKERS CO-OP
1239 Odlum
Vancouver, B.C.
(604) 299-6322

HEALTHWAY NATURAL FOODS
805 Denman
Vancouver, B.C.
(604) 684-4911

SOUTH GRANVILLE HEALTH FOODS LTD.
2861 Granville
Vancouver, B.C.

HEALTH FOOD SERVICE
209 City Centre
Vancouver, B.C.
(604) 632-7427

GRASSROOTS NATURAL FOODS LIMITED
124 E. Yale
Chilliwack, B.C.
(604) 792-0312

VIT-A-BAR HEALTH FOODS
221 Cranbrook

Cranbrook, B.C.
(604) 426-8563

MILNE'S MANNA
1451 Ellis
Kelowna, B.C.
(604) 762-5515

VALLEY NATURAL FOOD CENTRE
3 - 275 Seymour
Kamloops, B.C.
(604) 372-8614

FORT NELSON HEALTH FOOD CENTRE
Box 568, Dixie Lee Bldg.
Fort Nelson, B.C.
(604) 774-6226

NUTS TO YOU
Box 93
Winlaw, B.C.
(604) 226-7670
Small family business offering limited selection of nuts and dried fruits.
Almonds, raw $3.44 per lb.
Pecan pieces, raw $3.99 per lb.
Thompson Raisins, Organic $2.65 per lb.
Carob pieces $1.45 per lb.
(Prices do not include packing or shipping.)

YUKON HEALTH FOOD CENTRE INC.
504 Main St., Box 4519
Whitehorse, Yukon
(403) 667-2306

DELTA HEALTH FOODS
5008 Forrest Drive
Yellowknife, N.W.T.
(604) 873-3113

HILCOA PRODUCTS
Box 38, Station T
Calgary, Alberta
(403) 259-4411

VEGA HEALTH FOODS LTD.
1314a - 17th Avenue S.W.
Calgary, Alberta
(403) 245-2876

ALPHA OMEGA HEALTH FOODS
5213 - 50th Avenue
Grand Centre, Alberta
(403) 594-3533

NORTHERN HEALTH FOODS LIMITED
273 - 2nd Avenue S.
Saskatoon, Sask.
(306) 244-4644

BUCKLAND PEA FARMS
Box 2, Site 23, R.R.5
Prince Albert, Sask.
(306) 764-8027

Green soup peas and pea flour.
Send $1.00 for sample packet.

ANDERSON'S ORGANIC GRAINS
Box 186, Lowe Farm
Morris, Manitoba
(204) 746-8887

Well known for its uncontaminated grains, Anderson's has produced wheat, rye and other field crops for 10 years without resorting to chemicals. They ship both whole grains and their own stone ground flours.
Stone Ground Whole Wheat Flour 20 cents per lb.
Stone Ground Rye Flour 22 cents per lb.
Whole Peas $14 per 100 lbs.
Whole Grain Wheat or Rye $12 per 100 lbs.
(Shipping charges not included in prices.)

VITA-HEALTH CO. LTD.
1025 Dugald
St. Boniface, Manitoba
(204) 233-0203
also
1415 Henderson
Winnipeg, Manitoba
(204) 339-2600

HEALTH FOODS
107 Main Street
Flin Flon, Manitoba
(204) 687-7103

NATURE'S PANTRY
276 Main
Steinbach, Manitoba
(204) 326-6029

EAST HILL PURE MAPLE SYRUP
R.R.3
King City, Ontario
(416) 727-6278
(J. Kinnear)

Mail order maple syrup (prices change each year).
Last year's prices—
$18.00 for 1 gallon
$6.00 for 1 quart
$3.75 for 1 pint

SWISS HERBAL REMEDIES LIMITED
Mail order, Wholesale & Retail
2557 Yonge Street
Toronto, Ontario
(416) 489-3211

1558 Bloor Street West
Toronto, Ontario
(416) 537-3862

GOODBODIES NATURAL FOODSTUFFS
Main Street
Sutton, Quebec
(514) 538-3312

Attractive, slim catalogue of natural foods and grooming products (shampoos, toothpaste, shaving cream).

BACK TO NATURE NATURAL FOODS
Bear River, Nova Scotia
(902) 467-3526

THE GOOD LIFE LTD.
82 Main St., Box 97
Montague, P.E.I.
(902) 838-3393

Co-ops

PSC WORKERS CO-OP
424 Craigflower
Victoria, B.C.
(604) 386-3880

COLLECTIVE RESOURCE AND SERVICES WORKERS CO-OP
1239 Odlum
Vancouver, B.C.
(604) 299-6322

FED UP CO-OPERATIVE WHOLESALE
304 East First Avenue
Vancouver, B.C.
(604) 872-0712

Fed-Up means food to a growing number of B.C. residents who are truly fed up with Safeway and its ilk. It means getting the highest quality food on the market for a mere $5 membership fee initially; it means getting together with people who usually have the same interests in good living as you do; it means a greater amount of control exerted in what your family eats; and for many members, Fed-Up is a natural extension of their life style.

All is not roses, though. Safeway shopping might look attractive when you've just finished a day at work and your co-op group needs you for food distribution, which could add another six to eight hours onto your already exhausting day. Or the supermarket might be even more attractive at -20 degrees C when your sputtering car is plowing through a snowy driveway somewhere in the back of beyond on the night your own food order is ready to be picked up.

However, let your faith waver once and find yourself standing in a lineup at Safeway with a tiny package of lentils which is twice the price and half the quality of your co-op lentils and you're hooked again. Back to the co-op and damn the hassle.

Fed-Up has a huge warehouse in Vancouver where all our food is ordered. Workers from local co-ops are required to put in "work weeks" at the warehouse on a rotation basis. If the local doesn't send a worker, the local doesn't get its food. Fair. Not everyone from a local finds himself at a work week, but everyone should. It's a warmly personal experience with hard work from the moment of arrival on Monday morning to departure Friday afternoon. People learn firsthand what the word "cooperative" really means as orders from up to seven co-ops are processed.

The food is gathered and shipped from Vancouver to the local co-op and inside that particular co-op, groups are mobilized on an alternating basis to distribute the food in family orders. Good companionship and good conversation at distribution.

Regional co-ops, taking in large areas of interior B.C., are struggling for existence. In the North, Co-Operative Operative Group (COG) takes in the smaller

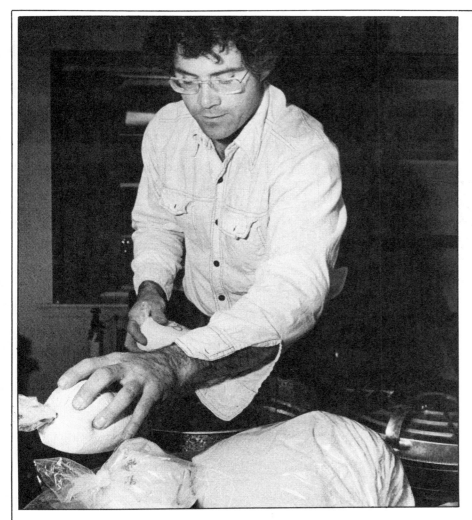

co-ops from Quesnel to Ootsa Lake; Edible Island regionalizes parts of Vancouver Island, and Kootenay Region takes in much of B.C.'s southeast section. Smaller co-ops can order together, and thereby take advantage of lower freight rates on the bulk food.

Storefront co-ops affiliated with Fed-Up are emerging in areas of concentrated population. Long overdue and especially good for smaller families who prefer to buy less than case lots.

Groups of talented people have banded together to form production co-ops, selling directly to Fed-Up—Uprising Breads, Canary Cannery, People's Share Granola and Wild West Organic Harvest all supply top quality food.

—Mary Ann Robertson
Quesnel, B.C.

PRAIRIE FOOD CO-OP FEDERATION

2344 Halifax Street
Regina, Sask.

ONTARIO FEDERATION OF FOOD COOPERATIVES AND CLUBS
680 King Street West
Toronto, Ontario M5V 1N3

Over half Ontario's food co-ops are active in the federation, which serves as an information source and central purchasing agent.

COOPERATIVE AUX PETITS OISEAUX
1596 St. Laurent
Montreal, Quebec
(514) 845-2824

One of the largest, most active single co-ops in the country, Cooperative aux Petits Oiseaux (Cooperative of Little Birds) is well-established and operates out of a three-storey building with a natural foods library and restaurant. They deal in both wholesale and retail orders and offer courses in nutrition and community action.

COOPERATIF ENTREPOT LA BALANCE
3508 Lionel Groux
Montreal, Quebec

Central cooperative supplier to a large number of Quebec co-ops.

L'ENGOULEVENT
330 rue St-Roch
Quebec City, Quebec

ENTREPOT DES ALENTOURS
Charles Provost
456 rue Florence
Sherbrooke, Quebec

This is a third central warehouse/supplier dealing with local co-ops in Quebec.

MARNAT CO-OP WAREHOUSE
Box 1163
Wolfville, N.S.
(902) 542-5818

This is the umbrella for 14 Maritime Co-Ops. They operate a large warehouse and publish a newsletter including current food and prices.

MANUFACTURERS, WHOLESALERS AND DISTRIBUTORS

SWAAN BULK NATURAL FOODS
1435 Store
Victoria, B.C.
(604) 382-6421

Retail and wholesale.

L'BEAR'S HEALTH FOODS LIMITED
1198 Pine Trail
Trail, B.C.
(604) 368-8318

ROGERS WHOLESOME FOODS LIMITED
R.R.3
Armstrong, B.C.
(604) 546-3155

Largest flour mill in British Columbia, specializing in whole grain products. Wholesale quantities, as well as a local outlet.

LIFESTREAM NATURAL FOODS LIMITED
12411 Vulcan Way
Richmond, B.C.
(604) 278-7571

Largest distributor of natural foods in Canada, selling in wholesale quantities across North America. Extensive catalogue listing everything from kasha buckwheat groats to organic blue cheese salad dressing.

GAHLER ENTERPRISES LIMITED
875 Shakespeare
N. Vancouver, B.C.
(604) 985-5649

ALBI IMPORTS LTD.
142 W. Hastings
Vancouver, B.C.
(604) 669-3626

ARDONA ENTERPRISES LIMITED
12200 Vulcan Way
Richmond, B.C.
(604) 278-4584

BACK TO EDEN NATURAL HEALTH FOODS
1214 William Street
Vancouver, B.C.
(604) 251-4452

DON BOSCO AGENCIES LTD.
7505 Victoria
Vancouver, B.C.
(604) 325-0711

CAN. SOYA INDUSTRIES
57 Lakewood
Vancouver, B.C.
(604) 255-1304

DOUG HEPBURN'S VILLAGE
Int. Health Products Ltd.
5 E. Broadway
Vancouver, B.C.
(604) 873-3684

FAMOUS FOODS LIMITED
1315 E. Hastings
Vancouver, B.C.
(604) 253-6414

FLORA DIST. LIMITED
8596 Fraser
Vancouver, B.C.
(604) 321-6641

GAHLER ENTERPRISES LIMITED
2435 Beta
Burnaby, B.C.
(604) 294-5126

GOLDEN NUTRITION LTD.
1975 Pine
Vancouver, B.C.
(604) 733-2116

I.G.E.
4517 E. Hastings
Burnaby, B.C.
(604) 298-2630

C.E. JAMIESON & CO. (DOMINION) LIMITED
8596 Fraser Avenue

Vancouver, B.C.
(604) 321-6641
Manufacture vitamins.

KIDD BROTHERS PRODUCE LIMITED
5312 Grummen
Burnaby, B.C.
(604) 437-9757

MERIT APPLIANCES
1 - 2934 Yew
Vancouver, B.C.
(604) 732-9436

NORTHERN GOLD FOODS LIMITED
6011 - 196A Street
Langley, B.C.
(604) 530-1131

NU-LIFE NUTRITION LTD.
871 Beatty
Vancouver, B.C.
(604) 682-4595

PARCO AGENCIES INTERNATIONAL LTD.
375 Terminal
Vancouver, B.C.
(604) 684-8301

PROGO PROTEIN LTD.
1035 Richards
Vancouver, B.C.
(604) 669-4626

QUEST VITAMIN SUPPLIES LIMITED
7475 Victoria
Vancouver, B.C.
(604) 324-0611

TRANS CANADA HEALTH FOOD JOBBERS LTD.
6829 Sillar
Burnaby, B.C.
(604) 433-1744

TROPHIC CANADA LTD.
260 E. Okanagan
Penticton, B.C.
(604) 492-8820

WILD WEST ORGANIC HARVEST
1275 - E 6th
Vancouver, B.C.
(604) 873-4488

TARA NATURAL FOODS
340 King Street E.
Kingston, Ontario
(613) 546-4439

Sells a wide selection of natural foods both retail and wholesale.

SANGSARA NATURAL FOODS LIMITED
682 George Street N.
Peterborough, Ont.
(705) 745-3674
Wholesale Division

(705) 748-4244
Retail Division

Sells mail order, wholesale and retail. Fresh organically grown fruits and vegetables available in season. An extensive selection of spices.

GIBSON SHORE LIMITED
45 Bowes Concord
Thornhill, Ontario
(416) 669-9626

GRAIN PROCESS ENTERPRISES
39 Golden Gate Court
Scarborough, Ontario
(416) 291-3226

Good prices on bulk orders of grain, nuts, flours, cereals, seeds, oils and dried fruits—some 170 items in all. Ships anywhere, prices F.O.B. Scarborough. Offers Triticale flour, a result of man-made cross-breeding of wheat and rye. Most products sold in 48, 24 or 12 kilo quantities, except the most expensive goods (e.g. whole raw cashews) which are also offered in smaller sizes.

Typical prices for 12 kilo quantities:
Cracked Wheat: $5.80
Durum Wheat Flour (stone ground) $6.40
Soya Beans: $6.50
Kidney Beans: $11.45
Bran Muffin Mix: $8.70
Rye Bread Mix: $10.10

MANNA FOODS INC.
Box 251, Station D
Scarborough, Ontario

Natural foods supplier to retail stores, registered co-ops, schools and other organizations. Everything from red lentils to horsetail soap and Bear Mush cereal. This firm is now organizing a tofu production facility to supply the Toronto area with bean curd made with imported Japanese Nigari and organic soybeans.

GREENLEAF WHOLE FOODS
Box 269
St. Jacobs, Ontario
(519) 745-5639

Greenleaf is, in my humble and totally biased opinion, the Farmer's Co-op-supermarket-Cadillac of "Health Food" stores.
It isn't really a health food store, it's a WHOLE food store.
Their warehouse in downtown Kitchener services restaurants, natural food stores, day care centres and other wholesale buyers in southern Ontario.
For those not within driving distance, Greenleaf will arrange large order shipments throughout most of southern Ontario.
—*Roger Nixon*
Dwight, Ontario

GOLDEN TOWN APPLE PRODUCTS LIMITED
Box 219
Clarksburg, Ontario
(519) 599-2415

Dried apples in bulk, both natural (no preservatives) and bleached (preservative S02).

HARVEY BURROWS & SON LIMITED
Wholesale and Retail
878 Cassells Street
North Bay, Ontario
(705) 472-2800

NATUR INC.
3600 Mtee St. Aubin
Chomedy, Quebec
(514) 331-1524

NUTRIFORCE INC.
(Natural Bakery)
2408 De La Province
Longueuil, Quebec
(514) 871-0043

BIO-FORCE CANADA LTD.
2404 de La Province
Longueuil, Quebec
(514) 871-1262

HOUSE OF HEALTH
1712 Granville Avenue
Halifax, N.S.
(902) 422-8331

WALNUT ACRES
Penns Creek, Penn. 17862
(717) 837-0601
A mail order supermarket of natural foods, without a trace of the supermarket mentality. Fascinating, 24-page catalogue that includes many foods grown or manufactured by Walnut Acres itself. The company farm has operated for 30 years without chemical fertilizers or pesticides. Will ship to Canada.

Cheese & Yogurt Making

HORAN-LALLY CO. LTD.
(Canadian Distributor)
1146 Aerowood Drive
Mississauga, Ontario L4W 1Y5
(416) 625-2560

CHR. HANSEN'S LABORATORY, INC.
9015 W. Maple Street
Milwaukee, WI 53214

Indispensable sources for anyone with a goat, cow or just a yearning for homemade dairy products. Hansen's now offers a non-animal, milk-coagulating agent for vegetarian cheese makers.
Acidophilus Yogurt Culture, $2.25
Buttermilk Culture, $2.25
Cheese Rennet Tablets, $6.50 for 25
Sour Cream Culture, $2.25
Dandelion Butter Colour, $2.10/3 oz.
Cheese Colour Tablets, $2.75/12

MARIKA DAIRY CULTURES

Natalex Corp.
Box 3060
Weehawken, N.J. 07087

The best yogurt you've ever tasted comes in little freeze-dried packages from Luxembourg via New Jersey. Marika Dairy Cultures, available by mail from Natalex Corp., can be used to prepare not only yogurt, but sour cream, buttermilk, cottage cheese and cream cheese. While the price of milk makes trying the other cultures financially unrewarding, this Bulgarian yogurt culture has proved itself simple to use and very inexpensive.

At $2.50 an envelope, use of the packaged culture at first glance seems more costly than simply buying a six-ounce container of plain yogurt to use as starter. If you use Marika wisely however, it becomes less expensive to have a far superior product. This is the way we do it: We use the packaged culture, which, incidentally, keeps indefinitely if unopened, to prepare one litre of yogurt using whole milk with extra skim milk powder stirred in. That original batch is then divided among three ice cube trays and frozen. When frozen, the cubes are divided into groups of six and packaged in plastic bags.

When we want to make yogurt, one cube goes into each yogurt machine jar and warm milk, with skim milk powder stirred in, is added. We eat five of those six jars and use the last to make the next batch of yogurt. The culture is only exhausted after that process is repeated four or five times so that a new batch of yogurt cubes is only needed, in our house, once a month. One $2.50 envelope lasts more than a year.

You can get a free 20-page information booklet on Marika Dairy Cultures from the company. If you write for yogurt culture from Canada, be sure to send U.S. funds.

—Sharon Airhart
Corbeyville, Ontario

HERBS

MURCHIE'S TEA & COFFEE LIMITED

560 Cambie Street
Vancouver, B.C. V6B 2N7

A hot cup of tea after class and an evening of tea drinking and studying early became a comfortable part of my married life. In those impoverished married student days, though, even a shared pot of tea had to be financially justified. Our ingenious—if tasteless—solution was to take one of those 100 for 89 cent tea bags and spear it over the stem of the electric coffee percolator we'd received as a wedding gift. We then perked 10 cups from one tea bag. As our finances improved, however, so did our taste, and we graduated from those bottom-of-the-line tea bags to "brand" name teas and occasional tins of Twining's tucked into Christmas stockings. A box of Constant Comment or lemon scented tea bags became special treats.

Recently, however, we discovered Murchie's, a Vancouver-based tea importing and blending house which specializes in mail orders. The Murchie family has been blending teas and coffees since 1894, offering more than two dozen original blends from Queen Victoria to Spider Leg Tea. Many kinds of coffee, along with herbs and spices are offered, some in distinctive gift packages, all available in bulk. The teas come in half-pound and one-pound bags and the prices, while slightly higher than ordinary supermarket brands, are often lower than those of specialty teas available in delicatessens. One pound of the very best orange pekoe sold by Murchie's is $3.25, a pound of Georgia blend, a lemon tea, is $2.70. A comparable specialty lemon tea, in bags, is about $12 per pound. Mailing costs add to the price of the tea, but that effect can be minimized if several families order together. Murchie's doesn't always have catalogues available but a price list can be obtained by mail.

—Sharon Airhart
Corbeyville, Ontario

LOOSE TEA

Irish Breakfast	*$1.45 per ½ lb.*
Green Gunpowder	*1.65 per ½ lb.*
Lapsang Souchong	*$1.75 per ½ lb.*
1976 Vintage Darjeeling	
(Moondakotee TGFBOP)	*$4 per ½ lb.*

In the sidehills of the majestic Himalayas in northern India is the district of Darjeeling. There are approximately 150 very distinctive tea gardens specializing in the world's most delicate teas.

Murchie's have decided to be the first in

the free world to bring to you these delicate flavours of muscatel teas by crop season, garden and vessel name.

WIDE WORLD OF HERBS
11 St. Catherine East
Montreal, Quebec H2X 1K3
or
WIDE WORLD OF HERBS
Box 266
Rouses Pt., New York 12979

Bitter=sweet

An herbalist's supply house—spices, teas, culinary herbs, rare botanicals, essential oils and mordants for natural dye processes. Minimum order is $5.00.

Frankincense 4 oz. $2.45
Myrrh Gum 4 oz. $4.36
Sarsaparilla Root 2 oz. $1.75
Mandrake Root 4 oz. $1.75
Sandalwood (soap or perfume essence) ¼ oz. $2.45

NEIGHBOURHOOD MAILBOX
1470 E. 22nd Street
Vancouver, B.C. V5N 2N7

Possibly the most extensive listing of ginseng products in the country, as well as common kitchen spices, herbs, natural toothpaste, kitchen items and herbal smoking mixes.

All Herbal Smoking Mix (If you don't smoke, drink as an herbal tea as well!) 50 cents per oz.

Bidis Indian Cigarettes (No tobacco: contains Holy Basil, Marjoram, Sour Orange, Papaya, Spearmint, Gigantic Swallow Wort, Thorn Apple) Pack of 20 -70 cents plus tax.

Tom's Natural Toothpaste (Spearmint or Fennel) 3 oz. $1.69

ATLANTIC MARICULTURE LIMITED
Box 2368
Dartmouth, N.S. B2Y 3Y4
(902) 434-6633

Hand-harvested vegetable products from the sea, including various flakes and powders derived from kelp and dulse. Inexpensive sample boxes are available, along with recipe suggestions.

GANDEN HERB FARM
Denman Island, B.C.
V0R 1T0
(604) 335-2426

New cottage industry offering dried herbs and their own blends of herbal teas under the Bodhi label.

THE HERB STORE
1913 Yew Street
Vancouver, B.C. V6K 3G3
(604) 733-4724

Going on eight years old, this is one of the oldest retail herb stores in North America. A large mail order service to all of North America.

The Herb Store
1913 Yew St.
Vancouver B.C.
Canada V6K 3G3

Benevolent Blood: *Is an excellent tea to*

take during all disorders of the blood as a purifier. It contains blessed thistle, burdock, sanicle, sarsaparilla, sassafras and yellow dock. 65 cents per oz.; $2.25/4 oz.; $7.10/16 oz.
Cloves: *Whole or ground $1.25 per oz.; $3.90/4 oz.; $12.90/16 oz.*
Coriander: *Whole or ground $.35 per oz.; $1.10/4 oz.; $2.30/16 oz.*
Dulse: *Fresh, Canadian, whole $.60 per oz.; $1.80/4 oz.; $5.85/16 oz.*
Mineral Mix: *Kelp, dulse and Irish moss $.70 per oz.; $2.30/4 oz.; $7.40/16 oz.*
Saffron: *Spanish, rare $3.95/¼ oz.; $850.00/lb.*

PEAT SMOKED IRISH TASTE

One of the great tastes of the world happens to be Irish ham and bacon smoked the traditional way with easy-to-procure peat moss.

Unlike hickory, oak, apple, alder and other wood used for meat and fish smoking, peat moss contains no resins, oils or tars that can impart a bitter flavour to the flesh.

To use peat, if it is purchased damp, spread it out in the sun until it is dry. It should be lit outdoors in a gallon-size can with a few holes in the bottom to permit air flow. I found it works very well if the dry moss is packed around a broken shovel handle or similar item placed in the centre of the can.

It should be lit from the bottom, and when smouldering well can be placed in whatever type of smokehouse you use.

I have had excellent smoking success using a 45-gallon clean steel barrel, or drum, having suspended a piece of mesh wire approximately four inches below the rim (to support the meat or fish) and using a piece of metal or plywood as a cover.

There should be at least four one-inch holes around the lower rim of the barrel and the can containing the burning peat moss must be raised off the bottom of the barrel with bricks or stones.

If properly done, the moss will burn for at least five hours, and if a darker smoke is required, the peat can may be filled again.

I use only peat moss to smoke up to 800 herring each year, as well as corned beef and bacon and find it superior to many other things I have tried.

—*George H. Johnson*
Belledune, New Brunswick

BEER & WINE

MOUNTMELLNICK MALTS
Duane's Imports
508 Canal Street
New York, New York 10013

Watered-down, freeze-dried, pumped up with CO_2 and filtered through asbestos—that's Twentieth Century Beer. How easy it is these days to drown in bad taste. *Fairy piss.* That's how lumberjacks order today's thin commercial beers. And they

drink it. Homebrew is the only way out.

But pity the poor cottage brewer: prone to creeping sloth (an occupational hazard) and to self-confessions that the stuff just doesn't justify all the fermenting and bottling mess-up. I confess that, up until a few months ago, I too was down on the old homebrew (this after writing a modestly successful booklet on the subject).

The problem seemed to be in the ingredients: canned syrups with a tinny taste. Canned syrup? A fatal shortcut, perhaps? Maybe I shouldn't have chucked out the rolling pin and black patent malt, but even in the woods we like a little progress. Finally giving up on the tinned syrups,

I let my brewing gear languish in a shroud of dust rolls beneath the gas refrigerator and spent unconscionable sums on Beck's imported German beer. Knowing that I could do better didn't overcome my reluctance to resume coarse-cracking malted grains.

Then one day a gift arrived: a box of exotic malts, canned and hopped extracts with English-Gaelic labels. I cooked up a crock right off, and two more the next day: light, dark, and stout. They worked, and after a month the caps came hissing off the finest beers I've ever bottled.

Mountmellnick, Ireland is the home of the outfit that turns out these all-barley malts—mostly for the Guiness brewery and a few pedigreed whiskey distilleries. Only a small portion of Mountmellnick products are extracted, hopped, and sold to homebrewers. Duane's Imports, a Manhattan homebrew supplier, tapes an envelope of carefully weighed and matched yeast to each can, christens them "Brewing Packs" and offers to ship them anywhere in the world. Even if you can't fathom the Gaelic on the label, these malts are noble enough to make a homebrewer realize why lager spelled backwards is regal. Hail!

The prices vary according to the quantity ordered, ranging from a stiff $7 per single can (35 oz.) to a reasonable $4.34 per can when ordered in cases of 12. (Your choice of any proportion of light, dark, and stout.) Shipping by UPS is free to any destination in the continental U.S., with different surcharges added for mailing elsewhere. (Canada is 25 per cent extra.) Duane's also offers a couple of "American" beers, hopped with no additives, as well as a complete stock of paraphernalia, including their own Home Brewing Handbook.

But it's their exclusive license to deal Mountmellnick malts that sets Duane's ahead of the pack. Two suggestions: try brewing these malts without sugar, especially the light for crystal clear beer. And write, don't call Duane's. They keep the number

secret. As the boss says, "When your customers are in varying stages of drunkenness at all hours, it's just something you have to do."

—*Tim Matson*
Thetford Center, Vermont

WINE ART

E.G. Arthurs & Sons Ltd.
2046 Avenue Road
Toronto, Ont. M5M 4A6
(416) 487-7124

Chain of wine and beer-making supply shops to be found in larger urban centres across Canada and the United States. Everything from fermentation vessels to rubber bungs, as well as concentrates made from varietal grapes in Europe, California, Australia, Canada and other wine growing countries. (One hundred ounces of concentrate yields about 5 gallons of wine.)

CALIFORNIAN:
Zinfandel—Red $28.95
SPANISH:
Red or Burgundy 160 oz. $32.95
Pommard 112 oz. $24.95
Red or Bordeaux 80 oz. $17.95
Premium Red 80 oz. $23.95
White or Chablis 160 oz. $29.95
Moselle 112 oz. $22.95
White 80 oz. $15.95
(Liebfraumilch not available)
Premium White 80 oz. $20.95
White 32 oz. $7.95
Red 32 oz. $8.95

WINE-ART SALES LTD.

3429 West Broadway
Vancouver, B.C. V6R 2B4
(604) 731-4726

THE WINE WORKS

392 Waterloo Street
London, Ont. N6B 2N8
(519) 438-9463

Well-stocked source of wine grape and fruit concentrates (more than 100 from which to choose), as well as brewing supplies and hardware. Publishes an informal newsletter and is equipped to handle mail orders.

French Pure Concentrates

Beaujolais $14.50 per 100 oz.
Burgundy $16.95 per 100 oz.
Bordeaux $16.95 per 100 oz.

Busby Hydrometer & Drake Trial jar $4.45
Mead Yeast (for 1-5 gals.) $.45
Rice Wine (Saki) Yeast $.45

THE VINTAGE SHOP LTD.

5766 Fraser Street
Vancouver, B.C. V5W 2Z5
(604) 325-5215

Specialty shop for home winemakers and amateur brewmasters. Grape concentrates (including Pinot Chardonnay and Baco Noir), malts, hops, equipment and how-to books. Will handle mail orders.

Wine Yeasts (Vierka—European Strains)

Types available: Beaujolais, Bordeaux, Bernkastler, Claret, Chianti, Chablis, Cold Ferment, Johannisberg-Riesling, Liebfraumilch, Madeira, Marsala, Niersteiner, Nahe, Perlschaum (Champagne), Pommard, Port, Ruedesheimer, Sauterne, Steinberger, Sherry, Tarragona, Tokaier. $1.15 ea.

Other Malts & Hops

Black Patent Malt 1 lb. $1.19
Pale Malt 1 lb. $1.19
Crystal Malt 1 lb. $1.19
Hops, Cluster No. 1, compressed 4 oz. $1.19
Golden Harvest Hops, compressed 4 oz. $1.19
Bramling Finishing Hops 1 oz. $1.19
Kent Finishing Hops 1 oz. $1.19
Indian Valley Hops, Pellets 2 oz. $1.29
German Hallertau Lager Hops 30 grams $1.19

Random Comment

WARNING: THIS HEALTH FOOD STORE MAY PROVE ADDICTIVE

Ah, the peace, quiet and privacy of a tranquil life in the country on an isolated road with no neighbours and 10 miles from the nearest hamlet. However—enter a distracting element—the children must not be deprived of all the 'advantages' of city life.

It was thus that my husband found himself chauffeuring our

eldest son each Friday evening to swimming lessons, 90 miles distant. While Andrew swam, my husband put in the time as best he could browsing through the stores. Not a dedicated, or even mildly interested shopper, he must surely have wished he were home by the fire instead of wandering this foreign terrain.

On his arrival home one Friday night he announced, "I have discovered a store you will love." When I finally managed to visit the store he had described so enthusiastically I did indeed love it. It was my first experience with a health food store; the most cluttered and interesting I have ever entered—it was necessary to move aside racks of books and literature to even get to some of the shelves. Enthused about cooking and always eager for new ideas, ingredients and recipes, I found this store a treasure trove of excitement and inspiration. I spent a delightful two hours which seemed like 20 minutes and had to be dragged away by my family. I visited this store at every opportunity and never lost my initial fascination.

Since then health food stores have proliferated and become almost commonplace. (A real symbol of their success is that most supermarkets now have specially designated health food sections). Influenced by the people I met through the health food store, I gradually became a convert and in the intervening years have altered our family's diet drastically.

Perhaps most symbolic of the change is the bread I bake, using it as a vehicle to introduce such wholesome ingredients as whole grain, wheat germ, rice polishings, Brewer's yeast, Triticale flour, bran, soya and pea flours. As well, I have mixed in squash, mashed potatoes, carrots (the family drew the line at cauliflower), cottage cheese, fruit, tomatoes, cheese, honey, blackstrap molasses, seeds, raisins, currants, other dried fruits and eggs—all sorts of nutritious fare that vary the taste and texture of the resulting bread.

In a Department of Agriculture course I attended recently, the instructors claimed there is no saving in making homemade

bread; in my personal experience this is simply not true. Even enriching your bread with many of the above mentioned, naturally nutritious additions, and using whole grain flours instead of 'enriched' supermarket white flour, homemade bread consistently costs less, adds more food value to the diet, and tastes better (much better!) than 'store' loaves. Perhaps the discrepancy arises because I purchase flour 100 pounds at a time through a natural food store, rolled oats in 20-pound bags, blackstrap molasses by the gallon, honey in 30-pound pails, powdered milk in 12-pound boxes and bake an oven full of bread or buns at a time rather than just one or two loaves, resulting in savings in energy costs and purchasing prices. The cost for my labour of love in making the bread is zero.

These bulk purchases entail savings, but the largest saving of all can be made by purchasing yeast in quantity. If you buy the familiar little yellow packages in the supermarket the yeast becomes probably the most expensive ingredient in your bread. Each package, costing almost 25 cents, contains slightly less than one tablespoon and will raise two loaves of bread (more if you are willing to wait longer for the bread to rise), thus adding 12 cents to the cost of each loaf. The small four ounce tins at $1.65 are less expensive, they contain enough yeast to make about 28 loaves at a cost per loaf for the yeast of approximately five and a half cents. Sometimes supermarkets carry two pound tins of Fleischmann's yeast; the most recent price I have seen was $3.39, which works out to one and a half cents per loaf for the yeast. The last yeast I purchased at the health food store cost $1.60 a pound, about 10 cents a pound less than the two pound tins, so that bread made with this yeast cost even less than one and a half cents per loaf for the yeast. Bulk yeast from a health food store keeps very well if you seal it in a glass jar and keep it in the refrigerator. I have been using it for several years and have never had any problem.

One may almost eliminate the need for purchasing yeast by using sourdough, fermenting cooked brown rice, making a raising mixture from hops, or making 'salt-rising bread' with water-ground cornmeal or potatoes as they do in the southern states. These methods are fun to try but they do take

longer; the breads have distinctive flavours and unfortunately they also often have a distinctive (one might even say unpleasant) aroma during the process.

I have great respect for nutritionists and home economists, but on the radio, in the newspaper and at the seminars and courses I have attended I have frequently detected in them a somewhat negative attitude toward health food stores and the natural products they represent. Favourite phrases seem to be, "All food is healthy," and, "We have to trust the government to ensure that our food is safe." Recently in a supermarket on a package labelled Chicken Noodle Soup I read the list of ingredients, (by law, ingredients must be labelled in order of quantity, beginning with the most plentiful): noodles, salt, hydrolyzed plant protein, malto-dextrin, chicken fat, sugar, vegetable oil shortening, wheat starch, spices, monosodium glutamate, onion powder, dehydrated chicken meat, parsley. Compare that with the homemade chicken soup you prepare for your family—that so-called soup in the package had scarcely the faintest of contact with a chicken and contained far more salt and sugar than chicken. Do you really want to trust a company or government who would foist that on an unsuspecting public?

In contrast, a good natural food store can offer confidence-inspiring ingredients and the motivation to use them. I'm addicted to health food stores, and I have no regrets.

—Lesley Rowsome
Cloyne, Ontario

Books

The greatest number of recipes published in modern cookbooks suffer seriously from Kraft dinner syndrome: stir together one package of jelly powder, one quart of pink and green miniature marshmallows, one box of Hamburger Helper and a gallon of Miracle Whip. Mix well and top with an edible oil product. It just doesn't fit the alternate life style; nowhere in the bountiful homestead harvest will you find a tin of potatoes or frozen bread dough.

In self defence, I turned to a variety of old fashioned and even antique recipes (receipts, they're often called) to prepare decent meals which begin with real foods. Some of my favourite cookbooks have been around for 40 years, others are modern printings of very old recipes, still others are new but sensible and interesting:

FOOD THAT REALLY SCHMECKS
Edna Staebler
McGraw-Hill Ryerson,
Toronto, 1968
There probably isn't a cook in southern Ontario who hasn't bought this book or borrowed it from a neighbour. Mennonite country cooking is its specialty and the recipes are plain, practical and incredibly good. Folksy notes add to the charm. I think it's a necessity in every country kitchen.

THE SETTLEMENT COOK BOOK
Simon and Schuster,
New York, 1976

This classic, subtitled "Treasured recipes of seven decades," was first published in 1901 and boasts 3,000 recipes, many new to this 33rd edition. The original cook book grew from cooking classes offered for immigrants in Milwaukee, Wisconsin by volunteer women at a "Settlement House." To spare students the tedium of copying recipes, the volunteers asked their Board of Directors for $18 to publish recipes. The conservative gentlemen refused. Undaunted, the women persevered and managed to attract advertisers to defray their slight cost. In 1901, 1,000 copies were printed. To date, 1,750,000 copies have been sold, producing enough profit to build a new Settlement House, establish the first nursery school in Milwaukee and grant scholarships to students. I've found recipes in this book unavailable anywhere else and it looks suspiciously as though those immigrant women may have

taught the Wisconsin ladies as much about cooking as the other way around.

LAURA SECORD CANADIAN COOK BOOK
McClelland and Stewart, Ltd.
Toronto, 1966
This well-designed and practical book was prepared for Laura Secord Candy Shops by the Canadian Home Economics Association and features regional specialties. A quality paperback, its recipes are well written and easy to follow. Another favourite.

THE AMERICAN HERITAGE COOKBOOK
Helen McCully, Ed.
American Heritage Press
New York, 1969
Drawings of 19th century kitchen utensils, historical notes and complete menus from feasts like Abraham Lincoln's Inaugural Luncheon and Nellie Grant's Wedding Breakfast, make this attractive book much more than a recipe collection. If it's recipes that interest, however, the 500 in this book are extraordinarily useful. Besides, it's great fun to tell the kids they're eating Ambushed Asparagus, Red Flannel Hash or Peach Crab Lantern.

HOME MADE, AN ALTERNATIVE TO SUPERMARKET LIVING
Sandra Oddo
Atheneum, New York, 1972
Another readable cookbook, this one has many recipes you'd never use and many you'll never find any other place. "Recipes from the Nineteenth Century, Rescued, Reinterpreted and Commented Upon" is the subtitle, and besides recipes, the book includes home remedies, processes and a section on utensils. Uniquely, the book is not divided into "fish, meat, cookies" or the like but lists recipes by the season. In May, you can concern yourself with Chapter 8—rhubarb, asparagus, dandelions and poke.

GUIDE TO COOKING
Nellie Lyle Pattinson
Airmont, New York, 1968

One of the few really decent paperback cooking books around, this basic book is based on the 1940s classic, the *Canadian Cook Book*. Not much different than other basic books, this one has advantages for the deeply disorganized. Everything is in list form, often recipes tell you what goes with what and when to start the potatoes.

—*Sharon Airhart
Corbeyville, Ontario*

SHOPPING FOR FOOD AND NUTRITION
Information Services
Agriculture Canada
Ottawa, K1A 0C7
A 32-page illustrated, colour booklet about buying, storing and cooking food. It shows the four food groups and how to sort out your nutrition score. Then, on to how to shop for them at a reasonable cost. Just great! Best yet, it is free.

—*William A. McLeish, M.D.
Ottawa, Ontario*

THE BOOK OF WHOLE GRAINS
by Marlene Anne Bumgarner
St. Martin Press,
New York
$10.95, hardcover.
The complete book of grains. Each chapter covers a different grain—wheat, oats, rye, buckwheat, corn, rice, etc.—and includes the history of the cereal, how to grow and harvest it, how to mill it, and how to use it, complete with a variety of traditional and ethnic recipes. Other chapters include nuts and seeds, dried peas and beans, equipment for milling, etc. and where to obtain it, and sources of whole grains. The suggested Canadian source is Anderson's Organic Grains, Box 186, Lowe Farm, Manitoba.

THE FOOD CO-OP DIRECTORY
106 Girard S.E.
Albuquerque
New Mexico 87106
(505) 265-7416

Information and listings of food co-ops, warehouses and buying clubs throughout North America.

Where Have All The Communes Gone?

Dreams vs. Realities: Meditation wouldn't fill the woodshed

Well, for those of us who have long since put away our beads and our black lights, it still smarts to think that here we are, 10 years after the Grand Revolution of which the Beatles sang, 10 years after all those swirling coloured dreams made everything clear to us — and nothing has really changed. Actually, the feeling that flowers and acid rock weren't going to bring down the walls was creeping insidiously into our minds in the late sixties, and it was then that those with sense (and those merely with incense) decided "the hell with the cities" and headed for greener pastures. In 1970 the back-to-the-land fervour among the psychedelic rebels was at its height and *Maclean's* informed the country with articles like "Green Power," describing the new force sweeping young people from the clutches of the establishment to the embrace of the countryside. In 1971 the Vancouver underground paper *Georgia Straight* proclaimed Harmony Gates to be "the most successful open commune in B.C."

Harmony Gates was a commune in the Slocan Valley, an area of picturesque mountain settings but no real economic base in the West Kootenays of southeastern British Columbia. If B.C. was Canada's commune centre — which it was — then the Slocan was its epicentre. With a magic mushrooming, no less than seven communes had appeared in the valley by '71, their names as whimsical and idealistic as those golden summer days of rebellion: The New Family, The Sun Blossoms, Harmony Gates, The Funkwells, The Flying Hearts Family, The Red and Blue Circus, Many Skies. Each had its own style, a different character from the next, but whatever the long-haired seeker sought, whether drugs or like-minded companions, creative expression or off-beat religions, escape from the U.S. draft, a chance at self-sufficiency or merely peaceful respite from the city, the odds were it could be found at one or another of these flower-powered retreats.

Where are they now? Since those halcyon days when a couple of dozen laughing hippies could be found at each location, giving the finger to CBC cameramen eager to document the beginnings of the New Revolution, the energy has not merely diminished — it has evaporated, almost completely. Left now are remnants of only two of those seven groups. In some cases just a single person or couple remains to carry on the struggle of existing in a remote mountain valley. Sometimes there is just the name left behind, which evokes curious smiles or nostalgic shakes of the head when you mention it to those who can remember when.

Ghost Town

To understand the rapid rise and fall of these communes, first bear in mind that they were mainly an imported phenomenon. The inspiration came from the California drug cult and the motivation was the Vietnam War. Over half of the Slocan commune founders were Californians, three-quarters Americans. But, like surfing, it turned out to be a cult which did not take well when transplanted to backwoods B.C.

The first to arrive, in the summer of '69, were five members of the New Family, headed by Eric Clough, who had attempted communal living in the Bay area of San Francisco. Clough, still around, still the energetic, bearded patriarch at 48, cheerfully describes himself as an anarchist. "We felt threatened by the menace of urban society in the States," he says. "We decided to look for the sanest possible place, and Canada looked like the sanest place to us. It still does." The original five, however, are now down to three after swelling to nearly 30 during the summers of 1970 and 1971. Eric Clough, Nancy Harris and Carol Gaskin each has a wing of the huge, 3,000-square-foot house the three of them built. Close by are several large A-frames, now empty. "The New Family Ghost Town" as Nancy terms it. What happened to the occupants? "One of our original members thought this life was going to be white picket fences, horses to ride and charming social evenings. That's not what was here. What *was* here was a lot of damned hard work. Leaving was really hard for her, but eventually she went."

Nancy looks thoughtful: "For some people, the *dream* was enough. The reality turned out to be more than they could cope with."

Hard work was one unexpected reality. Lack of stimulation amid the backwoods routine was another. A couple of the New Family originals got into Sufism, a more recent Californian cult. There were no Sufis with the New Family, so they left to join Meher Baba in the States. Others were turned off by the New Family's "no dope" rule, and insistence that everyone put in eight hours work per day. "We were always the most structured commune," says Nancy. That structure and their dedication kept them going, still the most mentioned group when one asks about communes in the Slocan.

In the beginning it was this work routine that built the houses (some other commune members seem to have drifted back to the cities because they never *could* manage to build themselves adequate

shelter) and grew the New Family's vegetables. The buildings are now built and the gardening is a matter of routine. The basics are now taken care of and the life style of the New Family stalwarts has changed considerably in recent years, an interesting object-lesson to those who never did conquer the issues of mere survival. Eric has returned to his former career as an architect, designing parks for the City of Nelson — his income allows him to fill two 300-gallon propane tanks every winter for their heating and lighting needs. Nancy is an actress with the local group Theatre Energy, which has become successful enough to have its performances broadcast on CBC radio and staged at Vancouver's Simon Fraser University. The income she gets from this is a modest $3,000 a year, but since they have everything paid for, that's enough for her to live on. More important, the theatre gives her an opportunity for creative expression, travel, and meeting new people outside the Valley. "Milking the cow and weeding the garden was suddenly not enough," says Nancy. It is a feeling echoed by many ex-commune members who came out of the super-stimulation of the sixties to find rural life at first quaint, then dull.

Gully Farm

It is a paradox that the survivors of the commune experience are stronger and more self-directed, but are hardly commune material: "It takes individualists to reject society in the first place, so what you end up with is a community of individualists — what a contradiction!" These are the words of Denton Coates, ex-University of British Columbia metallurgist who was a founding member of Gully Farm, one of the rare communes in which Canadians predominated. Coates, disillusioned with his experiences there, was staying with the New Family for a few months, writing. "The sixties gave rise to a generation disillusioned with the culture-at-large, Vietnam being its symbol. This created a strong, tight, 'us-versus-them' feeling that no longer exists. The reaction *against*

a domineering culture is just not there any more." Asks Coates, "How do you reconcile individual growth with the dissolving of individualism necessary for communality? It's a problem run into again and again. The communes that survive are those with a strong leader and a host of sheep."

Certainly, this seems borne out by the great success of the charismatic Steven Gaskin's Farm in Tennessee, whose membership continues to grow and grow, numbering well over 1,000 by now, and whose operations have spread to other farms in the U.S., as well as a whole network of natural food outlets. And the Sunburst family in Gaviota, California, keeps expanding with four stores, a gas station, three boats and members numbering in the hundreds, led by the powerful figure of Norm Krause. Both of these communes are known for their tight structure and organization, something none of the Slocan groups had, with the exception of the New Family.

In those early, glorious days, it was uncool to tell the hordes of transients who came to the farms each summer to quit smoking grass and start cutting it — it was time to get the hay in. The beautiful people preferred light duties like meditation to farm work. Why should they worry about getting the woodshed filled? Come winter they fled back to the cities or to California. Hence Louisa Marzicola, the lone female remnant of Harmony Gates, found herself hauling firewood and bales of hay through January snowdrifts more than once.

Trying to maintain friendly relationships with five men without sleeping with any of them proved too much at times for the diminutive Louisa. It also proved too much for the men, who eventually packed up and left her to fend for herself. Once, the distraught Louisa fell down on her knees and prayed — things were that bad. Minutes later, an unknown, unexpected priest knocked at her door — having slogged three miles through snow up the lonely road to the farm. This made Louisa think, and afterward she started praying regularly.

And who should then appear but Oreste from California, an old friend of the family. A Christian convert — and very handsome. Now Louisa and Oreste live with their three children in quiet domesticity on the farm which saw so many amazing scenes years ago. Communal living is definitely a thing of the past for Louisa. "If someone came whom we loved and who had accepted Christ like us, we *might* give them a place to build. But no, I don't want anybody sharing my home any more." Adds Oreste: "What motivated those people to come together — the Commune Spirit — was a dissatisfaction with their everyday lives, looking for a place to find love and peace and sharing. A Utopia. And they got very disillusioned when they didn't find that at Harmony Gates. Thing is, you don't find those things at any particular *place,* you find them when you have the right attitudes within yourself. I joined the Commune of God and found those feelings of love and peace. This is what people are *really* seeking."

"Emotional Garbage"

"Free love" was another beautifully naïve part of the hippie ideal that ran square into human possessiveness and jealousy, an ideal that created more problems than it solved.

"The emotional garbage can be very heavy," says Eric Clough, commenting on the non-monogamous style tried out by the New Family. "You have to be really dedicated, day-by-day, to make it work. For most people, it just wasn't worth the effort — it was easier to slip back into the safety of traditional relationships." A three-way tango that no one could dance to was the downfall of "Brain Damage," the rock group which was the unifying force of the Flying Hearts Family of Perry Siding. With a rush of enthusiasm and creative energy unequalled by other Slocan communes, "Brain Damage" emerged from the woods in 1972 to captivate audiences in Nelson, then in Vancouver.

They were a mixed group, with lead guitarist Bing Jensen from San José, his girlfriend and singer Helen Davis from Toronto and rhythm guitar player Gary Cramer

from Vancouver. The group attracted other musicians from California and New York, some $50,000-worth of equipment, and a family of 20 which grew with the group's popularity. Eventually they needed a school bus to handle them all, and a one-ton truck for the equipment. All this did not leave much time for growing a garden, but some effort was made by Bing and Helen. It didn't really matter — there was always *just* enough money from "gigs" for groceries. Living accommodations on the farm were unbelievable. No buildings were built, and often 20 people would share floor space in the old Perry Siding Store on their land. But none of this mattered while the group was making sweet music and packin' 'em in. They were moving . . . But this commune-on-wheels started to skid when Gary and Helen took a fancy to each other. Suddenly Bing and Gary

weren't in tune. The group broke up. Gary is now driving a cab in Vancouver and Bing and Helen are back together, but in Los Angeles. Having first moved to Hawaii — where the winters are a little kinder — they formed a new group, "Sweet Hearts," and went on to produce their first record. Now, like many other hopefuls, they await their big break in L.A.

Breakfast For 30

Peggy Hart, from Churchill, Manitoba, lived and travelled with the group for four years. After following them to Hawaii, she is now back in Vallican, a dozen miles from where it all started, living in a rented house. She doodles the Flying Hearts symbol while she talks. "I loved living communally: all the hustle and bustle of breakfast for 30. I get bored now, with just the baby and me. I'd give *anything* . . . I'd just love to get back to those times."

And off she goes to deal with the more prosaic realities of a balky washing machine.

But not even those who stuck to traditional relationships survived. The Funkwells, another California group, was comprised of three couples, four single adults and two kids. Judy Culwell is the only remaining member in the Slocan, and even she no longer lives on the old Russian farm the group bought nine years ago. (The Slocan is also the traditional home of the Doukhobors in Canada, whose descendants from the Doukhobor communes watched these latest, zany attempts to do what they had failed at with a certain amusement. The Doukhobor communes in the area lasted much longer than the hippies' — about 60 years, from the 1880s to the Second World War — an indication, perhaps, of the value of religious under-pinnings.) "It was really good when we started," says Judy. "Our aims were to become more self-sufficient and we worked really hard, growing gardens, planting fruit trees and keeping animals.

Then the personality hassles started. There was "a territorial struggle" between two of the men, one a vegetarian, the other not. This, plus "not enough action" prompted Steve Winegar, one of the two, to take his family and move to Idaho. Then Judy's house burned down in a chimney fire. A year later a converted barn housing one of the couples also burned in winter, forcing them to leave. One of the single men got busted for growing dope, and they were subjected to continual police hassles afterwards. Then Judy and her husband split up and he moved away. Country living can be as hard on traditional relationships as experimental ones, because the lack of external/city stimuli means couples are together all the time, and being *everything* for each other is a strain. Boredom can result.

Finally, only Judy and one other couple were left on the Funkwell's farm. It was a struggle for them to make ends meet in the economically depressed area. Judy says that lack of money was a big part of the Funkwell's demise — there just wasn't enough of it to go around. Eventually the other couple gave up and moved back to California, leaving Judy alone. A little more than a year ago, she moved in with Norman White, a potter who now makes his living tree planting for the B.C. government reforestation programme. This is a regular, spring-and-fall source of income for Slocan residents, and the tree-planting co-op that White helped to form has provided a large chunk of employment for those trying to live an alternative life style. In 1977 a total of 80 people worked, grossing over $200,000 in the spring planting. This capitalist venture that employs so many former commune members is in itself a democratic, open structure in which all have shares. It is the best example of the evolution of communality into something directed, and useful. "When you live in a tree-planting camp out in the mountains, it is an enforced communal situation," says White. "Maybe the ex-commune people get their satisfaction from this, these days. You get your fill of living and working with people for four to six weeks, then you go back to your own place." Certainly, says White, it's easy to pick out those in camp who have had communal living experience and those who haven't.

Judy Culwell's deserted farm is running down but can't be sold because Steve Winegar has a lien against it — a legacy of past disagreement and bitterness. "I don't know what's going to happen with the place now," she says. "I'm still emotionally attached to it. I hate to go back and look at it falling apart — it's horrible."

"The communes?" says Malcom Britton, one of the Flying Hearts when they were flying. "The communes have failed. They failed because of human failings." Says Nancy Harris: "A lot of people asked me why the New Family failed. This is like asking why your life failed. It didn't fail, it just changed. It has been hard to watch the energy run down, but for myself, I'm not the same human being. I'm thankful for the experience."

—Frank Appleton
Edgewood, British Columbia

SURVIVORS

If most communes did not survive the past decade, and if the word commune itself has fallen into disfavour, the ideal of establishing a successful intentional community remains alive, if feeble.

The most recent census of intentional communities, compiled by the Community Publications Cooperative, shows 84 such groups of people in North America, only five of which number more than 100 members. (Seven hundred and fifty surveys were mailed. The majority did not answer, and a number asked not to be identified in print.) Just 22 communities listed have more than 20 members, and a substantial proportion of the groups surveyed consist of less than 10 individuals.

The diversity, however, is exhilarating. While a number of groups have religious orientations (from Christ to Krishnamurti), others are held together by a common belief in everything from "anarchistic homesteading" to a "semi-monastic" life style. The majority are rural-based and involved in food production, but diets range from vegetarian to heavily carnivorous (wild game).

The best introduction to this world of intentional communities is found in *A Guide to Cooperative Alternatives*, which includes a fascinating chapter of community descriptions written by the members of the groups themselves:

COMMON CHOICE COMMUNITY
Box 389
Peoria, Illinois 58321
(102) 838-6666
Common Choice Community was founded in 1897 by a band of escaping Transylvanian intellectuals. Pleasantly situated on the banks of the Wabash River, the community combines the benefits of small-town casualness with the complex rituals of a Satanic cult. Presently there are 20 members in residence, ranging in age from six months to 175 years. We maintain a large mailing list, corresponding with a variety of werewolves, vampires and other exotica around the world.

Our chief economic support is

Hollywood films, as we are much in demand for "specialty" roles.

We are particularly interested in members who have exhibited signs of psychic power, or who tend to change form in the full moon. Visits should be arranged well in advance, as we make our neighbours nervous enough as it is.

Common Choice is legally incorporated as a complete fabrication.

KOOTENAY COOPERATIVE LAND SETTLEMENT SOCIETY
Argenta, British Columbia
Canada V0G 1B0

Kootenay Cooperative Land Settlement Society (est. '71) has 10 adult and three child residents, with about 40 "supporting" members. The adults' ages are between 22 and 33. Including children, the sex split is 50/50. We are located in a very rural area in the southeast corner of British Columbia. As a chartered co-op, we own 225 acres of forested slopes and benches. Our land is managed by the consensus of the group as a whole, with special regard for our role as caretakers. We have a system of small homesteads separated by common land. Hopefully, we will also develop communal houses. Some of us are political and ecological activists. We all subscribe to alternative values, a simpler life style, organic attempts toward self-sufficiency, and good non-sexist relationships with each other and our children. People (if Canadian or landed immigrants) can join and share payments after a three-month trial period.

ONE LIFE FAMILY
202 Pier Avenue
Santa Monica, California 90405
(213) 392-4501

One Life Family (est. '74) philosophy is to love one another, see only love, be only love, do only loving things, if you will. The 15 to 30 members, aged 18 to 40 years, (plus kids) meditate together often, play and hang-out as long as it feels good. We have an 18-acre ranch in the coastal mountain range and a large natural food store in Santa Monica. Twelve thousand dollars in annual sales leaves enough to do what we want. We do ranch work, store work, and all other levels and types of jobs

needed to keep a communal and commercial trip happening.

Our diet is vegetarian and junk foods. Our government is mostly flow and a benevolent dictatorship. Community members interact often, but follow no particular model. There are no real marriages, but plenty of couples, singles, gay folks, and crazies. Mothers watch their kids or make arrangements. Kids go to public schools.

New members are admitted unless they're real spacies. We are going to have a house for new folks to live in initially. Our goal is to refine and to become more loving, to make our space a better home, a better place to learn, a better place to share.

WILDERNESS SEEKERS
General Delivery
Chapleau, Ontario P0M 1K0

Wilderness Seekers is people, some of whom live in a small community. Our purpose is to use the wilderness in a sane manner, to sustain renewable natural resources, and to enjoy self-propelled wilderness activities: canoeing, dog sledding, snowshoeing, cross-country skiing, hiking, fishing, hunting and gathering. Within the community, some of us are attempting to live off the land in a self-reliant way, beyond agriculture, but within the existing game laws.

Members are free to establish their own enterprises in order to support personal interests and specializations. Members may be dependent or interdependent on the support systems of the community. There are opportunities to lead wilderness trips, teach tours, and

produce maple sugar, dried edible wild plants, medicines, smoked coarse fish, etc.

TWIN OAKS COMMUNITY
R. R. 4G
Louisa, Virginia 23093
(203) 894-5126

Twin Oaks Community (est. '67) is an intentional community of 75 on 300 acres of forest and farmland bordering the South Anna River in rural Virginia.

Since our beginnings, values of cooperation, nonviolence and equality have been central. We are continually striving to treat each other in a kind, honest and caring way and to create a gentle culture where women are encouraged to lead and men to nurture. We are an economically self-sufficient community with the farm and garden providing close to 60 per cent of our food needs. Each of us is required to work about a 45-hour work week which covers all domestic and income-producing labour. Our focus also includes finding solutions to problems of land use, food production, energy conservation, industrialization and use of technology. Integration of work and play is a key to community life.

We offer new friends, hard work, freedom from sex roles and a life rich with challenge. We seek members who want to join in the joy and struggle of living communally. All potential members must visit for three weeks and go through a six-month provisional period.

TOLSTOY FARM
Rt. 3, Box 70
Davenport, Washington 99122

Tolstoy Farm (est. '63) has 55 residents, 18 of them children. We hold 240 acres of land and 22 households. Each household is independent, having separate gardens, animals, income, etc., with the exception of a common milk cow and a hay field co-op. We are anarchistic homesteaders who believe in a simple, cooperative life. People here are on all levels of spiritual and political trips. We vary in our degrees of involvement with the alternative culture and local people. New people become part of Tolstoy Farm by buying or leasing the use of a house and the surrounding space. In recent years, houses have sold for

$50 to $1,000. Prospective visitors should write ahead.

How to Arrange a Visit

If you are interested in a particular community you should write for details about their arrangements and then try to make an appointment for a visit. Communities often are swamped with mail and requests for information. Be sure to enclose a stamped, self-addressed envelope and a dollar if you can afford it, to help with the cost of answering mail.

Remember that a community is not an institution, but the home of those who live there. Respect their home; don't make them a crash pad for your cross-country trip, or the object of a study for your college sociology class. If you do come to visit, here are some hints to make your visit pleasant both for you and your hosts.

1. Never go to visit unless they are expecting you.

2. Take along sleeping gear and plan to share in their work, their play and their expenses. Freeloaders can make a group decide to close its doors to further strangers.

3. Leave your pets at home unless you have permission to bring them.

4. One of the most important ingredients of community is compatible people. You cannot judge that well unless you spend enough time with the people you are considering living with. So try to arrange for an extended visit of a week or two if possible. Sometimes short-term visitors are regarded more as "sightseers" than as serious about community.

We welcome additions to the list and if you have any information about any of these communities or if you know of communities that would like to be listed in the next directory please have them get in touch with us.

Cooperative Lifeline

I have been living within the context of an intentional community since the spring of 1972 and my interest in this movement as a whole has been constant throughout the period. However, during the past four years of intensive effort to make our farm and living situation a success, I have had little time or energy to attend conferences, visit other groups or even to encourage others to visit our group.

My emotional and informational lifeline to other community and cooperative efforts has been a magazine called *Communities (Journal of Cooperative Living).*

Founded in 1972, as an amalgamation of three alternative life style magazines, *Communities* has evolved into a very useful and graphically pleasing publication. It is a magazine by, for and about cooperative ventures — most of them successful and on-going. *Communities,* itself, is an outstanding example of cooperation producing results: writing, publishing and distribution is done by volunteers.

Issue Number 38 is the 184-page *Guide to Cooperative Alternatives,* an attempt to present the "separate strands which make up the rich texture of the cooperative fabric." Included are chapters on cooperative efforts in: food distribution, health care, housing, communications and networking, energy, politics and, among others, anti-nuclear organizing.

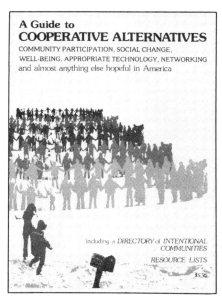

Communities has an annual directory of intentional communities, something I look forward to each year to see who is still listed and what new groups have formed. Although more than 80 groups were listed in the most recent directory, there are a great many group-living situations across the continent that are not found in this listing — for reasons of privacy, because they weren't aware of the directory or, perhaps, because they just didn't get around to sending information in on time.

—Ian Murray
Headlands Community
Stella, Ontario

Communities (Journal of Cooperative Living)
6 issues for $7.50 in the U.S.,
$9.00 everywhere else (U.S.funds)
A Guide to Cooperative Alternatives
$6.50 per copy in the U.S.,
$7.50 everywhere else (U.S. funds)
Guide plus 6 issues of Communities,
special offer, $11.00 in the U.S.,
$12.50 everywhere else (U.S. funds)

Available from:
COMMUNITIES,
P.O. Box 426
Louisa, Virginia 23093

COMMUNITIES IN CANADA

Canadian intentional communities are either (a) extremely difficult to identify, or (b) extremely few in number. Those extant as the eighties begin are:

INTEGRITY
Box 9,
100 Mile House,
British Columbia V0K 2E0
We number about 110 here at 100 Mile Lodge in south central British Columbia and are a point of orientation for a world-wide community of some 200 ranches, farms, orchards and communal homes. All this began back in the 1930s with one man, Lloyd Meeker, who saw something of his potential and the potential of mankind as a unified body, as we perhaps sense we are meant to be. By word of mouth and through lectures a few came close to this man, finding that his vision was not only akin to their own but carried their sense of purpose much further.

100 Mile Lodge has been in operation since 1930 when Lord

Martin Cecil, fresh from the British Royal Navy, came to the thinly settled wilderness of central British Columbia, recognizing there was more to life than the traditional comfort of British aristocracy. He met Lloyd Meeker in 1940. In 1948, 100 Mile Lodge was established as the Canadian headquarters for the Emissaries of Divine Light, when half a dozen people moved here to provide the base for our community. Our population now varies slightly as a few change location throughout our larger community. Ranks swell to as many as 200 during classes and various conferences.

We operate 15 businesses in town: a bakery, hotel, service station, building supply outlet, stereo and TV shop, the local newspaper, a cattle ranch and an accounting and management consulting firm to mention a few. Many of us work here in our communal home while others are employed in our various businesses. This balance in activities ensures that our home is taken care of and that we have toothpaste, good tennis balls and various other essentials to wholesome balanced living.

We also operate Educo, a rigorous wilderness training programme for boys and men. Having taken the one week adult course I can say without hesitation, the experience is remarkable! Faced with a raging torrent of white water while hurtling downstream in a frail canoe, or clinging 80 feet up sheer rock face with apparently nowhere to turn, one discovers a depth, a solidarity, a resource within never known before.

We meet four times a week to give special thought to our experience together from a spiritual perspective. It is always a pleasure, sometimes comfortable, sometimes uncomfortable, to come into a larger vision of spiritual living and so to further refine one's artistry and sensitivity in this. It's a

particular privilege to be able to openly share one's experience with others whose vision and ability has been well practised and proven over a long period of time.

Our children attend local schools where perhaps a half dozen of our family teach. We feel the primary influence upon our children is at home and as our children need to function in the world as it is, school is a good situation to learn the art of "being in the world but not of it." If what we are doing is right, it will ring true with them, as children are quite sensitive and alert. We also operate Twin Valleys, an alternative educational community near London, Ontario.

Occasionally we stage a theatrical presentation, usually written here. Many participate in our choir and orchestra. For a short period of time a few of us formed a rock/blues band and by playing locally were able to contribute substantially to our fledgling orchestra, providing instruments and other requirements.

We have a large organic garden here and an orchard and garden in the B.C. fruit belt to provide high quality food for our family. We keep our own bees and much more.

We publish a monthly newsletter, Integrity, ($10.00 per year) and hold numerous classes in the Art of Living in several locations around the world.

We also have a large property just north of Toronto (near King City) known as King View Farm, where perhaps 70 people are living. Coordinators are Bill and Lois Porter, who can be reached at Box 217, Aurora, Ontario (416) 884-4285.

Increasing numbers of centres are located all over the North American continent as well as overseas in England, Scotland, Holland, West Germany, Italy, Israel, Ghana, Nigeria, Rhodesia, South Africa, New Zealand, Australia, and we have friends in most other countries. From all these places people come to visit, attend classes, and to share with us the deepening experience of life.

As our accommodations are taxed with scheduled classes and visitors, visiting arrangements must be made in advance. It is often most

convenient to visit a centre near you to see if our experience meshes with yours.

And how does it all operate? Though we appear, in a sense, to be doing a lot, running several businesses, having scores of centres around the globe, it is no more than a training ground for us to grow up to reveal the real character of manhood and womanhood, not being at all impressed with our roles or with what we are doing. Rather, we learn to fulfill a responsibility as stewards of the Earth. We find that our identity may be beyond the world of effects, in spirit, and then effects sort themselves out quite easily and naturally.

An ancient Chinese proverb puts it neatly: "Before enlightenment, chopping wood and carrying water; after enlightenment, chopping wood and carrying water." The activities may appear the same but the perspective and purpose has ascended.

If this description of our experience is one you would like to know more about, I would welcome hearing from you.

—Dave Thatcher
100 Mile House, B.C.

NEW ROOTS COMMUNITY LAND TRUST
Box 1192
Wynyard, Saskatchewan
S0A 4T0
Information packet: $1.50
Access to farmland without paying $5,000 an acre. This non-profit organization leases land to people who agree to work it organically and to cooperate with others in the area in the use of intermediate technology and in community decision-making. Families and individuals are invited to apply for land through the lease arrangement.

Other land trust organizations can be located through:

National Community of Land Trusts
639 Massachusetts Avenue
Cambridge, Massachusetts 02139

THE FARM
R.R. 3
Lanark, Ontario K0G 1K0
(613) 278-2785

Twenty-eight member northern off-shoot of Stephen Gaskin's Tennessee Farm. (See following.)

THE FARM
156 Drakes Lane
Summertown, Tennessee 38483
(615) 964-3574

''Many communes haven't worked because the people in them wanted to live together so that nobody had to work very hard; they were built on the idea of leisure. We're built on the idea of doing something, so we have the advantage of pooling our labour and working hard, too.''

Founded when leader Stephen Gaskin led a 63-bus caravan of ''hippies'' out of San Francisco in 1970, The Farm is, numerically, the most successful of modern intentional communities, with more than 1,000 members and a million-dollar non-profit budget built with income from farming, publishing and distributing natural foods.

The Farm has distinguished itself

by providing aid to the underprivileged in the West Indies, Latin America and several U.S. cities. Their work in earthquake-torn Guatemala earned them the praise of the Canadian ambassador — and $100,000 in building supplies from Canada for use in rebuilding homes and schools.

Gaskin has become the spiritual leader of The Farm, which is working to spread his message beyond their borders:

Basically, the last depression was like this: The dudes with the heavy bread — the Rockefellers and Big Jim Fiske and the railroad barons and people like that — learned how to manoeuvre the stock market. They got it so they could move it up and make a little money at the top, and move it down and make a little money at the bottom. And they got so greedy and started running it up and down so hard that they broke it. It wasn't good for anybody, then — not even them.

So the government got it together a bit, as governments do sometimes, to keep that from happening again. They were dealing with an oscillation in the system, and they tried to put in some dampers and shock absorbers to keep the oscillation from happening so fast that it would break the machine.

And those dampers and shock absorbers were called the Interstate Commerce Commission and the Anti-Trust Act and Anti-Monopoly Act and things like that.

But we're in another place now. We have instant electronic communication around the world. Electronic communication moves at 186,000 miles per second, and it's only 25,000 miles around the world. And we have corporations like Exxon, which is bigger than Austria in gross national product; and Ford Motors, which is bigger than Denmark; and ITT, which is bigger than Portugal — and they can afford all the electronic communications equipment they need.

So now we have the phenomenon of the multinational corporation. That means that the corporations don't have any loyalty to any particular countries anymore, they're just totally out for themselves. The only thing that governs what they're doing is profit . . . . They are actually a very strange breed of creature without a soul. A corporation is a soulless entity which grows, reproduces, protects itself, and makes policy, even though it isn't anybody. People would have a harder time doing the kinds of things to each other than those entities regularly do. But if there's such a thing as a demon, it's a soulless entity with great material-plane powers. And so this is a time when there are demons and monsters loose upon the world. And their names are Exxon and General Motors and Phillips and Mobil and Gulf and Ford and ITT and Anaconda . . . .

An alternate life style is what you do about them. You can't attack them. To get violent with a thing like that turns you into the same thing it is, in the same way that we developed our own secret police who were as bad as the Nazis in order to compete with the Nazi secret police. We can't fight those things in that fashion. What we have to do is massively build an alternate culture.

—Stephen Gaskin

THE PRACTICING MIDWIFE

156 Drakes Lanes
Summertown, Tennessee 38483
Midwifery is also a major interest of The Farm, both in handling the considerable number of births among their own population and in educating midwives throughout the world.

Their quarterly newsletter, costing $5.00 a year, is a mixture of "professional" news and exchanges of information and opinion among practicing midwives:

Q.: What would you recommend as things to do when you've got a baby whose head is delivered but the shoulders are stuck?

Nancy: This is where home birth has an advantage over a hospital birth because there's something you can do about shoulder dystocia, and when I talked to Etta, I found that we both did the same thing; it's hands and knees. I've had a couple of cases of shoulder dystocia where there was nothing I could do — there was no room for me to do any manoeuvring the first time it happened to me. I was perplexed as to how I was going to get the baby out, so I flipped her on her hands and knees, because my initial thought was an advantage of gravity even though I'm not hot on hands and knees position. I do more tears that way because it's harder to control. I found that on her hands and knees the whole relationship of the baby to the pelvis changed and it appeared suddenly that I could get fingers in there to rotate the shoulders and deliver the baby. I've probably had it happen four times since that first time which was three years ago. In cases of cord around the neck, sometimes I couldn't get it off and I had to cut it and had a blue baby. I didn't want to wait. I just wanted the baby out now. So hands and knees and push, and I've never had it fail, on the first push.

A quarterly newsletter for Canadians interested in childbirth information and "family-centred maternity care" is also available from:

Barbara Reid
52 Burnham Court
Fredericton, New Brunswick
E3B 5T7

CARCROSS COMMUNITY

Box 26
Carcross, Yukon Y0B 1B0
This 40-member educational community strives for self-sufficiency in an adverse climate with difficult soil and growing conditions. Disadvantaged youths work and learn with adult members of the group.

ALTERNATIVE TO ALIENATION

Box 46
Postal Station M
Toronto, Ontario
(416) 925-9665
This eight-year-old commune now numbers about 15 adults. It owns a 15-room house in Toronto and a 230-acre farm, bought with the proceeds from a printing/graphics business, a marine hardware company and four restaurants, the first of which was Spice of Life. The group seeks to actively practice Erich Fromm's "Art of Loving" and is interested in self-psychoanalysis.

HEADLANDS

R.R.3
Stella, Ontario K0H 2S0
(613) 389-3444
Very small community on 400 acres involved in breeding sheep, candlemaking, and home construction/engineering. Has goal of growing into a "community of individuals living and working together in small consumer and producer cooperatives."

RUITER VALLEY COMMUNITY FOREST FARM

Dunkin, Quebec
(514) 292-3751
A community evolving on 700 acres of pastureland and valley slopes in the Sutton Mountains in the Eastern Townships area of Quebec.

Both resident and non-resident members participate in self-sufficiency-oriented activities (gardening, beekeeping, animal husbandry, home construction) and group meditation.

Newcomers may rent accommodation at the farm or build, with community help, their own shelter. Workshops are regularly scheduled, with varying themes:

Wilderness Experience:
A three-day training programme in camping and survival techniques, designed to provide challenge, adventure and growth for young people.
Animators: Keith Willcok, Russell Slater, Sandra Woods, Simon Bryant
Place: The Farm. Cost: $60.00

Weekend Without Words:
On the second weekend of every month anyone interested is invited to explore within themselves and others that rare experience . . . silence. Outdoor activities, eating, working, communication, playing . . . without words.

Animators: Joan Matthews, Robert Shepherd
Place: The Farm. Cost: $50.00

Renewal: A Weekend For Those Who Care For Others:
The community provides a quiet setting where people in the professional caring role can come and relax, share with others and be cared for.
Animators: Margaret Edgar, Robert Shepherd
Place: The Farm. Cost: $60.00

KOOTENAY COOPERATIVE LAND SETTLEMENT SOCIETY
Argenta, British Columbia
V0G 1B0
Small group of resident community members living on 225 acres in rural British Columbia, with individual small homestead and common land areas. The co-op also has some 40 supporting non-resident members. Non-sexist relationships and organic self-sufficiency are the goals, and prospective members go through a three-month trial period before joining.

LANARK HILLS
R.R.4
Perth, Ontario K7H 3C6
(613) 267-4819
Producers of non-competitive games for children (*Harrowsmith* Number Two), with a vegetarian kitchen and an involvement with the teachings of Krishnamurti.

DANDELION COMMUNITY CO-OPERATIVE
R.R.1
Enterprise, Ontario K0K 1Z0
Inspired by B.F. Skinner's *Walden Two*, Dandelion was established in 1975 and numbers about 12 adults. Economically self-sufficient, the community operates a successful tinnery (producing candle holders, planters and other items from recycled tin cans) and a new hanging rope chair industry.

Dandelion is open to visitors and new members and will send a free tinnery catalogue or a subscription to their bimonthly newsletter *Pappus* ($3.50 per year). They also offer a mail-order book service specializing in information on the community movement.

WILDERNESS SEEKERS
General Delivery
Chapleau, Ontario P0M 1K0
(See above)

THE BEAR TRIBE
Book Department
Box 9167
Spokane, Washington 99209
This is a self-described ''medicine society, called together by the medicine vision of Sun Bear, a Chippewa medicine person.''

Located in northwest Washington State, the Bear Tribe operates a self-reliance centre on 60 acres of land, where visitors may come for four-day intensive courses in Native ways of living and self-reliance, including an introduction to the Sweat Lodge.

The Bear Tribe has published *Many Smokes*, a newsletter about Native Life and social action, for 17 years, and they also offer a wide range of books and posters about Indian life. Write for current price list.

I am tired of fighting, our chiefs are killed. Looking Glass is dead, the old men are all dead.

It is the young men who say no and yes. He who led the young men is dead. It is cold and we have no blankets. The little children are freezing to death. My people, some of them have run away to the hills and have no blankets — no food, no one knows where they are — perhaps they are freezing to death.

I want to have time to look for my children and see how many of them I can find. Maybe I shall find them among the dead. Hear me, my

chiefs, I am tired, my heart is sick and sad. From where the sun now stands I will fight no more forever.
—*Surrender Speech of Chief Joseph*

COMMUNITY ACTION

RURAL RESOURCES AND INFORMATION
Box 567
Moyie Springs, Idaho 83845
RR & I is a rich compost produced by a single individual — known as Skeeter. His original concept was to help connect overworked country people with those who yearned to leave the cities.

The trade is labour for knowledge. Each summer Skeeter places many apprentices throughout the Northern Intermountain Region, including British Columbia.
—*Larry Geno*
Northport, Washington

ECOLOGY ACTION CENTRE
Forrest Building
Dalhousie University
Halifax, Nova Scotia B3H 3J5
(902) 422-4311
Up-to-the minute information on energy and ecological problems, with an open-to-the-public resource library and education centre. A small paid staff works to direct information to the media and the public, as well as to ''bring together people whose information, values and perspectives would not otherwise come into contact.''

Concerned with paper recycling, nuclear power, refillable bottle legislation, pesticide spraying, environmental law, electric rates, urban environment and other subjects.

GRINDSTONE CO-OP LTD.
Box 564, Station P
Toronto, Ontario M5S 2T1
Grindstone Island is a 12-acre wooded piece of land in Big Rideau Lake, north of Kingston, Ontario, that serves as an international centre for discussion of social issues. The Island and its facilities may be rented by groups wishing to stage conferences related to social change (recent

interest has centred on nuclear power, the media, defence policy, and co-ops).

CUSO
151 Slater Street
Ottawa, Ontario K1P 5H5
(613) 563-3648
You won't change the world, but you may change a few lives — most of all your own. CUSO (Canadian University Services Overseas) has sent some 6,000 volunteers around the world since 1961. The trend now is away from taking right-out-of-mortarboard university graduates and CUSO is looking for experienced people with skills in agriculture, technology and the trades.

CUSO pays travel, medical, insurance and orientation costs, while the host country pays the volunteer's salary — at local rates. Contracts are for two years.

THE EARTHCARE GROUP
Box 1048
Wynyard, Saskatchewan
S0A 4T0
(306) 554-3595
A Prairie information and resource centre focussing on ecological agriculture and initiated by the Earthcare Group, a Saskatchewan organization of farmers and gardeners.

The centre will attempt to gather

and disseminate information on "practical and viable ecological agriculture methods, organic gardening, urban agriculture, silviculture, farm and municipal composting, watershed management and land tenure systems."

CO-OP HOUSING

May I suggest an added category? Cooperative housing is becoming a biggish thing in the alternate culture, and as the four co-ops already built in the St. Lawrence neighbourhood in Toronto show, nothing to be sneezed at any more. (Indeed, at least part of the recent attack on "public housing" by the Toronto Real Estate Board, in my opinion, is a side-swipe at co-op housing; for one thing, co-ops get mortgages at eight per cent, whereas the market is now nearer 12 per cent for private housing mortgages. The CMHC mortgage is a bargain for the nation, however, because on a 50-year term the interest amounts to roughly twice the principal.

TREB won't tell you about that. *I* think that the obvious attractiveness of housing co-ops has the Real Estate Board running scared.)

COOPERATIVE HOUSING FEDERATION OF TORONTO

Suite 501, 299 Queen St. W.
Toronto, Ontario M5V 1Z9
(416) 598-1641

The four-year-old Cooperative Housing Federation of Toronto now has 25 member organizations. CHFT has several working teams, offering services such as development, lobbying (of all four levels of government), and so forth — brochures on request.

One of the original principles of cooperation is cooperation between co-ops, and CHFT helps see to that. It runs training workshops for maintenance committee members, finance committee members, boards of directors and so on. CHFT publishes a newsletter called *The Circuit* which is distributed free to all individual members of each member co-op.

CO-OP HOUSING FOUNDATION OF CANADA

237 Metcalfe Street
Ottawa, Ontario K2P 1R2
The national organization is 11 years old, and publishes *From the Rooftops*.

At its annual meeting this spring, CHF's president predicted that the 1979 investment in co-op housing would be $100,000,000 and that by 1984 there would be 100,000 people living in housing co-ops in Canada.

It has also been generally understood in both the Foundation and the Federation that it is now possible to generate most of the capital needed to build new or buy and rehabilitate old housing for co-ops from within the co-op movement itself: credit unions and co-op insurance companies. Boot-strapping.

I'm too tired to be persuasive any more. For more information, write CHF and CHFT. They'll be glad to send information. Both are into public education, and no doubt both will be more coherent than I.
—*Norman McKinney*
Toronto, Ontario

Clapping to the beat of their own drums, residents of Barnes Creek, B.C. take a break from the scheduled entertainment at their annual Country Faire.

EXPEDITIONS

GREAT EXPEDITIONS
Box 46499, Station G
Vancouver, B.C. V6R 4G7
(604) 738-4222
Travel information newsletter.
4 issues per year. $12.

As good as the old homestead is, which of us can resist thoughts of far-away places when the long Canadian winter drags out into April? For those with exotic tastes in travel, but a beer budget, I recommend Lawrence Buser's *Great Expeditions* newsletter as the best antidote to cabin fever or being bored in the bush.

Great Expeditions is a fledgling 100 per cent Canadian non-profit information service dealing exclusively with far-out group adventures in far-flung places. *Great Expeditions* doesn't sponsor anything itself, but is strictly in the business of getting groups who run scientific field exploration, adventure trips, outdoor activities, educational, ecological and cultural activities, together with those who might want to join them. It is a newsletter—they optimistically say it will be six times a year, but so far I've only received four—still okay at the price. They list, for example, a marine biology group you can join for three weeks in Honduras—scuba instruction provided—for $645; backpacking the Great Divide trail at Jasper for nine days ($180); archaelogical exploration of 7,000-year-old sites in southern Italy ($990 for 21 days); or floating down the Omo River in Ethiopia with a Sierra Club group for 22 days ($2,125).

Great Expeditions' newsletter is packed with dozens of such enticing listings, and gets bigger and better every issue. The "classified" section runs free ads from those individuals looking for people to join them as they chase up mountains, down rivers, into caves and across oceans. I haven't had any first-hand experience with G.E.-recommended adventures yet, but I'm dreaming . . . .

Frank Appleton
Edgewood, B.C.

In Canada (Whitehorse, Yukon Territory) the Pelly River flows through the Pelly Mountains flanked by the impressive Ansil and Glenlyon Ranges. Exploring the 195 miles of this uninhabited area will be the focus of this expedition of 10 days . The Pelly covers this land with its slough, sandbars and islands and the wildlife of the area flock to it for sustenance. The share of costs for this one will be $840.

On the water, but this time under sail, the Alliance is looking for eight participants for a Hawaiin sailing backpacking trip. This 10-day trip combines five days of sailing with five days of backpacking on the island of Kauai in the Na-pali-kona Forest Reserve. Leaving from Lihue, Hawaii, USA the cost for this trip will be $675.

HEADWATERS
Box 288
Temagami, Ont. P0H 2H0
No-fooling-around level wilderness trips by canoe, foot or ski. Trips designed to integrate discussion and instruction in outdoor survival, ecology, historical perspectives, natural studies. Summer and winter programmes.

Headwaters is located in the Temagami Region of Northern Ontario, some of finest canoe country in Canada. Our base is on Anamanipissing Lake, about 325 miles north of Toronto. The rustic camp of log buildings is nestled on a rocky point at the foot of a range of hills in the heart of the Precambrian Shield.

For many people a wilderness canoe

trip is merely a physical challenge. But, it can be a great deal more. At Headwaters a canoe trip is an activity which takes place within an historical tradition, and which offers to the individual a meaningful physical, social, personal and aesthetic experience.

Basic Core Programmes (15 days)
On these programmes the canoe trip is 12 days in length and travel is primarily on large and small lakes with some amount of small river and stream travel. Of the 12 days, 2 are set aside as rest days to allow ample opportunity for people to pursue their particular interests. These are ideal trips for someone especially interested in sketching, birding and photography. They are also the best programme for someone to join who has very little or no previous experience.
COST: $390/person (Can. dollars)

NEWFOUNDLAND Nature Tour 1

July 14-29. Canada's 10th province has great appeal to the visiting naturalist. Accordingly, we offer two tours—to show you the best it has to offer, from willow ptarmigan and puffins to merlins and mourning warblers. Many alpine-arctic plants offer the photographer and botanist a bonus. Our first tour begins at North Sydney to allow us to take the five-hour sailing to Port-aux-Basques, providing opportunity to observe petrels, shearwaters and other pelagic species. We then travel across the island, visiting Gros Morne and Terra Nova National Parks, the Great Northern Peninsula, L'Anse-au-Meadow—site of the only known Viking settlement in North America, fishing communities and other places of interest, finishing in St. John's. Leader: Gus Yaki. Cost, land arrangements, accommodation,

ferry and minibus transport from North Sydney, N.S./St. John's - $498.00. Charter airfare from Toronto/return, approx. $170.00

NATURE TRAVEL SERVICE
246 Queen Street E.
Toronto, Ont. M5A 1S3
(416) 363-6394

Organized tours across Canada and to far-flung parts of the world. Serious naturalist orientation.

POLAR BEARS—Churchill, Man.
Autumn finds dozens of magnificent polar bears awaiting the winter ice on the Hudson Bay shore near Churchill, Man. This tour provides a special opportunity to see and photograph these mammals in their natural habitat in the pristine wilderness of the Canadian tundra. You are taken safely into their midst in specially designed 4-wheel-drive vehicles—to observe at leisure, without harassing them. You will also see other wildlife—caribou, ptarmigan—and if the river is open, drift close enough to touch a beluga whale. Leaders: Gus Yaki and Al Chartier. Cost, complete from Winnipeg, except meals. $798.00. This activity is available on an individual basis from late September to early November. Contact us for further details.

SCOTLAND, including Shetlands and Orkneys.
Begin this tour at Prestwick (Glasgow) and travel through the highlands of Scotland. Include a visit to the delightful Shetland and Orkney Isles. See Britain's rarest birds, the ospreys at Aviemore, and reindeer in the Cairngorms. See such cliff-nesting seabirds as puffins and fulmars. Visit John O'Groat's. Your leader will be Dr. Peter Peach, President, Federation of Ontario Naturalists. Complete land costs, excluding dinners. $689. Airfare Toronto/return, approx. $325.

CAN. NATURE TOURS
355 Lesmill Road
Don Mills, Ont. M3B 2W7
(416) 469-0531 or 444-8419

Organized by the Federation of Ontario Naturalists and the Canadian Nature Federation, these tours range from bus trips through the Cariboo country of British Columbia to solar home visits in Ontario and backpacking expeditions to the high Arctic.

ELLESMERE — Cost: $1,200. Deposit $100.
High, high in the Arctic is Ellesmere Island, one of those rare places on earth where nature rules supreme and sets guidelines for the life it supports. Our jumping-off point is Resolute; from there we fly north to the coast of Ellesmere and camp out on the land. We will have 24 hours of daylight to appreciate the blaze of wildflowers and lichens and to observe the wildlife. The Island at various times is inhabited by musk ox, arctic fox, hare, polar bear and many birds—plovers, jaegers, terns, snowy owls and, perhaps, peregrine falcons. The marine life is incredible. We are likely to see belugas, ring and harp seals, walrus and, occasionally, narwhal, bearded seals and bowheads.

We would stress that only the hardy should consider registering for this trip, because of very little protection and challenging conditions. Furthermore, the chance of being fogged in entails the possibility of a lengthier stay and extra cost. Our leader is Allen Clarke. Experienced (see "Arctic Adventure" in the Autumn 1978 issue of Ontario Naturalist), resourceful, good natured and knowledgeable, he has all the qualities that make for a good Arctic leader. The fee covers all costs from Resolute.

THE ARCTIC LOWLANDS
Cost: $1,395. Deposit: $100.
The paradox: the land was crushed and scoured by the glaciers so that now, its very flatness, the barenness of the Barrens, makes it visually stunning. The flora is flamboyant—yellow poppies, purple saxifrage, red rhododendrons, orange lichen—while much of the fauna hides, dependent on camouflage in a land that offers little cover. Yet both are amazingly photogenic.

On this trip, nature photographer Barry Ranford takes us up the west side of Hudson Bay to three communities: Churchill and Rankin Inlet on the coast, and Baker Lake on the inland tundra. The surge of life where land meets sea will give us much to shoot; scores of nesting birds, hunters of the air and perhaps even herds of caribou, will come before our cameras on the land. Accommodation will be in local hotels. The fee covers all costs, including food, from Churchill.

ARNICA ADVENTURE
R.R.1
Nelson, B.C. V1L 5P4
(604) 825-9351

Wilderness expeditions in groups of 10 or less, with trips designed for beginner intermediate and advanced hikers.

Backpacking the Historic Earl Grey Pass Trail.
The idyllic little settlement of

Argenta will be the starting point for this 7 day hike from the West to the East Kootenays on a trail built in the early 1800s. Following this historic trail we get an insight into the strong determination of our pioneering forefathers. Soak up good mountain sunshine for a day or so at the Earl Grey Pass enjoying some of the spectacular scenery before completing the 34-mile hike to Toby Creek.
Tour cost for the 7 days (all inclusive) $200.00.

STRATHCONA PARK LODGE
Box 2160
Campbell River, B.C.
V9W 5C9

Non-profit lodge and outdoor education centre on Vancouver Island. Year-round programmes in canoeing, hiking, ocean kayaking, log building, nature photography, spelunking and many others. Write for catalogue.

SKI MOUNTAINEERING EXPEDITION.
A loop tour in the beautiful Forbidden Plateau area will expose students to elements of winter mountaineering. While travelling this enchanting area, participants will learn basic avalanche safety and snow cave construction. They will have the opportunity to improve their cross-country and downhill ski techniques. Those taking part are asked to bring their own equipment including alpine touring skis, touring bindings with safety releases, and, of course, sleeping bag and ensolite. Students will take part in provisioning as part of their trip preparation. $175.

OUTFITTERS

L.L. BEAN INC.
9910 Spruce Street
Freeport, Maine 04033
(207) 865-3111

Proof that quality lives. Known to insiders as "Leon's," L.L. Bean's reputation as a source of excellent outdoor equipment and garb spans several generations. Everything from English flycasting reels to handmade Canada Goose decoys. Commendable service, and shipments to Canada are easily handled. (Duty will have to be paid on most items, however.) Free catalogue upon request.

British Felt Bush Hat: A good looking, serviceable hat for canoeing, fishing and general field use. Styled after the traditional expeditionary hat worn by British soliders and made of substantial 1/8" thick Yorkshire wool felt. Naturally weather resistant. 2½" brim provides good shade and protection against rain. Pugaree cloth hatband. Hat will shrink slightly when wet, but stretches back to size as worn. Colour, loden green. Men's sizes: 6¾ to 7¾. $21.50 postpaid.

Wheatley Fly Boxes: English Wheatley fly boxes are prized by fishermen for their high standard of craftsmanship and utility. Sturdy, lightweight construction with piano type hinges. Wet fly boxes fitted with spring steel clips, hold flies flat for quick identification and selection. Dry fly boxes have individual spring lid compartments with transparent tops, flies are stored without crushing hackles and can be selected without exposing entire assortment. Trout fly with centre swing leaf. Holds 102 flies. Size 3½" x 2-3/8" x 1". $9.75 postpaid.

Chouinard Double Seated Trail Pants: Originally used by iron workers and adopted by Yvon Chouinard as highly functional rock climbing pants. For outdoors use where a tough, comfortable, non-binding pant is required. Made of 12 oz. polyester-cotton duck, double stitched and bartacked at all points of stress with polyester wrapped cotton thread for extra strength. Deep front pockets. Roomy double seat forms two large rear pockets secured at top by Velcro. Double layered front provides for long wear and will not bind. Machine washable and dryable. Colour, straw. Weight 21 oz. Men's even waist sizes: 28 to 38 (state finished inseam length desired). $25.00 postpaid.

Wool Knickers: Alpine design for cross-country skiing, climbing and hiking. Hard wearing, tightly woven 85 per cent wool and 15 per cent nylon fabric in a medium weight (16 oz.) twill weave. Cut full through thighs and knees for easy movement. Two deep side pockets, two hip pockets with button-flaps, belt loops, double seat

and adjustable Velcro knee closures. Colour, medium gray. Men's even waist sizes: 30 to 40. $32.75 postpaid.

THE HAPPY OUTDOORSMAN LTD.
433 St. Mary's Road, Box 190
St. Vital Post Office
Winnipeg, Man. R2M 4A5
(204) 233-6461

Canada's homegrown answer to L.L. Bean. In eight years, this small firm has developed an impressive catalogue of quality outdoor goods, mostly imported from the United States (of necessity). Descriptive content is generally detailed and honest, with useful consumer advice on buying skiis, tents, sleeping bags and other gear. Mail order source for Grumman canoes, River Runner kayaks, Vermont Tubbs snowshoes and furniture and a good selection of cross-country skiis. Send $1.00 for catalogue.

Gresshoppa Finse: There are (and, I hope, always will be) a segment of the cross-country skiing fraternity who have a soft spot for tradition—and that means good old wood skis. For those fine people, we offer the Gresshoppa Finse. And without apology—this is a good ski. We have been selling Gresshoppas longer than any other ski in this catalogue and most of our customers wouldn't trade them for any other make or model. Traditional Norwegian craftsmanship goes into each and every pair, producing a ski that performs very nicely, stands up faithfully and is pretty to look at. It is finished in either a clear, natural, pine tar or a stained and lacquered deck. The bases, being hickory with lignostone edges, require pine tarring. Width at the waist is 52 mm. Available in 180, 185, 190, 195, 200, 205, 210 and 215 cm lengths $79.95.
Gresshoppa Finse Tur Touring model, 57 mm wide $79.95

Materials from top to bottom:
hickory & beech deck
beech stabilizing layer
spruce core
beech sides
hickory base
lignostone edges

Plastic Emergency Tips: Fits over broken section, prevented from backing out by serrated metal plate. Compact and handy. Two sizes: Regular, fits widths to 55 mm $2.50 ea. Large, fits width to 60 mm $2.50 ea.
Kelty Backpacker's Rain Suit: This is unquestionably the best rain suit we have seen designed specifically by Kelty for the backpacker. It is constructed of a medium-weight (2.7 oz.) urethane-coated nylon with hand-coated seams—total weight of both jacket and pants is only 20 oz. Pants are a bib-front overall with adjustable suspenders and velcro tape side closure. Jacket features an attached hood with visor, zippered front with snap fastened storm flap, drawstring waist and two inside front pockets to keep small gear out of the weather. Both jacket and pants are full cut with generous allowance at neck, shoulder and cuffs for unrestricted movement. The most unique feature of the Kelty Foul-Weather Suit is the side slit design of both jacket and pants which allows the hip belt of your pack to be worn inside the front of the suit. This feature is not meant to keep the buckle dry—what it does is allow the front of the suit to hang loosely, ventilating freely and preventing condensation build-up. An expensive piece of gear—but if you are a serious backpacker the Foul-Weather Suit has features well worth while. Small, medium, large and extra large. Jacket $48.25; Pants $34.75

FABER & CO.
C.P. 100
Loretteville, Que. G2B 3W6

Canada's largest retail source of snowshoes, the Faber catalogue lists 58 different models, including Army snowshoes and models for racers, lumbermen and for other heavy-duty use. Quality white ash frames with full-grain rawhide filling. Distributors throughout Canada. Write for nearest outlet.

EDDIE BAUER
22 Bloor Street West
Toronto, Ontario M4W 1A1
(416) 789-0511

Eddie Bauer now has retail stores in Toronto, Edmonton and Calgary and is building its Canadian mail order business. Stock in trade is outdoor clothing, especially down-filled vests and jackets. Free catalogue.

HOLUBAR MOUNTAINEERING LTD.
Box 7
Boulder, Colorado 80306

Interesting catalogue of clothing and equipment for camping and hiking. Sexier models than the competition, not to mention Robin Williams' rainbow-coloured suspenders ($5.95/pr.).

Cathedral Dome Tent: A roomy, geodesic design that has been enhanced by the skillful, detailed construction techniques of Holubar. A geodesic structure provides the highest strength-to-weight ratio of known structural systems which gives you greater resistance against wind and snow loads over conventional tent designs. The hemisphere formed by the four pole system creates the most volume (efficient living space) with the least amount of surface thereby minimizing the total carrying weight.

Holubar's unique sewing details include lap feld seams for joining floor to sidewall and sidewall to canopy; double stitched canopy and rainfly seams (seam sealer included) and reinforced pullouts for anchoring poles and rainfly. $250.00

Bowser Bag: The Bowser Bag enables your dog to carry a seven to eight day food supply. The load bearing ''saddle'' is made of durable coated pack fabric, lined with a ¼'' thick foam pad and smooth Nylport for comfort and protection. Each pannier is made from 7.5 oz. coated duck with a double bottom extending partway up the sides for extra reinforcement. Access to the pannier compartment is a coil zipper with a protective weather flap.
Sew-it-Yourself Kit $13.50
Handcrafted by Holubar $23.50

Phoenix Dry Storage Bags: Invaluable gear for all outdoor people, particularly canoeists, kayakers and rafters. All Phoenix dry bags are made from heavy gauge vinyl and feature the same closure system that keeps water out and prevents pressure from breaking the water-proof seal.
13½'' wide x 16'' long $12.00
17½'' wide x 22'' long $15.00

TREBOR OUTDOORS
508 Current Ave., Box 3450
Thunder Bay, Ont. P7B 5J9
(807) 683-5542

Canadian-made sew-it-yourself outdoor clothing and backpacking equipment: down-filled jackets, vests, ski mitts, pants and comforters.
Men's Medium Down Vest
(10.5 oz.) $23.95

Down Comforter (double) $124.95
Bike Pannier $25.95

Bike Panniers: These bags are carried low, offsetting any top heavy tendency. Our set of two will fit any standard bicycle luggage rack. Made of waterproof, urethane coated, 7.9 oz. nylon, these bags measure 13'' long at the top, 11½'' at the bottom, is 12'' in height and 5'' thick. Rigidity is maintained by a stiffening plate, in the back of each pannier. This also serves to keep the rear corners out of the spokes. Fastened with hooks and nylon straps to your luggage rack they will not sway or flap when the going gets rough. With detachable carrying straps the panniers can be carried separately or fastened together. Two top strap holders can be used for carrying additional gear. Colours: international orange, kelly green. $25.95

SPORT SEWING SHOP
1659 Bayview Ave. Suite 201
Toronto, Ontario M4G 3C1
(416) 486-9666

Do-it-yourself down sportswear: vests, parkas, sleeping bags and comforters in kit form. Satisfaction guaranteed.
Ripstop Nylon Down Vest $34.65
Ripstop Down Parka $62.35
Polar Guard Sleeping Bag $63.00
Down Comforter, Double $182.70

VERMONT TUBBS INC.
Forestdale, Vermont 05745
(802) 247-3414

Admiral Bird took Vermont Tubbs snowshoe furniture to the South Pole, and this New England Yankee company continues to market a unique line of webbed arm chairs, rocking chairs, tables and footstools. Made of rawhide and hardwoods, with a protective urethane finish. Vermont Tubbs, of course, remains a traditional name in the manufacture of snowshoes, with a complete line of wood and babiche models, some now with cross-country ski bindings.

Snowshoe Rocker: A clubby, comfortable addition to any porch, deck or room. A full-size chair, but still just right for a large gentleman or a small lady. The same sturdy construction used in our world-famous snowshoes. All joints are secured by countersunk screws pegged over with matching wood. $115.00

Flat Bear Paw: 13 x 28. This small, light shoe is used by mountain climbers, orchard growers and snowmobilers. It will support

weights up to 200 lbs. and is useful where manoeuvrability is important. Because of the flatness of the shoe, its tip is easily caught in the snow and is therefore not recommended for beginners. But, because of its flatness, the shoe is excellent for executing kick turns used by mountaineers. $60/pr.

ATOM RESEARCH FOUNDATION
Route 1, Box 159
Troy, Texas 76579
(817) 984-2255

Manufacturers of ''Cameleons''— fabric constructions that allow a single garment to serve as an entire wardrobe, as well as providing camping shelter. If this seems incomprehensible, read it from Atom Research themselves:

Synergetic Environmental Ecological Devices. The Atom Research Foundation is dedicated to the development of tools and lifestyles for the freeing of the individual in the universe.

Currently, a man's home is not designed to work harmoniously with his toothbrush, nor his toothbrush with his underwear, nor his underwear with his telephone, nor his telephone with his car. However, it is possible through the application of nature's coordinate system for all of our physical tools to work together in harmony.

The term ''synergy'' represents the integrated behaviours of aggregate whole systems. The universe is operating on a totally comprehensive set of generalized principles which can be applied to our everyday life. These principles are the governing laws of all naturally found universal patternings. By the application and imitation of these natural patterns, the Atom Research Foundation is developing a system of components

which has the potential to fulfull all a human being's physical life support needs. We call these integral components the seed system. The cameleon is one component of the seed system.

Cameleon catalogue sent free.

CAMELEON: 4 oz. waterproof nylon pack cloth with two way zippers. Use as raingear, backpack, tent component, or a groundcloth. Finished: $66.00, Kit $45.00

PROVIDENCE BAY BOAT WORKS
Providence Bay, Ontario
P0P 1T0

Plans for building rowing, sailing or motor-powered dories from 14 to 27 feet. Step-by-step instructions and plans, $15 per set.

E.B.S. MARINE
41 Cantin
Jonquiere, Quebec G7X 8S6

Manufacturers of the two-person, collapsable aluminum Instaboat.

WOODSTREAM CANADA
Niagara Falls, Ont. L2E 6T3

Source of Lexan polycarbonate snowshoes, which are guaranteed for life against breakage.

CAMPERS WORLD LTD.
633 Windmill Road
Dartmouth, N.S. B3B 1B6

Lightweight gear for camping and hiking.

KAISER DISTRIBUTORS LIMITED
5660 Minoru Blvd.
Richmond, B.C. V6X 2A9
(604) 273-5481

Distributors of the German-made Metzeler line of inflatable boats.

DOG SLEDDING

While the current popular image of the sled dog is one of a sleek racing animal or just an unusual household pet, the fact is that a sled dog can still be an excellent working animal. Although many teams have, like the draft horse, fallen victim to mechanization, it is heartening to note that in the last little while dog sledding seems to have acquired a new lease on life.

Sledding was never confined to the Northwest Territories and the Yukon, but is an integral part of the heritage of the northern portions of most provinces. While the sport of dog sledding is growing (even into tropical southern Ontario), numbers of people are now recognizing the potential usefulness of the sled dog in winter. For hauling firewood or water, a sturdy sled dog can't be beat. One dog working alone can pack in all the groceries from the end of that long snowed-in driveway, can pull the kids to their hearts' content and provide the kind of companionship and affection that only a loyal canine can. As few as three dogs harnessed in a team can be used for transportation over fairly long distances, a team of five dogs would be sufficient for all transportation needs.

The most popular sled dog breeds are the Siberian Husky, Alaskan Malamute and the cross-bred MacKenzie Huskies and Alaskan Huskies. Another uniquely Canadian breed that has only just been saved from extinction is the Canadian Eskimo dog.

It is true that working sled dogs require good care, top quality feed, and training, but there is nothing like the satisfaction of working with an animal that is doing exactly what generations of selective breeding have equipped it to do.

There is no shortage of knowledge available concerning working with sled dogs and the use and manufacture of equipment. Various suppliers are willing to provide further information.

—*Jeffrey Dinsdale*
Quesnel, B.C.

THE B.C. SLED DOG ASSOCIATION
R.R.1 Geddies Road
Prince George, B.C.

Write for sample copy of the B.C. Musher.

HUSKY FEVER
Box 2212
Yellowknife, N.W.T.

A northern-oriented publication dealing with sled dogs.

KELSON RACING EQUIPMENT
Box 208
Hudson, Quebec J0P 1H0
(514) 458-4788

North America's largest supplier of sled dog racing equipment:
trainer sled $325 FOB Montreal
pleasure harness $6
racing harness $7
pro harness $9
collars $3
ganglines $4/dog
snow hooks $18
semi pro sled $175 FOB Montreal

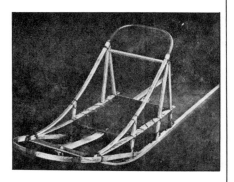

THE KELSON PRO SLED: A tried and proven design, being used by most of the top professional mushers. Features: Constructed from selected ash, mortise and tenon joints, nylon lashed, H.D. plastic shoeing, complete with bridle and foot pads. $250.

BIG BEAR WILDERNESS SERVICES LIMITED
Box 2640
Edson, Alberta T0E 0P0
(403) 723-2212

Publishers of Wilderness Arts and Recreation, a quarterly collection of authoritative articles on wilderness survival, natural crafting, edible and medicinal plants, ecology. Their mail order catalogue also offers hard-to-get outdoor items. Subscription $5/year ($5.50 outside Canada.)

MAJOR DOG SLED KENNEL
Box 4274
Quesnel, B.C. V2J 3J3
(604) 992-9143

Now going into its fourth year of business, this small outfit offers, in its own words, "dog mushing gear and equipment for all working dogs." Harnesses are made from white, heavy-duty nylon webbing or polypropylene webbing. Prices from $7 to $10 per dog. Also available are tow lines, sled runner shoeing and other hardware.

Send 25 cents for catalogue.

DOG PACKS: *We are now distributors for famous Wenaha dog packs, in our opinion, the best dog pack on the market. These packs, for use when packing with your dog on cross-country hikes have many plus features which include: spacious pockets, double stitched for strength, made from the finest 8 ounce coated nylon pack cloth, neoprene brush guards for protection of the lower pockets from brush and rocks, a wide yoke across the back for better weight distribution, a 1" nylon breast strap with padded buckle secures the pack in front, six D-rings are strategically placed on yoke for tying on such items as a tent or tarp, underneath a 1½" poly cinch strap with padded buckle is comfortable even for short-haired dogs . . . there are many other excellent features to these packs. These packs come in sizes Small (under 70 pounds), Medium (70 to 100 pounds), Large (100 pounds and over). Price per pack — $40.00*

BOOTIES: *If you're going to tackle the Iditarod, or if you just want to guard against occasional foot problems, or protect an injured paw, these booties are recommended. Made from Cordura fabric, these booties have a single seam, they also are fastened with Velcro fasteners. The Velcro keeps the bootie in place. These booties will last for many miles of hard use. Price per bootie $1.50*

BIRD WATCHERS

CONSERVATION ENTERPRISES
58 Edgar Avenue
Thornhill, Ont. L4J 1S6
(416) 221-2304

Kathleen Wilson stocks supplies for bird watchers. Feeders, seed mixtures, books, records, Hummingbird feeders, Bushnell binoculars and scopes.

PIGEON-PROOF FEEDER: *(suspended) This grill feeder permits entry to all birds up to the size of and including the Blue Jay. $23.95*

STARLING PROOF FEEDER: *is similar but with smaller grill $24.95*

7x50 HIGH LIGHT GATHERING BINOCULARS:
(Exit pupil 7.1mm; relative light efficiency 76.5). Often called the "Marine Glass" since it became the standard for Navy use at sea, under day and night light conditions, with emphasis on performance under poor light conditions.

WATER WARMERS *for keeping bird-baths ice-free: $27.95*

Savu Sauna Kit

SAUNA
The best transition from outdoors to in

SAVU SAUNA PRODUCTS LTD.
132 University Ave. E.
Waterloo, Ont. N2J 2W3

Pre-built and build-it-yourself solid cedar saunas and accessories. Prices from $1,375 to $2,390 including heater, wiring assembly, thermostatic control, igneous sauna rocks, vapour proof light, benches and flooring. The do-it-yourself kits range from $633 to $1,588. Heaters from $249 to $595.

THE SAVU SAUNA pre-built kit *was designed to fill the growing need for a professional-looking sauna that can be assembled easily in hours by anyone, and fit almost anywhere: in the basement, garage, beside the pool, or at the cottage as no plumbing, floor drain,*

nor special venting is required. Those deluxe features previously characteristic of fine custom-built saunas, are now available in every pre-built Savu Sauna.

JASON WILLIAMS INDUSTRIES LTD.
3317 Dufferin Street
Toronto, Ont. M6A 2T7
(416) 783-1280

Sauna Lodge Finnish baths in kit form, from $1,550 to $2,465 complete. Elektro Sauna Heaters (electric), $269 to $699. Hot tubs also available.

SOLAR SAUNA
Box 466
Hollis, New Hampshire 03049
Clarke Davis (603) 465-7811

Designs for a combination sauna/solar greenhouse, in which heat from the sauna helps warm the growing area. A complete "solar amenities module" design encompasses greenhouse, solarium, hot tub, sauna and outdoor deck space. Plans $7.50. Colour brochure $1.00.

SAUNA STOVE: *Wood fires the Aito sauna stove. Lined with mineral wool and firebrick, the Finnish-made stove contains heat-retaining periodotite stones and is said to provide two days of sauna bathing on one firing of wood. $350.*

THE SOLAR AMENITIES MODULE: *An integrated energy system, with efficiently designed solar greenhouse as its basic thermal collector, with optional solar collectors on the roof of the sauna or elsewhere on your roof, with three-way possible transfer of heat to the greenhouse directly (open sauna door), to the adjacent house (open sliding doors to house, possibly automated with freon devices), or via copper water coils in the sauna ceiling to hot tub which will consequently act as a massive heat sink which you may enjoy while it stores heat/humidity for the greenhouse, using your gas/oil/electric/coal/wood/solar fired hot water baseboard system as back-up when greenhouse temperatures drop below minimum levels.*
Heavily insulated quarry tile floors conduct and retain heat, and are tough, washable and waterproof.
Modularity of the SAM allows for sauna to be added later, greenhouse or deck area to be expanded in four foot increments.
Heavily insulated double glazed throughout, using only proven top quality components.
Simple plans make it possible for even a layman to easily construct the SAM.

CONTACT

THE NEW ALCHEMY INSTITUTE

Box 432
Woods Hole, Mass. 02543
(617) 563-2655

I am perhaps not the best individual to comment on this organization, since I am one of its associate members.

However, if I may say so, I think the Institute is a striking instance of combined scientific research method, applied appropriate technology, and loving humanist attitudes. It must be a remarkable group with which to live and work.

The Journal of the N.A.I., a yearbook, is always a pleasure to see and read; staff members and their children do it all, and well. Long months of patient observation and days of thought have plainly gone into its annual make up. I believe it to be one of the more important publications of its kind. Certainly, it lives up to that part of the Institute's slogan which reads, " . . . to inform the Earth's stewards."

I think it is possible, for example, to credit the New Alchemists with the current interest in backyard aquaculture, in which, so far as I know, it was a pioneer. The implications of this could be great: suppose we could export the technology to underdeveloped lands;

New Alchemist John Todd near aquaculture tank at The Ark Project, R.R.4, Souris, Spry Point, P.E.I. C0A 2B0.

would that not go a long way towards alleviating the protein shortage from which so many people suffer? This could change world history—for the better.

N.A.I. also developed the Ark concept, which has had such striking acceptance in alternative architecture recently. The Ark on Cape Cod and that in P.E.I. are open to visitors at regular hours, and one may buy publications and plans about either or both. This is a combination of housing, greenhouse, acquaculture, solar and wind energy technologies in a micro-ecology—an *intentional* micro-ecology—which bids fair to revolutionize housing in North America, and has applications all over the temperate zones.

—*Norman McKinney*
Toronto, Ontario

Subscription membership, $10, brings newsletters and annual Journal. Associate membership, $25, helps sponsor research. Write for list of publications and posters. Include S.A.S.E.

POLLUTION PROBE — TORONTO

43 Queen's Park Cres. E.
Toronto, Ontario
(416) 978-6477

Pollution Probe in Toronto is currently working on "Ecology House," retrofitting an aging brick residence into a solar age home—complete with composting toilets, active and passive solar systems and energy-conserving appliances. The group is also a clearinghouse for information on recycling, pollution, nuclear power and food additives. Publishes the lively *Probe Post*, a bimonthly tabloid for members ($20/yr; $30/yr for institutions).

POLLUTION PROBE — WINNIPEG

Room 102N, Box 29
University Centre
University of Manitoba
Winnipeg, Manitoba
(204) 474-8211 ext. 22

Publishers of "Ecospeak," an environmental/ecological magazine.

POLLUTION PROBE — OTTAWA

53 Queen Street
Ottawa, Ontario K1P 5C5
(613) 231-2742

SPEC (Canadian Scientific Pollution and Environmental Control Society)

1603 West 4th Avenue
Vancouver, B.C. V6J 1L8
(604) 736-5601

Public interest group organized to reduce pollution, conserve energy and work for responsible management of fish, forest and land resources. Memberships $8.00 per individual, with special fees arranged for students, senior citizens and groups.

CANADIAN ENVIRONMENTAL LAW ASSOCIATION

Suite 303, 1 Spadina Cr.
Toronto, Ontario

Publishes newsletter *Canadian Environmental Law News,* keeping its readers abreast of court cases and decisions.

THE ENVIRONMENTAL SOURCE BOOK

Information Services
Dept. of the Environment
Ottawa, Ontario K1A 0H3

Directory of government bodies involved with environmental issues, as well as sources of information. (Also available from each provincial department or ministry of the environment.)

ECOLOGY ACTION CENTRE

Forrest Building
Dalhousie University
Halifax, Nova Scotia

Membership $5.00

RECYCLING COUNCIL OF ONTARIO

477 Dupont Street
Toronto, Ontario M6G 1H6
(416) 531-3548

Network of recycling groups in Ontario. Information source.

STOP (Society To Overcome Pollution)

1361 Greene Avenue
Montreal, Quebec H3Z 2A5

Citizen's environmental organization which serves to gather and disseminate information, with publications, meetings and a quarterly magazine. Membership $50.

WORLD WILDLIFE FUND (CANADA)
60 St. Clair Ave E., Suite 201
Toronto, Ontario M4T 1N5
(416) 923-8173 or 923-8272

Free newsletters and educational materials. Children's newsletter—$2.00/yr.

WORLDWATCH INSTITUTE
1776 Massachusetts Ave. N.W.
Washington, D.C. 20036

Independent non-profit research organization created to analyze and focus attention on global problems. Membership $25/yr. List of publications available.

THE BIOMASS ENERGY INSTITUTE INC.
Box 129, Station C
Winnipeg, Manitoba R3M 3S7
(204) 284-0472

Publishes the bimonthly newsletter *Bio-Joule*, and offers a booklet detailing the results of this group's research into energy recovery from animal manures. Membership, $10 per year. $250 per year for corporate members.

CANADIAN WILDLIFE FEDERATION
1673 Carling Avenue
Ottawa, Ontario K2A 1C4

CONSERVATION COUNCIL OF ONTARIO
6th Floor, 45 Charles St. E.
Toronto, Ontario M4Y 1S2
(416) 961-6830
Publish "Ontario Conservation News" 12 times a year. Subscription $10 a year. Membership: (regular affiliate) $10.

NUCLEAR OPPOSITION

CANADIAN COALITION FOR NUCLEAR RESPONSIBILITY (CCNR)
2010 Mackay Street
Montreal, Quebec H3G 2J1

ONTARIO COALITION FOR NUCLEAR RESPONSIBILITY
Box 872
Waterloo, Ontario

GREENPEACE
2108 West 4th Avenue
Vancouver, B.C.

MARITIME ENERGY COALITION
77 rue Germaine
St. John, New Brunswick

SASKATOON ENVIRONMENTAL SOCIETY
Box 1372
Saskatoon, Sask. S7K 3N9

SOCIETE POUR VANCRE LA POLLUTION
Box 65, Place d'Armes
Montreal, Quebec

FRIENDS OF THE EARTH
124 Spear Street
San Francisco, Ca 94105

THE PRIME MINISTER OF CANADA
Parliament Hill
Ottawa, Ontario
(613) 992-4211

ENVIRONMENTAL POLICY CENTER
317 Pennsylvania Ave. S.E.
Washington, D.C. 20003
(202) 547-6500

NATIONAL PUBLIC INTEREST RESEARCH GROUP
1329 E Street N.W.
Suite 1127
Washington, D.C. 20004
(202) 347-3811

ENERGY PROBE
43 Queen's Park Cr. E.
Toronto, Ontario

THE BIRCH BARK ALLIANCE
Trent University
Peterborough, Ont. K9J 7B8

Working to become a widely heard voice of concern about nuclear development in Ontario. Quarterly newsletter, $4 per two years. Institutions $8.

OPIRG (Ontario Public Interest Research Group)
Physics 226
University of Waterloo
Waterloo, Ontario
(519) 884-9020

Central coordinating office for a number of local chapters.

BOOK SERVICES

MANDALA BOOK SHOP
427 Dufferin Avenue
London, Ontario N6B 1Z7
(519) 432-9488

From the philosophic *(The Phenomenology of Internal Time Consciousness)* to the mundane *(How To Build A Barrel Stove)*, Mandala offers some 4,000 unusual titles. A 64-page catalogue strong on religious and esoteric studies is offered free.
—*Sharon Airhart*
Corbeyville, Ontario

WHOLE EARTH TRUCK STORE
c/o Zen Center
300 Page Street
San Francisco, Ca 94102

Excellent selection of alternative books.

THE CO-EVOLUTION QUARTERLY
Box 428
Sausalito, Ca 94965

Limited selection of books *(Soft Tech, Space Colonies)* from the publishers of CQ and the Whole Earth Epilog. Also offered are a number of posters, T-shirts and back issues of Co-Evolution Quarterly.

NATURE CANADA BOOKSHOP/CANADIAN NATURE FEDERATION
75 Albert St., Suite 203

Ottawa, Ontario K1P 6G1
(613) 238-6154

Mail order book service specializing in natural history and the environment.

THE FARALLONES INSTITUTE
15290 Coleman Valley Road
Occidental, Ca 95465
(707) 874-3060

Limited selection of publications dealing with alternative architecture, organic agriculture, waste management. Plans for solar greenhouses, composting toilets and other projects. Membership, $25 per year. For information package send $1.00.

HARROWSMITH BOOKS
Camden East, Ont. K0K 1J0
(613) 378-6661

Books on country living, gardening, small stock and alternative energy. Titles selected by readers and editors of *Harrowsmith* magazine.

MAGICAL BOOKS AND LETTERS LTD.
1588 Barrington Street
Halifax, Nova Scotia B3J 1Z6
(902) 423-5470

Specialty bookstore dealing with alternatives in living and life styles, spiritual development and awareness. Mail order catalogue available.

GARDEN WAY PUBLISHING
Charlotte, Vermont 05445
(802) 425-2171

Many well-known country living titles. Books imported into Canada are dutiable, but Customs occasionally lets orders slip through without question.

THE CAN-DO BOOKSTORE
120 Cumberland Street
Toronto, Ont. M5R 1A6
(416) 922-9543

The ultimate in how-to bookstores—more than 10,000 titles, 3,000 listed (without description or author, unfortunately) in their mail order catalogue. Good people to deal with and they will search out difficult-to-find books on request.

GOVERNMENT PUBLICATIONS

Government presses continue to churn out publications by the thousands, some excellent, some reprehensible, most somewhere in between. In the fields of agriculture and food, most offerings are reasonably useful, despite the prevailing agribusiness mentality. A book on grape culture, for example, will devote chapters to fungicides and pesticides, with not a word about natural controls and defences. To balance this there will be information on vineyard location and cultural practices. The price is, almost always, right. Write for lists of available publications. (Most are free within the province in which you live, while nominal charges are made for non-resident purchasers.)

AGRICULTURE CANADA
Information Division
Sir John Carling Bldg.
Ottawa, Ontario K1A 0C7

PROVINCIAL GOVERNMENTS

Alberta:
Dept. of Agriculture
Communications Branch
9718 - 107th Street
Edmonton, Alta. T5K 2C8

British Columbia:
Information Branch
Ministry of Agriculture
Parliament Buildings
Victoria, B.C. V8W 2Z7

Manitoba:
Department of Agriculture
Publications Section
200 Vaughan Street
Winnipeg, Man. R3C 0V8

New Brunswick:
Department of Agriculture
Box 6000 - Research Station
Fredericton, N.B. E3B 5H1

Newfoundland:
Department of Forestry
and Agriculture
Agriculture Branch
Headquarters
Building 812 - Pleasantville
St. John's, Nfld. A1A 1R1

Nova Scotia:
Department of Agriculture
Hollis Bldg., Box 190
Halifax, N.S. B3J 2M4

Ontario:
Ministry of Agriculture
and Food
Information Division
Queen's Park
Toronto, Ontario M7A 1A5

Prince Edward Island:
Information Section
Department of Agriculture
& Forestry
Box 2000
Charlottetown, P.E.I.
C1A 7N8

Quebec:
Department of Agriculture
Information Branch
200A Chemin Ste-Foy
Quebec, P.Q. G1R 4X6

Saskatchewan:
Communications
Department of Agriculture
Admin. Building
Regina, Sask. S4S 0B1

SUPERINTENDENT OF DOCUMENTS
U.S. Government
Printing Office
Washington, D.C. 20402

The titles available from this panjandrum of pragmatic knowledge are almost countless. State the subjects in which you are interested to receive a free listing, or, if you choose, a biweekly newsletter describing selected titles in your area of interest. There is also a *Monthly Catalog of U.S. Government Publications,* for which a subscription price is charged. Ships to Canada.

NEW YORK STATE COLLEGE OF AGRICULTURE AND LIFE SCIENCES
or
NEW YORK STATE COLLEGE OF HUMAN ECOLOGY
Mailing Room, Bldg. 7
Cornell University
Ithaca, New York 14853

Cornell seems to be the bellwether in leading the agricultural schools from the straight and narrow agribusiness path, with increasing numbers of research projects investigating non-chemical alternatives for farmers and food producers. The booklets and brochures Cornell disseminates to the public are beginning to reflect this shift, with many titles for small farmers, organic gardeners and those who prepare and preserve food. Ask for *The Know How Catalogue.*

PERIODICALS

ALTERNATIVE SOURCES OF ENERGY
107 S. Central Avenue
Milaca, Minnesota 56353
(612) 983-6892

Digest-length (or shorter) articles and snippets of information about renewable energy developments, primarily in the United States. $15 per year (six issues).

CANADIAN RENEWABLE ENERGY NEWS
Box 4869, Station E
Ottawa, Ontario K1S 5B4
(613) 232-1208

Monthly news tabloid dealing with developments in the field of energy. Especially strong on coverage of governmental policy and shifts therein. $7.50 per year. $15 per year for institutions.

CO-EVOLUTION QUARTERLY
Box 428
Sausalito, Ca 94965
(415) 332-1716

Stewart Brand is, I think, the only editor of a (surviving) English language periodical to state, in permanent type, " . . . We don't care at all what our readers think." To what extent he belives this is open to question, but his magazine (and it is *his* magazine—issues without the *SB* initial are almost invariably lacking the whole spirit that keeps this non-profit quarterly together) remains unique in North America. If you loved the *Whole Earth Catalog,* you should love CQ. What other magazine would tell you how astronauts urinate in space? One year $14 (four issues).
No advertising.

BLAIR & KETCHUM'S COUNTRY JOURNAL
139 Main Street
Brattleboro, Vermont 05301

Intelligent writing about country matters, centred in New England. $13.50 per year (12 issues). ($15.50 to Canada.)

COUNTRY LIFE
King's Reach Tower
Stamford Street
London, England

Proof that the world of P.G. Wodehouse still exists in rural Great Britain. *Country Life* provides a glimpse into the homes and thought processes of Britain's landed gentry, along with the world's most fascinating real estate advertising. $96 per year, airmail to North America (weekly).

COUNTRYSIDE
312 Portland Road
Waterloo, Wisconsin 53594

$12 per year, monthly
($14 to Canada)

From the same address:

BACKYARD POULTRY
$7 per year, monthly
($9 to Canada)

RABBITS
$7 per year, monthly
($9 to Canada)

These three magazines represent the best regular sources of information on small livestock rearing, although long-time readers feel that the mother ship *Countryside,* has suffered, as editorial material is diverted into the two new publications. Editor Jerome Belanger edits lightly and with integrity, producing magazines that sound like everyday people talking.

THE DRAFT HORSE JOURNAL
Box 670
Waverly, Iowa 50677

The best source of information about heavy horses, especially good for locating breeders, breeding stock and information from breed associations. $8.50 per year (4 issues). $10.00 per year to Canada.

ENVIRONMENT
4000 Albemarle Street N.W.
Washington, D.C. 20016
(202) 362-6445

International review of ecological problems and trends. Serious, non-sensational, readable. $12.75 per year (10 issues). $16.75 to Canada.

INTERNATIONAL WILDLIFE
Canadian Wildlife Federation
1673 Carling Avenue
Ottawa, Ontario K2A 1C4
Membership with subscription $10.50 (6 issues).

INTERNATIONAL WILDLIFE
National Wildlife Federation
1412 - 16th Street
Washington, D.C. 20036
Membership with subscription $10.50 (6 issues).

The combined effort of these two non-profit organizations, *International Wildlife* is a beautiful and highly readable magazine about endangered (or just fascinating) animals throughout the world. Each issue brings an inserted report from the Canadian offices.

ORGANIC GARDENING
Rodale Press, Inc.
Emmaus, Pennsylvania 18049

The grandfather of all North American "organic" and "back-to-the-land" magazines. Extremely short articles on all how-to facets of gardening. Rodale is also the largest publisher of gardening and country living books in the world. $9.00 per year (12 issues). $10.00 to Canada.

SOLAR AGE
Church Hill
Harrisville, N. H. 03450
(603) 827-3347

The growing professionalism of this monthly reflects the sophistication of the industry it covers editorially. Articles are aimed either at professionals or serious solar buffs. $20 per year (12 issues). $26 per year to Canada.

SOFT ENERGY NOTES
124 Spear Street
San Francisco, Ca 94105
(415) 495-5210

Amory Lovins has put his name to this thick-ish newsletter, and the content is generally up to his high standards of scrutiny. Objective, in-depth articles on energy matters are perhaps the best available to serious lay readers, but the price ($50 per year, published "irregularly") restricts *Notes* mainly to those professionally or academically interested in renewables.

SMALL FARMER'S JOURNAL
"Featuring Practical Horse Farming"
94262 Oaklea Drive
Junction City, Oregon 97448

Nice photographs of horse-drawn farm implements, reprints of old farm magazine articles and, mixed throughout, material and advertising of interest to the non-mechanized farmer. $11.50 per year (4 issues).

WIND POWER DIGEST
54468 CR 31
Bristol, Indiana 46507

Essential reading for wind power advocates and involved wind system owners. $8 per year (quarterly). $9 to Canada.

RAIN
Journal of Appropriate Technology
2270 N.W. Irving
Portland, Oregon 97210
(503) 227-5110

RAIN is pure (no advertising) and simple (short articles), mainly of use for listing new books in the soft-tech field, as well as sources of information and contact points. $15/year for 10 issues (22-pages each).

Personal Subscription Order Form

Please start a *Harrowsmith* subscription in my name.

☐ One year (8 issues) for $10.00

☐ Two years (16 issues) for $18.00

☐ Payment enclosed.

☐ Please bill me.

Name_____

Street/Rural Route_____

Town_____

Province/State_____ Postal Code_____

Harrowsmith is published on a bimonthly schedule with two special issues published during the course of a year. Should this frequency of publication change, each subscriber will receive the full number of issues originally ordered.

Gift Subscription Order Form

Please enter a Gift Subscription in the name of the person listed below.

☐ One year (8 issues) for $10.00

☐ Two years (16 issues) for $18.00

☐ Payment enclosed.

☐ Please bill me.

Gift Name_____

Street/Rural Route_____

Town_____

Province/State_____ Postal Code_____

Your Name_____

Street/Rural Route_____

Town_____

Province/State_____ Postal Code_____

A tasteful gift card will be sent to you for personalization and forwarding to the gift subscription recipient. Should the recipient of this gift already be a *Harrowsmith* subscriber, his or her subscription will be extended by the number of issues ordered.

Gift Subscription Order Form

Please enter a Gift Subscription in the name of the person listed below.

☐ One year (8 issues) for $10.00

☐ Two years (16 issues) for $18.00

☐ Payment enclosed.

☐ Please bill me.

Gift Name_____

Street/Rural Route_____

Town_____

Province/State_____ Postal Code_____

Your Name_____

Street/Rural Route_____

Town_____

Province/State_____ Postal Code_____

A tasteful gift card will be sent to you for personalization and forwarding to the gift subscription recipient. Should the recipient of this gift already be a *Harrowsmith* subscriber, his or her subscription will be extended by the number of issues ordered.

BUSINESS REPLY MAIL
No postage stamp necessary
if mailed in Canada

POSTAGE WILL BE PAID BY

MAGAZINE
CAMDEN EAST, ONTARIO
CANADA K0K 1J0

BUSINESS REPLY MAIL
No postage stamp necessary
if mailed in Canada

POSTAGE WILL BE PAID BY

MAGAZINE
CAMDEN EAST, ONTARIO
CANADA K0K 1J0

BUSINESS REPLY MAIL
No postage stamp necessary
if mailed in Canada

POSTAGE WILL BE PAID BY

MAGAZINE
CAMDEN EAST, ONTARIO
CANADA K0K 1J0